Contents

Teaching Masters

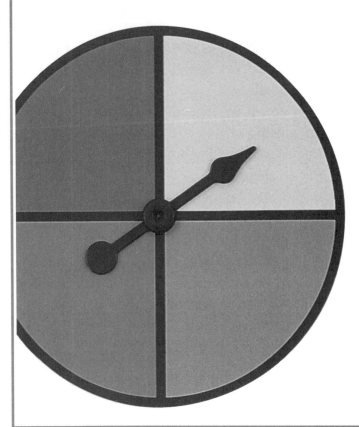

Study Link Masters

Clear
Mode
Frac
Fac
Unit
Simp
Op1
Op2
Fix
1000.
100.
10.
1.
0.1
0.01
0.001
Enter

Name Date Time

Array Dot Paper

Name Date Time

Grid Paper (1 cm)

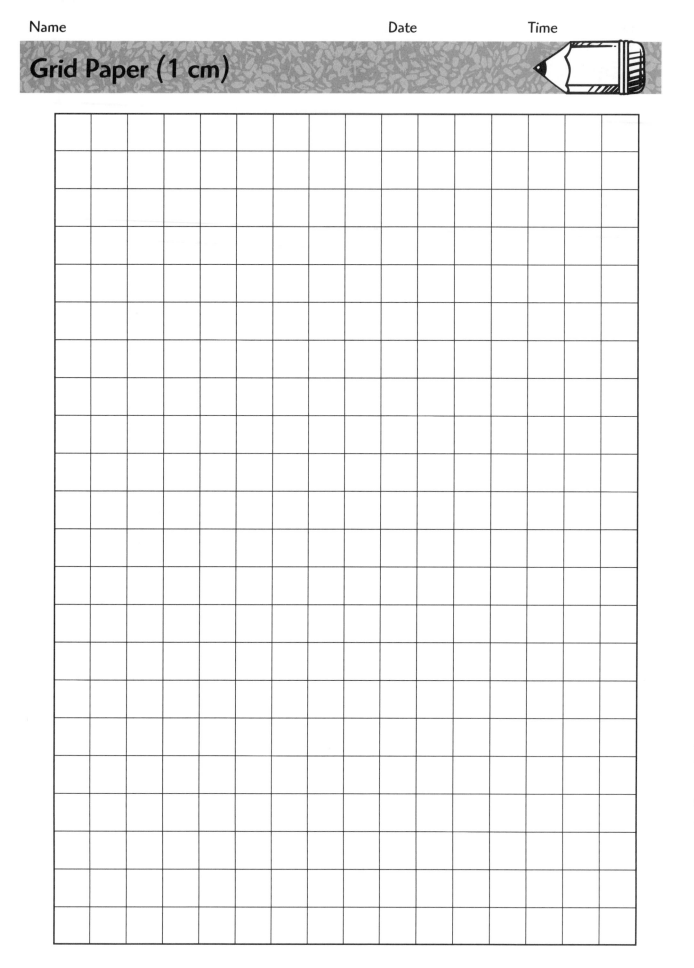

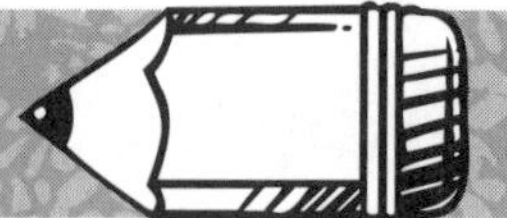

Name Date Time

Multiplication Facts

A List					
3 * 6 = 18					
6 * 3 = 18					
3 * 7 = 21					
7 * 3 = 21					
3 * 8 = 24					
8 * 3 = 24					
3 * 9 = 27					
9 * 3 = 27					
4 * 6 = 24					
6 * 4 = 24					
4 * 7 = 28					
7 * 4 = 28					
4 * 8 = 32					
8 * 4 = 32					
4 * 9 = 36					
9 * 4 = 36					
5 * 7 = 35					
7 * 5 = 35					
5 * 9 = 45					
9 * 5 = 45					
6 * 6 = 36					
6 * 7 = 42					
7 * 6 = 42					
6 * 8 = 48					
8 * 6 = 48					
6 * 9 = 54					
9 * 6 = 54					
7 * 7 = 49					
7 * 8 = 56					
8 * 7 = 56					
7 * 9 = 63					
9 * 7 = 63					
8 * 8 = 64					
8 * 9 = 72					
9 * 8 = 72					
9 * 9 = 81					

B List					
3 * 3 = 9					
3 * 4 = 12					
4 * 3 = 12					
3 * 5 = 15					
5 * 3 = 15					
4 * 4 = 16					
4 * 5 = 20					
5 * 4 = 20					
5 * 5 = 25					
5 * 6 = 30					
6 * 5 = 30					
5 * 8 = 40					
8 * 5 = 40					
6 * 10 = 60					
10 * 6 = 60					
7 * 10 = 70					
10 * 7 = 70					
8 * 10 = 80					
10 * 8 = 80					
9 * 10 = 90					
10 * 9 = 90					
10 * 10 = 100					

Bonus Problems					
11 * 11 = 121					
11 * 12 = 132					
5 * 12 = 60					
12 * 6 = 72					
7 * 12 = 84					
12 * 8 = 96					
9 * 12 = 108					
10 * 12 = 120					
5 * 13 = 65					
15 * 7 = 105					
12 * 12 = 144					
6 * 14 = 84					

Name Date Time

Baseball Multiplication Playing Mat

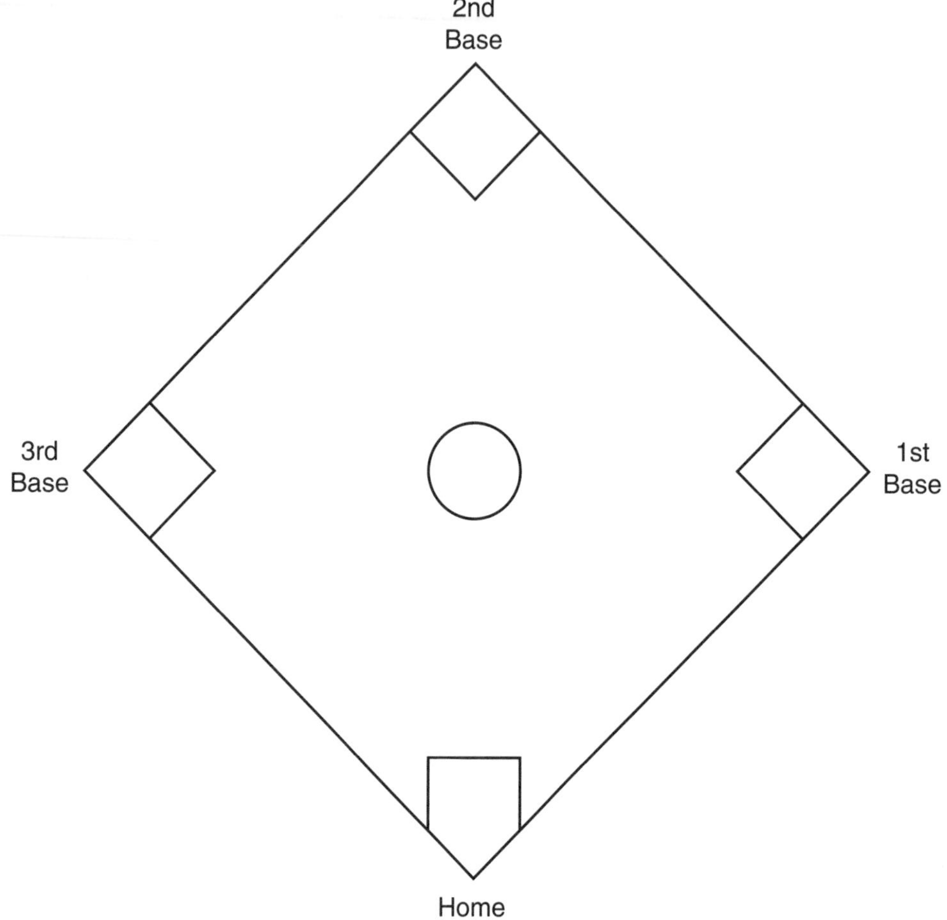

Scoreboard

Inning		1	2	3	Total
Team 1	outs				
	runs				
Team 2	outs				
	runs				

Hitting Tables

1- to 6-Facts	
Use 2 six-sided dice	
1 to 9	Out
10 to 18	Single (1 base)
20 to 28	Double (2 bases)
30 to 35	Triple (3 bases)
36	Home Run (4 bases)

1- to 10-Facts	
Use number cards 1–10	
1 to 21	Out
24 to 45	Single (1 base)
48 to 70	Double (2 bases)
72 to 81	Triple (3 bases)
90 or 100	Home Run (4 bases)

2- to 12-Facts	
Use 4 six-sided dice	
4 to 24	Out
25 to 49	Single (1 base)
50 to 64	Double (2 bases)
66 to 77	Triple (3 bases)
80 to 144	Home Run (4 bases)

Name Date Time

Factor Captor Grid 1 (Beginning Level)

1	2	2	2	2	2
2	3	3	3	3	3
3	4	4	4	4	5
5	5	5	6	6	7
7	8	8	9	9	10
10	11	12	13	14	15
16	18	20	21	22	24
25	26	27	28	30	32

Name Date Time

Factor Captor Grid 2 (Advanced Level)

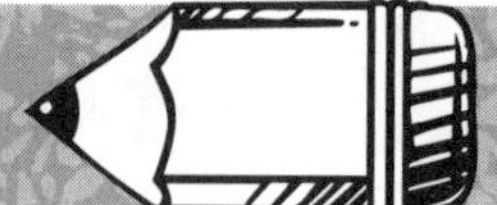

1	2	2	2	2	2	3
3	3	3	3	4	4	4
4	5	5	5	5	6	6
6	7	7	8	8	9	9
10	10	11	12	13	14	15
16	17	18	19	20	21	22
23	24	25	26	27	28	30
32	33	34	35	36	38	39
40	42	44	45	46	48	49
50	51	52	54	55	56	60

Use with Lesson 1.4.

Name Date Time

Divisibility by 4

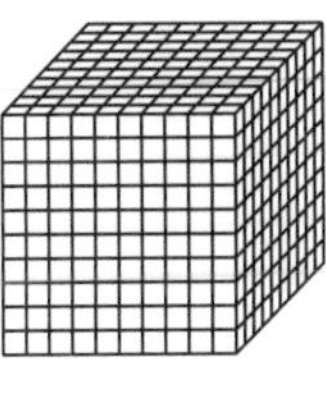
1,000 cubes

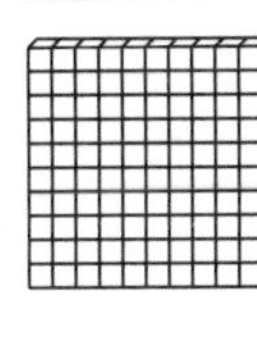
100 cubes

10 cubes

1 cube

1. What number is shown by the base-10 blocks? ________

2. Which of the base-10 blocks could be divided evenly into 4 piles of cubes?

____

____

3. Is the number shown by the base-10 blocks divisible by 4? ________

4. Circle the numbers that you think are divisible by 4.

324 5,821 7,430 35,782,916

Use a calculator to check your answers.

Challenge

5. Use what you know about base-10 blocks to explain why you only need to look at the last two digits of a number to decide if it is divisible by 4.

____

____

____

____

6. Complete the following statement:

A number is divisible by 4 if ____

____.

Name Date Time

Goldbach's Conjecture

1. Write each of the following numbers as the sum of two prime numbers.

Examples 56 = 43 + 13 26 = 13 + 13

a. 6 = ____________ **b.** 12 = ____________

c. 18 = ____________ **d.** 22 = ____________

e. 24 = ____________ **f.** 34 = ____________

The answers to these problems are examples of **Goldbach's Conjecture.** Christian Goldbach lived in the eighteenth century. He had a theory that every even number greater than 2 can be written as the sum of two prime numbers.

A **conjecture** is something you believe is true even though you can't be certain that it is true. Goldbach's Conjecture may be true, but no one has ever proved it. Anyone who can either prove or disprove Goldbach's Conjecture will become famous.

2. Can any of the numbers above be written as the sum of two prime numbers in more than one way? If so, give an example. Show all possible ways.

____

____

____

Challenge

3. Write 70 as the sum of two primes in as many ways as you can.

____

____

Name Date Time

Number Patterns

Draw the dot pattern that comes next and record the number of dots in the pattern.

Example

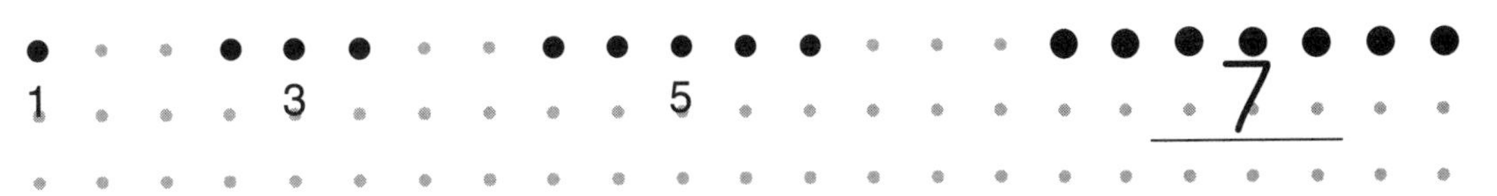

1.

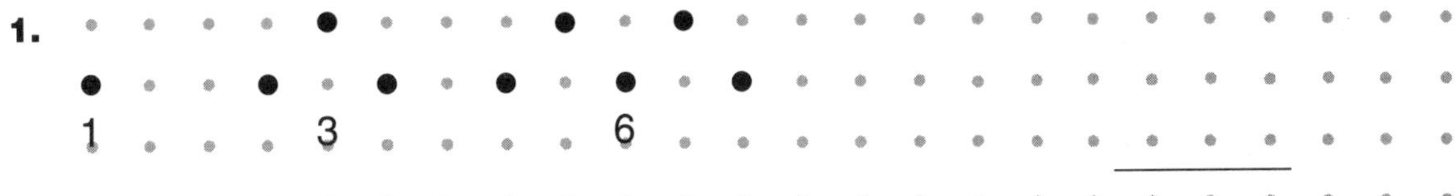

2.

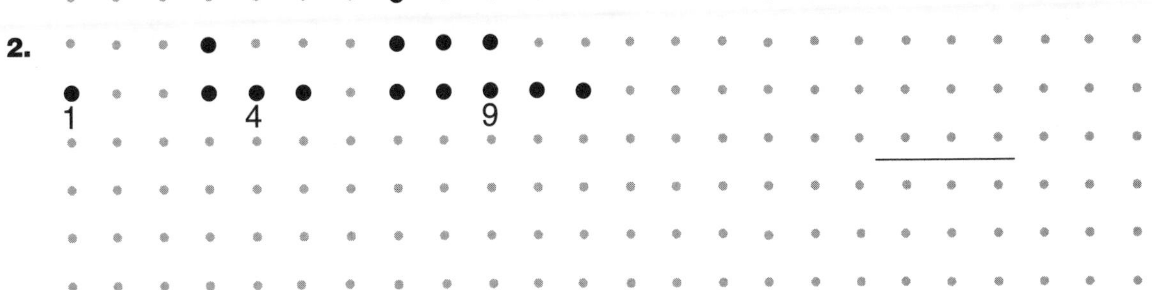

3.

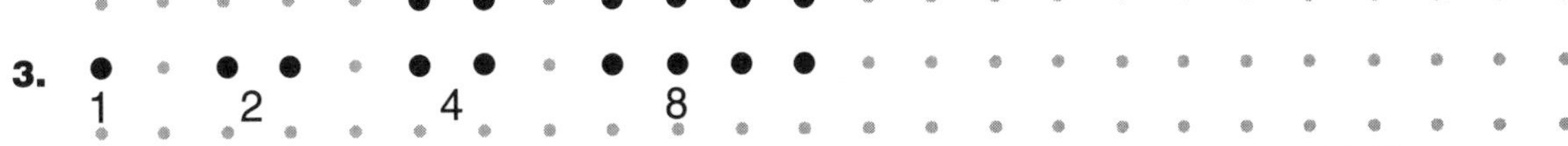

Challenge

4.

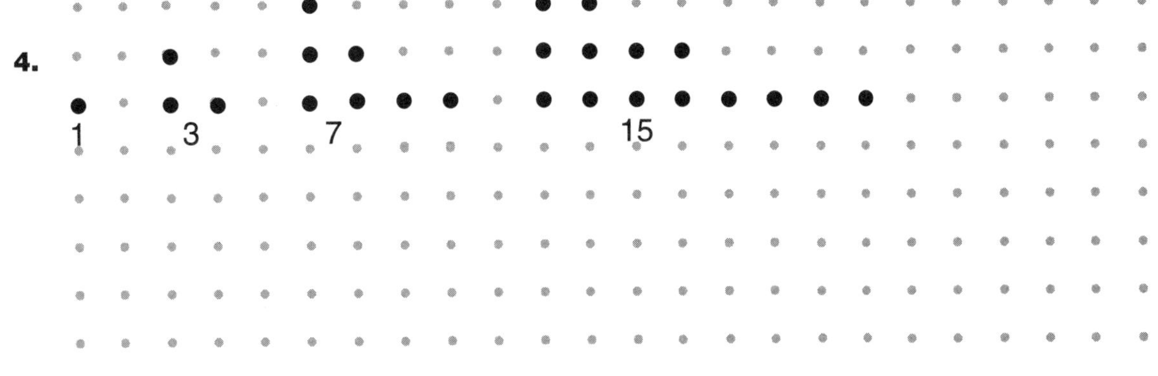

Name Date Time

Factor Bingo Game Mat

Write any of the numbers from 2 through 90 on the grid above. You may use a number only once. Keep track of the numbers you use by circling them in the list below.

	2	3	4	5	6	7	8	9	10
11	12	13	14	15	16	17	18	19	20
21	22	23	24	25	26	27	28	29	30
31	32	33	34	35	36	37	38	39	40
41	42	43	44	45	46	47	48	49	50
51	52	53	54	55	56	57	58	59	60
61	62	63	64	65	66	67	68	69	70
71	72	73	74	75	76	77	78	79	80
81	82	83	84	85	86	87	88	89	90

Name Date Time

Multiplication Facts Master List

Make a check mark next to each fact for which you beat the calculator.

1s	3s	5s	7s	9s
1 * 1	3 * 1	5 * 1	7 * 1	9 * 1
1 * 2	3 * 2	5 * 2	7 * 2	9 * 2
1 * 3	3 * 3	5 * 3	7 * 3	9 * 3
1 * 4	3 * 4	5 * 4	7 * 4	9 * 4
1 * 5	3 * 5	5 * 5	7 * 5	9 * 5
1 * 6	3 * 6	5 * 6	7 * 6	9 * 6
1 * 7	3 * 7	5 * 7	7 * 7	9 * 7
1 * 8	3 * 8	5 * 8	7 * 8	9 * 8
1 * 9	3 * 9	5 * 9	7 * 9	9 * 9
1 * 10	3 * 10	5 * 10	7 * 10	9 * 10

2s	4s	6s	8s	10s
2 * 1	4 * 1	6 * 1	8 * 1	10 * 1
2 * 2	4 * 2	6 * 2	8 * 2	10 * 2
2 * 3	4 * 3	6 * 3	8 * 3	10 * 3
2 * 4	4 * 4	6 * 4	8 * 4	10 * 4
2 * 5	4 * 5	6 * 5	8 * 5	10 * 5
2 * 6	4 * 6	6 * 6	8 * 6	10 * 6
2 * 7	4 * 7	6 * 7	8 * 7	10 * 7
2 * 8	4 * 8	6 * 8	8 * 8	10 * 8
2 * 9	4 * 9	6 * 9	8 * 9	10 * 9
2 * 10	4 * 10	6 * 10	8 * 10	10 * 10

Name Date Time

Computation Grid

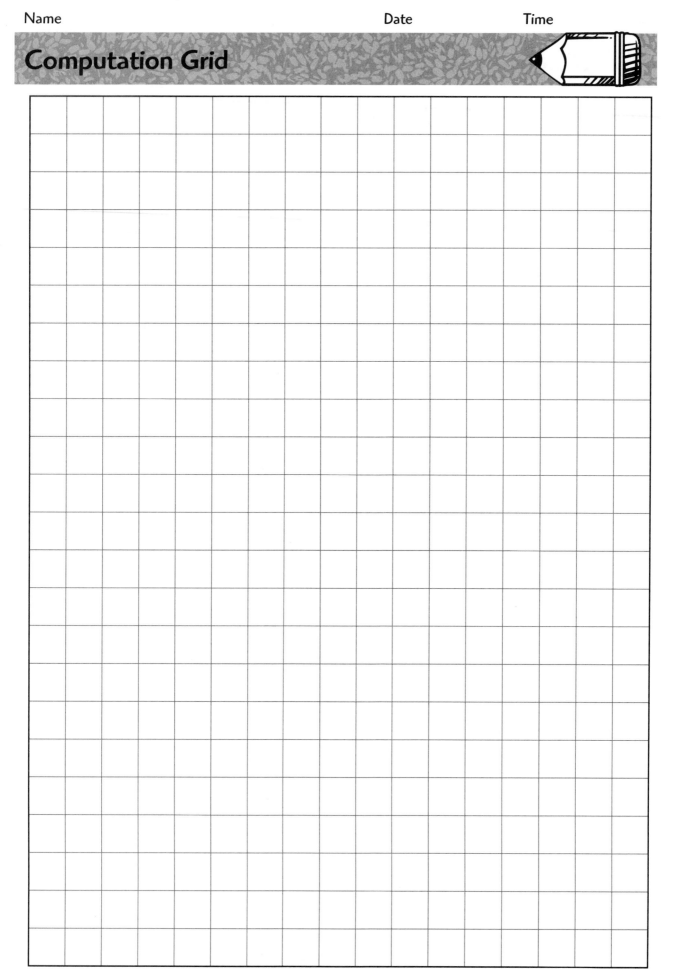

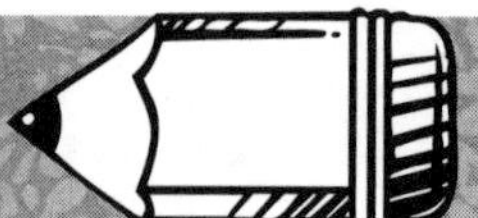

Name Date Time

Place-Value Puzzles

Millions			Thousands			Ones		
Hundred-millions	Ten-millions	Millions	Hundred-thousands	Ten-thousands	Thousands	Hundreds	Tens	Ones

Use the clues to solve the puzzles.

Puzzle 1

- The value of the digit in the **thousandths** place is equal to the sum of the measures of the angles in a triangle (180°) divided by 30.
- If you multiply the digit in the **tens** place by 1,000; the answer will be 9,000.
- Double 35. Divide the result by 10. Write the answer in the **tenths** place.
- The value of the digit in the **hundreds** place is $\frac{1}{2}$ the value of the digit in the thousandths place.
- When you multiply the digit in the **ones** place by itself, the answer is 0.
- Write a digit in the **hundredths** place so that the sum of all six digits in this number is 30.

What is the number? _____ _____ _____ . _____ _____ _____

Puzzle 2

- Double 12. Divide the result by 8. Write the answer in the **millions** place.
- If you multiply the digit in the **tens** place by 10, the answer will be 40.
- The digit in the **ten-thousands** place is a prime number. If you multiply it by itself, the answer will be 49.
- Multiply 7 and 3. Subtract 12. Write the answer in the **ones** place.
- Multiply the digit in the tens place by the digit in the millions place. Subtract 7 from the result. Write the answer in the **hundreds** place.
- The digit in the **thousands** place is an odd digit that has not been used yet.
- The value of the digit in the **hundred-thousands** place is the same as the number of sides of a quadrilateral.

What is the number? _____, _____ _____ _____, _____ _____ _____

Check: The sum of the answers to both puzzles is 3,471,939.756.

Name Date Time

Number Story Challenge

Solve each problem.

1. Lucas was comparing prices on a pair of mini-speakers. At one store, the pair of speakers cost $19.95. At a second store, the same speakers cost $24.70. At a third store, they cost $18.50. If he buys the speakers at the lowest price, how much will he save over the highest price?

a. List the numbers needed to solve the problem. ____________________

b. Describe what you want to find. ____________________

____

c. Open sentence: ____________________

d. Solution: __________ **e.** Answer: ____________________

2. Lucas earned $45.50 babysitting. Could he buy both the lowest-priced speakers and a CD costing $12.99? __________

Describe what you did to solve the problem. ____________________

____

3. Lucas decided to buy only the lowest-priced speakers. His brother Max wanted to pay half of the cost so that he could share the speakers. Lucas agreed. How much money did Lucas have left after paying for half of a set of speakers?

a. List the numbers needed to solve the problem. ____________________

b. Describe what you want to find. ____________________

____

c. Open sentence: ____________________

d. Solution: __________ **e.** Answer: ____________________

4. On the back of this page, write a number story of your own using the information on this page. Then solve the problem.

Name Date Time

Statistical Landmarks

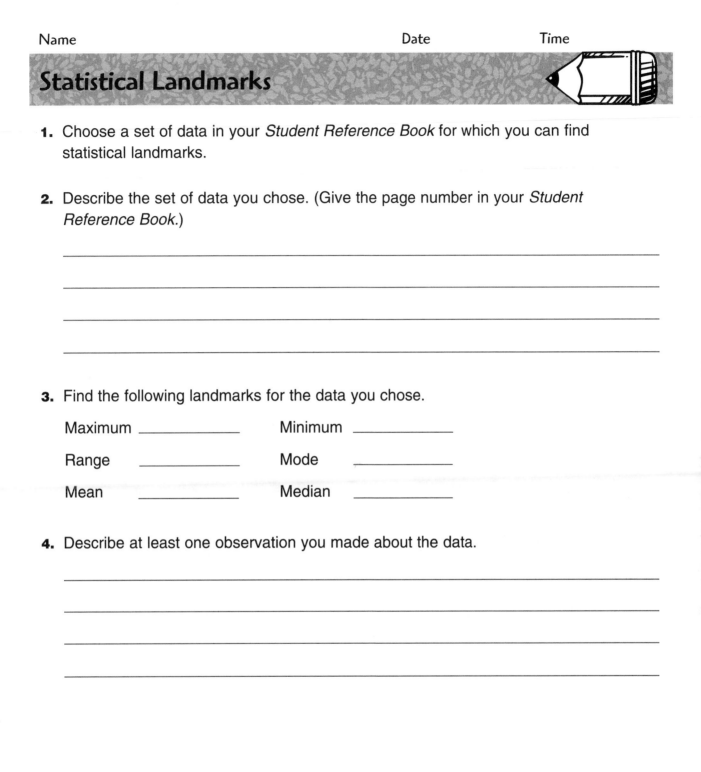

1. Choose a set of data in your *Student Reference Book* for which you can find statistical landmarks.

2. Describe the set of data you chose. (Give the page number in your *Student Reference Book.*)

____

____

____

____

3. Find the following landmarks for the data you chose.

Maximum ____________ Minimum ____________

Range ____________ Mode ____________

Mean ____________ Median ____________

4. Describe at least one observation you made about the data.

____

____

____

____

Name Date Time

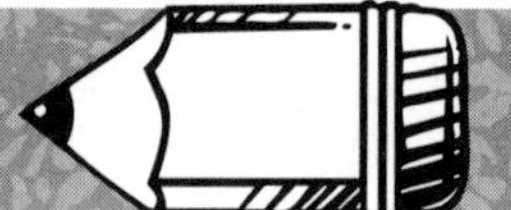

Spinner Experiments

You can make a spinner by dividing a circle into different-color parts and holding a large paper clip in place with the point of a pencil.

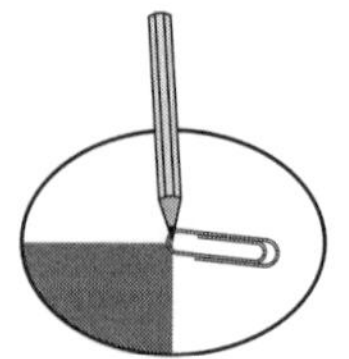

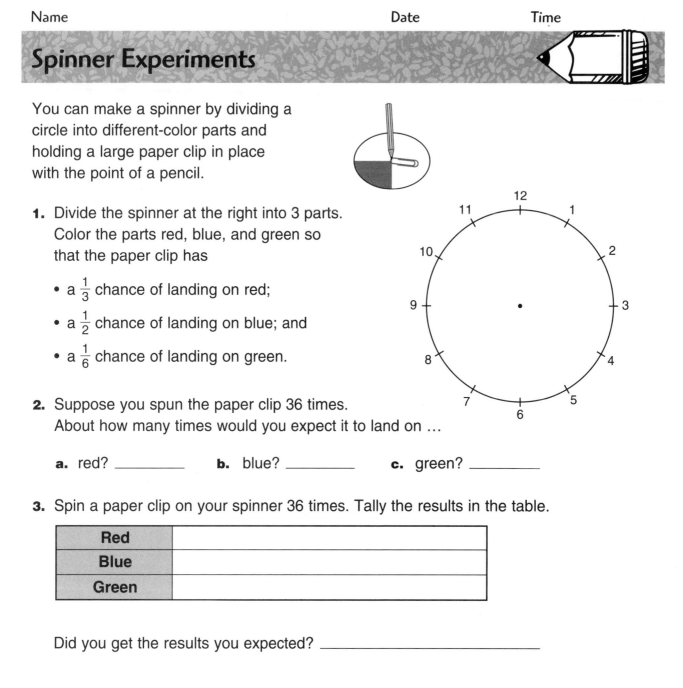

1. Divide the spinner at the right into 3 parts. Color the parts red, blue, and green so that the paper clip has

   - a $\frac{1}{3}$ chance of landing on red;
   - a $\frac{1}{2}$ chance of landing on blue; and
   - a $\frac{1}{6}$ chance of landing on green.

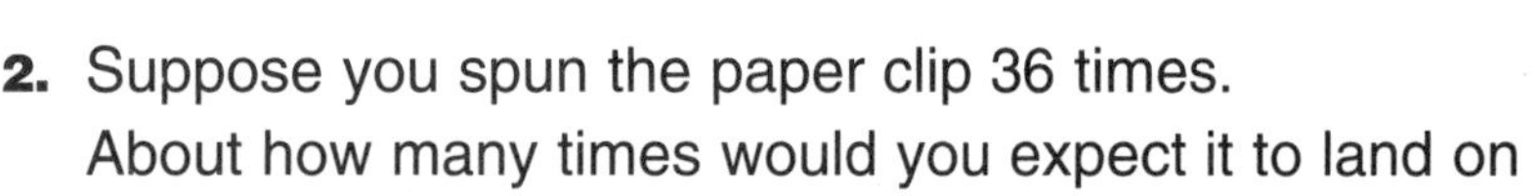

2. Suppose you spun the paper clip 36 times. About how many times would you expect it to land on …

   a. red? ________ **b.** blue? ________ **c.** green? ________

3. Spin a paper clip on your spinner 36 times. Tally the results in the table.

Red	
Blue	
Green	

Did you get the results you expected? ____________________

4. Suppose you spun the paper clip 90 times. About how many times would you expect it to land on …

   a. red? ________ **b.** blue? ________ **c.** green? ________

5. Spin a paper clip on your spinner 90 times. Tally the results in the table.

Red	
Blue	
Green	

Did you get the results you expected? ____________________

Name Date Time

Array Grid

GLUE OR PASTE EDGE OF PAGE 18 HERE

Start here.

Name Date Time

Array Grid (cont.)

Use with Lesson 2.8.

Name Date Time

Lattice Multiplication Table

9	8	7	6	5	4	3	2	1	0	
0/0	0/0	0/0	0/0	0/0	0/0	0/0	0/0	0/0	0/0	0
0/0	0/8	0/7	0/6	0/5	0/4	0/3	0/2	0/1	0/0	1
1/8	1/6	1/4	1/2	1/0	0/8	0/6	0/4	0/2	0/0	2
2/7	2/4	2/1	1/8	1/5	1/2	0/9	0/6	0/3	0/0	3
3/6	3/2	2/8	2/4	2/0	1/6	1/2	0/8	0/4	0/0	4
4/5	4/0	3/5	3/0	2/5	2/0	1/5	1/0	0/5	0/0	5
5/4	4/8	4/2	3/6	3/0	2/4	1/8	1/2	0/6	0/0	6
6/3	5/6	4/9	4/2	3/5	2/8	2/1	1/4	0/7	0/0	7
7/2	6/4	5/6	4/8	4/0	3/2	2/4	1/6	0/8	0/0	8
8/1	7/2	6/3	5/4	4/5	3/6	2/7	1/8	0/9	0/0	9

Name Date Time

An Ancient Multiplication Method

Over 4,000 years ago, the Egyptians developed one of the earliest multiplication methods. This method, with some modifications, was then used by the ancient Greeks and, in the Middle Ages, by people living in other parts of Europe.

Study the examples of the Egyptian method below. Each problem has been solved by this method of multiplication. Try to figure out how the method works.

13 * 25 = 325	**18 * 17** = 306	**26 * 31** = 806
✓1 25 (1 * 25)	~~1 17~~	~~1 31~~
~~✓2 50 (2 * 25)~~	✓2 34	✓2 62
✓4 100 (4 * 25)	4 68	~~4 124~~
8 200 (8 * 25)	8 136	✓8 248
325 (13 * 25)	✓16 272	✓16 496
	306	806

Make up a multiplication problem. Then solve it using the Egyptian method.

Name Date Time

Lattice-Computation Grids

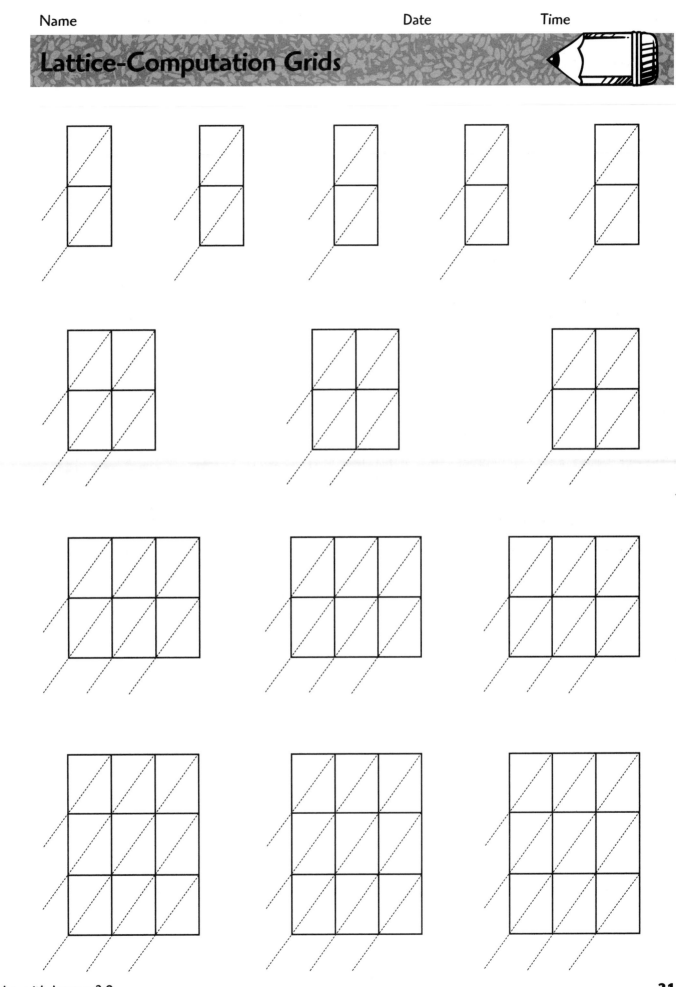

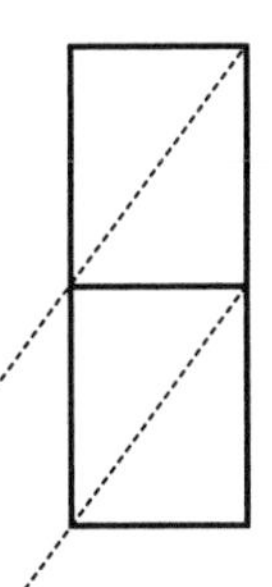
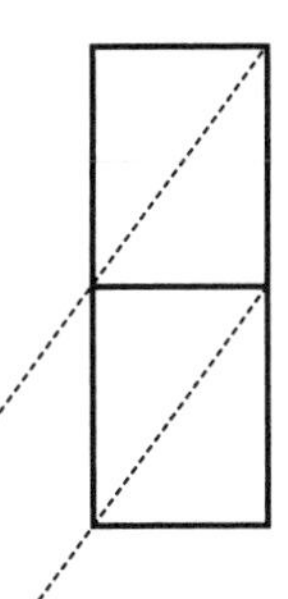
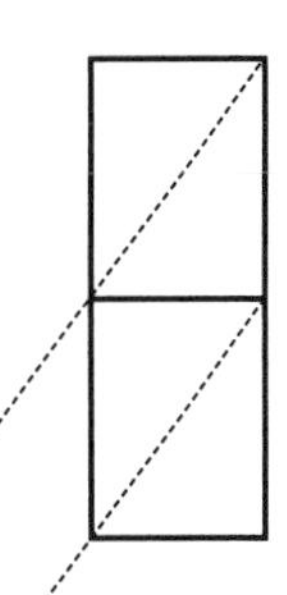
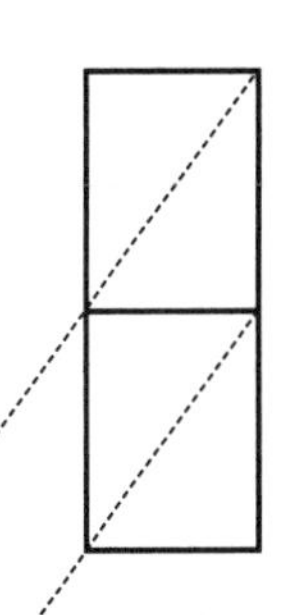
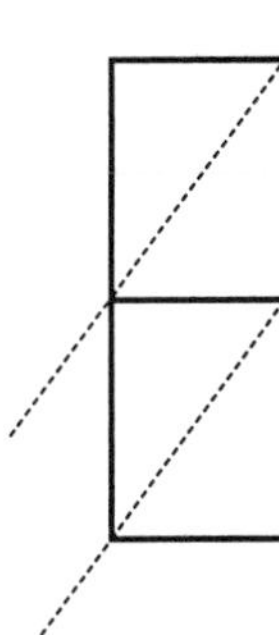

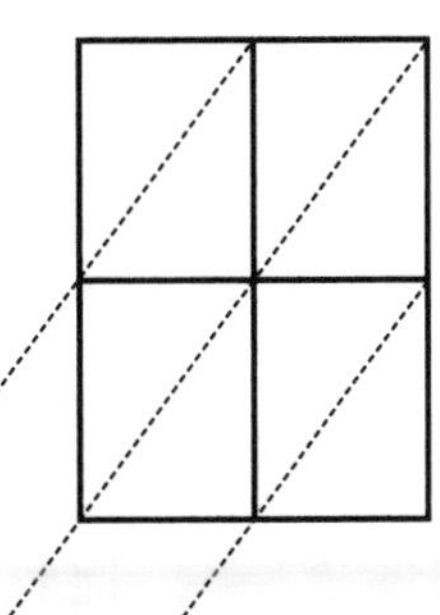
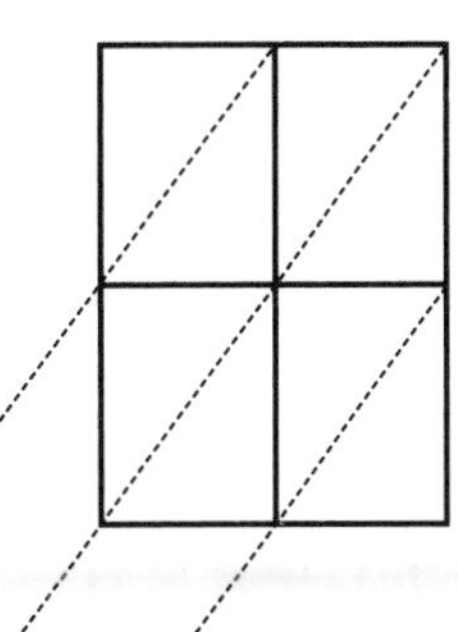
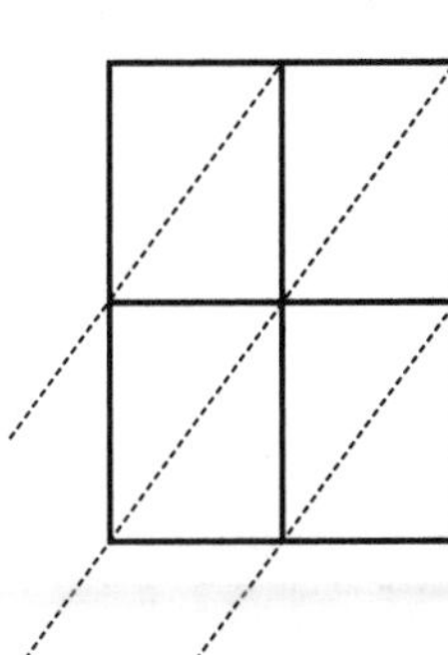

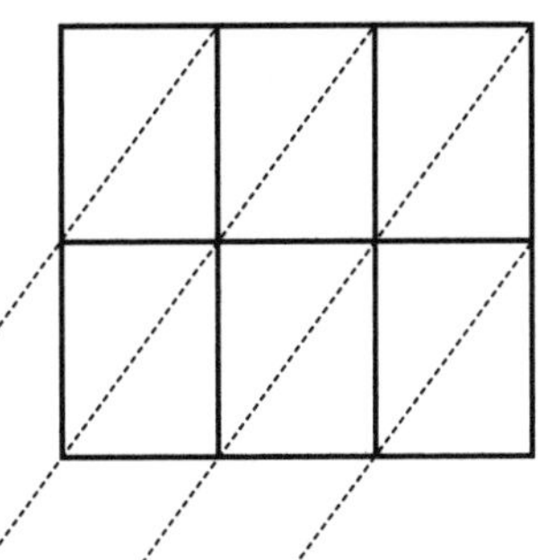
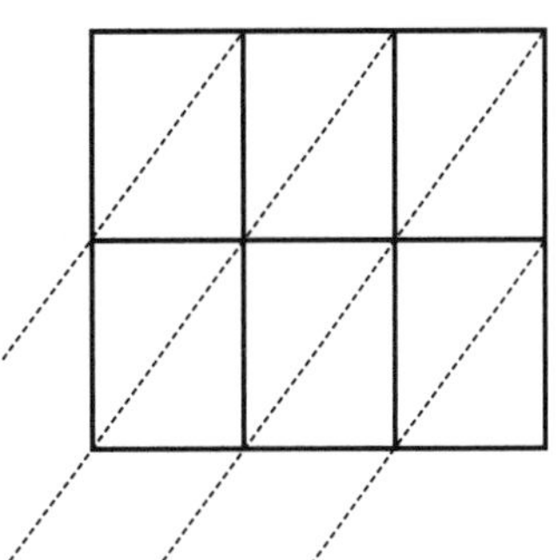
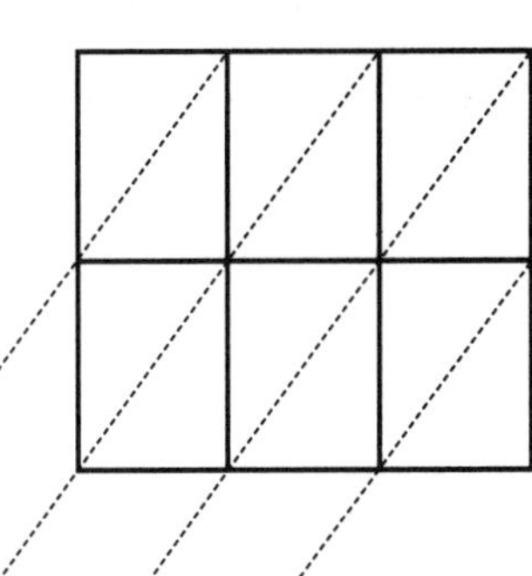

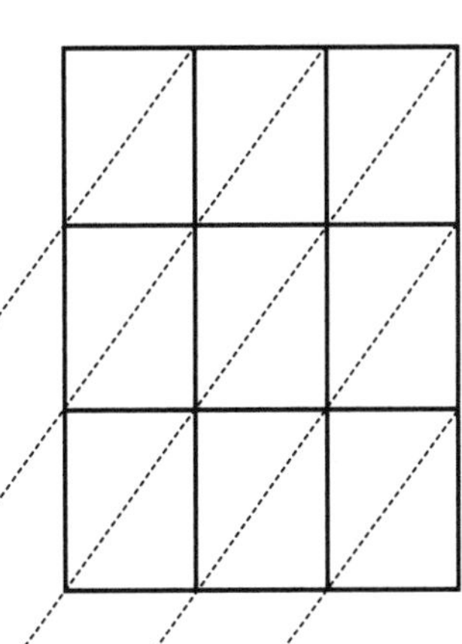
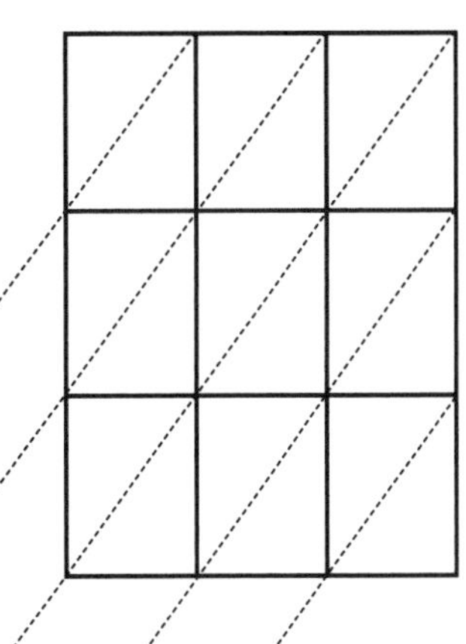
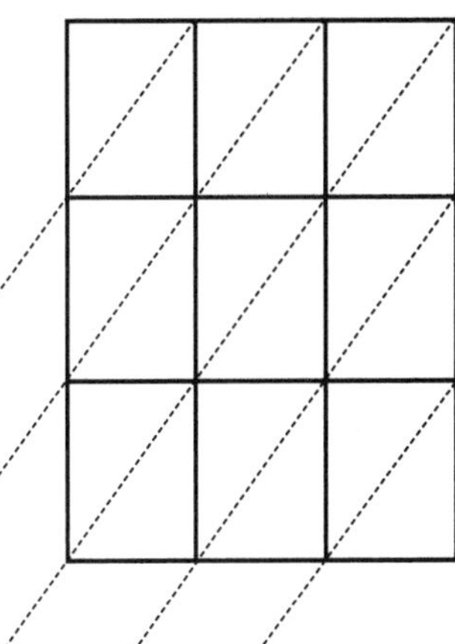

Name Date Time

Place-Value Mat

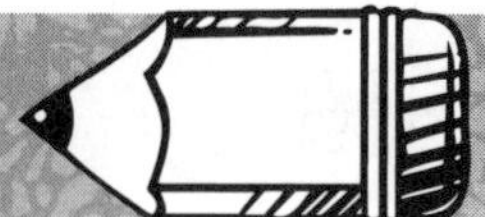

Millions

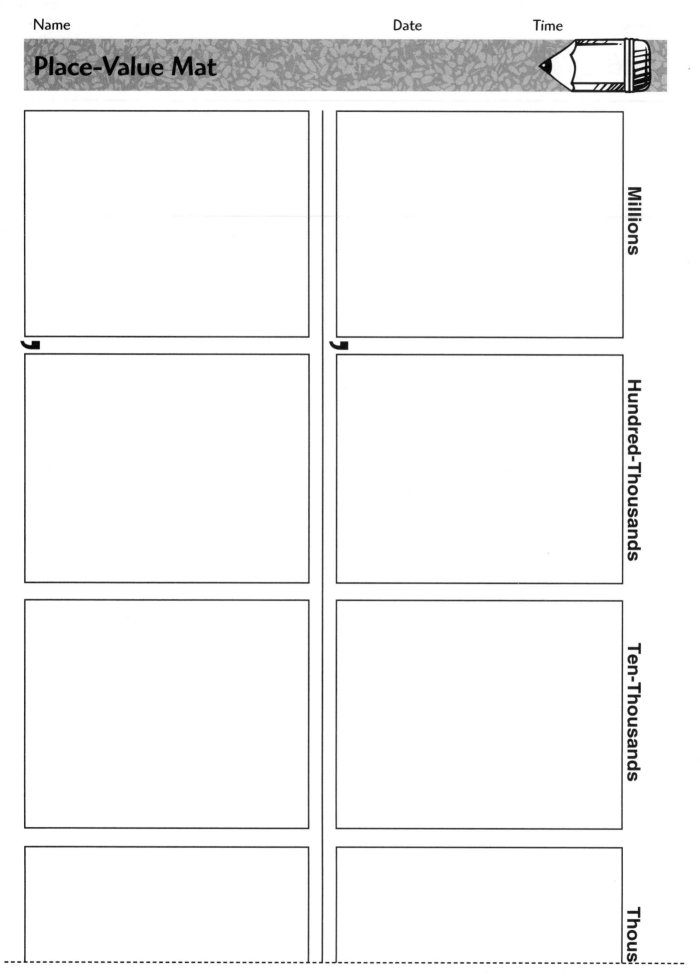

Hundred-Thousands

Ten-Thousands

Thous

Use with Lesson 2.10.

Name Date Time

Place-Value Mat (cont.)

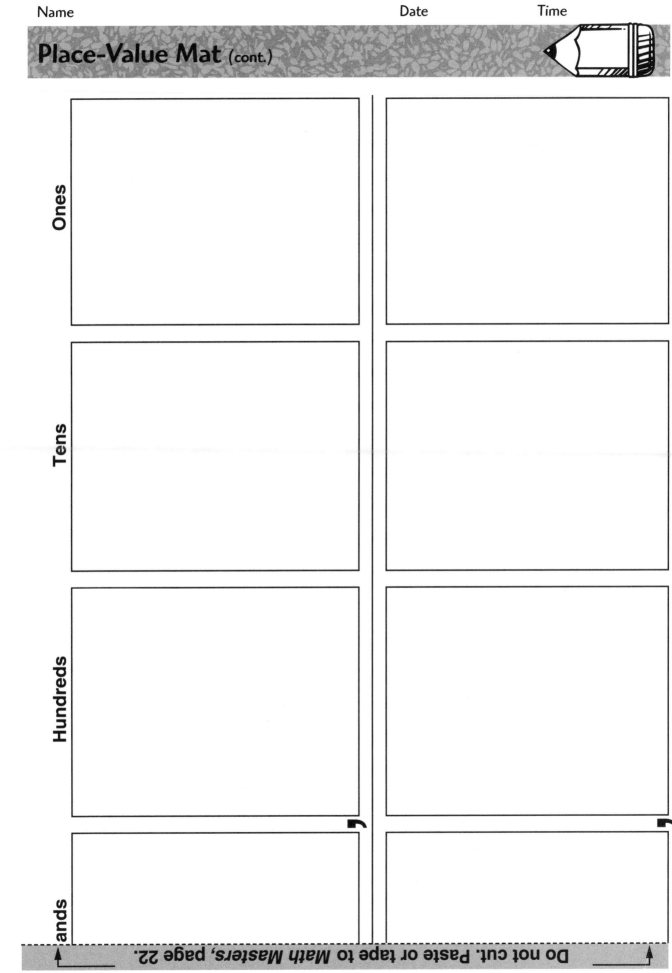

Ones

Tens

Hundreds

ands

Do not cut. Paste or tape to *Math Masters*, page 22.

Name Date Time

U.S. Census Questions

Here are some of the questions from both the short and long forms of the U.S. Census. Answer the questions *for yourself.* Mark and fill in the boxes with your answers. Then put this sheet in the collection box.

1. What is this person's sex? Mark one box.

☐ Male ☐ Female

2. a. What is this person's date of birth? *Print numbers in boxes.*

Month ☐☐ Day ☐☐

Year of birth ☐☐☐☐

b. What was this person's age on April 1 of this year?

☐☐☐

3. Where was this person born?

☐ In the United States—*Print name of state.*

☐☐☐☐☐☐☐☐☐☐☐☐☐☐☐

☐ Outside the United States—*Print name of foreign country, or Puerto Rico, Guam, etc.*

☐☐☐☐☐☐☐☐☐☐☐☐☐☐☐

4. a. Does this person speak a language other than English at home?

☐ Yes ☐ No → *Skip to 5.*

b. What is this language?

☐☐☐☐☐☐☐☐☐☐☐☐☐☐☐

(For example: Korean, Italian, Spanish, Vietnamese)

5. Is there telephone service available in this house, apartment, or mobile home from which you can both make and receive calls?

☐ Yes ☐ No

Name Date Time

The Geometry Template

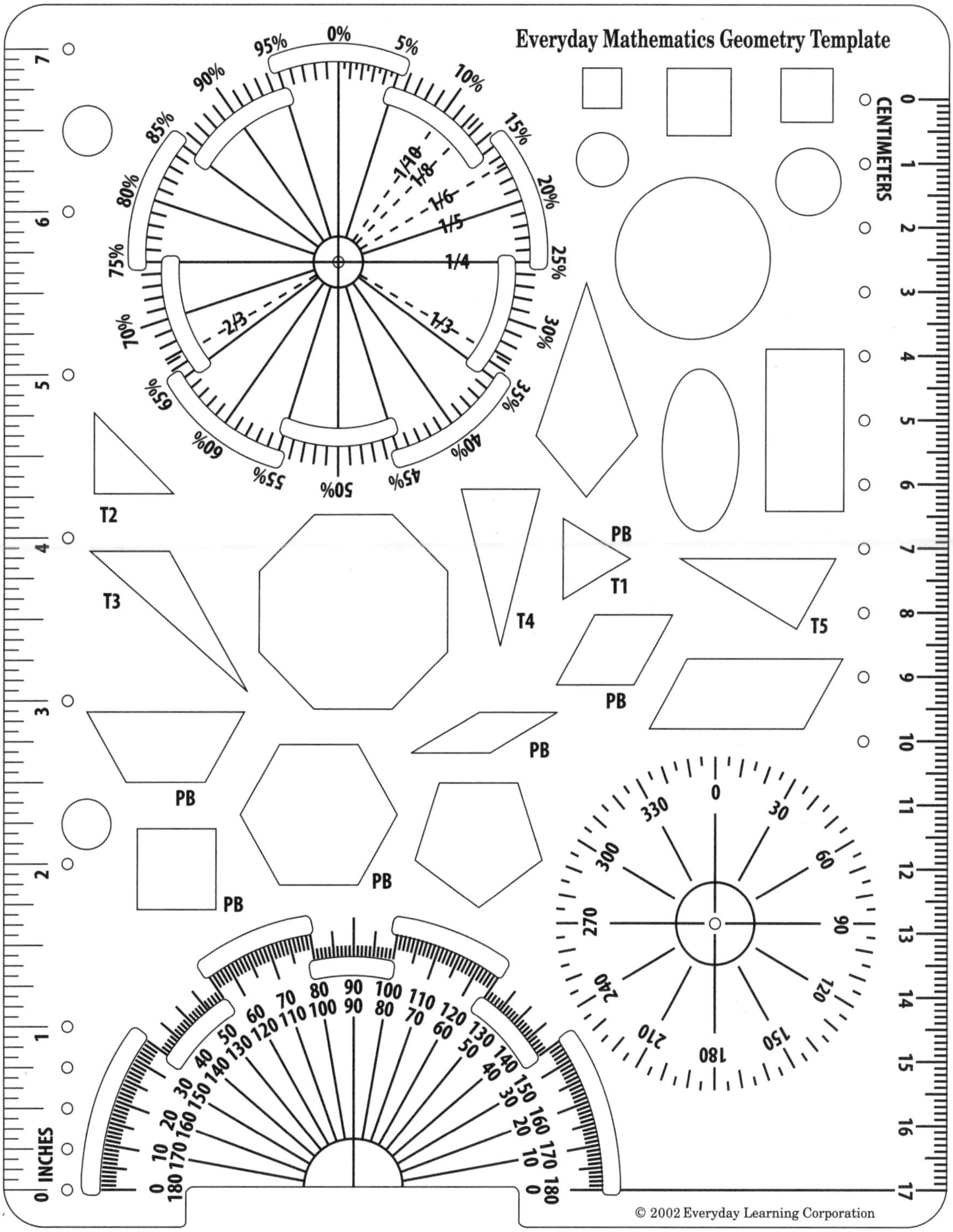

Everyday Mathematics Geometry Template

Name Date Time

Measuring and Drawing Angles with a Protractor

3. Martha used her half-circle protractor to measure the angle at the right. She said it measures about 30°. Terri measured it with her half-circle protractor. Terri said it measures about 150°. Bob measured it with his full-circle protractor. Bob said it measures about 330°.

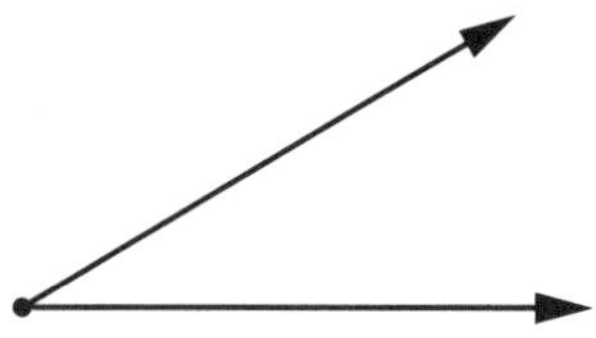

a. Use both of your template protractors to measure the angle. Do you agree with Martha, Terri, or Bob? ______________________

b. Why? ______________________

____

____

4. Use your half-circle protractor. Measure each angle as accurately as you can.

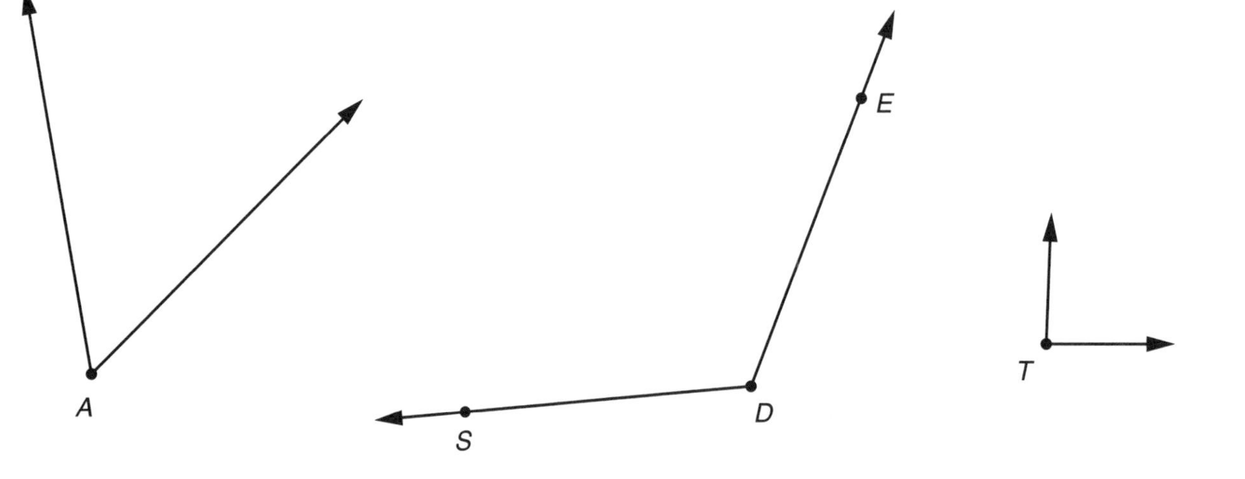

m ∠*A* is about ________°. m ∠*EDS* is about ________°. m ∠*T* is about ________°.

Name Date Time

Measuring and Drawing Angles (cont.)

5. Use your full-circle protractor to measure each angle.

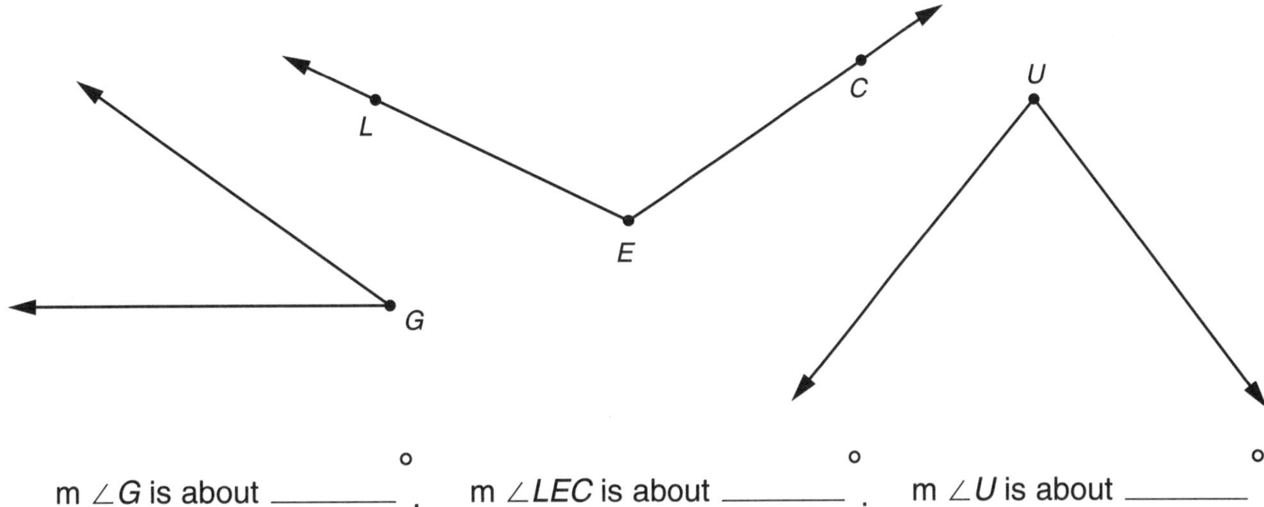

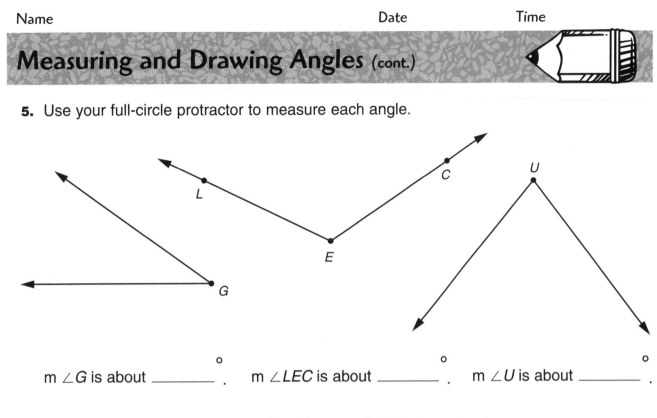

m ∠*G* is about ________°. m ∠*LEC* is about ________°. m ∠*U* is about ________°.

6. Draw and label the following angles. Use your half-circle protractor.

∠*CAT:* 62° ∠*DOG:* 135°

Name Date Time

Baseball Angles

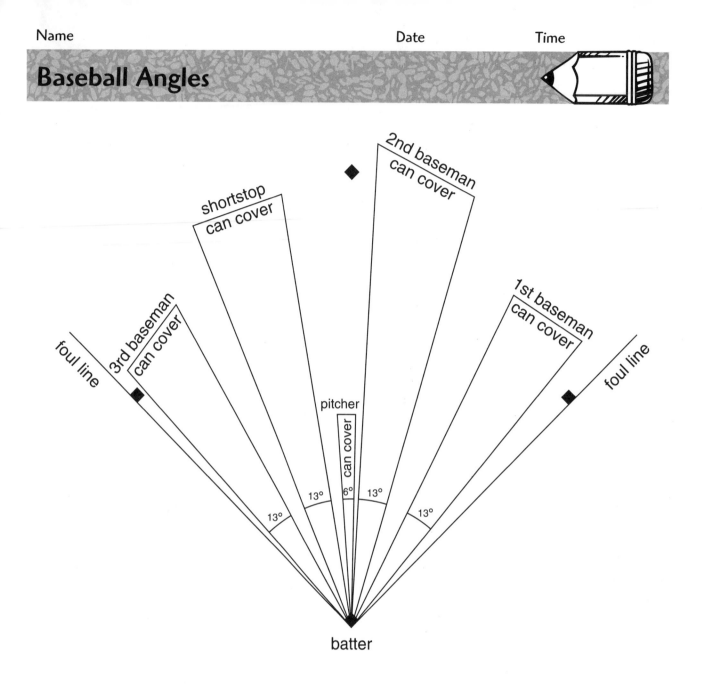

The playing field for baseball lies between the foul lines, which form a 90° angle. Suppose that each of the four infielders can cover an angle of about 13° on a hard-hit ground ball, and that the pitcher can cover about 6°. (See the diagram above.)

Source: Applying Arithmetic, Usiskin, Z. and Bell, M. © 1983 University of Chicago

1. How many degrees are left for the batter to hit through? ________°

Name Date Time

Designs with a Compass and a Straightedge

If you know how to inscribe a hexagon in a circle, you can make a 6-pointed star, or **hexagram,** inside a circle.

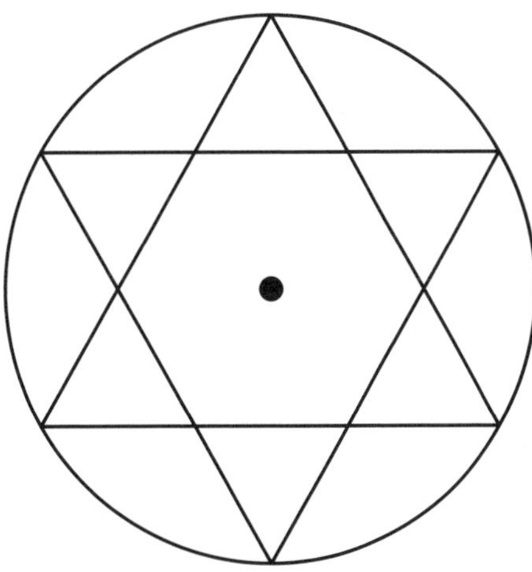

1. On a separate piece of paper, make a 6-pointed star. (*Hint:* Mark the circle as you do for a hexagon. Connect every other mark.)

2. Divide the angles of your star in half as shown below.

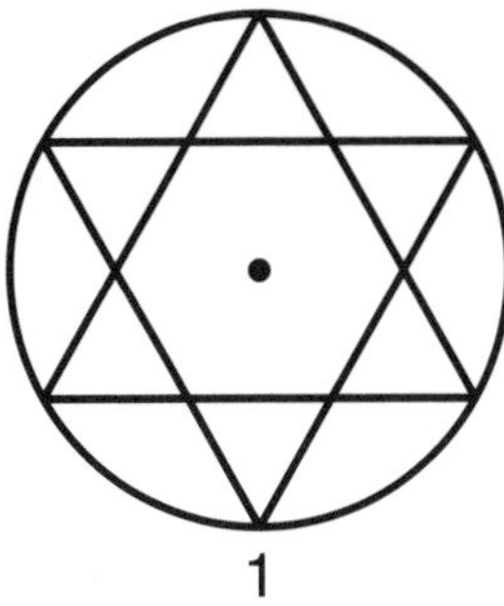

1

2

3. Color your design in some pattern.

4. Reproduce the following designs, using a compass and a straightedge to draw hexagons and hexagrams. Then find patterns and color them. (*Hint:* Use a pencil and draw lightly so you can erase unwanted lines.)

Name Date Time

Polygon Capture Pieces

H

J

O

C

B

M

N

A

I

D

K

G

L

F

P

E

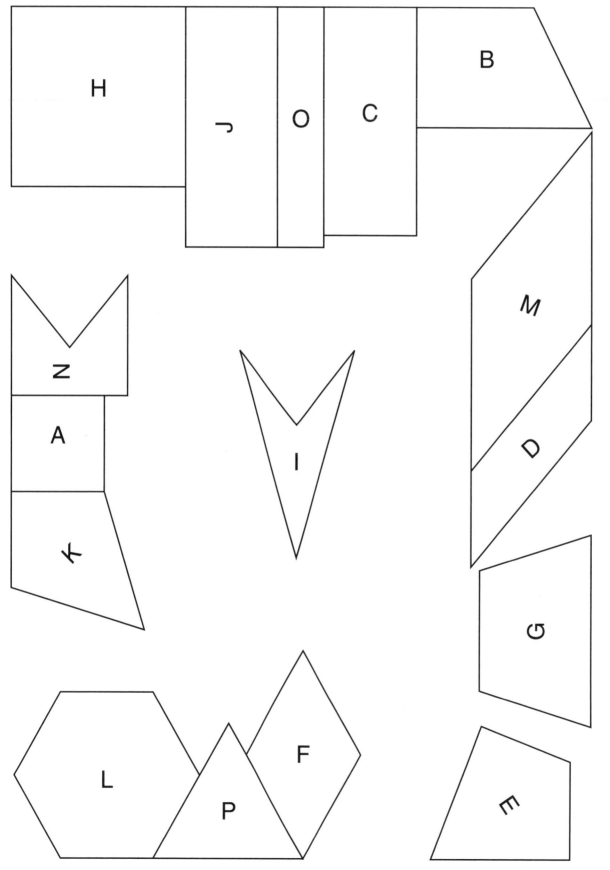

Use with Lesson 3.7.

Name Date Time

Regular Polygons

Fold the page like this.

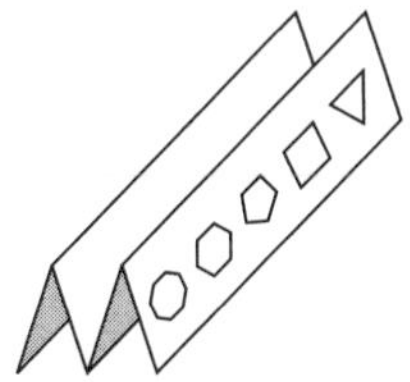

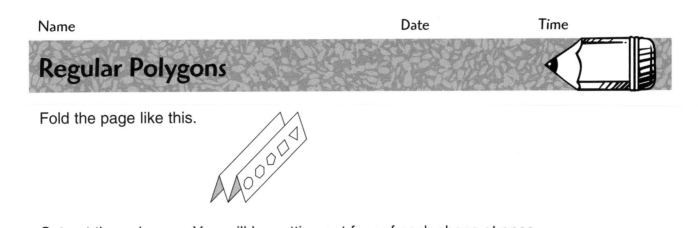

Cut out the polygons. You will be cutting out four of each shape at once.

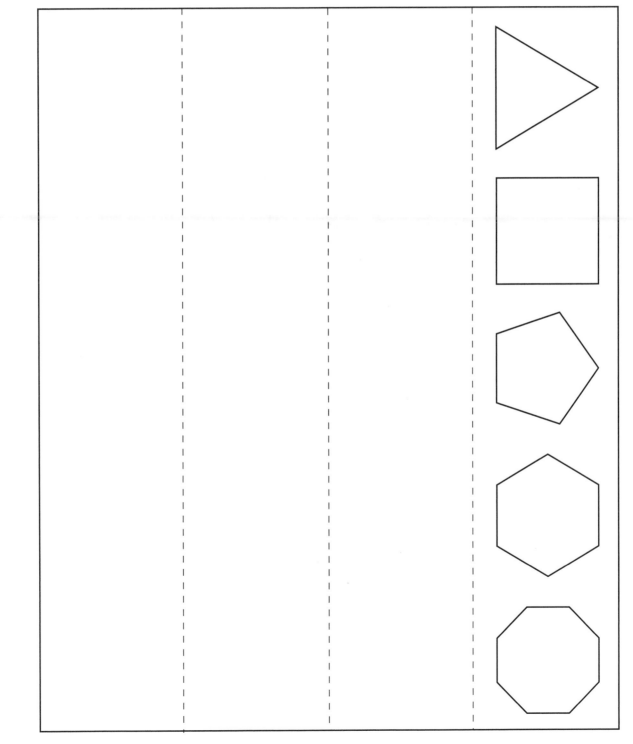

Name Date Time

Sums of Angles in Quadrangles and Pentagons

Sum of the Angles in a Quadrangle

Group	Group Median

Sum of the Angles in a Pentagon

Group	Group Median

Sums of Polygon Angles

Polygon	Class Median
triangle	
quadrangle	
pentagon	
hexagon	

Use with Lesson 3.9.

Name Date Time

A Quadrangle Investigation

The sum of the angles in a quadrangle is equal to 360°. Since there are 360° in a circle, you might predict that every quadrangle will tessellate. Follow the procedure below to investigate this prediction.

1. Fold a piece of paper ($8\frac{1}{2}$" by 11") into six parts by first folding it into thirds and then into halves.

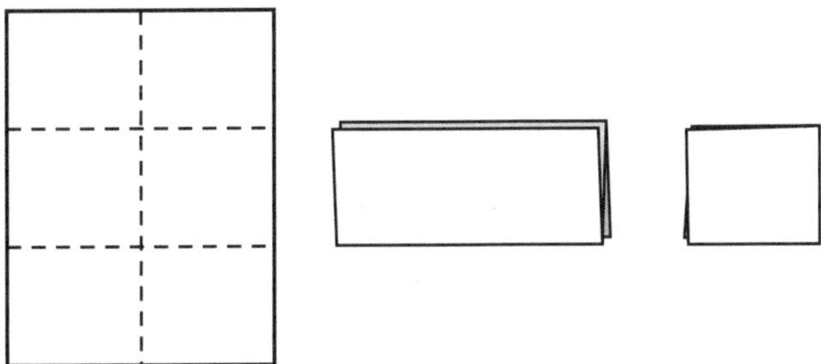

2. Using a straightedge, draw a quadrangle on the top layer of the folded paper. Label each of the four vertices with a letter *inside* the figure—for example, *A, B, C,* and *D.*

3. Cut through all six layers so that you have six identical quadrangles. Label the vertices of each quadrangle in the same manner as the quadrangle on top.

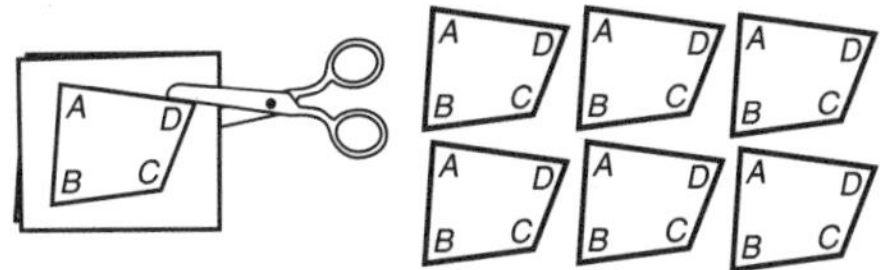

4. Arrange the quadrangles so that they tessellate.

5. When you have a tessellating pattern, tape the final pattern onto a separate piece of paper. Color it if you want.

6. Talk with other students who did this investigation. Were their quadrangles a different shape than yours? Do you think any quadrangle will tessellate?

Option To make a pattern that has more than six quadrangles, draw your original quadrangle on a piece of cardstock, cut it out, and use it as a stencil. By tracing around your quadrangle, you can easily cover a half-sheet of paper with your pattern. Label the angles on your stencil so you can be sure you are placing all four angles around points in the tessellation. Color your finished pattern.

Name Date Time

Problems for the Geometry Template

Record your solutions on *Math Masters,* page 35. Include the problem numbers.

Challenging

Examples

1. Without using a ruler to measure, enlarge the octagon on the Geometry Template to approximately 2 times its size and 3 times its size. (6 points for the double-size octagon and 9 points for the triple-size octagon)

2. Using the triangles on the template, draw three different **kites.** Describe your procedure. Remember, a kite has two pairs of equal sides, but not four equal sides. The equal sides must share an endpoint. (3 points each)

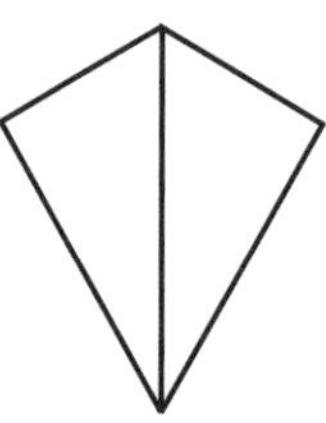

3. Describe how you would draw the largest circle possible with the Geometry Template, without tracing any of the circles on the template. Draw this circle if you have a sheet of paper that is large enough. (15 points)

4. Use your template to draw at least four **parallel lines.** Describe your procedure. (10 points)

5. Each side of the hexagon is 1 unit long. Each side of the equilateral triangle is 1 unit long. Use at least one hexagon and at least one equilateral triangle to make each of the following:

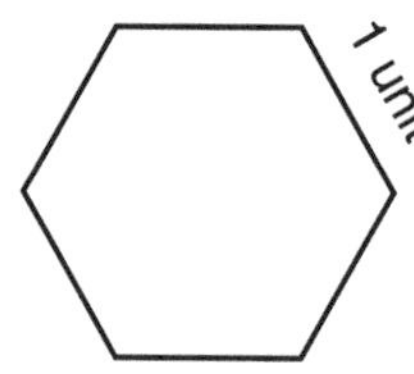

   - An equilateral triangle with sides 3 units long
   - An equilateral triangle with sides 4 units long
   - An equilateral triangle with sides 5 units long
   (10 points each)

6. Draw as many polygons as you can inside each box on *Math Masters,* page 35. The polygons must not overlap. None of the polygons may be used more than once. (1 point for each polygon used)

Name Date Time

Problems for the Geometry Template (cont.)

Solutions

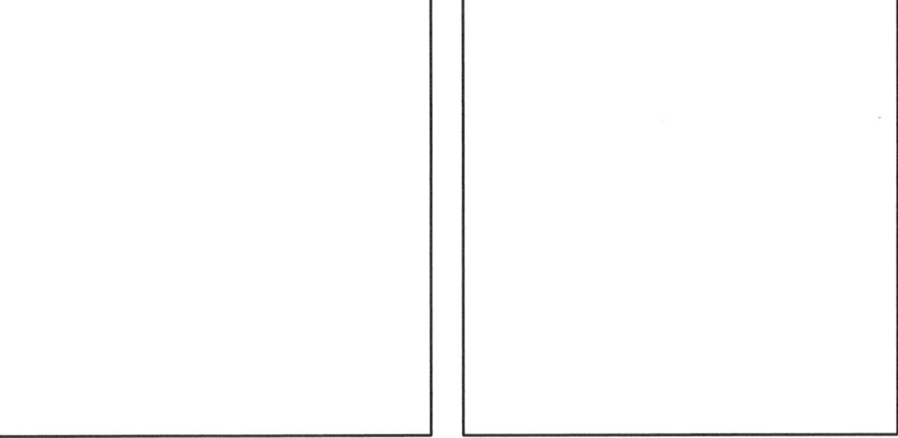

Name Date Time

Tangram Puzzles

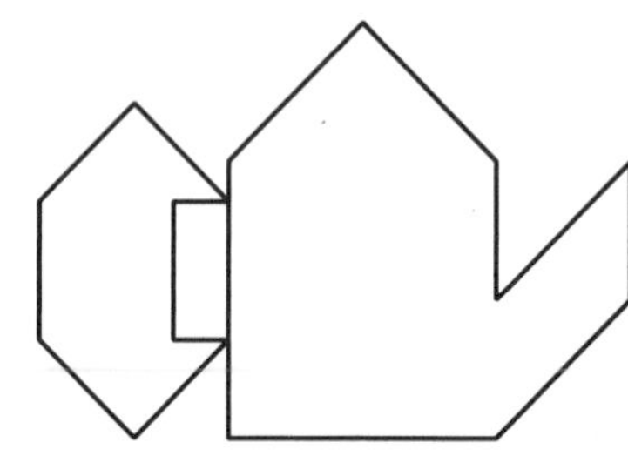

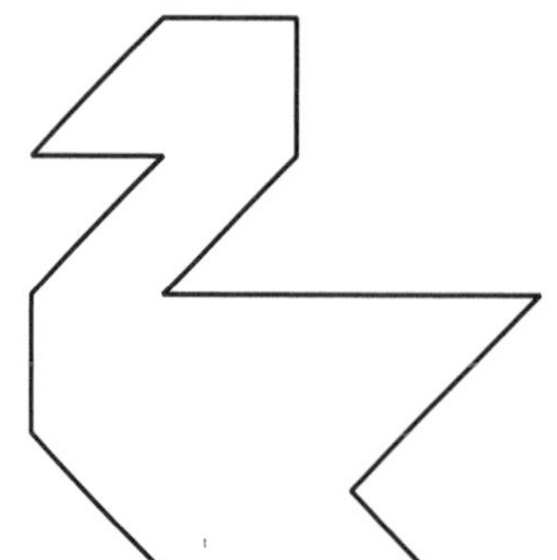

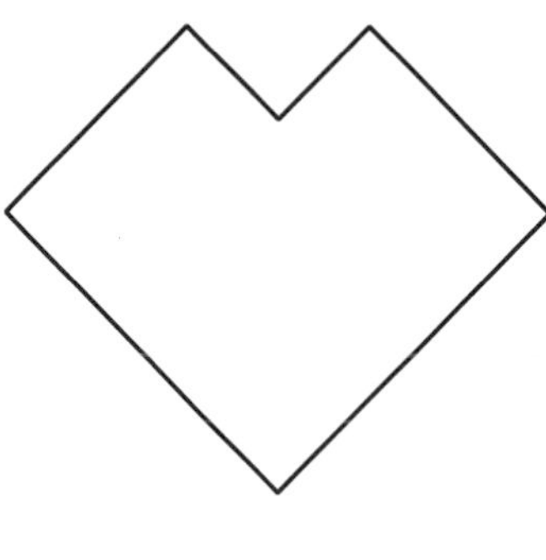

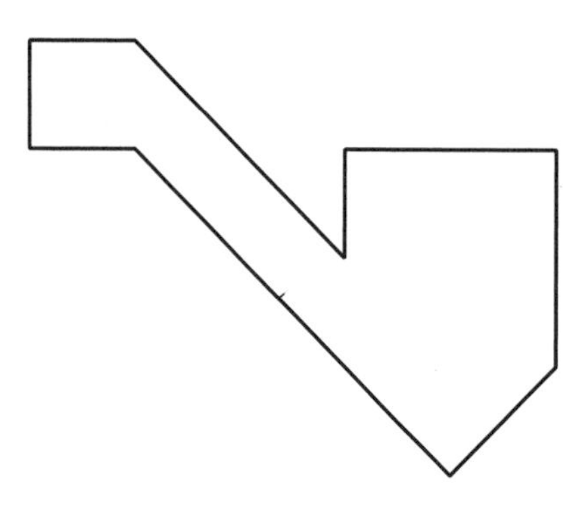

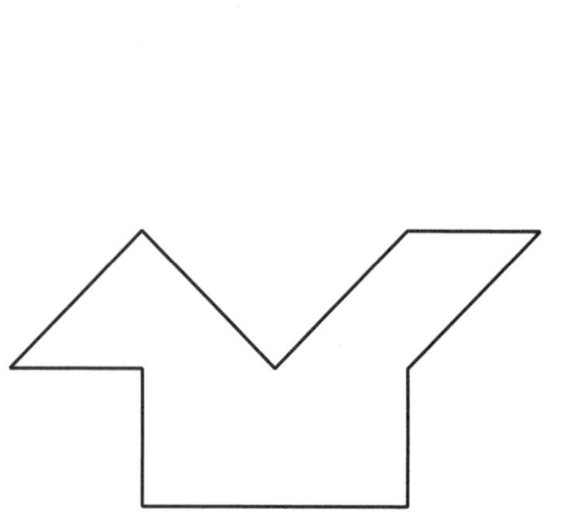

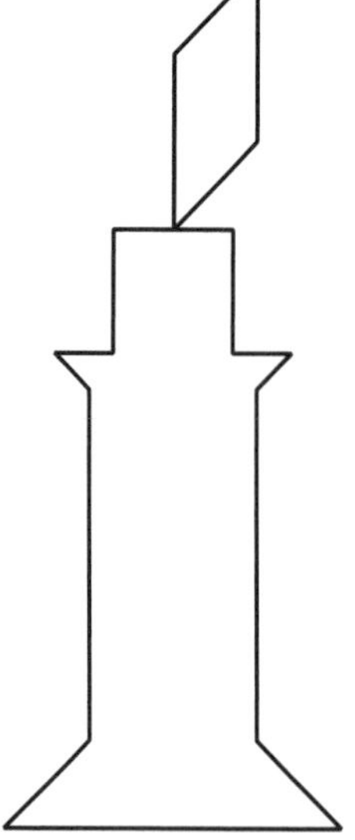

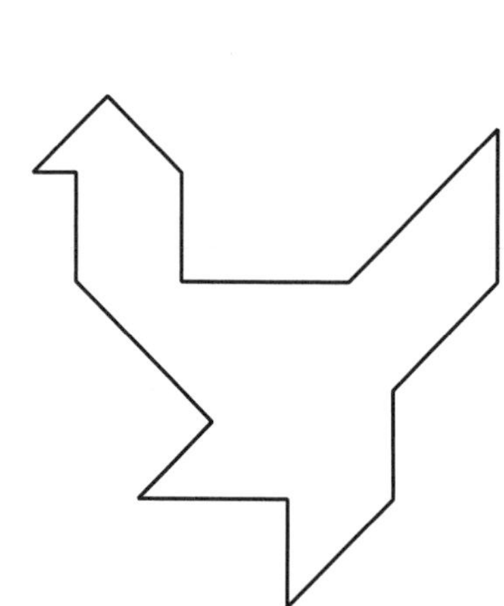

Name Date Time

Tangram Pieces

Name Date Time

Fact Families

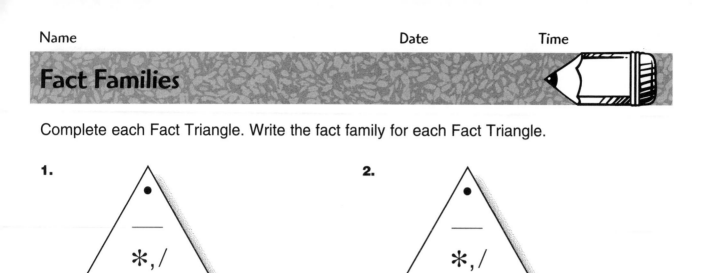

Complete each Fact Triangle. Write the fact family for each Fact Triangle.

1.

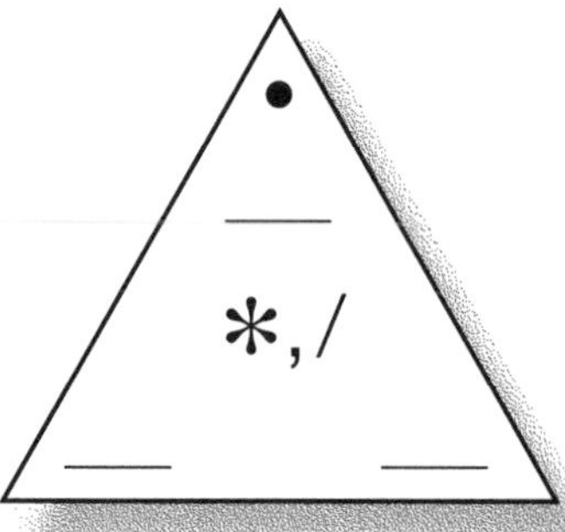

2.

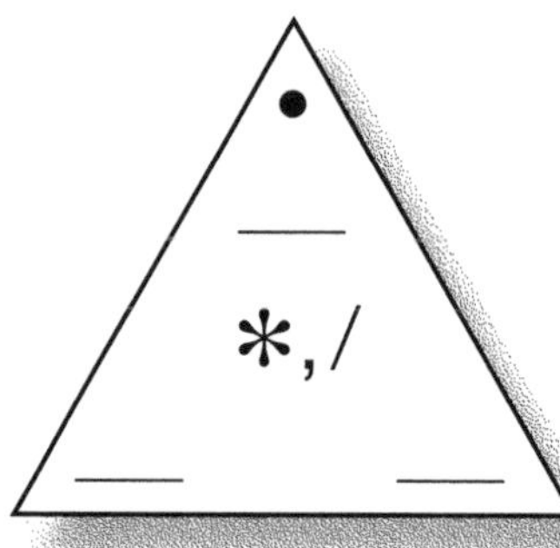

3.

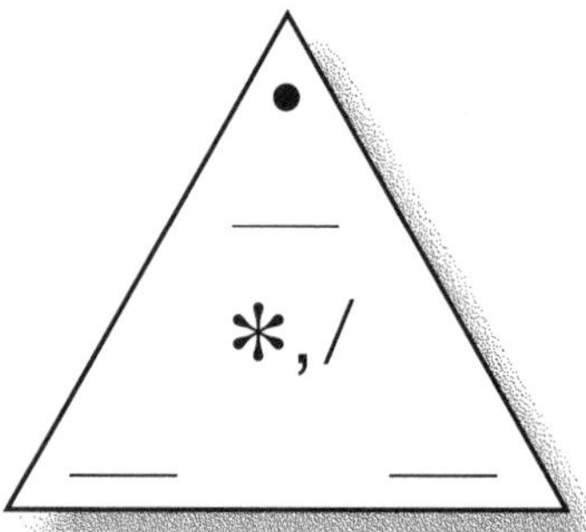

4.

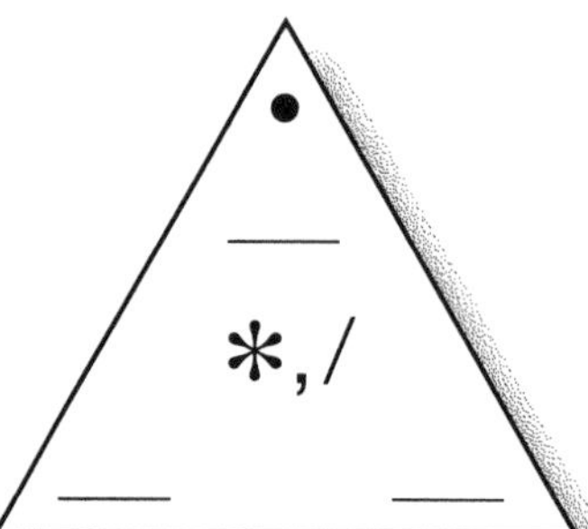

Use with Lesson 4.1.

Name Date Time

Easy Multiples

100 * ______ = ______	100 * ______ = ______
50 * ______ = ______	50 * ______ = ______
20 * ______ = ______	20 * ______ = ______
10 * ______ = ______	10 * ______ = ______
5 * ______ = ______	5 * ______ = ______
1 * ______ = ______	1 * ______ = ______
100 * ______ = ______	100 * ______ = ______
50 * ______ = ______	50 * ______ = ______
20 * ______ = ______	20 * ______ = ______
10 * ______ = ______	10 * ______ = ______
5 * ______ = ______	5 * ______ = ______
1 * ______ = ______	1 * ______ = ______
100 * ______ = ______	100 * ______ = ______
50 * ______ = ______	50 * ______ = ______
20 * ______ = ______	20 * ______ = ______
10 * ______ = ______	10 * ______ = ______
5 * ______ = ______	5 * ______ = ______
1 * ______ = ______	1 * ______ = ______

Name Date Time

Division Practice

For each division problem, complete the multiples of the divisor. Then divide.

1. $\overline{)}$

Answer: ________

200 * ________ = ________

100 * ________ = ________

50 * ________ = ________

20 * ________ = ________

10 * ________ = ________

5 * ________ = ________

1 * ________ = ________

2. ________ ÷ ________

Answer: ________

200 * ________ = ________

100 * ________ = ________

50 * ________ = ________

20 * ________ = ________

10 * ________ = ________

5 * ________ = ________

1 * ________ = ________

3. ________ / ________

Answer: ________

200 * ________ = ________

100 * ________ = ________

50 * ________ = ________

20 * ________ = ________

10 * ________ = ________

5 * ________ = ________

1 * ________ = ________

4. ________ ÷ ________

Answer: ________

200 * ________ = ________

100 * ________ = ________

50 * ________ = ________

20 * ________ = ________

10 * ________ = ________

5 * ________ = ________

1 * ________ = ________

Name Date Time

A Trip through the Panama Canal

The Panama Canal crosses the country of Panama near its capital city, Panama City. The canal connects the Atlantic and Pacific Oceans.

Pretend that you will travel by ship from New York, through the Panama Canal, to Los Angeles.

1. Use the map below to decide on a route that your ship will take. Then use a pencil to draw this route on the map.
2. Estimate the length of the route you have chosen. Use a ruler, string, compass, paper and pencil, or any other tool. ________ miles
3. How much longer is your route than the straight-line distance from New York to Los Angeles? ________ miles

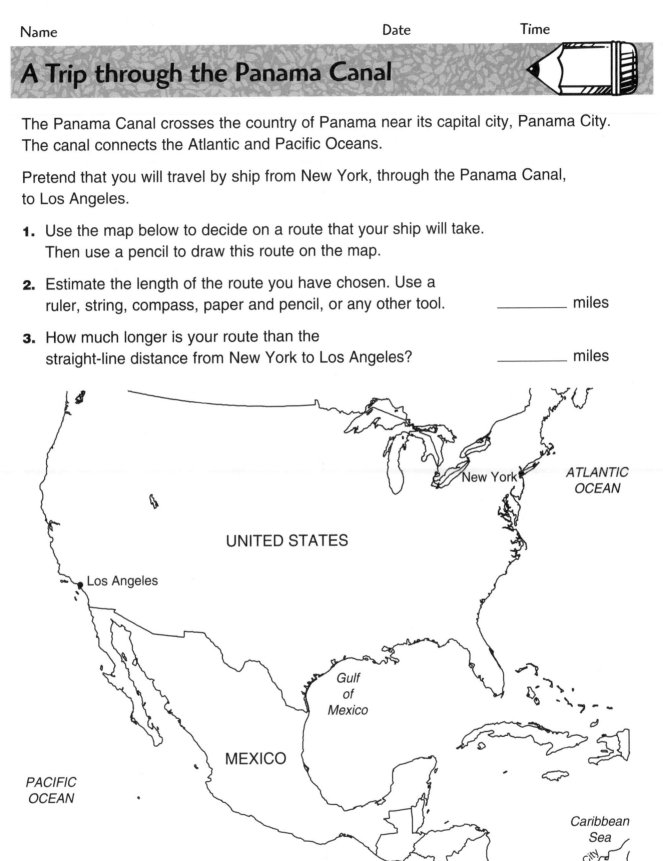

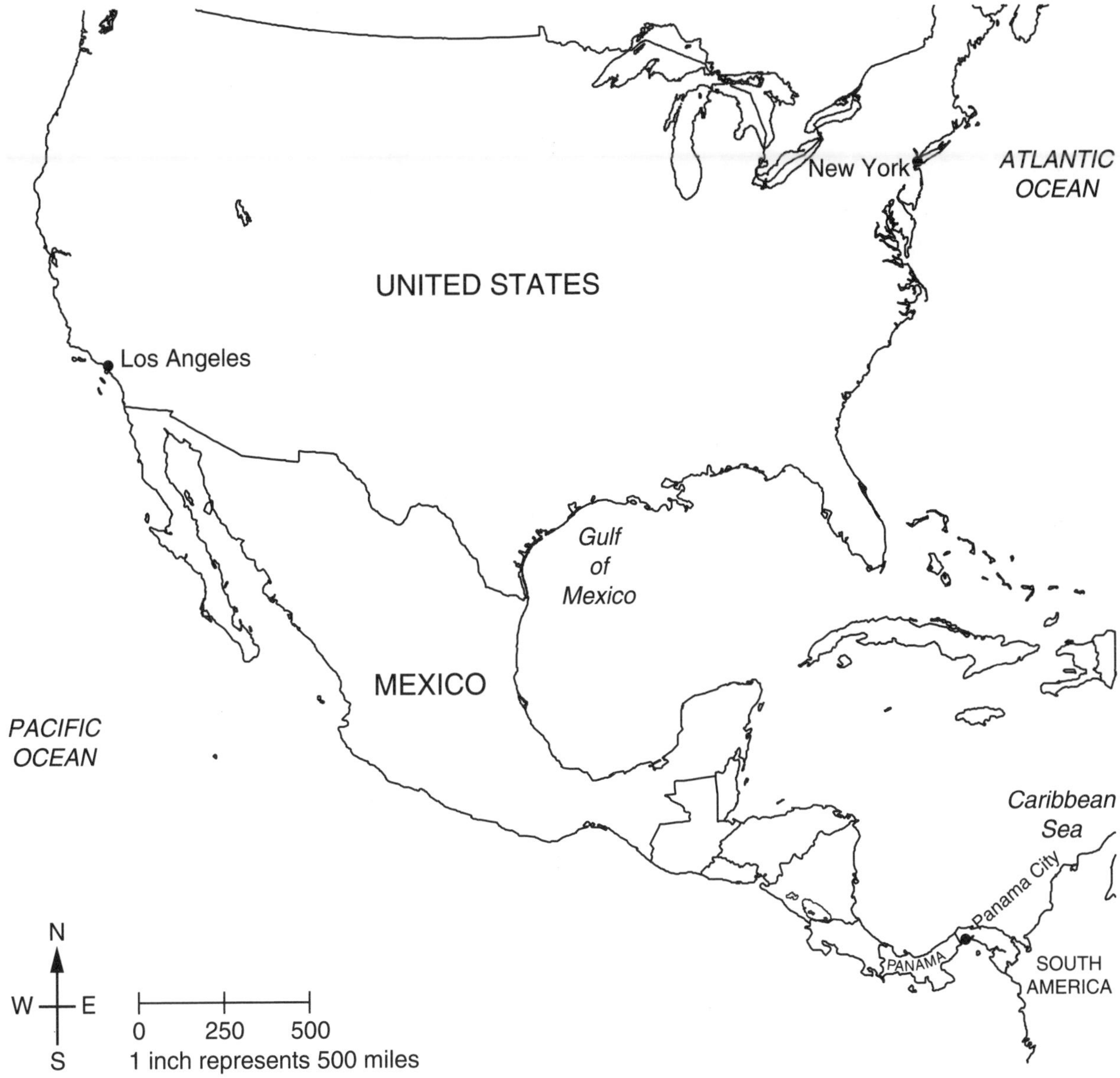

Name Date Time

Division with Base-10 Blocks

For each problem:

- First, use □ | . to represent the dividend with base-10 blocks.
- Then use □ | . to show how you would distribute the blocks in equal groups to represent the division.
- Record your answer with digits.

Example 5)689 □□□□□□ ||||| ||| ::::.

□ ||| ::...	□ ||| ::...	□ ||| ::...	□ ||| ::...	□ ||| ::...

....

Answer: 5)689 137 R4

1. 3)427

- Show the dividend:
- Show equal groups below.

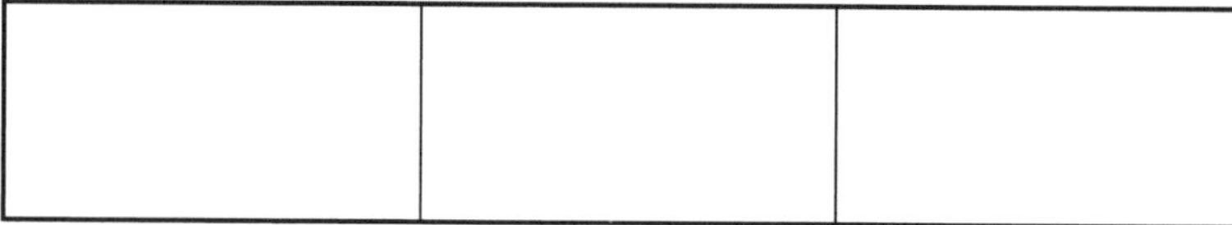

- Write the answer. 3)427

2. 4)555

- Show the dividend:
- Show equal groups below.

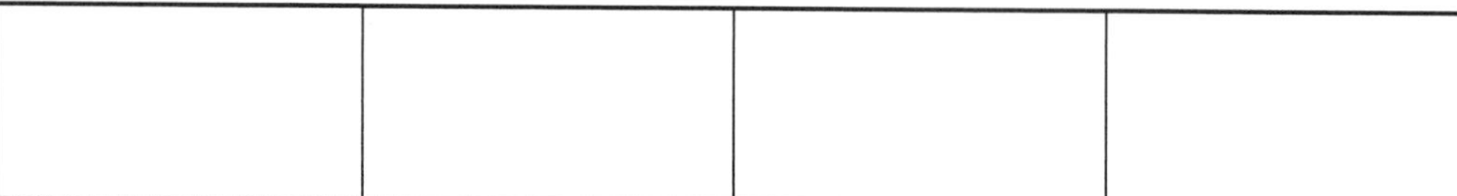

- Write the answer. 4)555

Name Date Time

A Division Challenge

Judy and two friends bought a raffle ticket at the school fundraiser. They agreed that if they won, they would share the winnings equally. They won $145! They received one $100 bill, four $10 bills, and five $1 bills.

Judy used the division algorithm shown below to calculate how much money each person should get. She wanted to calculate the answer to the penny. Can you figure out how the algorithm works?

(*Hint:* There were 3 people in all. Judy realized that in order to share the $100 bill, they needed to trade it for ten $10 bills. Then they would have fourteen $10 bills and five $1 bills.)

	100s	10s	1s	10ths	100ths
		4	8 •	3	3
3	1	4	5	0	0
		14	25	10	10
		12	24	9	9
		2	1	1	1

1. Explain how you think the algorithm works. ____________________

2. Explain what Judy did when she had $1 left. ____________________

3. How much money did each person get? ____________________

4. Use the algorithm to divide: $4\overline{)51.6}$ ____________________

Name Date Time

Practice with Remainders

For each number story:

- Draw a picture to represent the problem. Make sure to show the remainder in your picture.
- Write a number sentence.
- Use a division algorithm to solve the problem.
- Decide what to do about the remainder and explain your decision.
- Record your solution to the problem.

1. Ms. Haag is rearranging her classroom. There are 30 students in the classroom. The students sit at tables. Four students can sit at each table. How many tables does she need?

Number sentence: ______________________________

Explain what you did with the remainder. ______________________________

____

____

Solution: ________ tables

2. Marc needs 3 square yards of fabric to make a cape for a costume party. His friends want a cape to match his. If Marc has 17 square yards of fabric, how many capes can he make?

Number sentence: ______________________________

Explain what you did with the remainder. ______________________________

____

____

Solution: ________ capes

Name Date Time

Math Message

Math Message

Name: ____________________

1st die ______________

2nd die ______________

Product (P) ______________

$20 * P =$ ______________

Math Message

Name: ____________________

1st die ______________

2nd die ______________

Product (P) ______________

$20 * P =$ ______________

Math Message

Name: ____________________

1st die ______________

2nd die ______________

Product (P) ______________

$20 * P =$ ______________

Math Message

Name: ____________________

1st die ______________

2nd die ______________

Product (P) ______________

$20 * P =$ ______________

Math Message

Name: ____________________

1st die ______________

2nd die ______________

Product (P) ______________

$20 * P =$ ______________

Math Message

Name: ____________________

1st die ______________

2nd die ______________

Product (P) ______________

$20 * P =$ ______________

Name Date Time

First to 100 Problem Cards

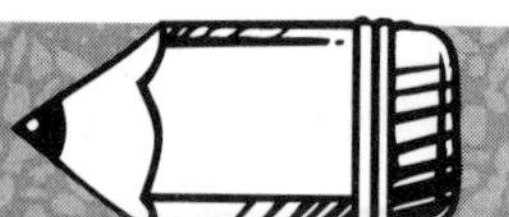

How many inches are there in x feet? How many centimeters are there in x meters? 1	How many quarts are there in x gallons? 2	What is the smallest number of x's you can add to get a sum greater than 100? 3	Is $50 * x$ greater than 1,000? Is $\frac{x}{10}$ less than 1? 4
$\frac{1}{2}$ of $x = ?$ $\frac{1}{10}$ of $x = ?$ 5	$1 - x = ?$ $x + 998 = ?$ 6	If x people share 1,000 stamps equally, how many stamps will each person get? 7	What time will it be x minutes from now? What time was it x minutes ago? 8
It is 102 miles to your destination. You have gone x miles. How many miles are left? 9	What whole or mixed number equals x divided by 2? 10	Is x a prime or a composite number? Is x divisible by 2? 11	The time is 11:05 A.M. The train left x minutes ago. What time did the train leave? 12
Bill was born in 1939. Freddy was born the same day, but x years later. In what year was Freddy born? 13	Which is larger: $2 * x$ or $x + 50$? 14	There are x rows of seats. There are 9 seats in each row. How many seats are there in all? 15	Sargon spent x cents on apples. If she paid with a \$5 bill, how much change should she get? 16

Name Date Time

First to 100 Problem Cards (cont.)

The temperature was 25°F. It dropped x degrees. What is the new temperature? 17	Each story in a building is 10 feet high. If the building has x stories, how tall is it? 18	Which is larger: $2 * x$ or $\frac{100}{x}$? 19	$20 * x = ?$ 20
Name all of the whole-number factors of x. 21	Is x an even or an odd number? Is x divisible by 9? 22	Shalanda was born on a Tuesday. Linda was born x days later. On what day of the week was Linda born? 23	Will had a quarter plus x cents. How much money did he have in all? 24
Find the perimeter and area of this square. x cm x cm 25	What is the median of these weights? 5 pounds 21 pounds x pounds What is the range? 26	$x°$?° 27	$x^2 = ?$ 50% of $x^2 = ?$ 28
$(3x + 4) - 8 = ?$ 29	x out of 100 students voted for Ruby. Is this more than 25%, less than 25%, or exactly 25% of the students? 30	There are 200 students at Wilson School. x% speak Spanish. How many students speak Spanish? 31	People answered a survey question either Yes or No. x% answered Yes. What percent answered No? 32

Name Date Time

Algebra Election Gameboard

WA
Washington
11

MT
Montana
3

ND
North Dakota
3

OR
Oregon
7

ID
Idaho
4

SD
South Dakota
3

WY
Wyoming
3

5

NV
Nevada
5

NE
Nebraska
5

UT
Utah
5

CO
Colorado
9

CA
California
55

KS
Kansas
6

AZ
Arizona
10

NM
New Mexico
5

OK
Oklahoma
8

TX
Texas
34

AK
Alaska
3

HI
Hawaii
4

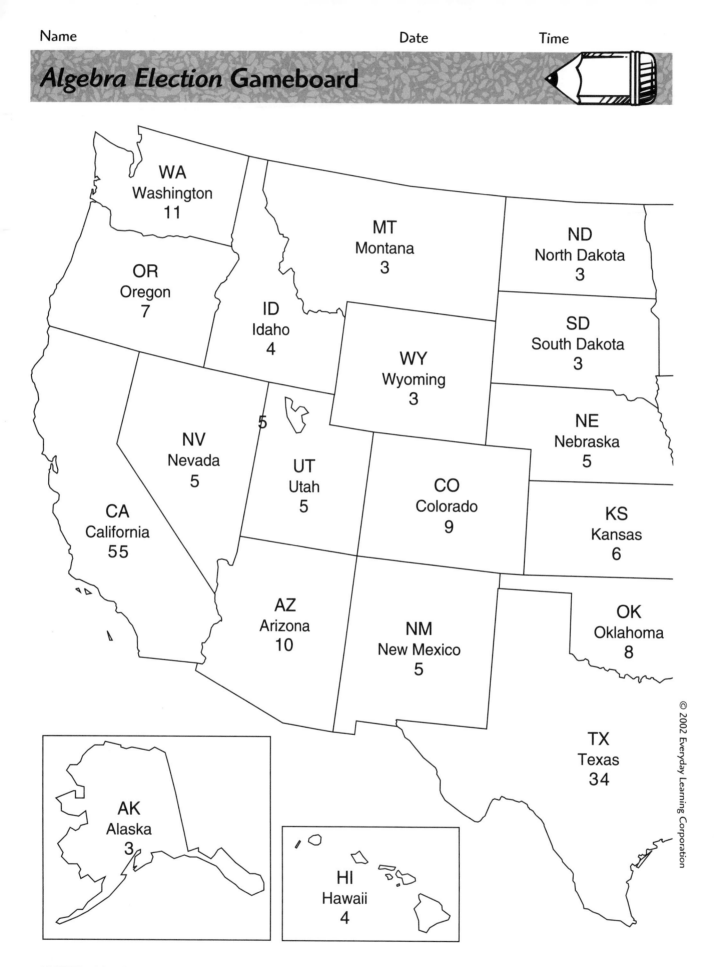

NOTE: Alaska and Hawaii are not drawn to scale.

Use with Lesson 4.6.

Name Date Time

Algebra Election Gameboard (cont.)

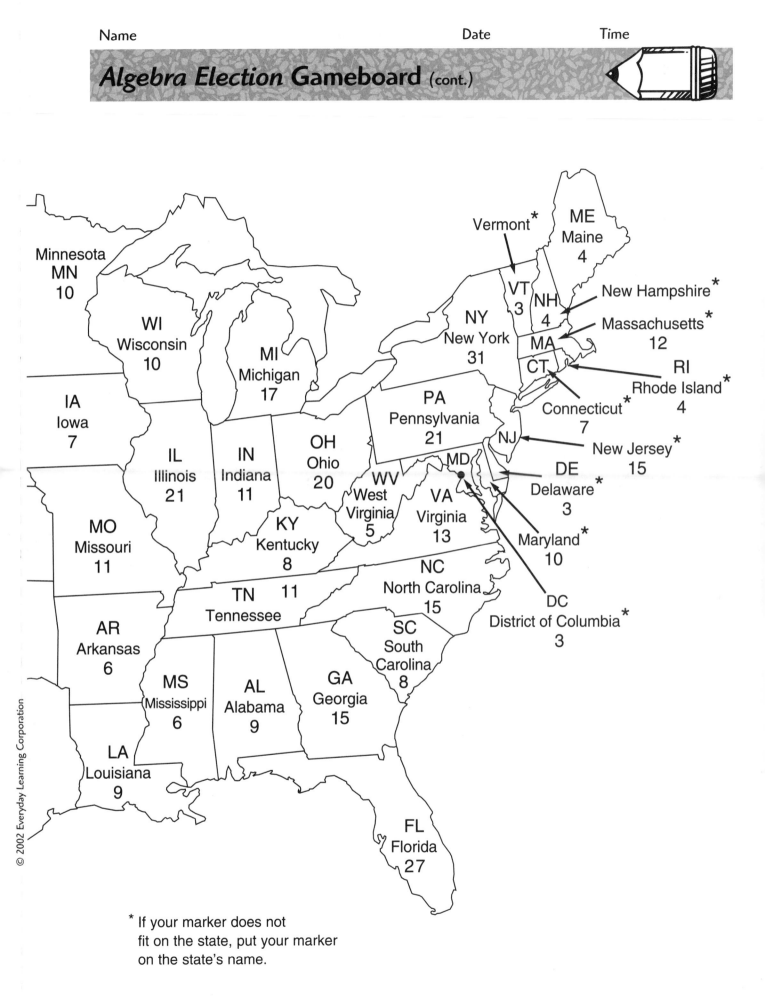

Minnesota
MN
10

WI
Wisconsin
10

MI
Michigan
17

Vermont*

ME
Maine
4

VT
3

NH
4

New Hampshire*

NY
New York
31

MA

Massachusetts*
12

CT

RI
Rhode Island*
4

IA
Iowa
7

IL
Illinois
21

IN
Indiana
11

OH
Ohio
20

PA
Pennsylvania
21

Connecticut*
7

NJ

New Jersey*
15

MD

DE
Delaware*
3

WV
West Virginia
5

VA
Virginia
13

MO
Missouri
11

KY
Kentucky
8

Maryland*
10

NC
North Carolina
15

TN 11
Tennessee

DC
District of Columbia*
3

AR
Arkansas
6

SC
South Carolina
8

MS
Mississippi
6

AL
Alabama
9

GA
Georgia
15

LA
Louisiana
9

FL
Florida
27

* If your marker does not fit on the state, put your marker on the state's name.

Name Date Time

Ruler Close-Up

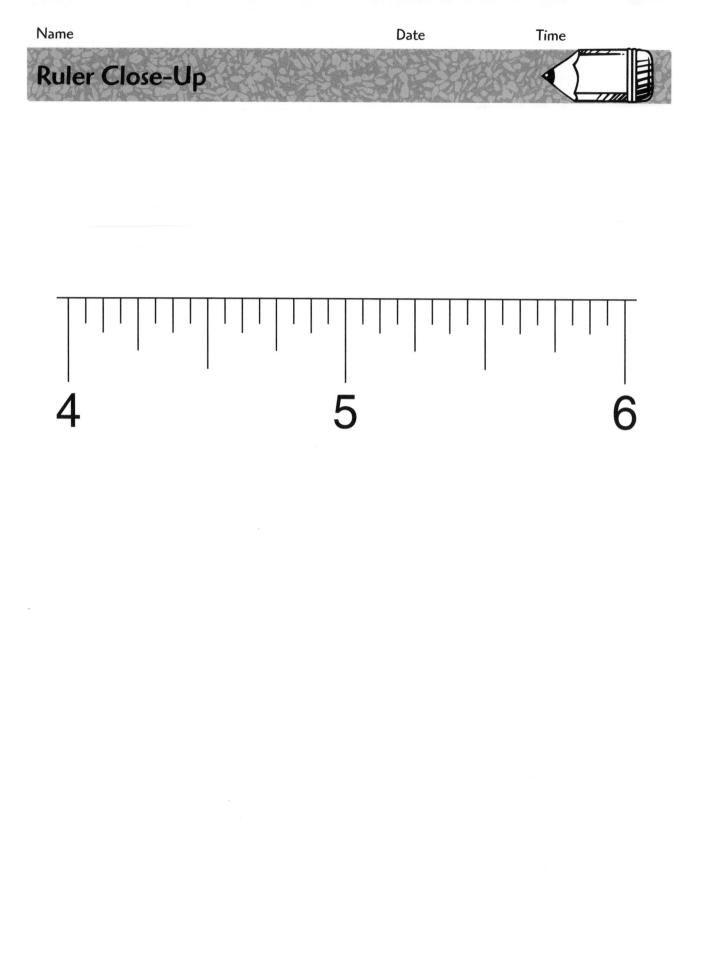

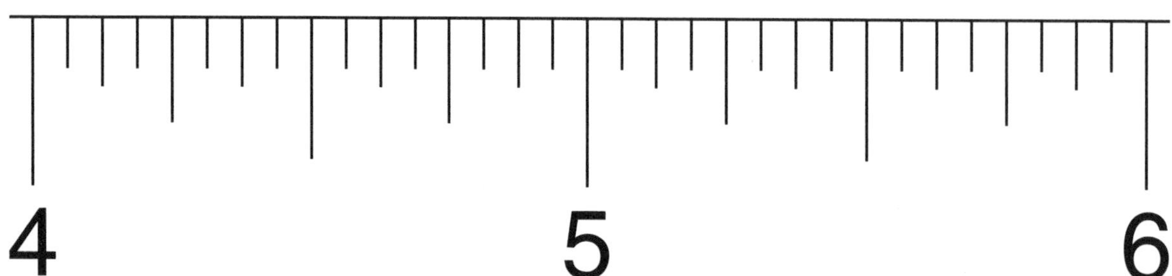

Name Date Time

Pattern-Block Fractions

For Problems 1–3, Shape A is the Whole.

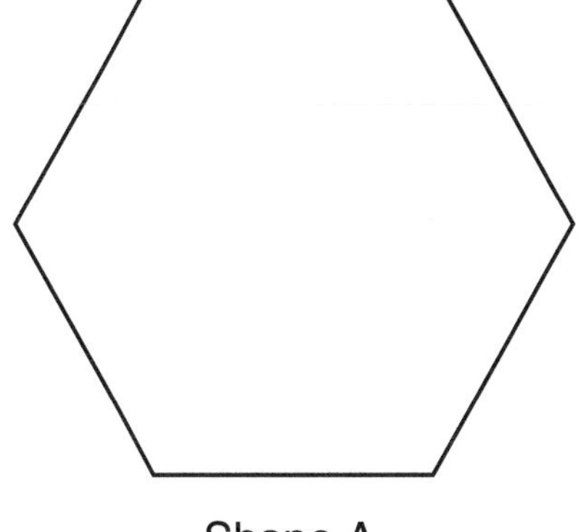

Shape A

1. What fraction of the shape is covered by 1 trapezoid?

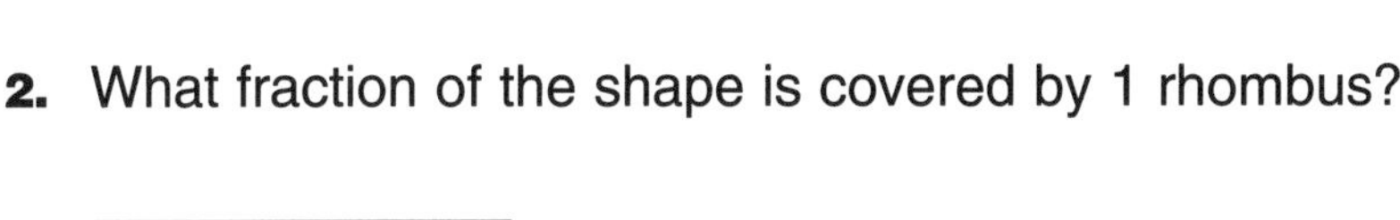

____

2. What fraction of the shape is covered by 1 rhombus?

____

3. What fraction of the shape is covered by 1 triangle?

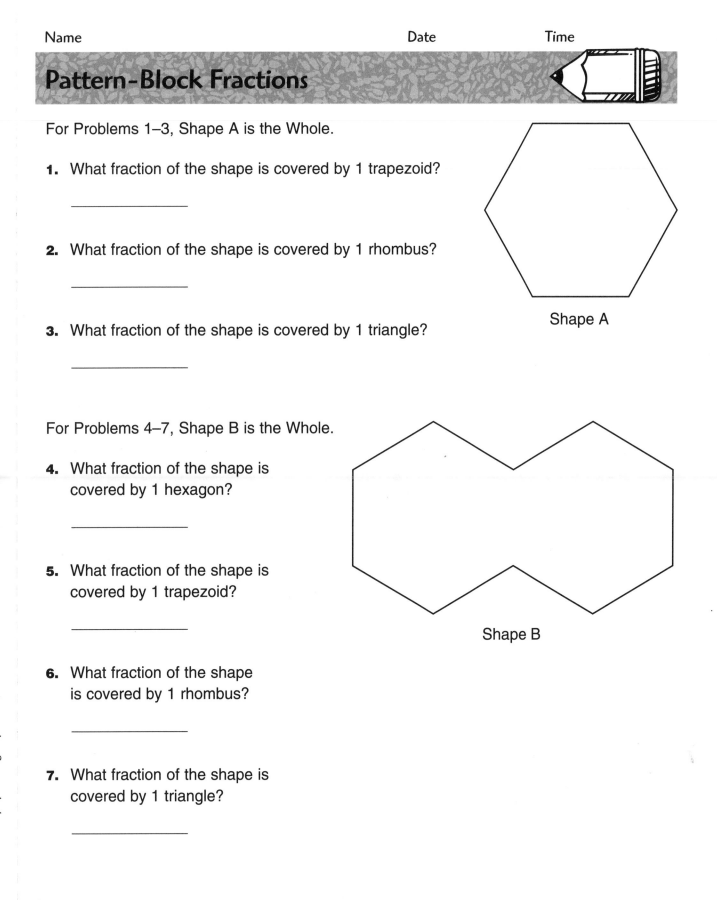

____

For Problems 4–7, Shape B is the Whole.

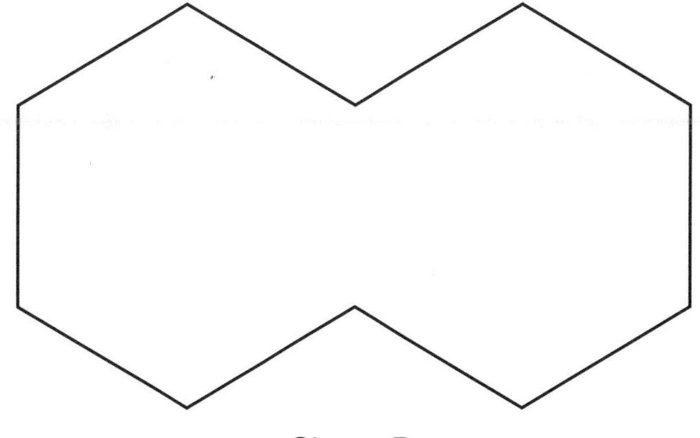

Shape B

4. What fraction of the shape is covered by 1 hexagon?

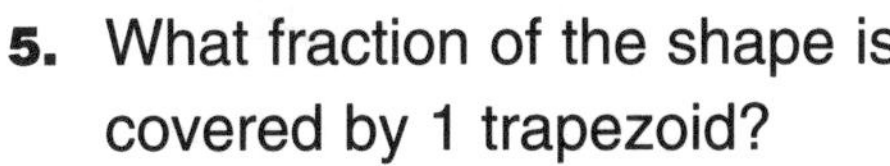

____

5. What fraction of the shape is covered by 1 trapezoid?

____

6. What fraction of the shape is covered by 1 rhombus?

____

7. What fraction of the shape is covered by 1 triangle?

____

Name Date Time

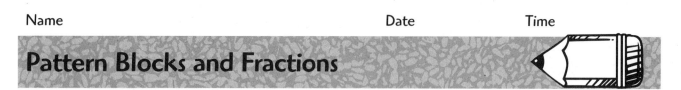

Pattern Blocks and Fractions

Make up your own problem like Problem 9 on journal page 128. Follow the same steps.

1. Choose one pattern block and give it a value. The block can be worth ONE or a fraction of ONE. Draw the block and record its value.

The ____________ is worth ____________.

2. Fill in the chart below, based on your choice.

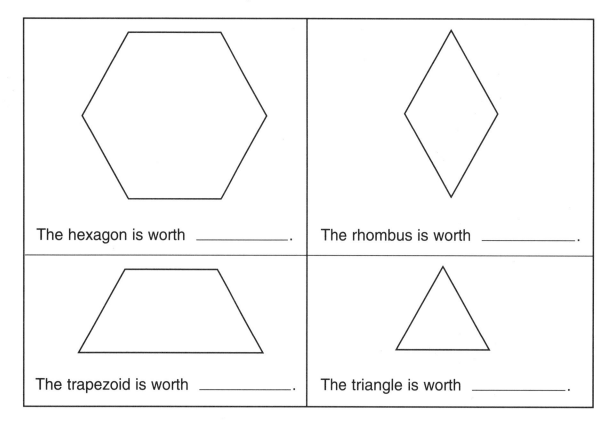

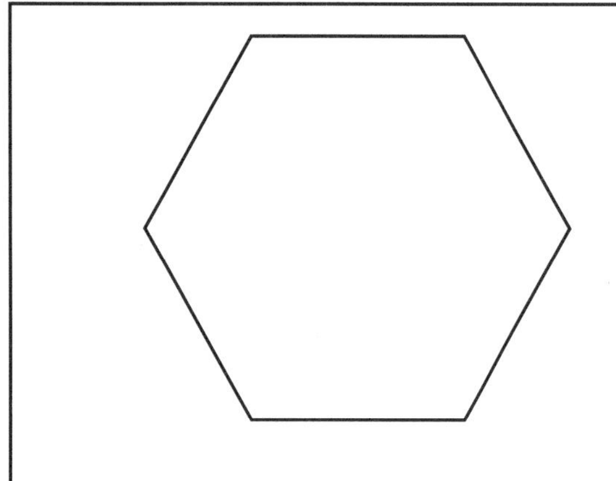 The hexagon is worth ____________.	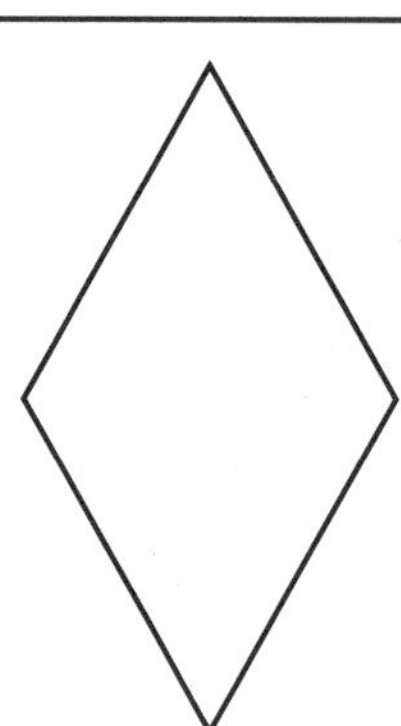 The rhombus is worth ____________.
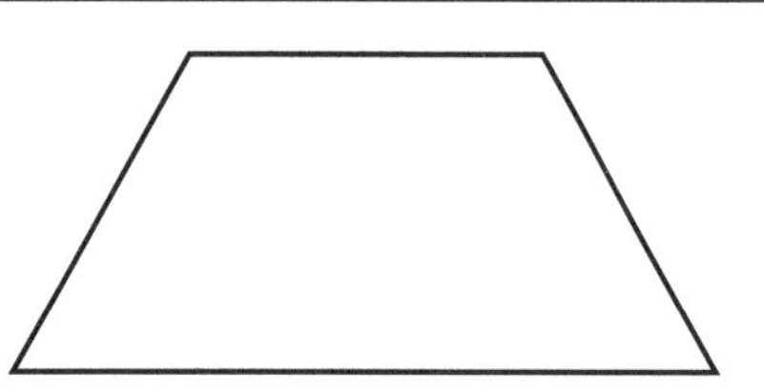 The trapezoid is worth ____________.	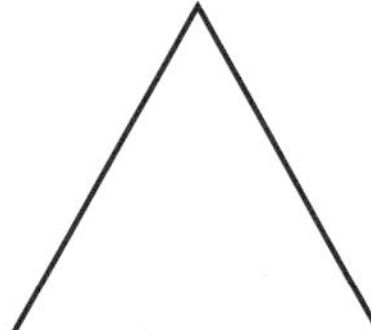 The triangle is worth ____________.

3. In the space below or on another piece of paper, make a design with about 10 pattern blocks. Trace the outline of each block. (Or use the pattern-block shapes on the Geometry Template.)

4. Label each part of your design with a fraction. How much is the design worth? ______

5. Write a number model to show how you calculated the value of the design.

____

Name　　　　Date　　　　Time

Fraction-Stick Chart

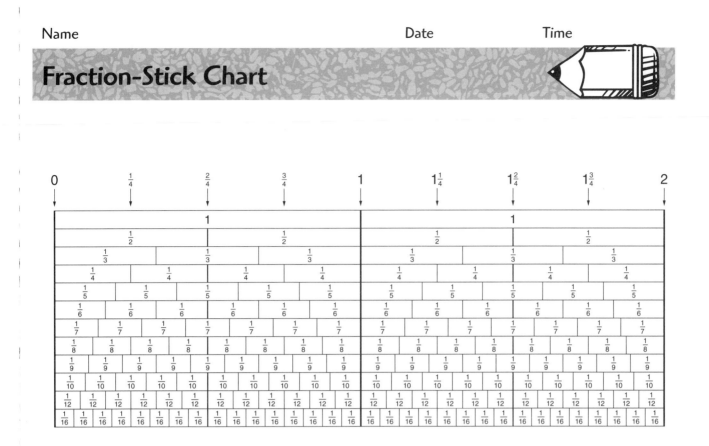

0　$\frac{1}{4}$　$\frac{2}{4}$　$\frac{3}{4}$　1　$1\frac{1}{4}$　$1\frac{2}{4}$　$1\frac{3}{4}$　2

1 | 1

$\frac{1}{2}$ | $\frac{1}{2}$ | $\frac{1}{2}$ | $\frac{1}{2}$

$\frac{1}{3}$ | $\frac{1}{3}$ | $\frac{1}{3}$ | $\frac{1}{3}$ | $\frac{1}{3}$ | $\frac{1}{3}$

$\frac{1}{4}$ | $\frac{1}{4}$ | $\frac{1}{4}$ | $\frac{1}{4}$ | $\frac{1}{4}$ | $\frac{1}{4}$ | $\frac{1}{4}$ | $\frac{1}{4}$

$\frac{1}{5}$ | $\frac{1}{5}$ | $\frac{1}{5}$ | $\frac{1}{5}$ | $\frac{1}{5}$ | $\frac{1}{5}$ | $\frac{1}{5}$ | $\frac{1}{5}$ | $\frac{1}{5}$ | $\frac{1}{5}$

$\frac{1}{6}$ | $\frac{1}{6}$ | $\frac{1}{6}$ | $\frac{1}{6}$ | $\frac{1}{6}$ | $\frac{1}{6}$ | $\frac{1}{6}$ | $\frac{1}{6}$ | $\frac{1}{6}$ | $\frac{1}{6}$ | $\frac{1}{6}$ | $\frac{1}{6}$

$\frac{1}{7}$ | $\frac{1}{7}$ | $\frac{1}{7}$ | $\frac{1}{7}$ | $\frac{1}{7}$ | $\frac{1}{7}$ | $\frac{1}{7}$ | $\frac{1}{7}$ | $\frac{1}{7}$ | $\frac{1}{7}$ | $\frac{1}{7}$ | $\frac{1}{7}$ | $\frac{1}{7}$ | $\frac{1}{7}$

$\frac{1}{8}$ | $\frac{1}{8}$ | $\frac{1}{8}$ | $\frac{1}{8}$ | $\frac{1}{8}$ | $\frac{1}{8}$ | $\frac{1}{8}$ | $\frac{1}{8}$ | $\frac{1}{8}$ | $\frac{1}{8}$ | $\frac{1}{8}$ | $\frac{1}{8}$ | $\frac{1}{8}$ | $\frac{1}{8}$ | $\frac{1}{8}$ | $\frac{1}{8}$

$\frac{1}{9}$ | $\frac{1}{9}$ | $\frac{1}{9}$ | $\frac{1}{9}$ | $\frac{1}{9}$ | $\frac{1}{9}$ | $\frac{1}{9}$ | $\frac{1}{9}$ | $\frac{1}{9}$ | $\frac{1}{9}$ | $\frac{1}{9}$ | $\frac{1}{9}$ | $\frac{1}{9}$ | $\frac{1}{9}$ | $\frac{1}{9}$ | $\frac{1}{9}$ | $\frac{1}{9}$ | $\frac{1}{9}$

$\frac{1}{10}$ | $\frac{1}{10}$ | $\frac{1}{10}$ | $\frac{1}{10}$ | $\frac{1}{10}$ | $\frac{1}{10}$ | $\frac{1}{10}$ | $\frac{1}{10}$ | $\frac{1}{10}$ | $\frac{1}{10}$ | $\frac{1}{10}$ | $\frac{1}{10}$ | $\frac{1}{10}$ | $\frac{1}{10}$ | $\frac{1}{10}$ | $\frac{1}{10}$ | $\frac{1}{10}$ | $\frac{1}{10}$ | $\frac{1}{10}$ | $\frac{1}{10}$

$\frac{1}{12}$ | $\frac{1}{12}$ | $\frac{1}{12}$ | $\frac{1}{12}$ | $\frac{1}{12}$ | $\frac{1}{12}$ | $\frac{1}{12}$ | $\frac{1}{12}$ | $\frac{1}{12}$ | $\frac{1}{12}$ | $\frac{1}{12}$ | $\frac{1}{12}$ | $\frac{1}{12}$ | $\frac{1}{12}$ | $\frac{1}{12}$ | $\frac{1}{12}$ | $\frac{1}{12}$ | $\frac{1}{12}$ | $\frac{1}{12}$ | $\frac{1}{12}$ | $\frac{1}{12}$ | $\frac{1}{12}$ | $\frac{1}{12}$ | $\frac{1}{12}$

$\frac{1}{16}$ | $\frac{1}{16}$ | $\frac{1}{16}$ | $\frac{1}{16}$ | $\frac{1}{16}$ | $\frac{1}{16}$ | $\frac{1}{16}$ | $\frac{1}{16}$ | $\frac{1}{16}$ | $\frac{1}{16}$ | $\frac{1}{16}$ | $\frac{1}{16}$ | $\frac{1}{16}$ | $\frac{1}{16}$ | $\frac{1}{16}$ | $\frac{1}{16}$ | $\frac{1}{16}$ | $\frac{1}{16}$ | $\frac{1}{16}$ | $\frac{1}{16}$ | $\frac{1}{16}$ | $\frac{1}{16}$ | $\frac{1}{16}$ | $\frac{1}{16}$ | $\frac{1}{16}$ | $\frac{1}{16}$ | $\frac{1}{16}$ | $\frac{1}{16}$ | $\frac{1}{16}$ | $\frac{1}{16}$ | $\frac{1}{16}$ | $\frac{1}{16}$

Name Date Time

Number Lines

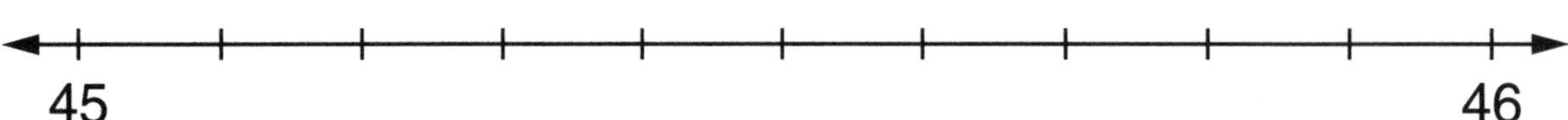

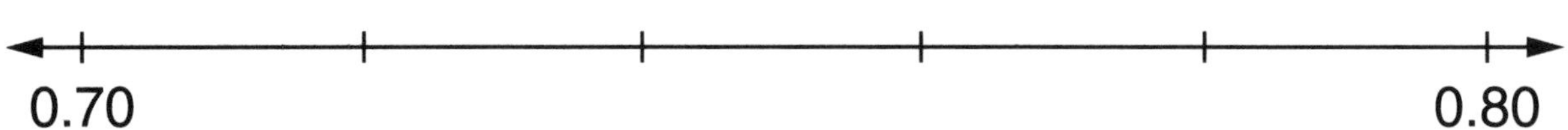

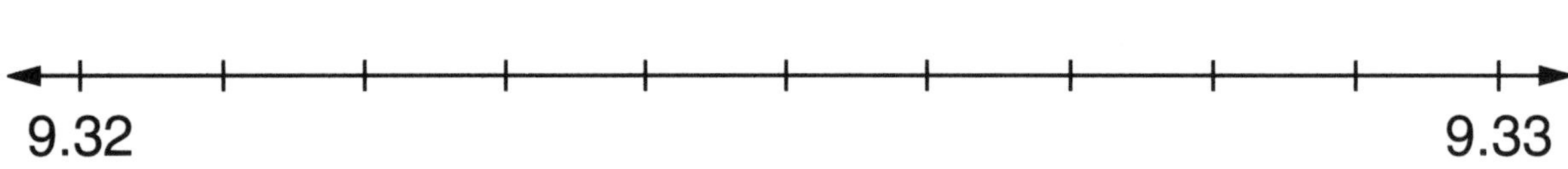

 Use with Lesson 5.5.

Name Date Time

Base-10 Grids

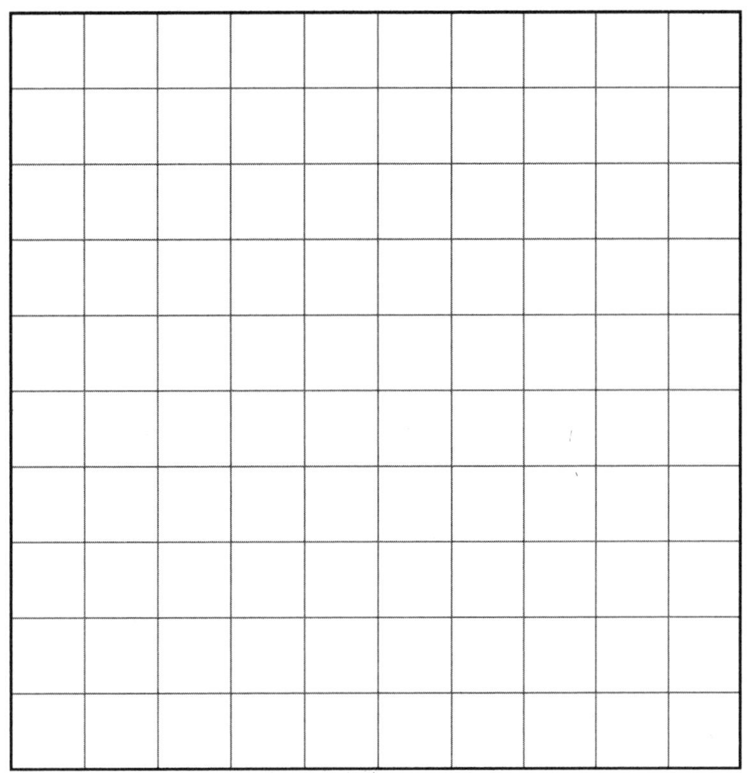

Name Date Time

Rounding Whole Numbers and Decimals

Draw number lines to help you round the numbers below.

Example Round 37 to the nearest ten.

- Draw and label a number line from the first multiple of 10 less than 37 (that is, 30) to the first multiple of 10 greater than 37 (that is, 40). Mark and label the point halfway between these endpoints (35).
- Find 37 on the number line. Mark and label it.
- Since 37 is closer to 40, round 37 up to 40.

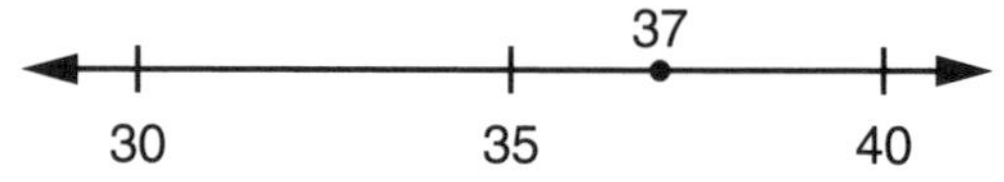

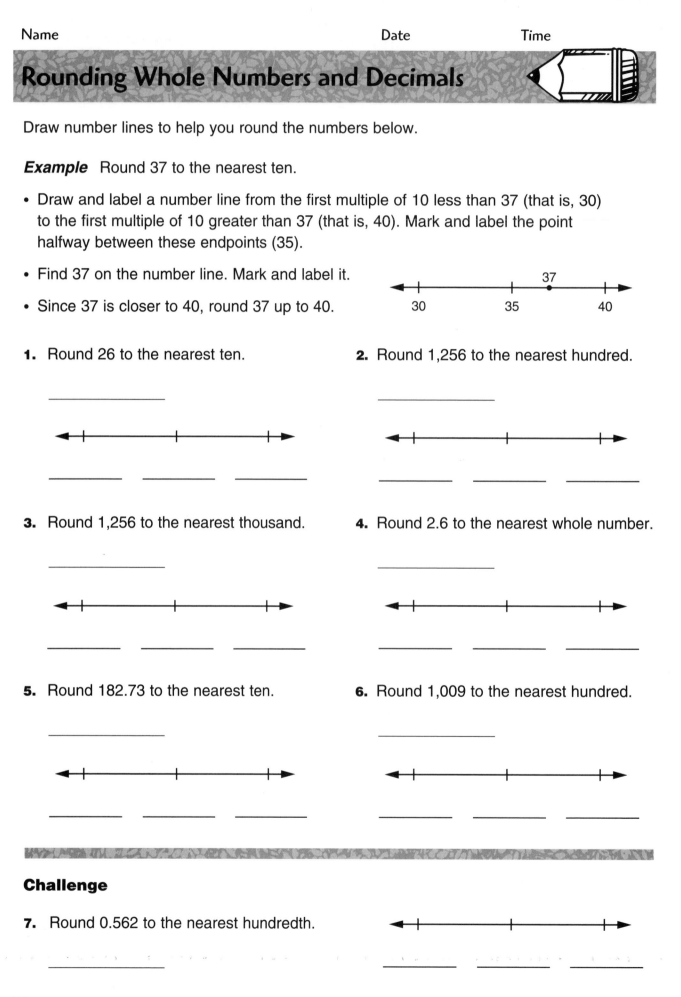

1. Round 26 to the nearest ten.

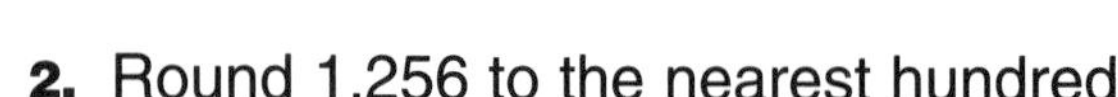

2. Round 1,256 to the nearest hundred.

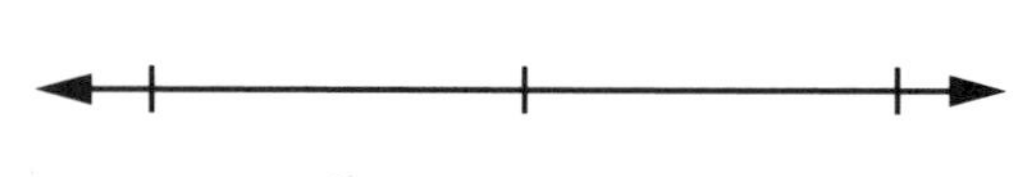

3. Round 1,256 to the nearest thousand.

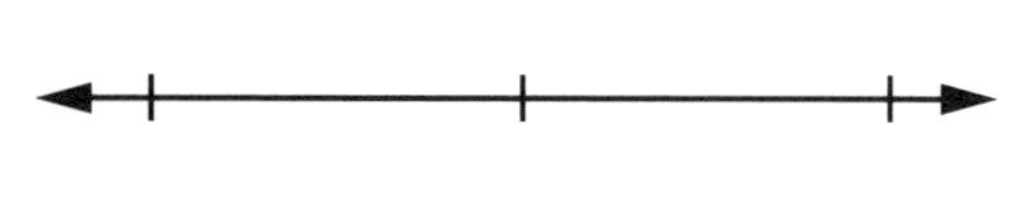

4. Round 2.6 to the nearest whole number.

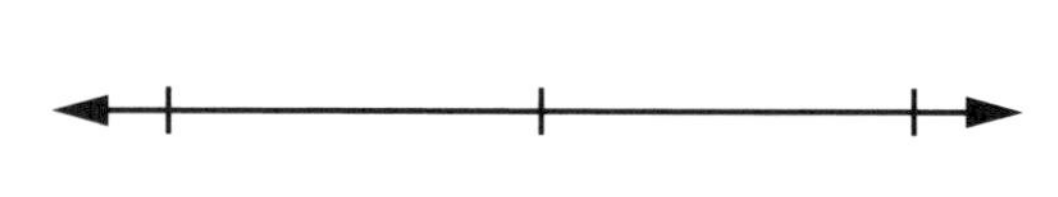

5. Round 182.73 to the nearest ten.

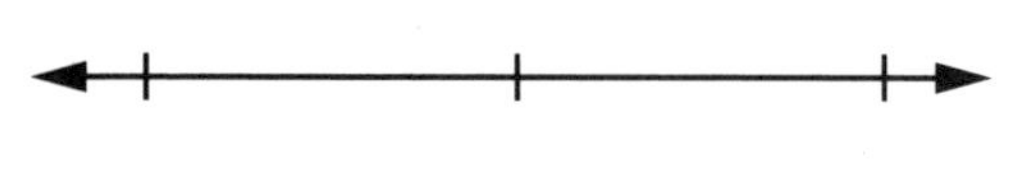

6. Round 1,009 to the nearest hundred.

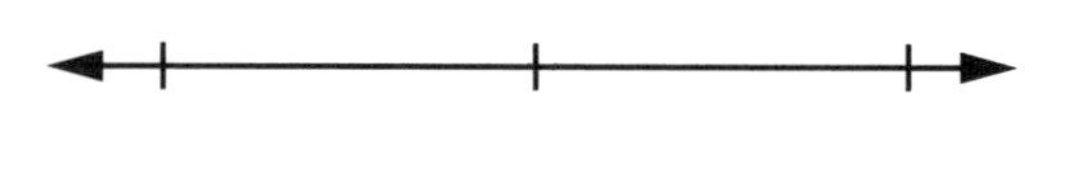

Challenge

7. Round 0.562 to the nearest hundredth.

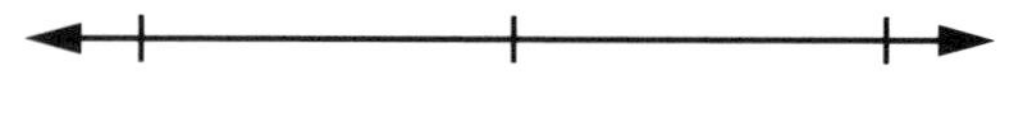

Name Date Time

Fraction-Stick Chart and Decimal Number Line

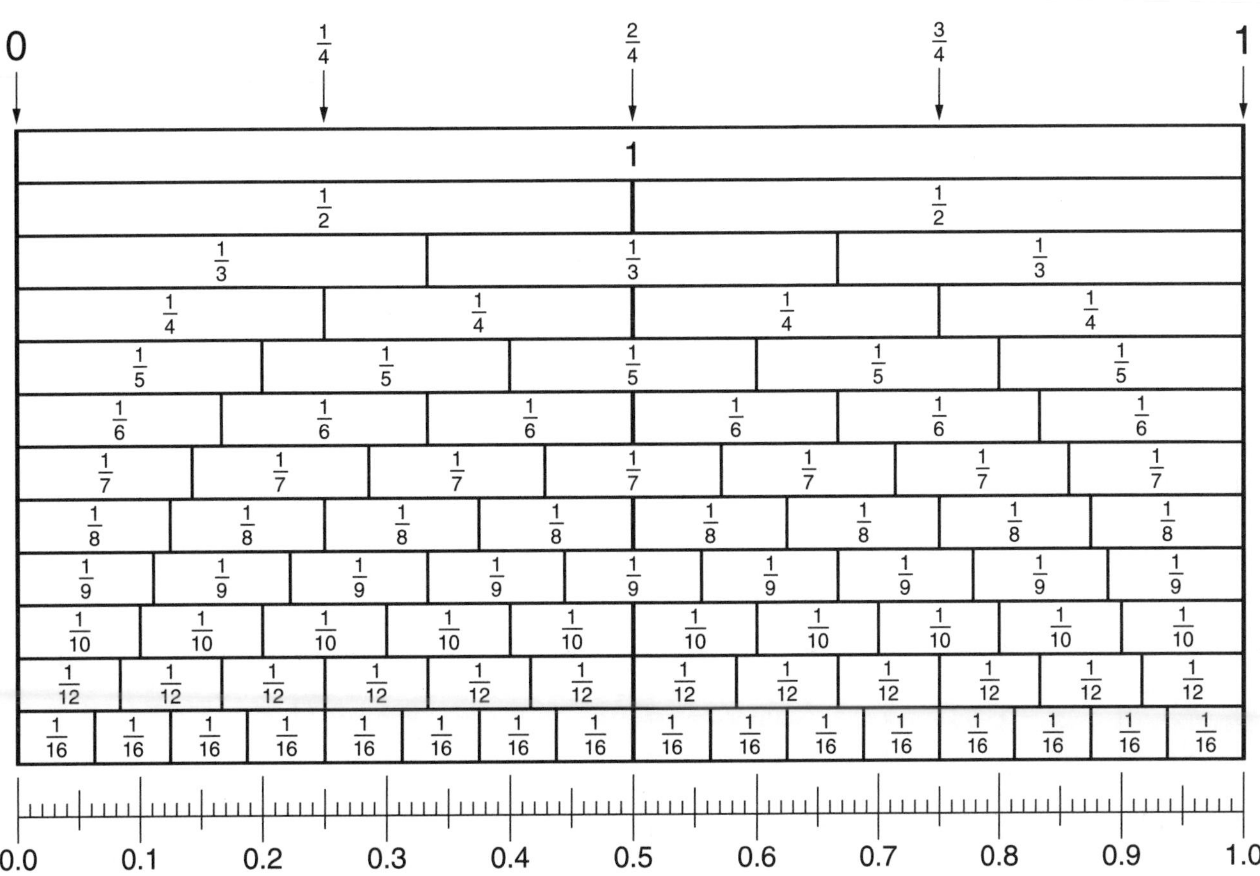

Name Date Time

Table of Decimal Equivalents for Fractions

Example To find the decimal equivalent for $\frac{1}{4}$, use the row for the denominator 4. Go to the column for the numerator 1. The box where the row and the column meet shows the decimal 0.25.

Numerator

Denominator	**1**	**2**	**3**	**4**	**5**	**6**	**7**	**8**	**9**	**10**
1	1.0	2.0	3.0							
2	0.5	1.0	1.5							
3							$2.\overline{3}$			
4	0.25				1.25					
5	0.2				1.0					
6										$1.\overline{6}$
7	$0.\overline{142857}$									
8					0.625					
9								$0.\overline{8}$		
10	0.1									

Name Date Time

Fractions and Decimals

Write the fraction name and decimal name for the shaded portion of each square. Use your transparent 100-grid to check your answer. For Problem 9, color the grid to show a fraction and then write the fraction and decimal name for the shaded portion of the square.

1. 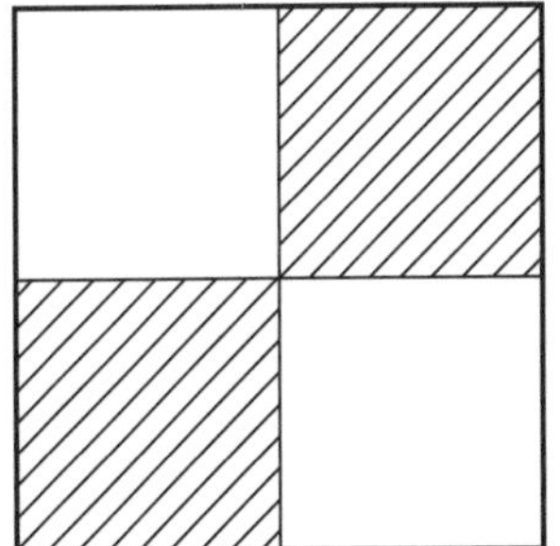

2 / 4 = 0. 5

2. 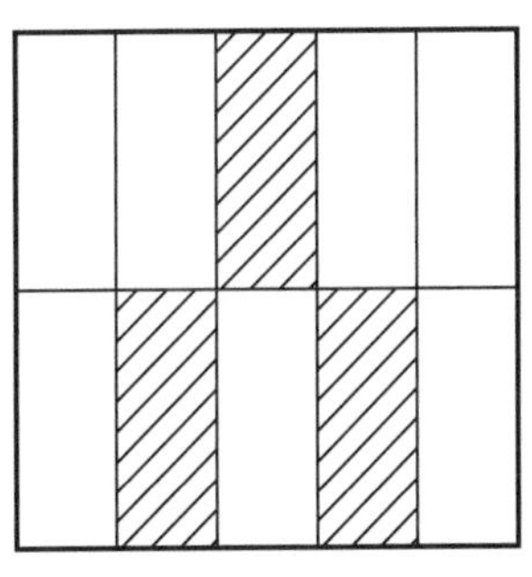

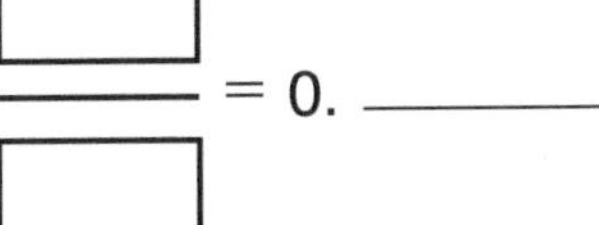

□ / □ = 0. ______

3. 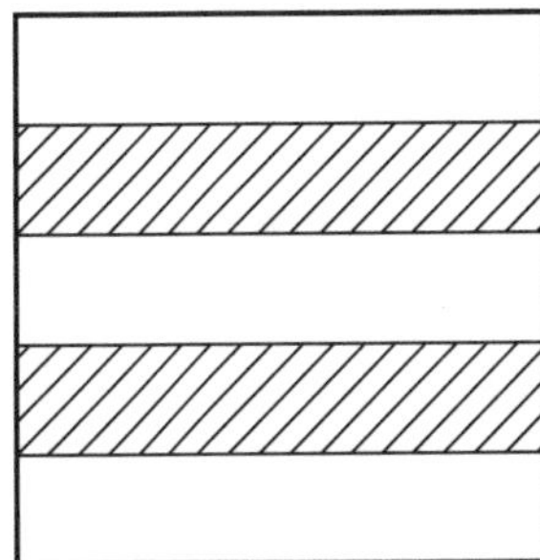

□ / □ = 0. ______

4. 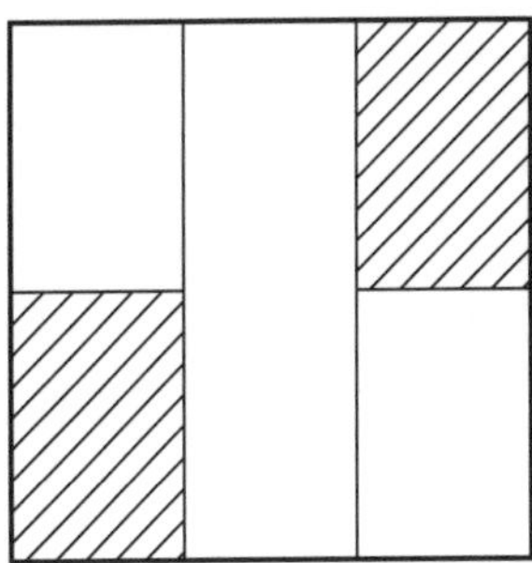

□ / □ = 0. ______

5. 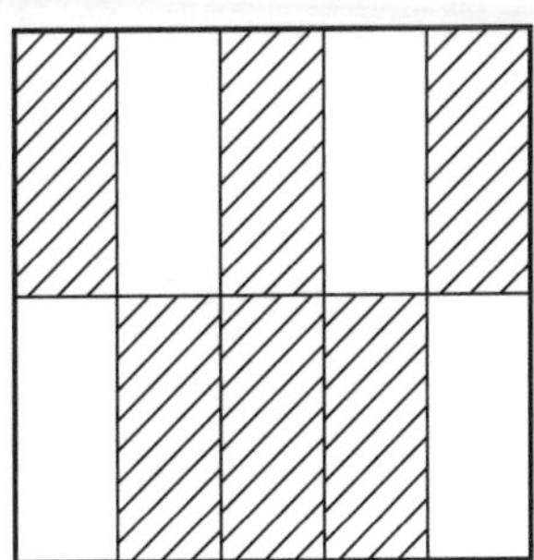

□ / □ = 0. ______

6. 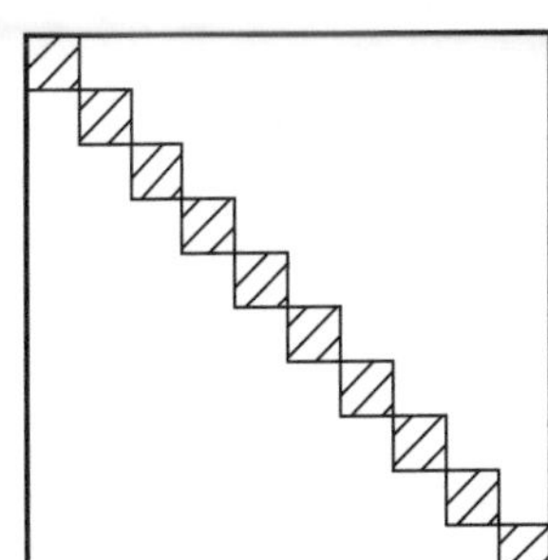

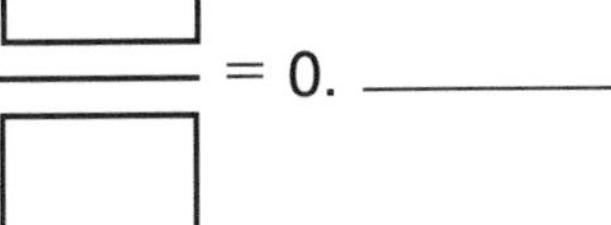

□ / □ = 0. ______

7. 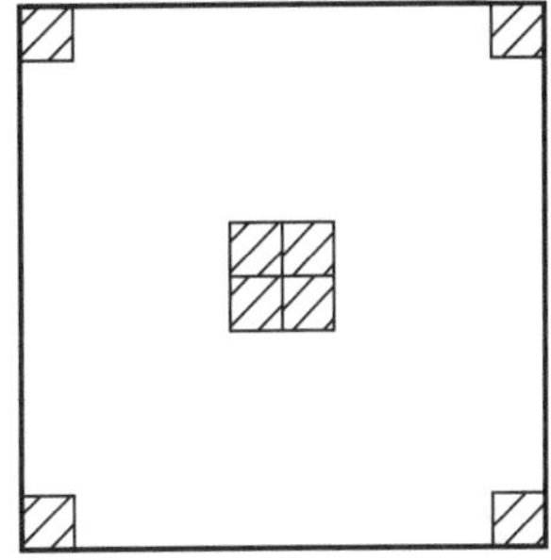

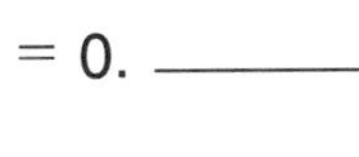

□ / □ = 0. ______

8. 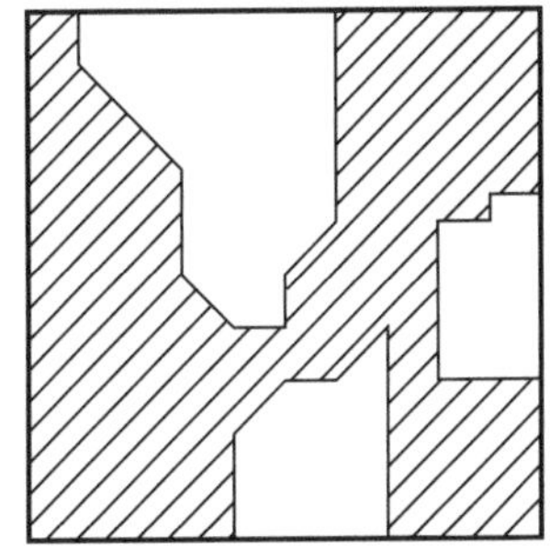

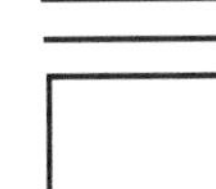

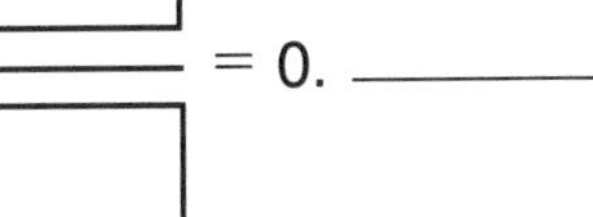

□ / □ = 0. ______

9. 

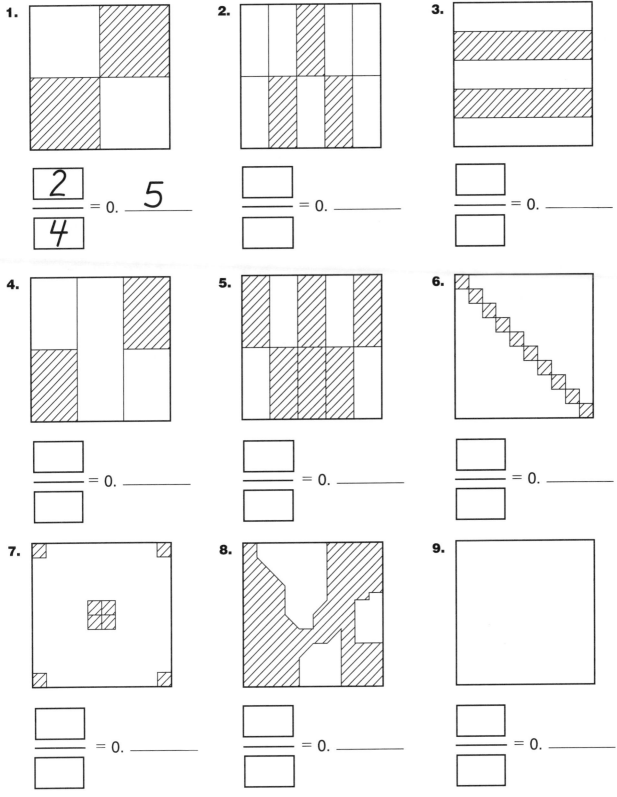

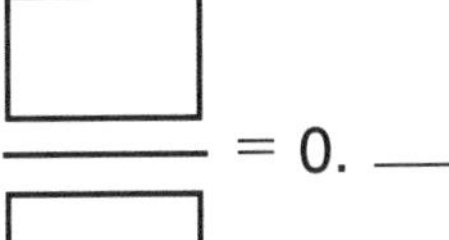

□ / □ = 0. ______

Name Date Time

100-Grids

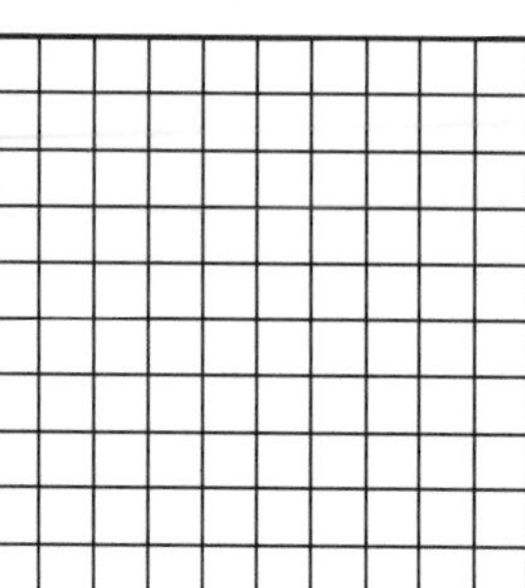

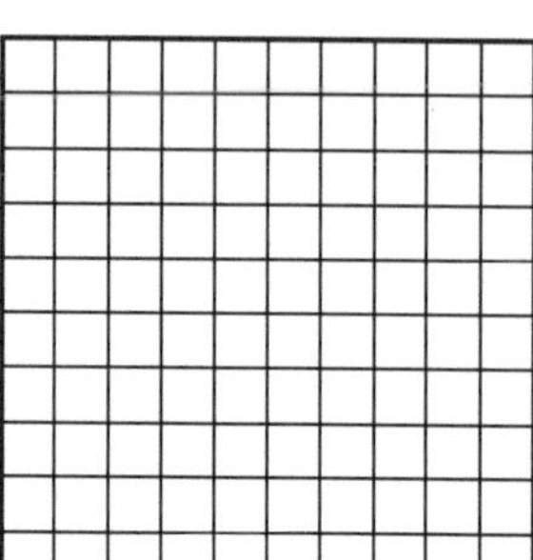

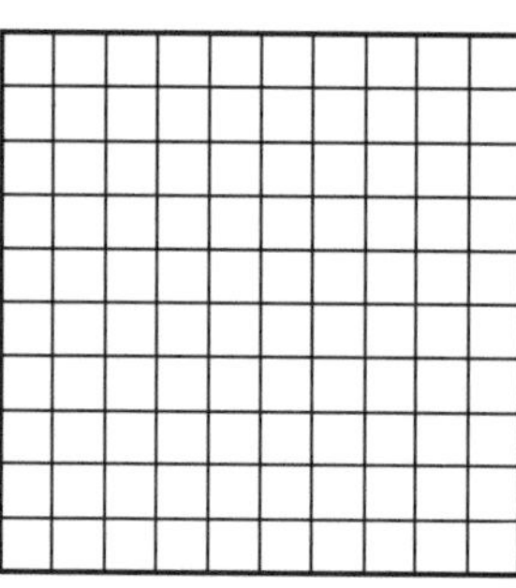

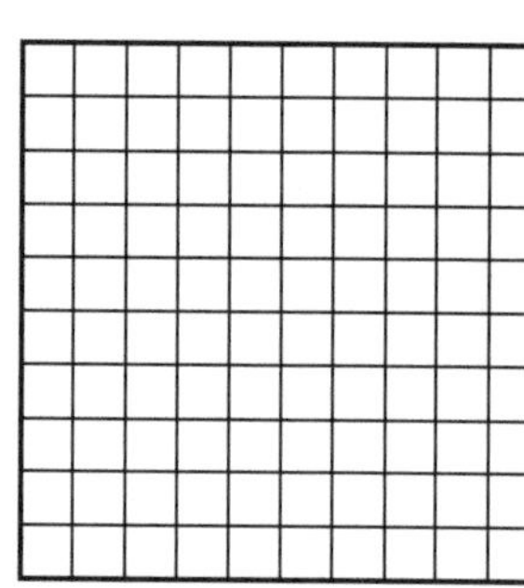

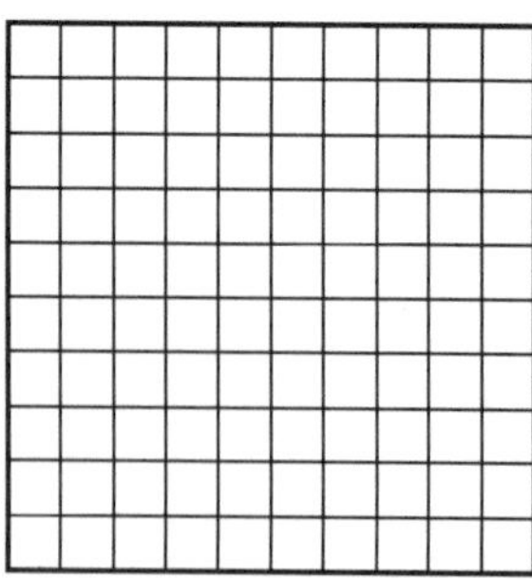

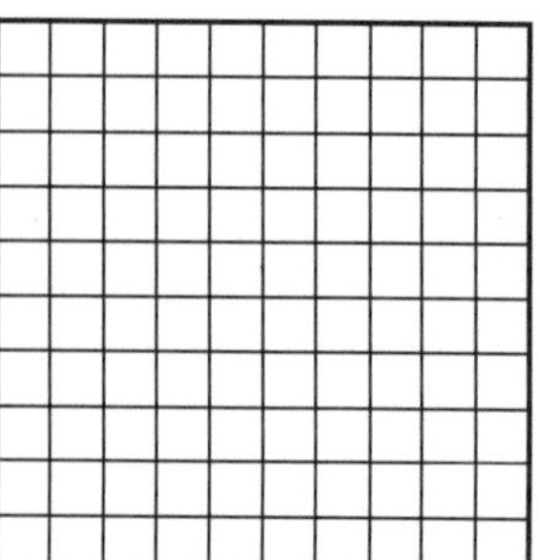

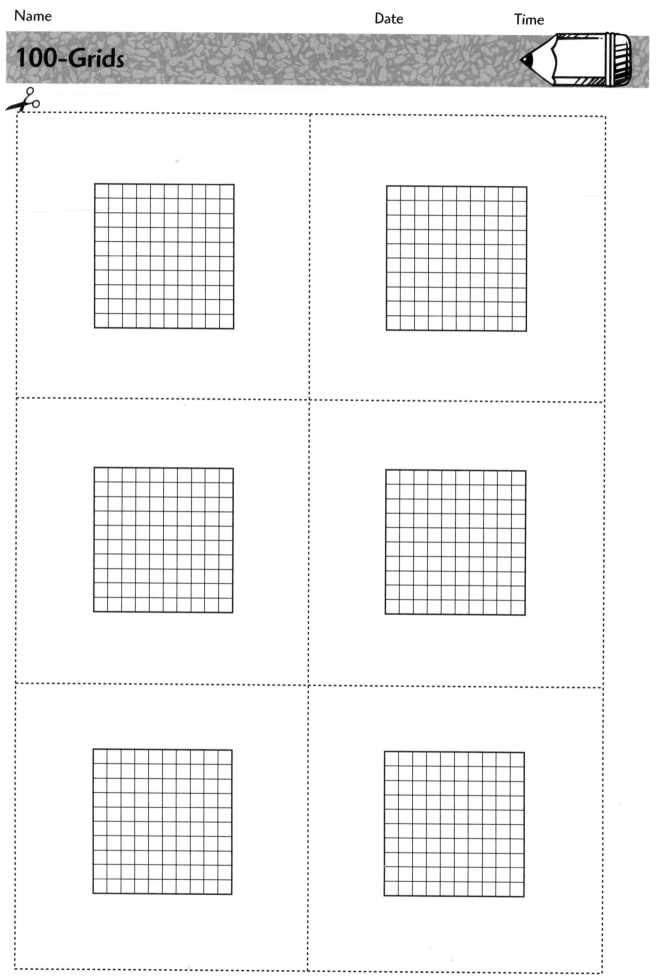

Use with Lesson 5.6.

Name Date Time

Decimal Comparisons

1. Mark each of the following points on the ruler below. Write the letter above the point. Point *A* has been done for you.

A: 3.4 cm *B:* 0.7 cm *C:* 8.3 cm *D:* 1.5 cm *E:* 10.6 cm *F:* 6.8 cm

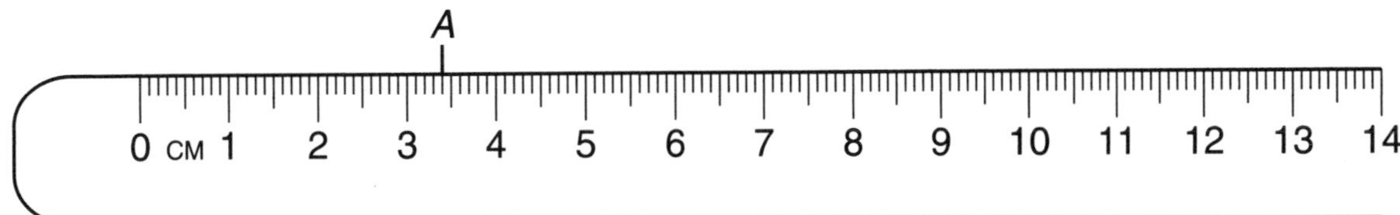

Write three numbers between each pair of numbers.

2. 0 and 1 ________, ________, ________

3. 2 and 3 ________, ________, ________

4. 0.6 and 0.8 ________, ________, ________

5. 0.3 and 0.4 ________, ________, ________

6. 0.06 and 0.05 ________, ________, ________

Circle the correct answer to each question.

7. Which is closer to 0.6? 0.5 or 0.53

8. Which is closer to 0.3? 0.02 or 0.2

9. Which is closer to 0.8? 0.77 or 0.85

10. Which is closer to 0.75? 0.6 or $0.\overline{8}$

11. Which is closer to 0.04? 0.3 or 0.051

12. Arrange the decimals below in order from least to greatest.

0.12 0.05 0.2 0.78 0.6 0.043 0.1

______ ______ ______ ______ ______ ______ ______

Name Date Time

Frac-Tac-Toe Number-Card Board

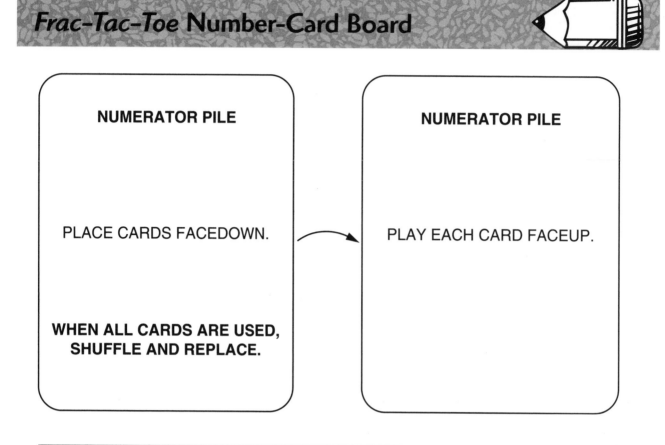

NUMERATOR PILE

PLACE CARDS FACEDOWN.

WHEN ALL CARDS ARE USED, SHUFFLE AND REPLACE.

NUMERATOR PILE

PLAY EACH CARD FACEUP.

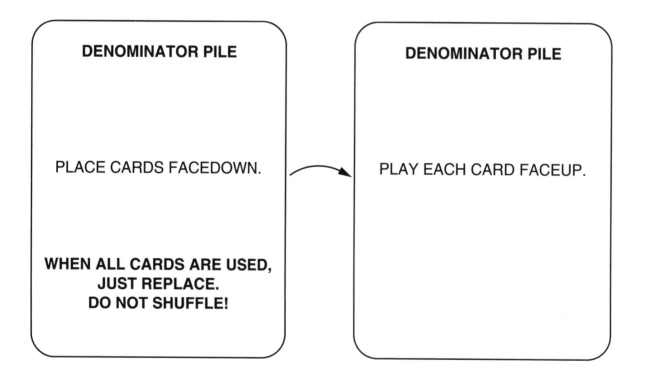

DENOMINATOR PILE

PLACE CARDS FACEDOWN.

WHEN ALL CARDS ARE USED, JUST REPLACE. DO NOT SHUFFLE!

DENOMINATOR PILE

PLAY EACH CARD FACEUP.

Name Date Time

2-4-5-10 Frac-Tac-Toe (Decimal Version)

If you use a standard deck of playing cards:

- Use Queens as zeros (0).
- Use Aces as ones (1).
- Discard Jacks, Kings, and Jokers.

If you use an Everything Math Deck, discard cards greater than 10.

Use different color counters or coins as markers. If you use coins, one player is "heads" and the other player is "tails."

If you use a pencil to initial the squares, print lightly so you can erase and use the board again.

Numerator Pile
All remaining cards

Denominator Pile
Two each of 2, 4, 5, and 10 cards

> 1.0	0 or 1	> 2.0	0 or 1	> 1.0
0.1	0.2	0.25	0.3	0.4
> 1.5	0.5	> 1.5	0.5	> 1.5
0.6	0.7	0.75	0.8	0.9
> 1.0	0 or 1	> 2.0	0 or 1	> 1.0

Name Date Time

2-4-8 Frac-Tac-Toe (Decimal Version)

If you use a standard deck of playing cards:

- Use Queens as zeros (0).
- Use Aces as ones (1).
- Discard Jacks, Kings, and Jokers.

If you use an Everything Math Deck, discard cards greater than 10.

Use different color counters or coins as markers. If you use coins, one player is "heads" and the other player is "tails."

If you use a pencil to initial the squares, print lightly so you can erase and use the board again.

Numerator Pile

All remaining cards

Denominator Pile

Two each of 2, 4, and 8 cards

> 2.0	0 or 1	> 1.5	0 or 1	> 2.0
1.5	0.125	0.25	0.375	1.5
> 1.0	0.5	0.25 or 0.75	0.5	> 1.0
2.0	0.625	0.75	0.875	2.0
> 2.0	0 or 1	1.125	0 or 1	> 2.0

Use with Lesson 5.7.

Name Date Time

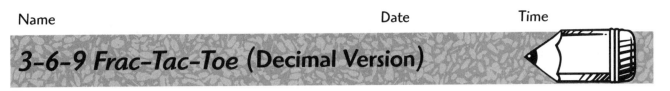

3-6-9 Frac-Tac-Toe (Decimal Version)

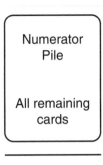

If you use a standard deck of playing cards:

- Use Queens as zeros (0).
- Use Aces as ones (1).
- Discard Jacks, Kings, and Jokers.

If you use an Everything Math Deck, discard cards greater than 10.

Use different color counters or coins as markers. If you use coins, one player is "heads" and the other player is "tails."

If you use a pencil to initial the squares, print lightly so you can erase and use the board again.

Numerator Pile
All remaining cards

Denominator Pile
Two each of 3, 6, and 9 cards

> 1.0	0 or 1	$0.\overline{1}$	0 or 1	> 1.0
$0.1\overline{6}$	$0.\overline{2}$	$0.\overline{3}$	$0.\overline{3}$	$0.\overline{4}$
> 2.0	$0.\overline{5}$	> 1.0	$0.\overline{6}$	> 2.0
$0.\overline{6}$	$0.\overline{7}$	$0.8\overline{3}$	$0.\overline{8}$	$1.\overline{3}$
> 1.0	0 or 1	$1.\overline{6}$	0 or 1	> 1.0

Name Date Time

2-4-5-10 Frac-Tac-Toe (Percent Version)

If you use a standard deck of playing cards:

- Use Queens as zeros (0).
- Use Aces as ones (1).
- Discard Jacks, Kings, and Jokers.

If you use an Everything Math Deck, discard cards greater than 10.

Use different color counters or coins as markers. If you use coins, one player is "heads" and the other player is "tails."

If you use a pencil to initial the squares, print lightly so you can erase and use the board again.

Numerator Pile

All remaining cards

Denominator Pile

Two each of 2, 4, 5, and 10 cards

>100%	0% or 100%	>200%	0% or 100%	>100%
10%	20%	25%	30%	40%
>100%	50%	>200%	50%	>100%
60%	70%	75%	80%	90%
>100%	0% or 100%	>200%	0% or 100%	>100%

Name Date Time

2-4-5-10 Frac-Tac-Toe (Decimal Bingo Version)

If you use a standard deck of playing cards:

- Use Queens as zeros (0).
- Use Aces as ones (1).
- Discard Jacks, Kings, and Jokers.

If you use an Everything Math Deck, discard cards greater than 10.

Fill in the gameboard by entering these numbers in the empty spaces:

0	0	0.1	0.2	0.25	0.3	0.4	0.5
0.5	0.6	0.7	0.75	0.8	0.9	1	1

Numerator Pile

All remaining cards

Denominator Pile

Two each of 2, 4, 5, and 10 cards

> 1.0		> 2.0		> 1.0
> 1.5		> 1.5		> 1.5
> 1.0		> 2.0		> 1.0

Name Date Time

2-4-5-10 Frac-Tac-Toe (Percent Bingo Version)

If you use a standard deck of playing cards:

- Use Queens as zeros (0).
- Use Aces as ones (1).
- Discard Jacks, Kings, and Jokers.

If you use an Everything Math Deck, discard cards greater than 10.

Fill in the gameboard by entering these numbers in the empty spaces:

0%	0%	10%	20%	25%	30%	40%	50%
50%	60%	70%	75%	80%	90%	100%	100%

Numerator Pile

All remaining cards

Denominator Pile

Two each of 2, 4, 5, and 10 cards

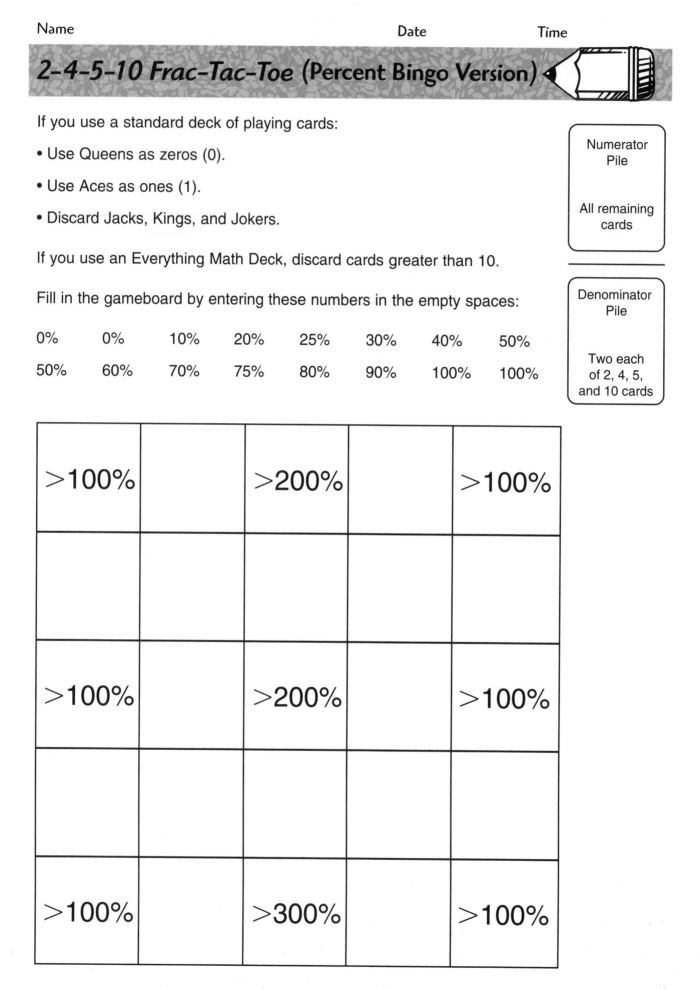

>100%		>200%		>100%
>100%		>200%		>100%
>100%		>300%		>100%

Name Date Time

2-4-8-10 Frac-Tac-Toe (Percent Version)

If you use a standard deck of playing cards:

- Use Queens as zeros (0).
- Use Aces as ones (1).
- Discard Jacks, Kings, and Jokers.

If you use an Everything Math Deck, discard cards greater than 10.

Use different color counters or coins as markers. If you use coins, one player is "heads" and the other player is "tails."

If you use a pencil to initial the squares, print lightly so you can erase and use the board again.

Numerator Pile

All remaining cards

Denominator Pile

Two each of 2, 4, 8 and 10 cards

>200%	0% or 100%	>150%	0% or 100%	>200%
150%	$12\frac{1}{2}\%$	25%	$37\frac{1}{2}\%$	150%
>100%	50%	25% or 75%	50%	>100%
200%	$62\frac{1}{2}\%$	75%	$87\frac{1}{2}\%$	200%
>200%	0% or 100%	$112\frac{1}{2}\%$	0% or 100%	>200%

Name Date Time

2-4-8 Frac-Tac-Toe (Decimal Bingo Version)

If you use a standard deck of playing cards:

- Use Queens as zeros (0).
- Use Aces as ones (1).
- Discard Jacks, Kings, and Jokers.

If you use an Everything Math Deck, discard cards greater than 10.

Fill in the gameboard by entering these numbers in the empty spaces:

0	0	0.125	0.25	0.375	0.5	0.5	0.625
0.75	0.875	1	1	1.5	1.5	2	2

Numerator Pile
All remaining cards

Denominator Pile
Two each of 2, 4, and 8 cards

> 2.0		> 1.5		> 2.0
> 1.0		0.25 or 0.75		> 1.0
> 2.0		1.125		> 2.0

Name Date Time

2-4-8 Frac-Tac-Toe (Percent Bingo Version)

If you use a standard deck of playing cards:

- Use Queens as zeros (0).
- Use Aces as ones (1).
- Discard Jacks, Kings, and Jokers.

If you use an Everything Math Deck, discard cards greater than 10.

Fill in the gameboard by entering these numbers in the empty spaces:

0%	0%	$12\frac{1}{2}\%$	25%	$37\frac{1}{2}\%$	50%	50%	$62\frac{1}{2}\%$
75%	$87\frac{1}{2}\%$	100%	100%	150%	150%	200%	200%

Numerator Pile
All remaining cards

Denominator Pile
Two each of 2, 4, and 8 cards

>200%		>150%		>200%
>100%		25% or 75%		>100%
>200%		$112\frac{1}{2}\%$		>200%

Use with Lesson 5.7.

Name Date Time

3-6-9 Frac-Tac-Toe (Percent Version)

If you use a standard deck of playing cards:

- Use Queens as zeros (0).
- Use Aces as ones (1).
- Discard Jacks, Kings, and Jokers.

If you use an Everything Math Deck, discard cards greater than 10.

Use different color counters or coins as markers. If you use coins, one player is "heads" and the other player is "tails."

If you use a pencil to initial the squares, print lightly so you can erase and use the board again.

Numerator Pile
All remaining cards

Denominator Pile
Two each of 3, 6, and 9 cards

>100%	0% or 100%	11.1%	0% or 100%	>100%
$16\frac{2}{3}\%$	22.2%	$33\frac{1}{3}\%$	33.3%	44.4%
>200%	55.5%	>100%	66.6%	>200%
$66\frac{2}{3}\%$	77.7%	$83\frac{1}{3}\%$	88.8%	$133\frac{1}{3}\%$
>100%	0% or 100%	$166\frac{2}{3}\%$	0% or 100%	>100%

Use with Lesson 5.7.

Name Date Time

3-6-9 Frac-Tac-Toe (Decimal Bingo Version)

If you use a standard deck of playing cards:

- Use Queens as zeros (0).
- Use Aces as ones (1).
- Discard Jacks, Kings, and Jokers.

If you use an Everything Math Deck, discard cards greater than 10.

Fill in the gameboard by entering these numbers in the empty spaces:

0	0	$0.1\overline{6}$	$0.\overline{3}$	$0.\overline{3}$	$0.\overline{6}$
$0.\overline{6}$	$0.8\overline{3}$	1	1	$1.\overline{3}$	$1.\overline{6}$

Numerator Pile

All remaining cards

Denominator Pile

Two each of 3, 6, and 9 cards

<table>
<tr><td>>1.0</td><td></td><td>$0.\overline{1}$</td><td></td><td>>1.0</td></tr>
<tr><td></td><td>$0.\overline{2}$</td><td></td><td></td><td>$0.\overline{4}$</td></tr>
<tr><td>>2.0</td><td>$0.\overline{5}$</td><td>>1.0</td><td></td><td>>2.0</td></tr>
<tr><td></td><td>$0.\overline{7}$</td><td></td><td>$0.\overline{8}$</td><td></td></tr>
<tr><td>>1.0</td><td></td><td></td><td></td><td>>1.0</td></tr>
</table>

Name Date Time

3-6-9 Frac-Tac-Toe (Percent Bingo Version)

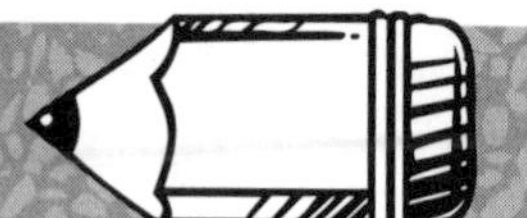

If you use a standard deck of playing cards:

- Use Queens as zeros (0).
- Use Aces as ones (1).
- Discard Jacks, Kings, and Jokers.

If you use an Everything Math Deck, discard cards greater than 10.

Numerator Pile
All remaining cards

Denominator Pile
Two each of 3, 6, and 9 cards

Fill in the gameboard by entering these numbers in the empty spaces:

0%	0%	100%	$16\frac{2}{3}\%$	$33\frac{1}{3}\%$	$33\frac{1}{3}\%$
$66\frac{2}{3}\%$	$83\frac{1}{3}\%$	100%	$133\frac{1}{3}\%$	$166\frac{2}{3}\%$	$166\frac{2}{3}\%$

>100%		11.1%		>100%
	22.2%			44.4%
>200%	55.5%	>100%		>200%
	77.7%		88.8%	
>100%				>100%

Name Date Time

Fraction/Percent Concentration Tiles (front)

10%	20%	25%	30%
40%	50%	60%	70%
75%	80%	90%	100%
$\frac{1}{2}$	$\frac{1}{4}$	$\frac{3}{4}$	$\frac{1}{5}$
$\frac{2}{5}$	$\frac{3}{5}$	$\frac{4}{5}$	$\frac{1}{10}$
$\frac{3}{10}$	$\frac{7}{10}$	$\frac{9}{10}$	$\frac{2}{2}$

Name Date Time

Fraction/Percent Concentration Tiles (back)

%	%	%	%
%	%	%	%
%	%	%	%
$\frac{a}{b}$	$\frac{a}{b}$	$\frac{a}{b}$	$\frac{a}{b}$
$\frac{a}{b}$	$\frac{a}{b}$	$\frac{a}{b}$	$\frac{a}{b}$
$\frac{a}{b}$	$\frac{a}{b}$	$\frac{a}{b}$	$\frac{a}{b}$

Use with Lesson 5.8.

Name Date Time

Percent Circle

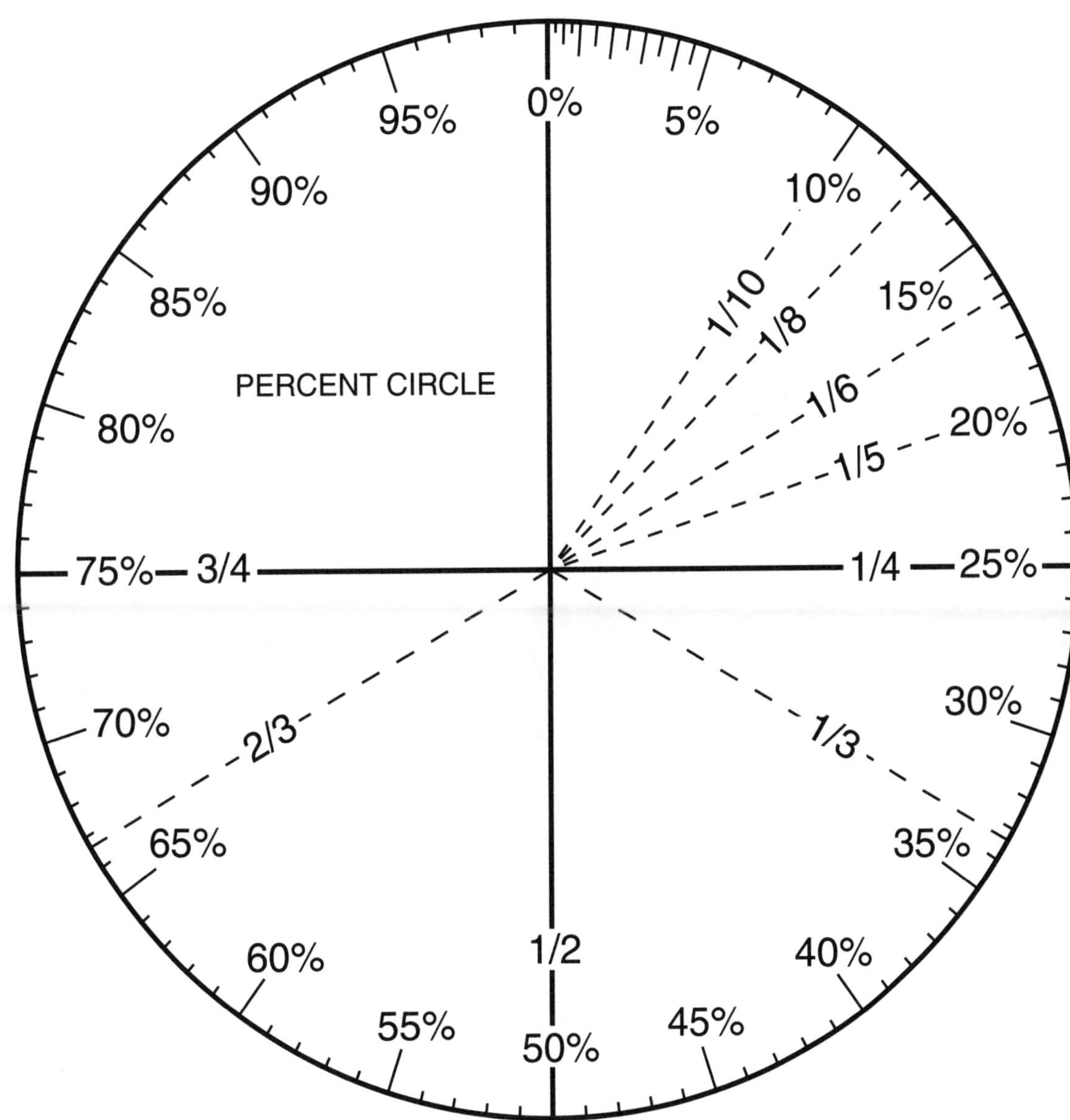

Name Date Time

Circle Graph

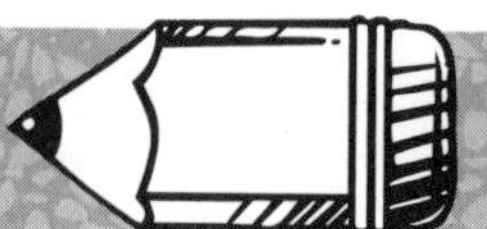

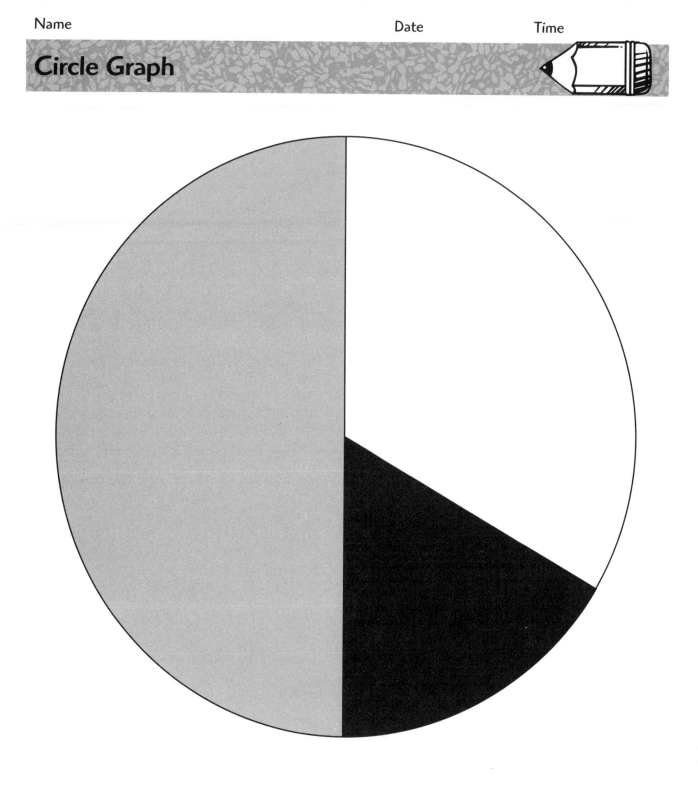

Use with Lesson 5.10.

Name Date Time

Percent Circles

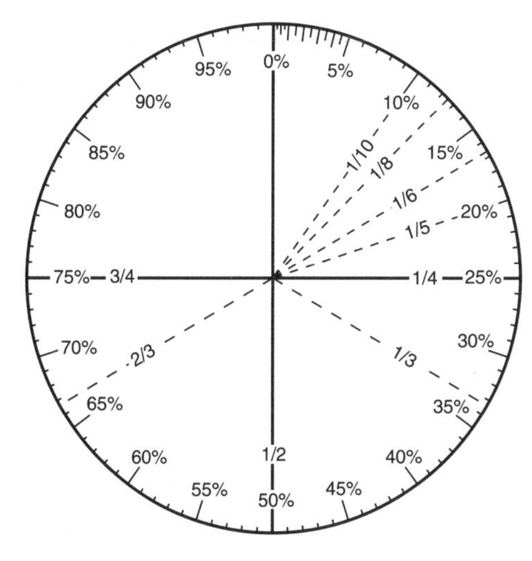

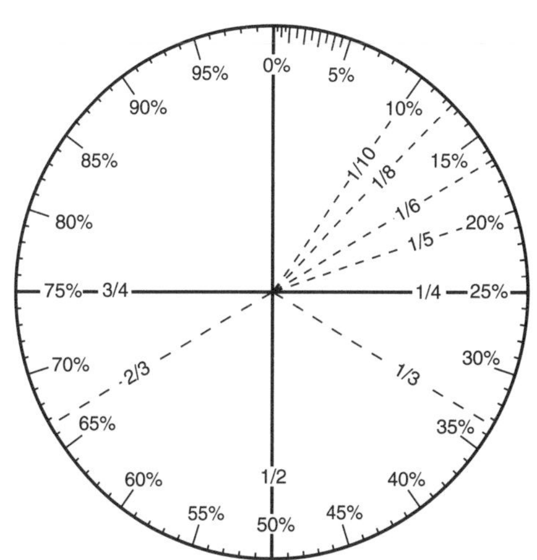

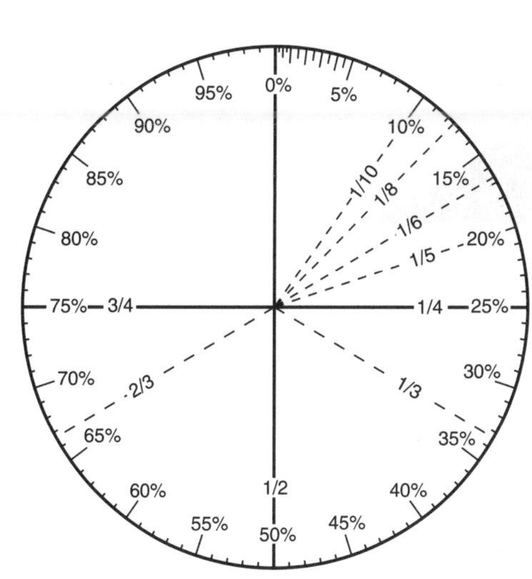

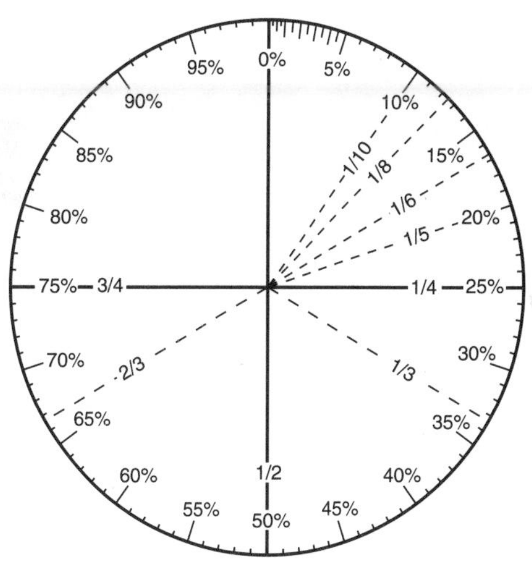

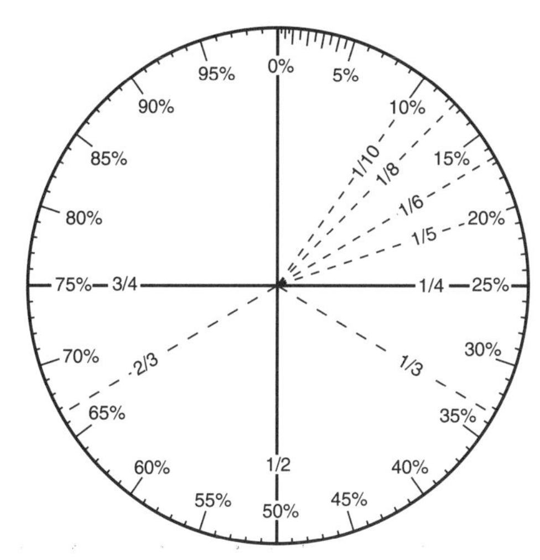

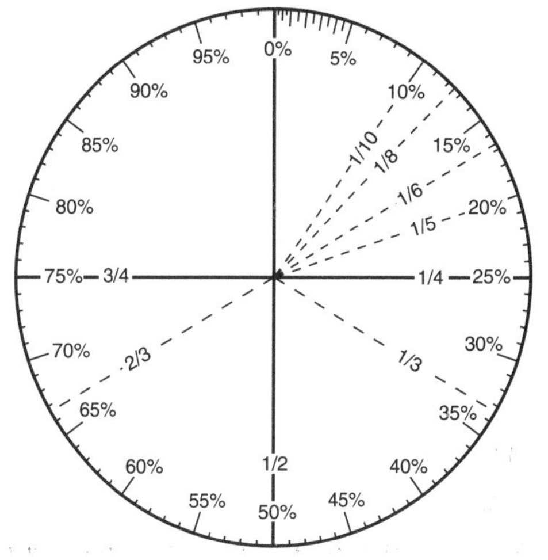

Name Date Time

Measuring Circle-Graph Sections

Use your Percent Circle to find what percent each piece (sector) is of the whole circle.

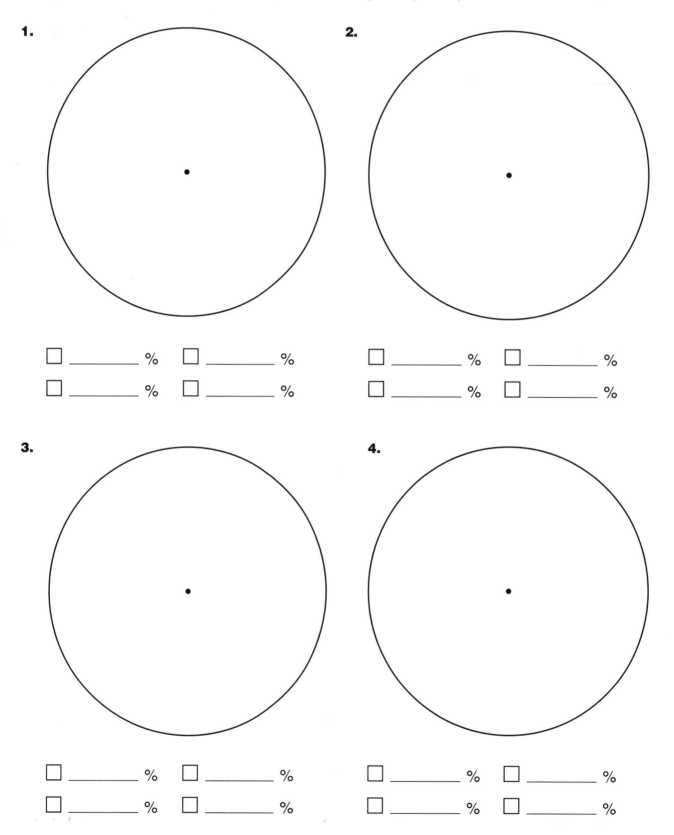

1.

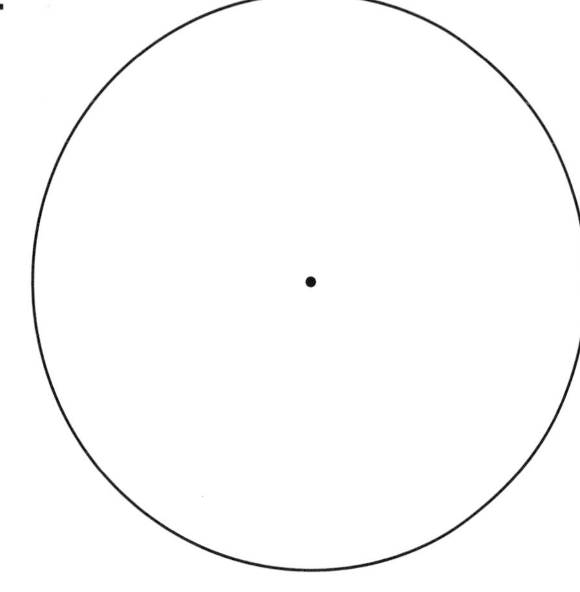

☐ ________ % ☐ ________ %

☐ ________ % ☐ ________ %

2.

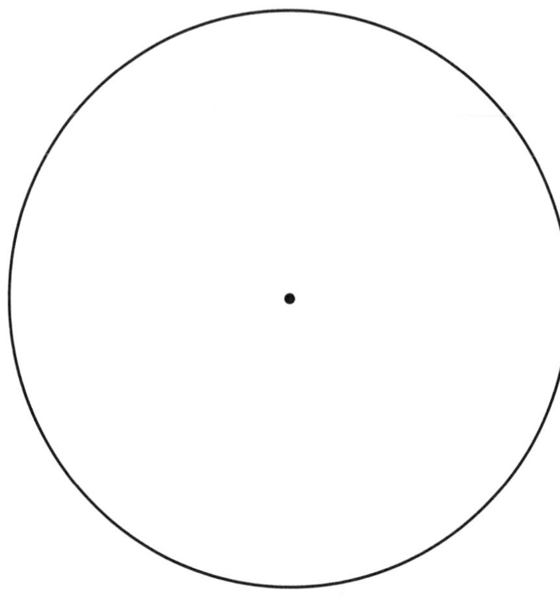

☐ ________ % ☐ ________ %

☐ ________ % ☐ ________ %

3.

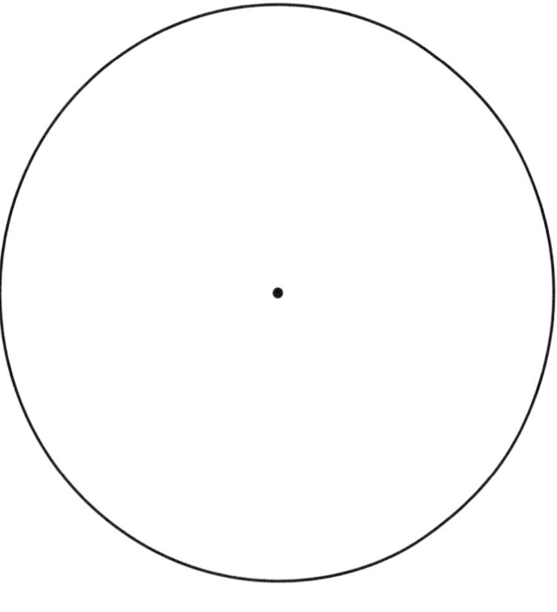

☐ ________ % ☐ ________ %

☐ ________ % ☐ ________ %

4.

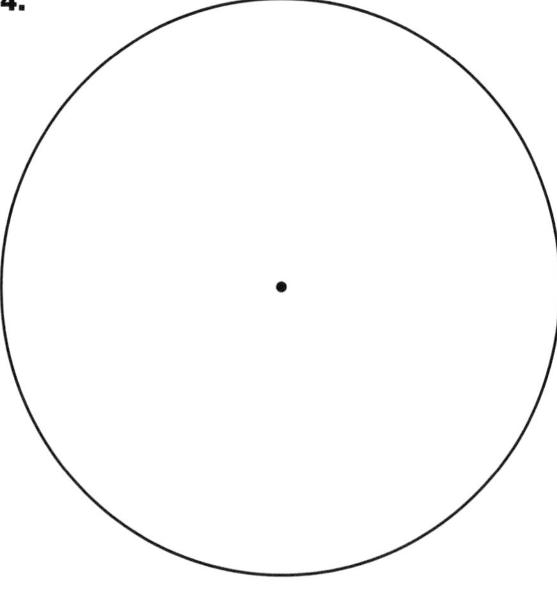

☐ ________ % ☐ ________ %

☐ ________ % ☐ ________ %

Name Date Time

Measuring Practice

1. Measure each line segment below to the nearest centimeter.

 a. ____________

 ________ cm

 b. ____________________________

 ________ cm

 c. ____

 ________ cm

2. Measure each line segment below to the nearest millimeter.

 a. ___

 ________ mm

 b. _____

 ________ mm

 c. ____

 ________ mm

3. Measure each line segment below to the nearest $\frac{1}{8}$ inch.

 a. ____

 ________ in.

 b. _________

 ________ in.

 c. ________

 ________ in.

 d. ________________

 ________ in.

4. Draw line segments having the following lengths:

 a. $2\frac{1}{8}$ inches

 b. 9 centimeters

 c. 22 millimeters

Name Date Time

Organizing Spelling-Test Scores

Ms. Hallaran wanted to collect information on how her class was doing in spelling. After a test, she had students record their score on a sheet of paper. She listed all the scores on the board:

75	85	80	80	85	80	95	100	100	90	80	85
70	85	100	95	70	95	95	100	90	80	75	80

1. Would it have been better if Ms. Hallaran had displayed the data in a stem-and-leaf plot? Explain your answer.

____

____

2. Make a stem-and-leaf plot for the spelling-test data.

Stems (10s)	**Leaves** (1s)

Use your stem-and-leaf plot to answer Problems 3 and 4.

3. a. What is the median score for the class? ________

   b. What was the mode for the class? ________

Challenge

4. How many questions do you think there were on the test? ________________

____

5. On the back of this page, explain how you figured out your answer to Problem 4.

Name Date Time

Comparing Left and Right Hands

Which is more flexible—the hand you write with or your other hand? This activity will help you find out.

Read the instructions below.

Trace Your Hands

Step 1 In the air, stretch to make the largest possible angle between the thumb and little finger on one of your hands.

Step 2 Now, lay that hand down on the back of this paper and use your other hand to trace around that hand with a pen or pencil. Label the tracing "right" or "left."

Step 3 Repeat Steps 1 and 2 for your other hand.

Mark and Measure

1. On each tracing, draw straight lines through the middle of the little finger and thumb outlines. Be sure the lines intersect, forming an angle. (See the picture below.)

2. Use a protractor on your Geometry Template to measure the angle formed by each hand. Record your answers below.

   Measure of angle formed by right thumb and little finger: ____________________

   Measure of angle formed by left thumb and little finger: ____________________

   I write with my ______________________ hand.
   (right or left)

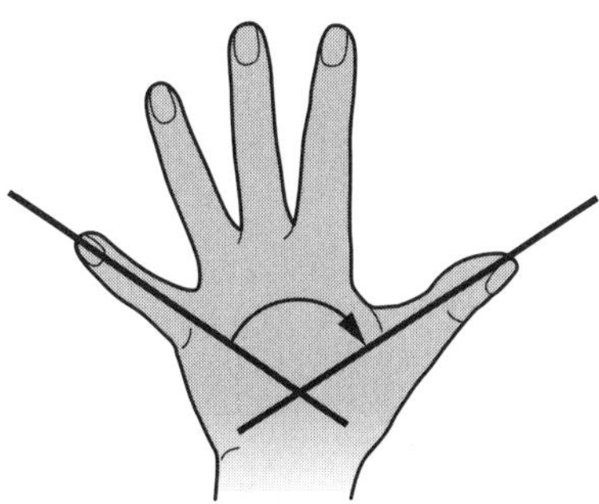

Measure this angle.

Name Date Time

Circles

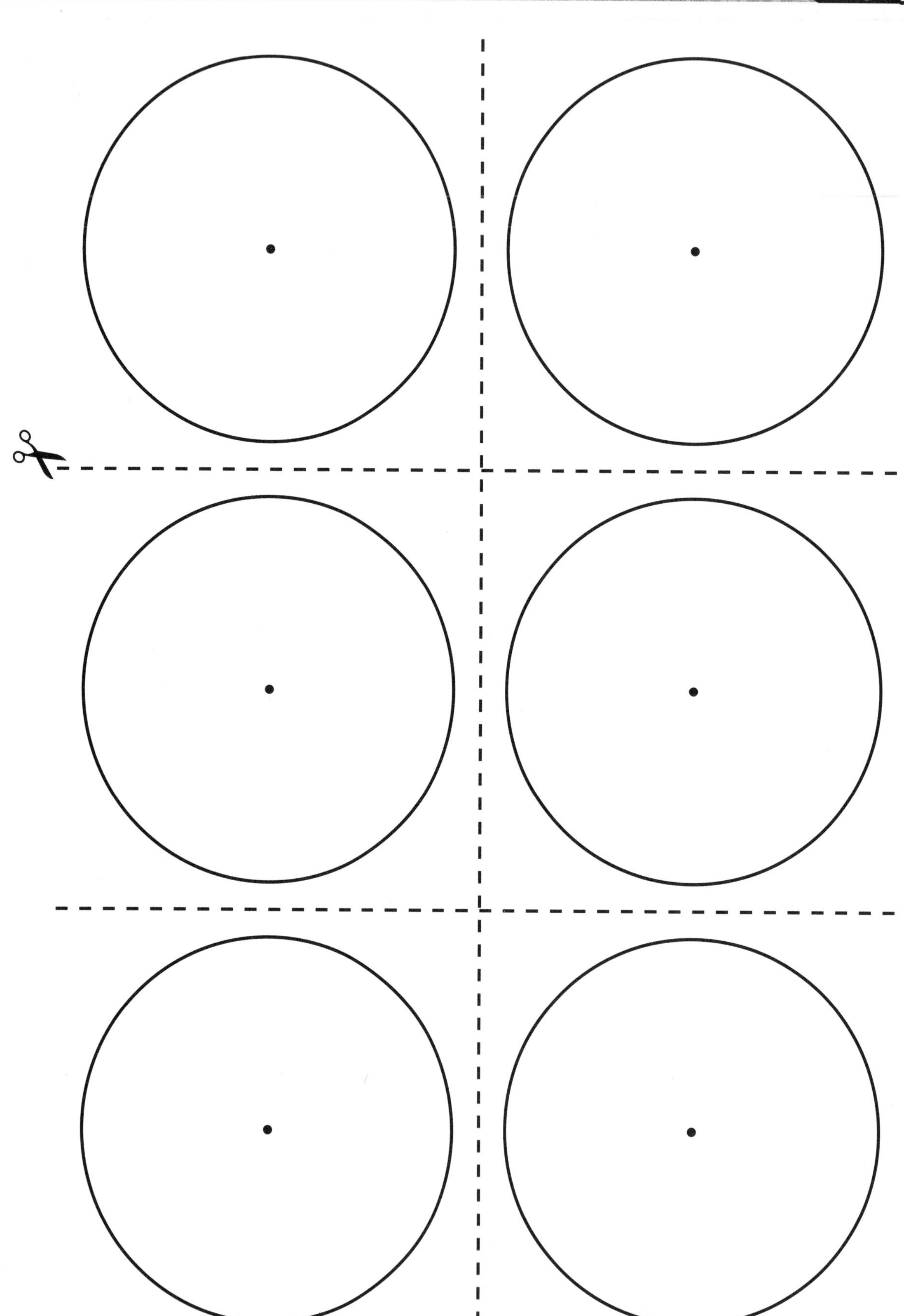

Use with Lesson 6.5.

Name

Overhead Slide Rule

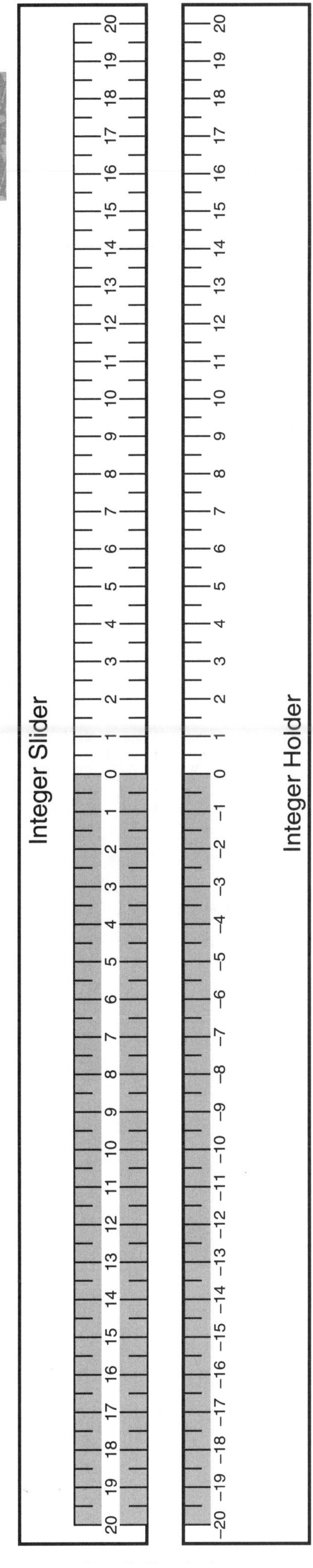

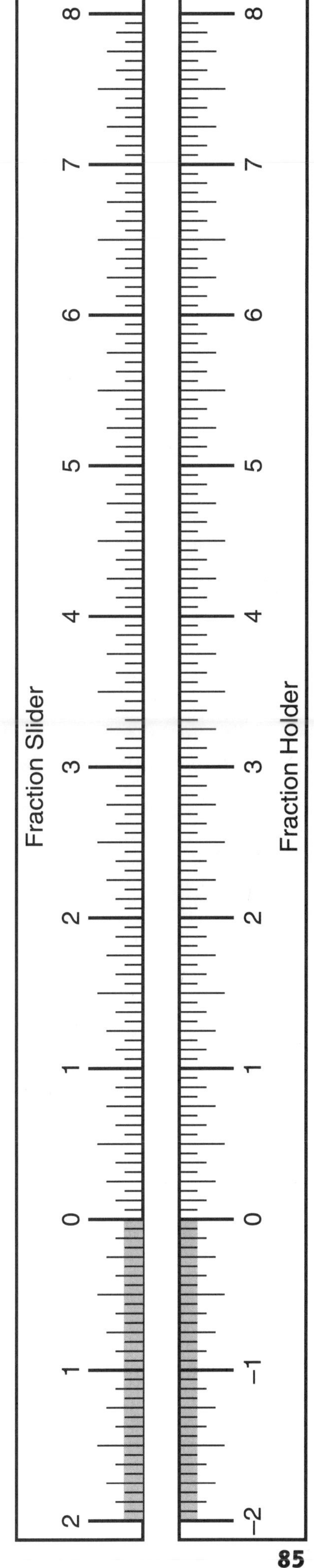

Name Date Time

Fraction Operations with Pattern Blocks

Whole
hexagon

Use your △, ◇, ⏢, and ⬡ pattern blocks to solve the problems.

1. A trapezoid is worth ________.

2. A rhombus is worth ________.

3. A triangle is worth ________.

4. Use your blocks to cover the shape at the right. Trace the outline of each block. Label each part with a fraction.

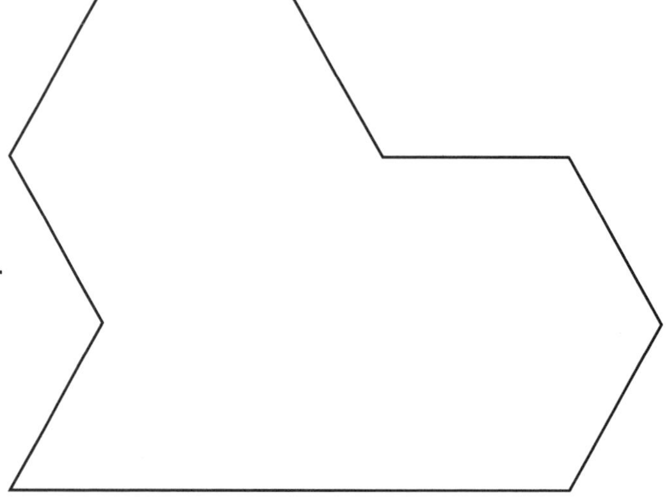

5. Write a number sentence to describe how you covered the shape in Problem 4.

____

6. Arrange your blocks to make a shape that is worth $3\frac{1}{6}$. Trace your block design on the back of this page. Label each part with a fraction.

7. Write a number sentence to describe how you covered the shape you made in Problem 6. ____

Challenge

8. Build your shape from Problem 6 again. Use different blocks to build the shape. Trace your new block design on the back of this page. Label each part with a fraction. Write the number sentence for your shape. ____________________

9. Explain why the number sentence you wrote in Problem 7 is equivalent to the number sentence you wrote in Problem 8. ____________________

____

____

Name Date Time

Fraction Capture

Materials *Fraction Capture* Gameboard
2 six-sided dice

Players 2

Object To capture the most squares on the *Fraction Capture* Gameboard. A player captures a square if he or she shades **more than** $\frac{1}{2}$ of it.

Directions

1. Player 1 rolls two dice and makes a fraction with the numbers that come up. The number on either die can be the denominator. The number on the other die becomes the numerator.

   A fraction equal to a whole number is NOT allowed. For example, if a player rolls 3 and 6, the fraction can't be $\frac{6}{3}$, because $\frac{6}{3}$ equals 2.

2. Player 1 initials sections of one or more gameboard squares to show the fraction formed. This **claims** the sections for the player.

   Example The player rolls a 4 and 5 and makes $\frac{5}{4}$. The player claims five $\frac{1}{4}$ sections by initialing them.

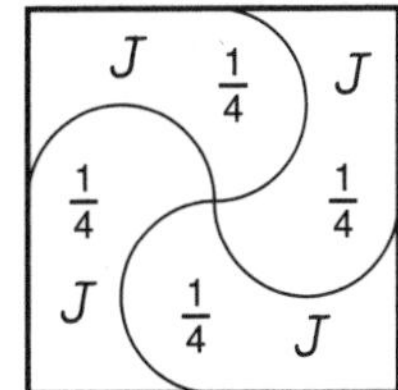

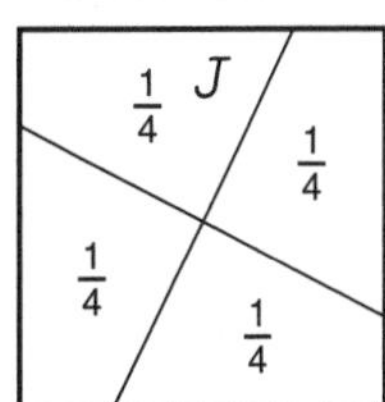

   - Equivalent fractions can be claimed. For example, if a player rolls 1 and 2 and makes $\frac{1}{2}$, the player can initial one $\frac{1}{2}$ section of a square, or two $\frac{1}{4}$ sections, or three $\frac{1}{6}$ sections.
   - The fraction may be split between squares. For example, a player can show $\frac{4}{3}$ by claiming $\frac{2}{3}$ on one square and $\frac{2}{3}$ on another square. However, **all** of the fractions must be shown.

3. Players take turns. If a player can't form a fraction and claim enough sections to show that fraction, the player's turn is over.

4. A player **captures** a square when that player has claimed sections making up **more than** $\frac{1}{2}$ of the square. If each player has initialed $\frac{1}{2}$ of a square, no one has captured that square.
   - Blocking is allowed. For example, if Player 1 initials $\frac{1}{2}$ of a square, Player 2 may initial the other half, so that no one can capture the square.

5. Play ends when all of the squares have either been captured or blocked. The winner is the player who has captured the most squares.

Name Date Time

Fraction Capture Gameboard

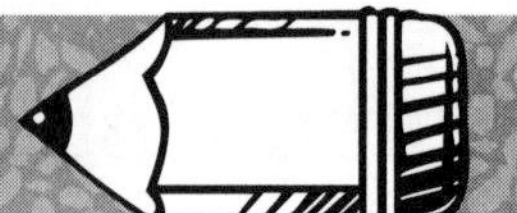

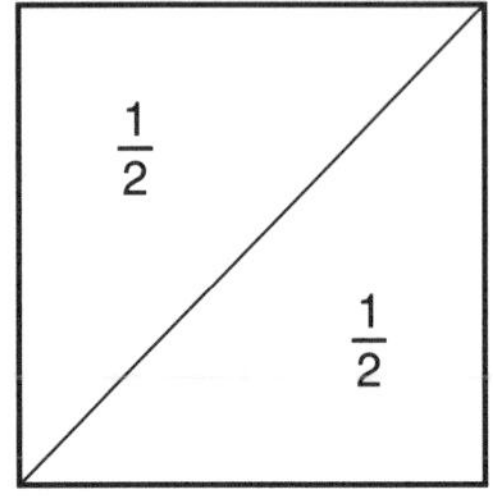

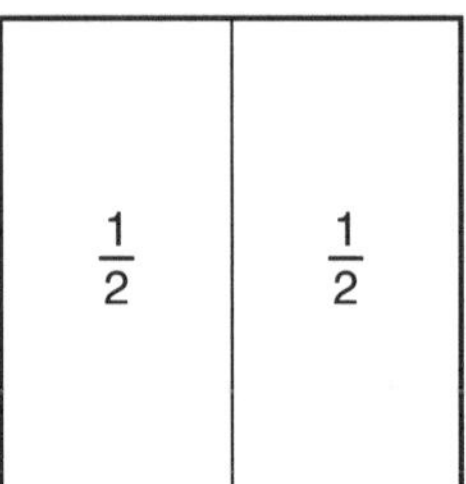

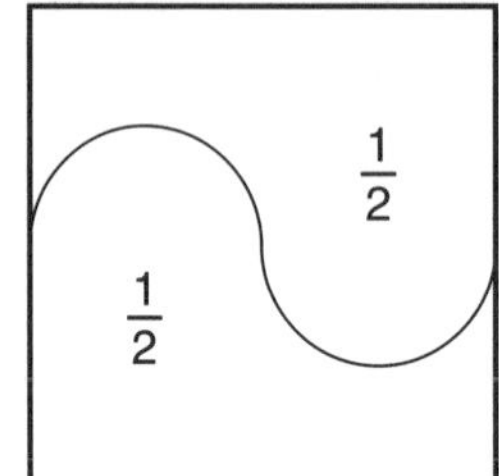

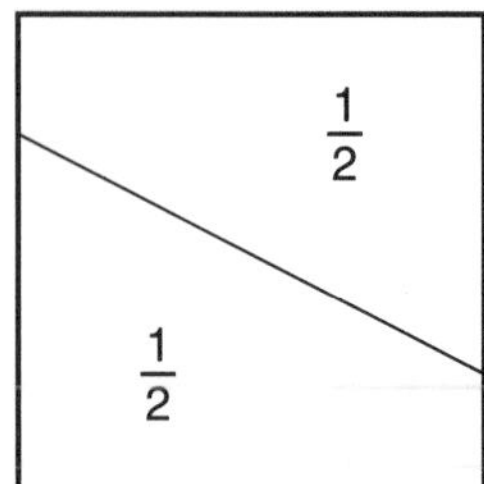

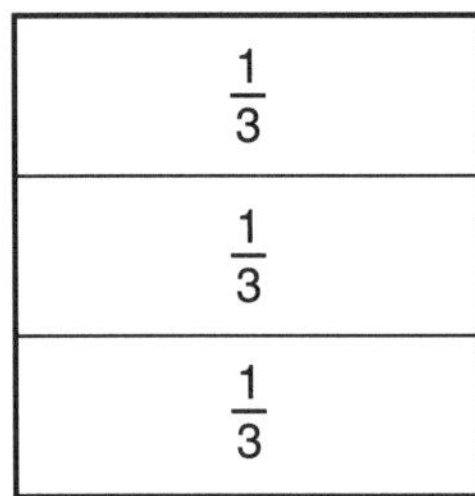

1/3 1/3 1/3

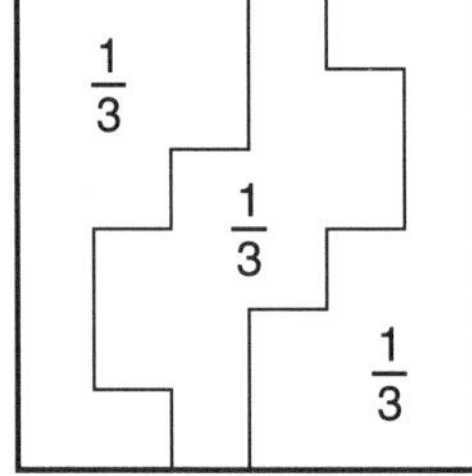

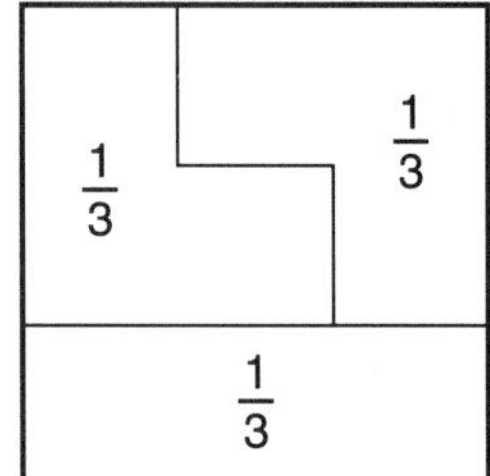

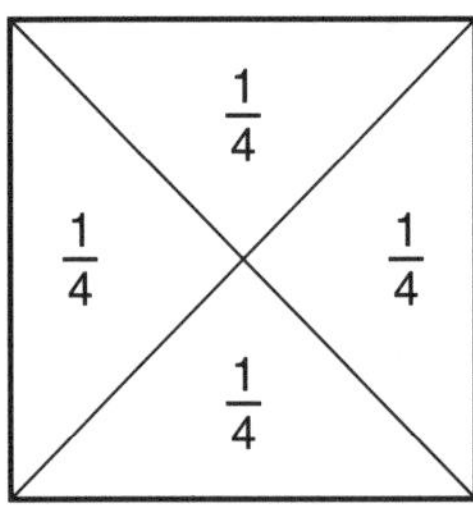

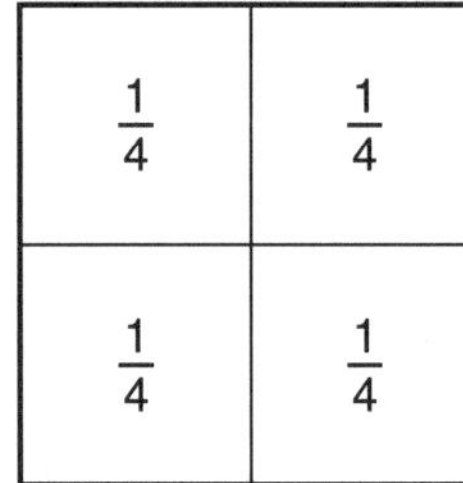

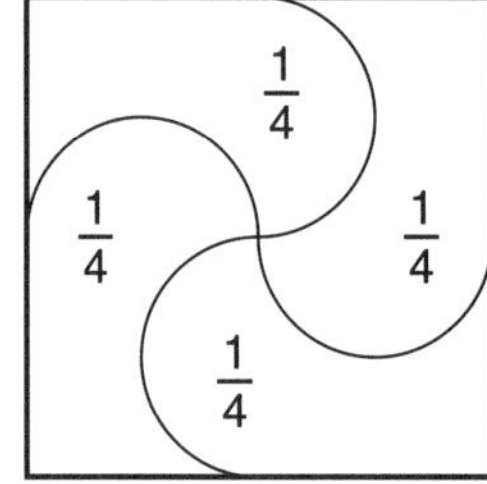

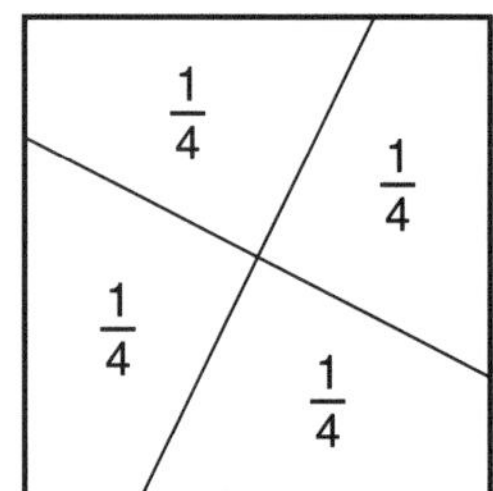

1/5 1/5 1/5 1/5 1/5

1/5 1/5 1/5 1/5 1/5

1/5 1/5 1/5 1/5 1/5

1/5 1/5 1/5 1/5 1/5

1/6 1/6 1/6 1/6 1/6 1/6

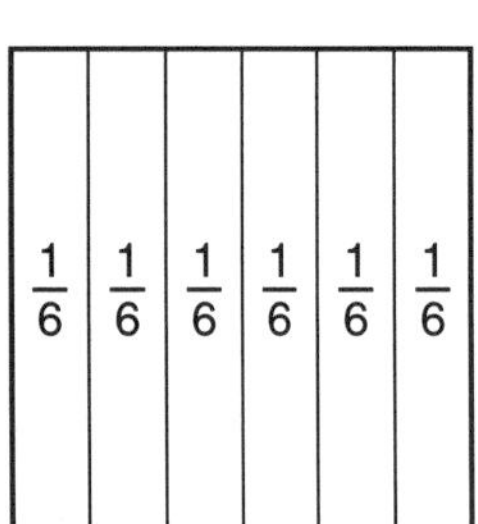

1/6 1/6 1/6 1/6 1/6 1/6

1/6 1/6 1/6 1/6 1/6 1/6

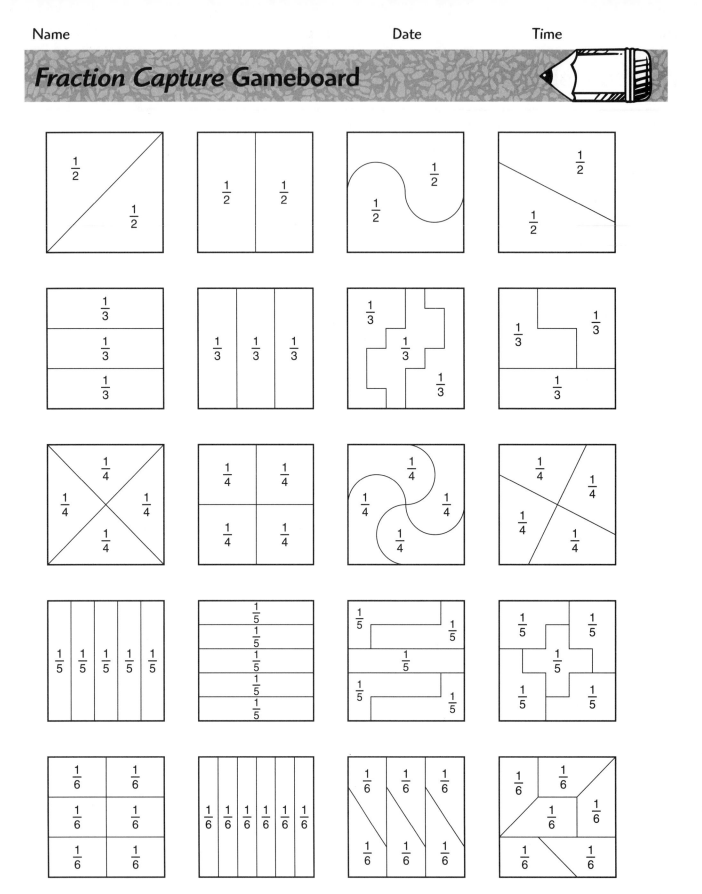

Use with Lesson 6.9.

Name Date Time

Common Denominators

1. For each pair of fractions below:

- Find a common denominator.
- Rewrite the fractions with this common denominator.
- Add the fractions.

Original Fractions	Fractions with a Common Denominator	Sum
$\frac{1}{2}$ and $\frac{3}{4}$		
$\frac{2}{9}$ and $\frac{7}{3}$		
$\frac{3}{8}$ and $\frac{5}{16}$		
$\frac{3}{5}$ and $\frac{9}{20}$		
$\frac{7}{14}$ and $\frac{6}{8}$		
$\frac{8}{10}$ and $\frac{15}{25}$		
$\frac{6}{9}$ and $\frac{8}{12}$		
$\frac{2}{3}$ and $\frac{3}{4}$		
$\frac{1}{5}$ and $\frac{3}{8}$		
$\frac{3}{10}$ and $\frac{6}{7}$		

2. Explain how you found a common denominator for one of the fraction pairs above.

____

____

Name Date Time

Exponent Ball Gameboard

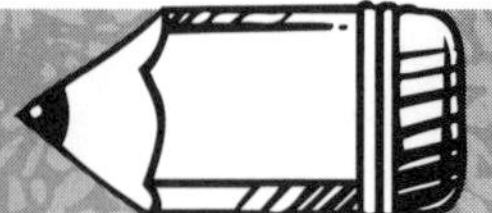

Goal Line

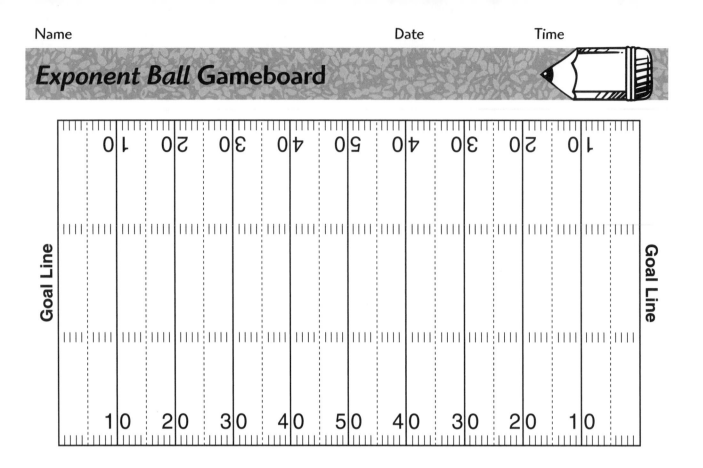

10 20 30 40 50 40 30 20 10

Goal Line

Table 1: Runs		
Value of Roll	**Move Ball**	**Chances of Gaining on the Ground**
1	−15 yd	−15 yards: 1 out of 6 or about 17%
2 to 6	+10 yd	10 yards or more: 5 out of 6 or about 83%
8 to 81	+20 yd	20 yards or more: 4 out of 6 or about 67%
in the 100s	+30 yd	30 yards or more: 13 out of 36 or about 36%
in the 1,000s	+40 yd	40 yards or more: 7 out of 36 or about 19%
in the 10,000s	+50 yd	50 yards: 1 out of 18 or about 6%

Table 2: Kicks		
Value of Roll	**Move Ball**	**Chances of Kicking**
1	+10 yd	10 yards or more: 6 out of 6 or 100%
2	+20 yd	20 yards or more: 5 out of 6 or about 83%
3	+30 yd	30 yards or more: 4 out of 6 or about 67%
4	+40 yd	40 yards or more: 3 out of 6 or about 50%
5	+50 yd	50 yards or more: 2 out of 6 or about 33%
6	+60 yd	60 yards: 1 out of 6 or about 17%

Name Date Time

Patterns with Fibonacci Numbers

1. The sequence of numbers 1, 1, 2, 3, 5, 8, 13, ... is called the **Fibonacci sequence.** In the Fibonacci sequence, every number, starting with the third number, is equal to the sum of the two numbers that come before it.

Examples

Third number: $1 + 1 = 2$ Fourth number: $1 + 2 = 3$

Fill in the next three Fibonacci numbers. 1, 1, 2, 3, 5, 8, 13, _____, _____, _____

2. Study the following pattern: $1^2 + 1^2 = 1 * 2$

$1^2 + 1^2 + 2^2 = 2 * 3$

$1^2 + 1^2 + 2^2 + 3^2 = 3 * 5$

$1^2 + 1^2 + 2^2 + 3^2 + 5^2 = 5 * 8$

a. Write the next two number sentences in the pattern.

____

____

b. Describe the pattern in words.

____

____

____

3. **a.** Solve the following problems: $2^2 - (1 * 3) =$ _______

$3^2 - (2 * 5) =$ _______

$5^2 - (3 * 8) =$ _______

$8^2 - (5 * 13) =$ _______

b. Write the next two number sentences in the pattern.

____

____

c. Describe the pattern in words.

____

____

____

Name Date Time

Powers of 10

Use the patterns you see to complete the table below. Do not use your *Student Reference Book.*

1,000,000	100,000	10,000	1,000	100	10	1

Describe at least three patterns that you see in the table.

1. ______

2. ______

3. ______

Name Date Time

Scientific Notation on a Calculator

Scientific calculators usually display numbers greater than 9,999,999,999 in scientific notation.

When calculators display numbers in scientific notation, they usually give the exponent but not the base. They also leave out the multiplication sign.

- A calculator display of 2 04 means $2 * 10^4$.
- A calculator display of 5 08 means $5 * 10^8$.

1. Complete the following table:

Calculator Display	Scientific Notation	Number-and-Word Notation	Standard Notation
2 08	$2 * 10^8$	200 million	200,000,000
4 09	$4 * 10^9$	4 billion	4,000,000,000
5 09			
8 10			
6 11			
7 12			

2. How can you enter a number in scientific notation into your calculator?

____

____

____

____

Quick Thinking

As you read these words, computers in the United States are making 25 trillion decisions each second, or more than 100,000 decisions per person in the United States each second.

Name Date Time

Confusion

Robin asked her friends to help figure out how much money she needed to go to the movies. She asked her friends, "How much is 4 plus 5 times 8?" Frances and Zack said, "72." Ann and Ricky said, "44."

1. How did Frances and Zack get 72? ______

2. How did Ann and Ricky get 44? ______

Robin's friends couldn't agree who was right. Finally Robin said, "I need to buy one under-12 ticket for $4 and 5 adult tickets for $8." Then Robin's friends knew who was right.

3. Who do you think was right? Explain your answer. ______

Name Date Time

Confusion

Robin asked her friends to help figure out how much money she needed to go to the movies. She asked her friends, "How much is 4 plus 5 times 8?" Frances and Zack said, "72." Ann and Ricky said, "44."

1. How did Frances and Zack get 72? ______

2. How did Ann and Ricky get 44? ______

Robin's friends couldn't agree who was right. Finally Robin said: "I need to buy one under-12 ticket for $4 and 5 adult tickets for $8." Then Robin's friends knew who was right.

3. Who do you think was right? Explain your answer. ______

Name Date Time

Changes in Stock Prices

The stock-market pages of a newspaper report how much the price of a share of stock went up or down during the previous business day.

The table below lists the change in price of one share of stock for each of nine well-known companies. The fraction or mixed number shown for each company gives the increase or decrease in price for one share of that company's stock from one day to the next. Stock prices are changing all day long. The changes in prices given below are the differences between the prices at the closing bell on March 9, 2000, and the closing prices on March 10, 2000. The *actual* price of a share of stock is not given. The change in price is reported as a fraction or mixed number and omits the dollar sign.

Company	Change in Price of 1 Share of Stock as Shown in a Newspaper	Change in Price of 1 Share of Stock in Dollars and Cents
America Online	$-1\frac{3}{4}$	−\$1.75
Coca-Cola	$-1\frac{3}{8}$	
Disney	$-1\frac{1}{8}$	
Gap	$-\frac{7}{8}$	
IBM	$-1\frac{3}{16}$	
McDonald's	$+\frac{3}{16}$	+\$0.19
Microsoft	+1	
Pepsi-Cola	$-\frac{5}{8}$	
Target	$+\frac{3}{4}$	

1. Which companies' stocks increased in price? ______

2. Which companies' stocks went down in price by \$0.50 or more? ______

3. Which company's stock did not change in price? ______

4. Write each change in price as a dollar-and-cents amount in the last column of the table. You may use your calculator to convert fractions to decimals. Round to the nearest cent.

Name Date Time

Cash and Debt Cards

+ $1 Cash	+ $1 Cash	− $1 Debt	− $1 Debt
+ $1 Cash	+ $1 Cash	− $1 Debt	− $1 Debt
+ $1 Cash	+ $1 Cash	− $1 Debt	− $1 Debt
+ $1 Cash	+ $1 Cash	− $1 Debt	− $1 Debt
+ $1 Cash	+ $1 Cash	− $1 Debt	− $1 Debt

Use with Lesson 7.7.

Name Date Time

Credits/Debits Game Record Sheet

Game 1				
	Start	Change		End, and Next Start
		Addition or Subtraction	Credit or Debit	
1	+$10			
2				
3				
4				
5				
6				
7				
8				
9				
10				

Game 2				
	Start	Change		End, and Next Start
		Addition or Subtraction	Credit or Debit	
1	+$10			
2				
3				
4				
5				
6				
7				
8				
9				
10				

Name Date Time

Comparing Elevations

The number line below is marked to show the elevation of several well-known places.

Elevation is a measure of how far a location is above or below sea level. For example, an elevation of 5,300 feet for Denver means that some point in Denver is 5,300 feet above sea level. An elevation of −280 feet for Death Valley means that some point in Death Valley is 280 feet below sea level.

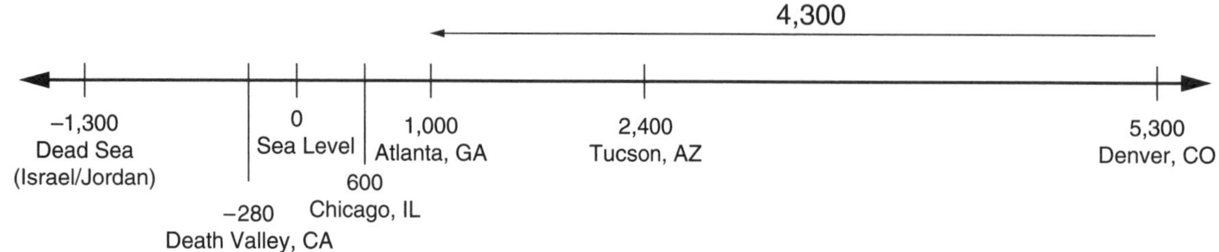

Elevation (Feet from sea level)

Fill in the table below. Use the example as a guide.

Example If you start at Denver and travel to Atlanta, what is your change in elevation?

Solution Draw an arrow above the number line. Start it at the elevation for Denver (5,300 feet). End it at the elevation for Atlanta (1,000 feet). Use the number line to find the length of the arrow (4,300 feet). Your final elevation is lower, so report the change in elevation as 4,300 feet down.

Start at	**Travel to**	**Change in Elevation (up or down)**
Denver	Atlanta	4300 feet down
Chicago	Tucson	_____ feet _____
Death Valley	Dead Sea	_____ feet _____
Dead Sea	Death Valley	_____ feet _____
Tucson	Death Valley	_____ feet _____
Dead Sea	Atlanta	_____ feet _____

Use with Lesson 7.9.

20 19 18 17 16 15 14 13 12 11 10 9 8 7 6 5 4 3 2 1 0 1 2 3 4 5 6 7 8 9 10 11 12 13 14 15 16 17 18 19 20

Integer slider

Fraction slider

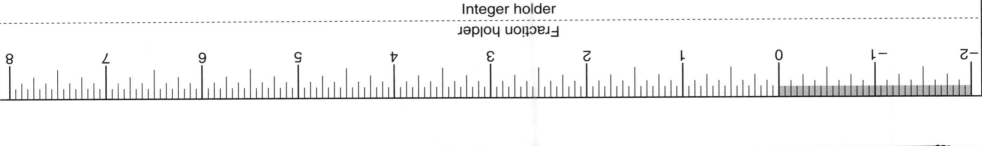

2 1 0 1 2 3 4 5 6 7 8

–20 –19 –18 –17 –16 –15 –14 –13 –12 –11 –10 –9 –8 –7 –6 –5 –4 –3 –2 –1 0 1 2 3 4 5 6 7 8 9 10 11 12 13 14 15 16 17 18 19 20

Integer holder

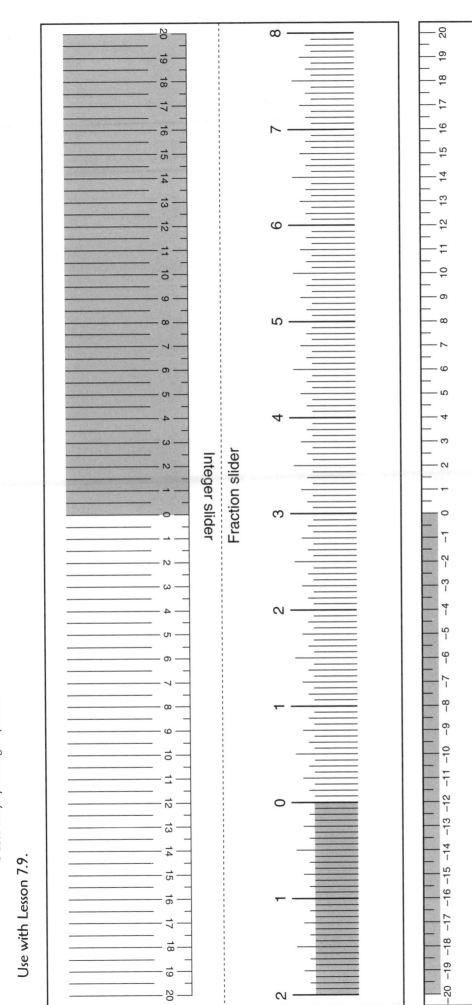

Fraction holder

8 7 6 5 4 3 2 1 0 –1 –2

Slide Rule

Name Date Time

Broken Calculator Problems

Change the display in the calculator without using the broken key. *You may only add and subtract negative numbers to reach the ending number.* The first one is done for you.

Starting Number	Ending Number	Broken Key	Keystrokes
38	48	0	38 [−] [(−)] 5 [−] [(−)] 5 [Enter =]
24	70	6	
200	89	1	
351	251	0	
1,447	1,750	3	

Make up five problems of your own. When you have finished, trade papers with your partner and solve each other's problems. *You may only add and subtract negative numbers to reach the ending number.*

Starting Number	Ending Number	Broken Key	Keystrokes

Use with Lesson 7.10.

Name Date Time

Build-It Card Deck

$\frac{5}{9}$	$\frac{1}{3}$	$\frac{11}{12}$	$\frac{1}{12}$
$\frac{7}{12}$	$\frac{3}{8}$	$\frac{1}{4}$	$\frac{1}{5}$
$\frac{2}{3}$	$\frac{3}{7}$	$\frac{4}{7}$	$\frac{3}{4}$
$\frac{3}{5}$	$\frac{4}{5}$	$\frac{7}{9}$	$\frac{5}{6}$

Name Date Time

Build-It Gameboard

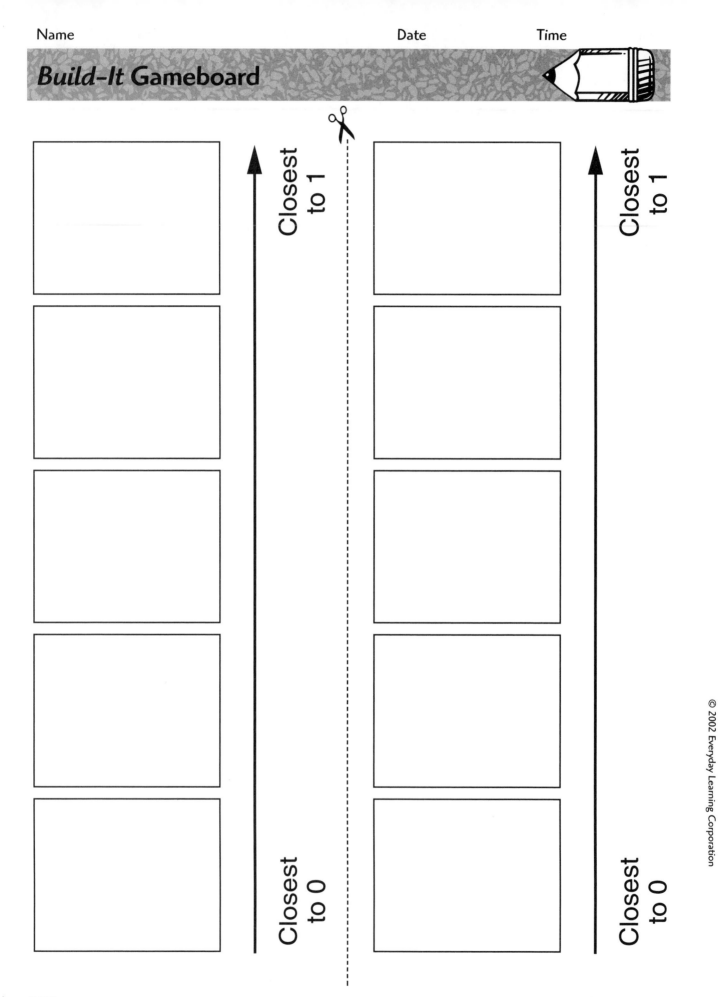

Closest to 1

Closest to 0

Closest to 1

Closest to 0

Name Date Time

Six-Inch Ruler

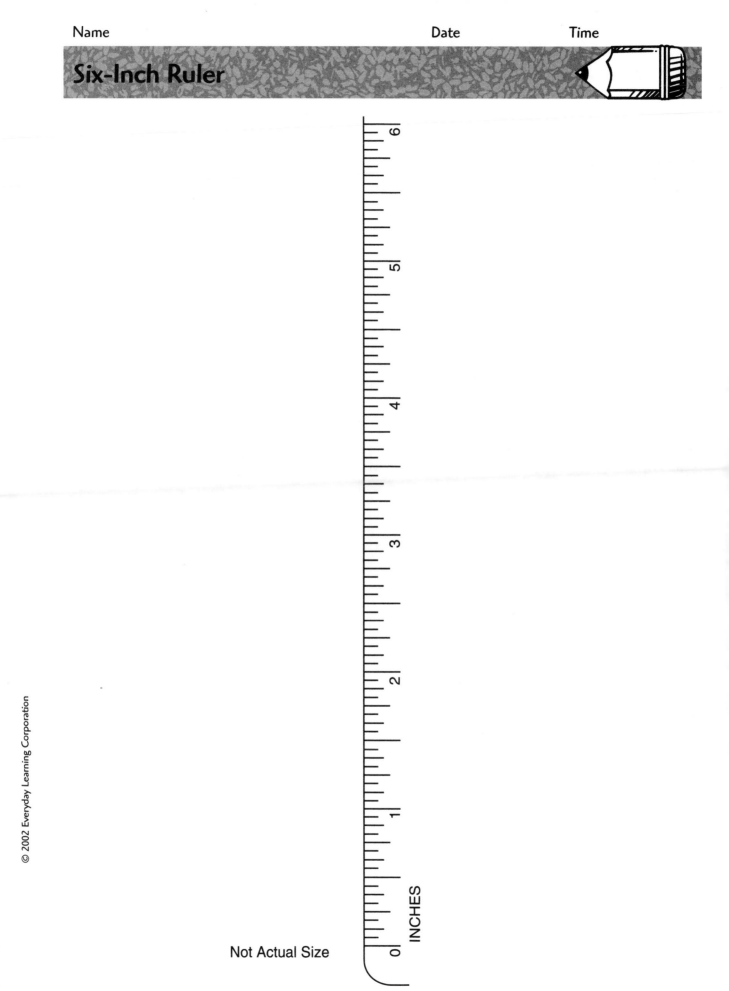

0 INCHES 1 2 3 4 5 6

Not Actual Size

Name Date Time

Addition of Mixed-Numbers Practice

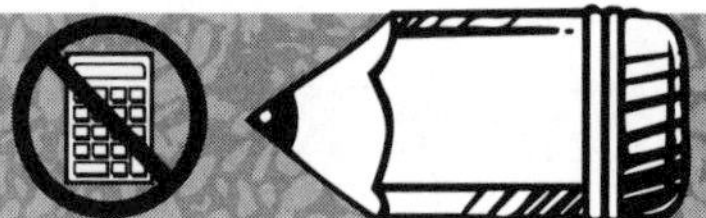

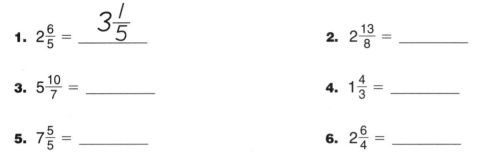

Rename in simplest form.

1. $2\frac{6}{5}$ = $3\frac{1}{5}$

2. $2\frac{13}{8}$ = ________

3. $5\frac{10}{7}$ = ________

4. $1\frac{4}{3}$ = ________

5. $7\frac{5}{5}$ = ________

6. $2\frac{6}{4}$ = ________

Add. Write each sum as a whole number or mixed number in simplest form.

7. $6\frac{2}{4} + 7\frac{3}{4}$ = ________

8. $2\frac{3}{5} + 6\frac{2}{5}$ = ________

9. $4\frac{2}{3} + 7\frac{2}{3}$ = ________

10. $3\frac{6}{8} + 4\frac{3}{8}$ = ________

11. $4\frac{2}{6} + 6\frac{1}{6}$ = ________

12. $8\frac{4}{5} + 3\frac{5}{5}$ = ________

Add. Rename the sum in simplest form, and circle your final answer.

13. $4\frac{7}{8} + 7\frac{1}{4}$

14. $3\frac{1}{2} + 8\frac{4}{7}$

15. $5\frac{1}{6} + 7\frac{8}{10}$

16. $3\frac{3}{4} + 6\frac{4}{9}$

Name Date Time

Mixed-Number Spin

Materials *Math Masters,* p. 106
large paper clip

Players 2

Directions

1. Each player writes his or her name in one of the boxes below.
2. Take turns spinning. When it is your turn, write the fraction or mixed number you spin in one of the blanks below your name.
3. The first player to complete 10 true sentences is the winner.

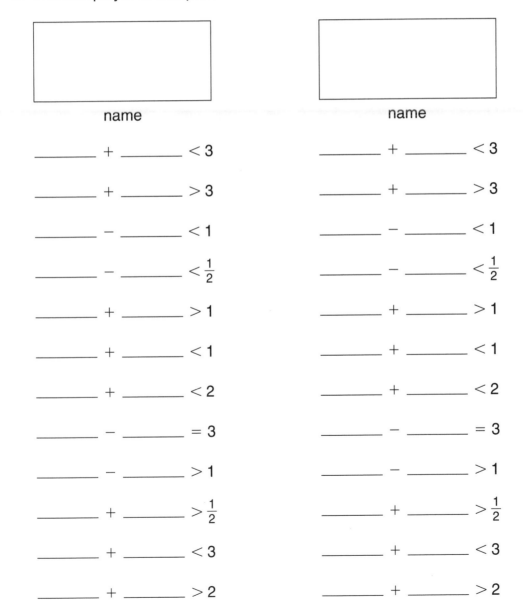

name	name
______ + ______ < 3	______ + ______ < 3
______ + ______ > 3	______ + ______ > 3
______ − ______ < 1	______ − ______ < 1
______ − ______ $< \frac{1}{2}$	______ − ______ $< \frac{1}{2}$
______ + ______ > 1	______ + ______ > 1
______ + ______ < 1	______ + ______ < 1
______ + ______ < 2	______ + ______ < 2
______ − ______ $= 3$	______ − ______ $= 3$
______ − ______ > 1	______ − ______ > 1
______ + ______ $> \frac{1}{2}$	______ + ______ $> \frac{1}{2}$
______ + ______ < 3	______ + ______ < 3
______ + ______ > 2	______ + ______ > 2

Name Date Time

Mixed-Number Spinner

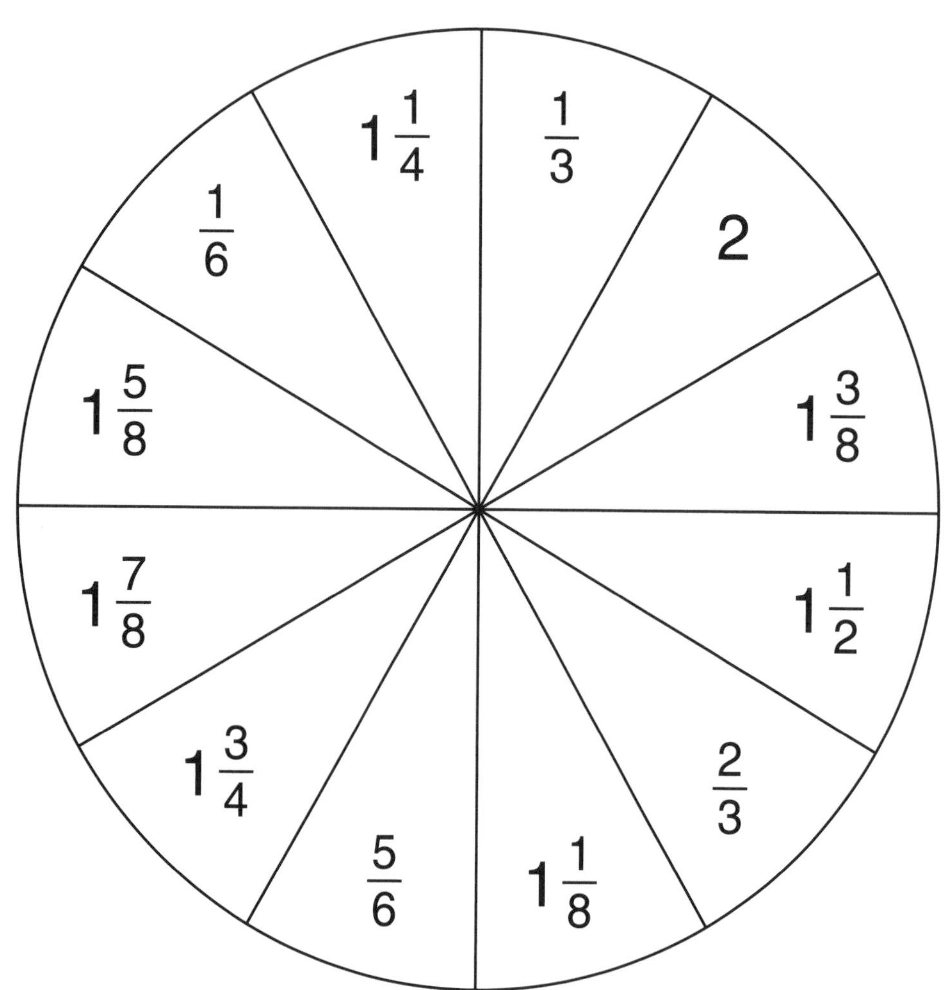

Use with Lesson 8.3.

Name Date Time

Subtraction of Mixed-Numbers Practice

Subtract. Write your answers in simplest form.

1. $2\frac{3}{4} - 1\frac{1}{4} =$ ______

2. $7\frac{2}{3} - 5\frac{1}{3} =$ ______

3. $6\frac{6}{10} - 4\frac{2}{10} =$ ______

4. $4\frac{7}{8} - 2\frac{3}{8} =$ ______

5. $5\frac{2}{9} - 4\frac{7}{9} =$ ______

6. $7\frac{1}{8} - 5\frac{5}{8} =$ ______

7. $6\frac{2}{5} - 2\frac{4}{5} =$ ______

8. $3\frac{1}{7} - 2\frac{5}{7} =$ ______

9. $7\frac{4}{8} - 4\frac{5}{8} =$ ______

10. $4\frac{1}{6} - 2\frac{4}{6} =$ ______

Name Date Time

Fraction Action, Fraction Friction Card Deck

$\frac{1}{2}$	$\frac{1}{3}$	$\frac{2}{3}$	$\frac{1}{4}$
$\frac{3}{4}$	$\frac{1}{6}$	$\frac{1}{6}$	$\frac{5}{6}$
$\frac{1}{12}$	$\frac{1}{12}$	$\frac{5}{12}$	$\frac{5}{12}$
$\frac{7}{12}$	$\frac{7}{12}$	$\frac{11}{12}$	$\frac{11}{12}$

Name Date Time

Number-Line Models

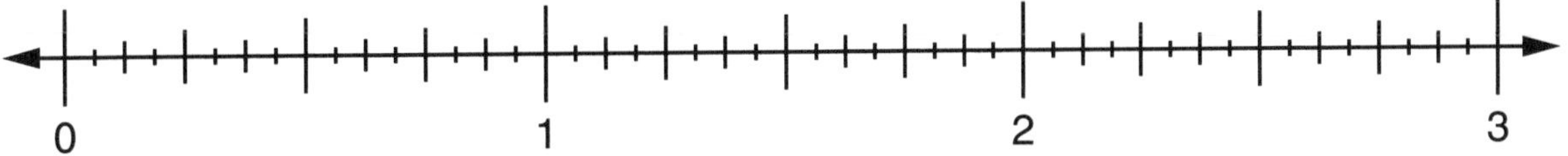

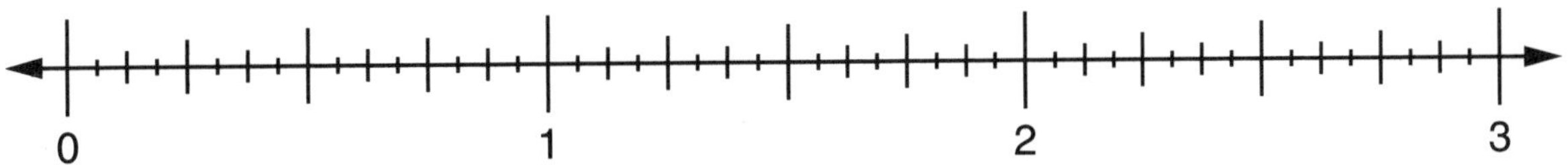

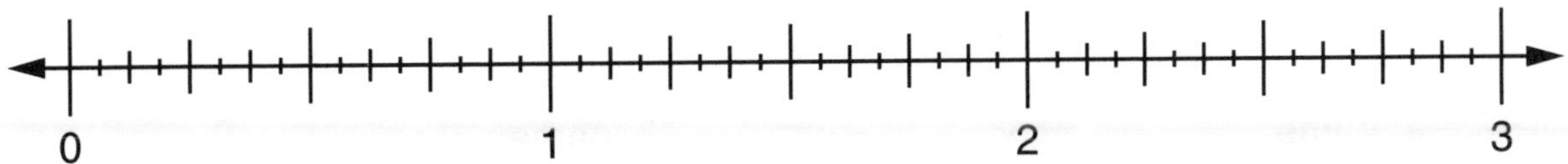

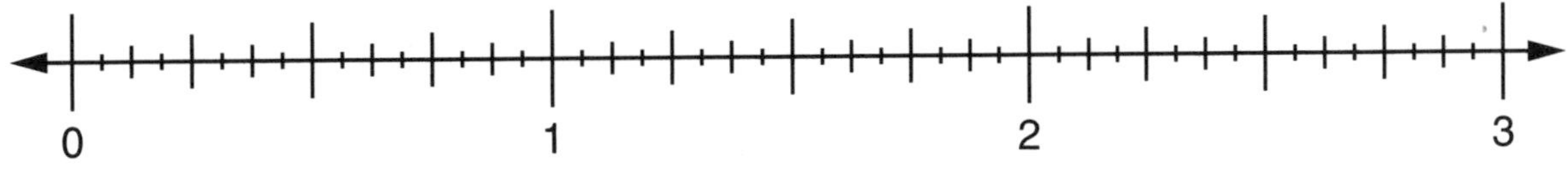

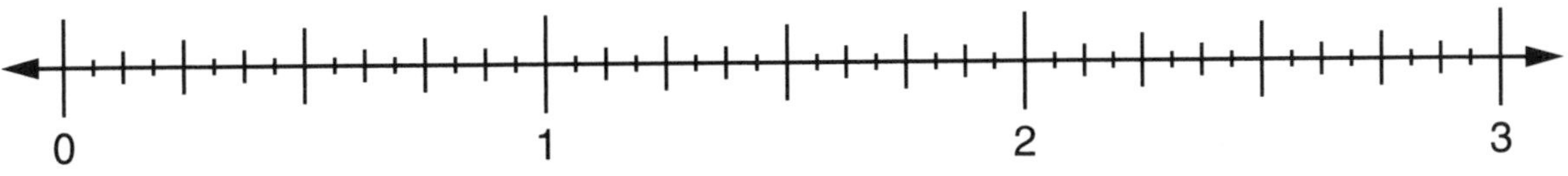

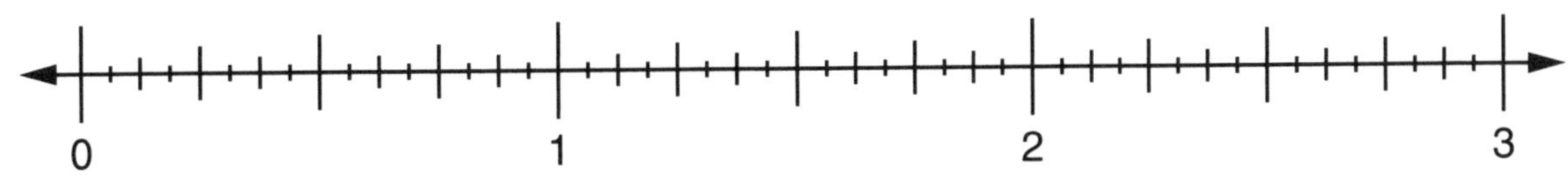

Name Date Time

Fraction Spin

Materials *Math Masters,* p. 111
large paper clip

Players 2

Directions

1. Each player writes his or her name in one of the boxes below.

2. Take turns spinning. When it is your turn, write the fraction you spin in one of the blanks below your name.

3. The first player to complete 10 true sentences is the winner.

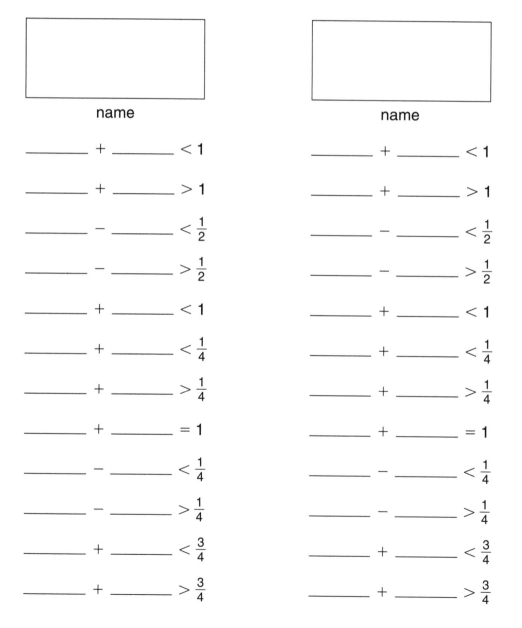

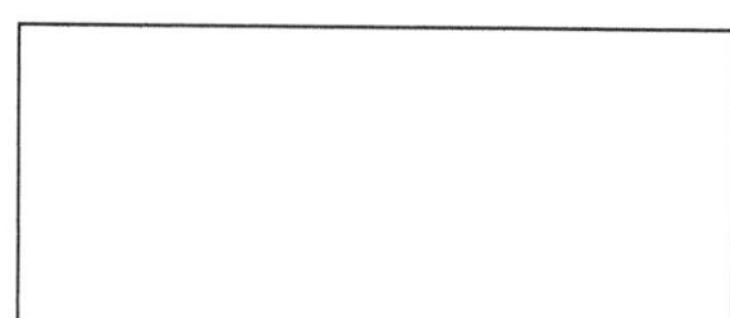

name	name
$\underline{\qquad} + \underline{\qquad} < 1$	$\underline{\qquad} + \underline{\qquad} < 1$
$\underline{\qquad} + \underline{\qquad} > 1$	$\underline{\qquad} + \underline{\qquad} > 1$
$\underline{\qquad} - \underline{\qquad} < \frac{1}{2}$	$\underline{\qquad} - \underline{\qquad} < \frac{1}{2}$
$\underline{\qquad} - \underline{\qquad} > \frac{1}{2}$	$\underline{\qquad} - \underline{\qquad} > \frac{1}{2}$
$\underline{\qquad} + \underline{\qquad} < 1$	$\underline{\qquad} + \underline{\qquad} < 1$
$\underline{\qquad} + \underline{\qquad} < \frac{1}{4}$	$\underline{\qquad} + \underline{\qquad} < \frac{1}{4}$
$\underline{\qquad} + \underline{\qquad} > \frac{1}{4}$	$\underline{\qquad} + \underline{\qquad} > \frac{1}{4}$
$\underline{\qquad} + \underline{\qquad} = 1$	$\underline{\qquad} + \underline{\qquad} = 1$
$\underline{\qquad} - \underline{\qquad} < \frac{1}{4}$	$\underline{\qquad} - \underline{\qquad} < \frac{1}{4}$
$\underline{\qquad} - \underline{\qquad} > \frac{1}{4}$	$\underline{\qquad} - \underline{\qquad} > \frac{1}{4}$
$\underline{\qquad} + \underline{\qquad} < \frac{3}{4}$	$\underline{\qquad} + \underline{\qquad} < \frac{3}{4}$
$\underline{\qquad} + \underline{\qquad} > \frac{3}{4}$	$\underline{\qquad} + \underline{\qquad} > \frac{3}{4}$

Name Date Time

Fraction Spinner

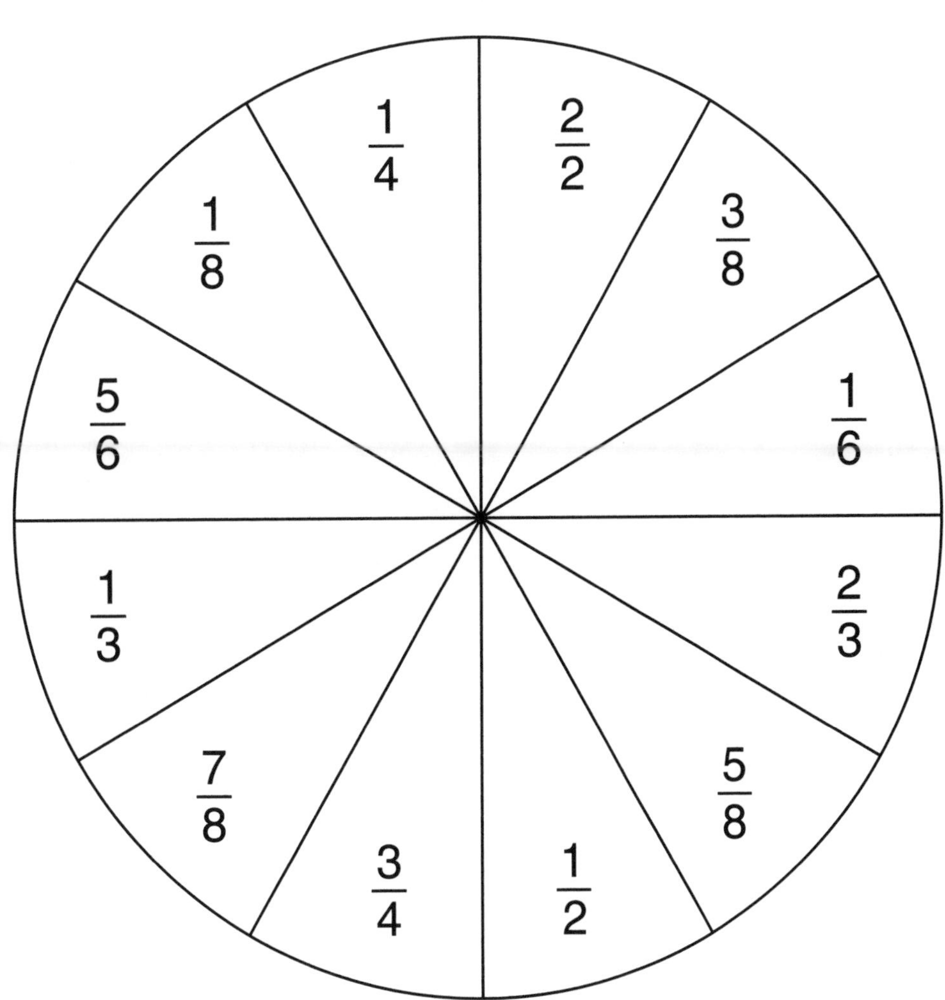

Name Date Time

An Area Model for Fraction Multiplication

1. Use the rectangle at the right to find $\frac{2}{3} * \frac{3}{4}$.

$\frac{2}{3} * \frac{3}{4} =$ ____________

Your completed drawing in Problem 1 is called an **area model.**

Use area models to complete the following.

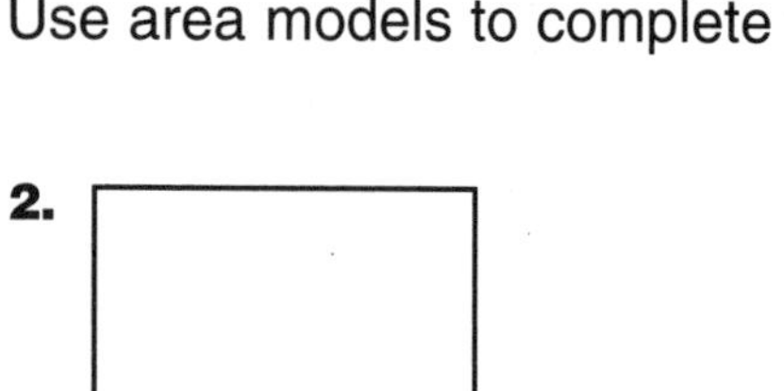

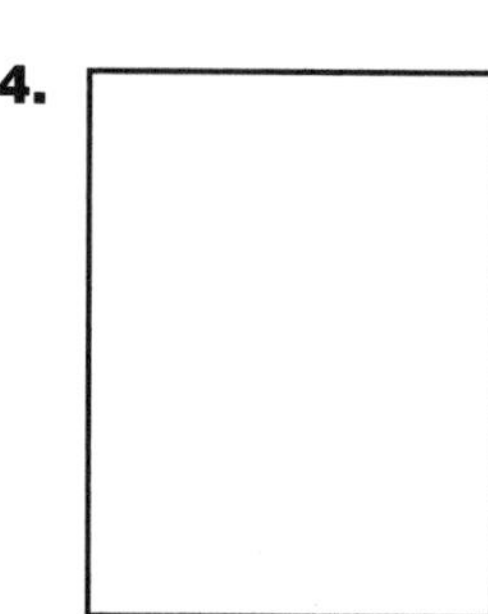

2. $\frac{2}{3} * \frac{1}{5} =$ ______

3. $\frac{3}{4} * \frac{2}{5} =$ ______

4. $\frac{1}{4} * \frac{5}{6} =$ ______

5. $\frac{3}{8} * \frac{3}{5} =$ ______

6. $\frac{1}{2} * \frac{5}{8} =$ ______

7. $\frac{5}{6} * \frac{4}{5} =$ ______

8. Make up your own fraction multiplication problem. Use an area model to help you solve it.

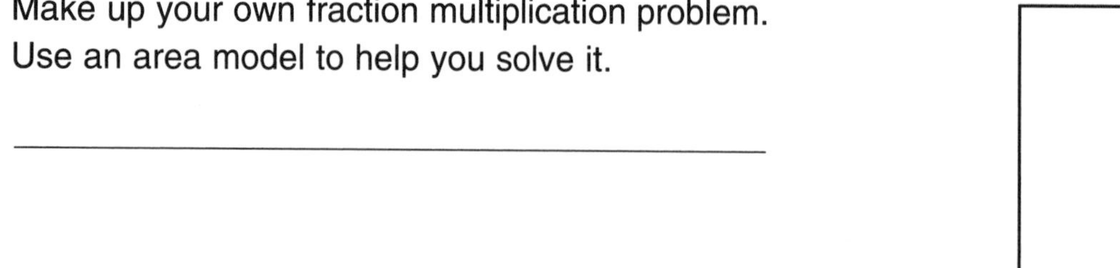

____

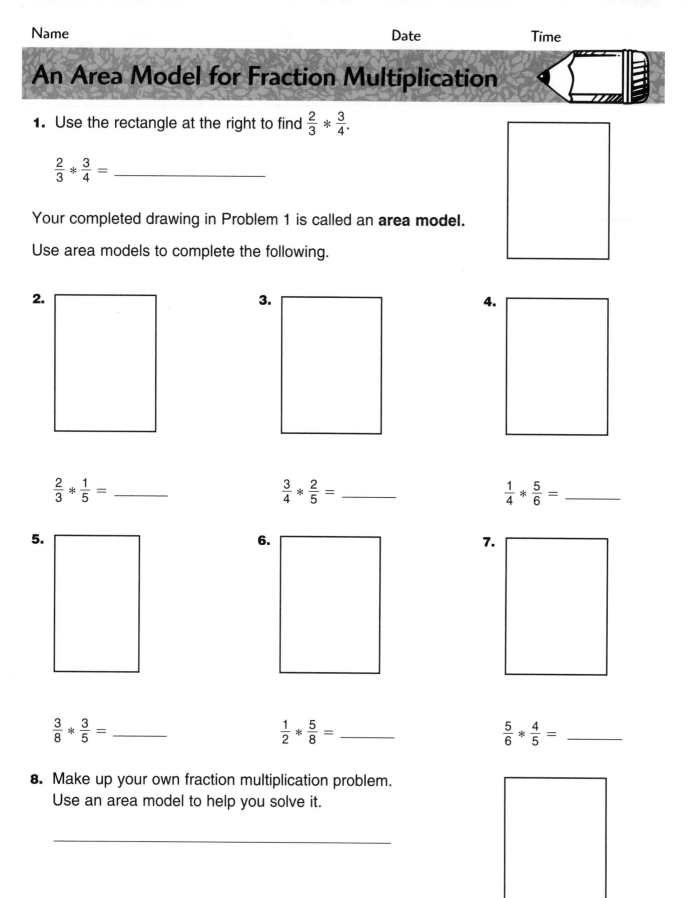

Name Date Time

Using Area Models to Multiply Fractions

Use area models to complete the following.

1. 

_____ = _____

2. 

_____ = _____

3. 

_____ = _____

4. 

_____ = _____

5. 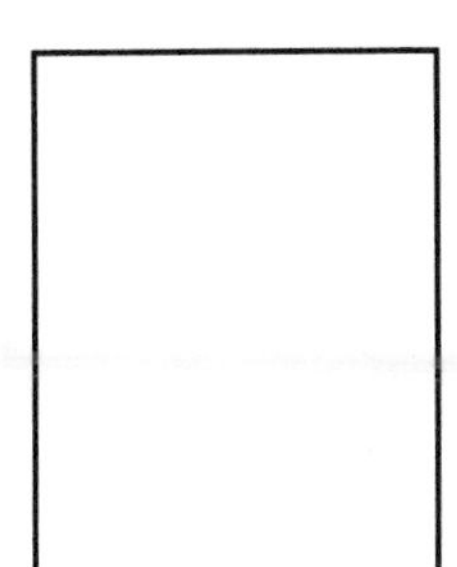

_____ = _____

6. 

_____ = _____

Make up your own fraction multiplication problems. Use area models to help you solve them.

7. 

____

8. 

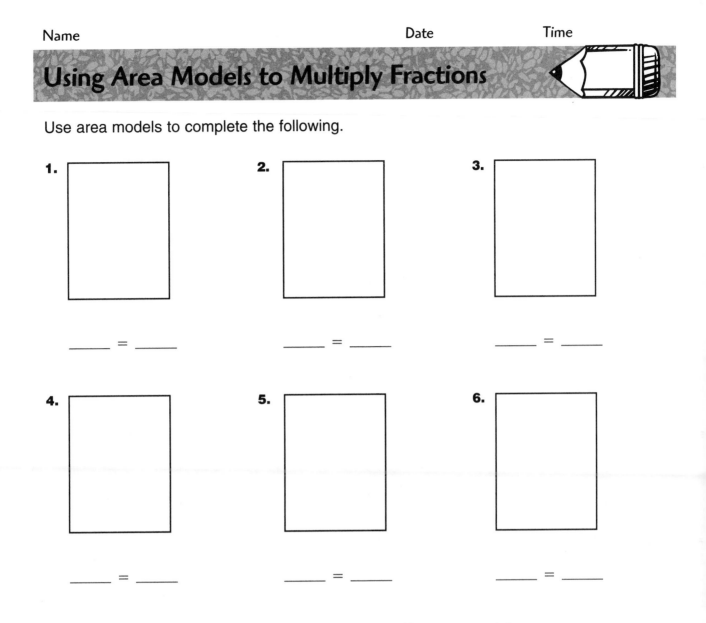

____

Name Date Time

Percent Problems

1. Alice baked a batch of cookies. 24 cookies are 40% of the cookies she baked. Complete the table showing the number of cookies for each percent.

%	10%	20%	30%	40%	50%	60%	70%	80%	90%	100%
Number of cookies				24						

2. Explain how you found 100% or the total number of cookies Alice baked.

____

____

____

____

3. Complete the table showing how far Melissa ran during her 60-minute run. She ran at a steady rate for the entire time.

Time	15 minutes	30 minutes		60 minutes
Miles		4 miles	6 miles	

4. What percent of the run is 30 minutes? _______________

5. a. What percent of her total distance is 6 miles? _______________

   b. Explain. _______________

   ____

6. How can constructing a table help solve a percent problem?

____

____

____

Name Date Time

"What's My Rule?"

1. Rule: out = 25% of in

in	out
44	
	25
64	
	31
304	
116	

2. Rule: out = 60% of in

in	out
100	
60	
	42
110	
	72
35	

Find the rule. Then complete the table.

3. Rule: out = ________ of in

in	out
100	40
45	18
60	24
	32
	16
125	

4. Rule: out = ________ of in

in	out
24	9
72	27
56	21
80	30
	15
32	

Make up two of your own.

5. Rule: out = ________% of in

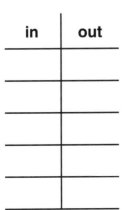

in	out

6. Rule: out = ________% of in

in	out

Name Date Time

Classroom Survey

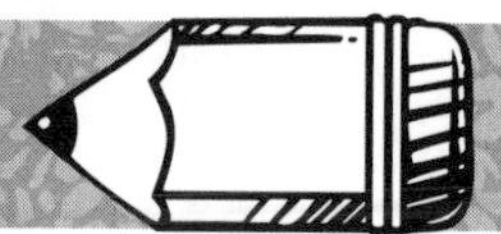

Number in Household	Number of Students
1–2	
3–5	
6 or more	

Language at Home	Number of Students
English	
Spanish	
Other	

Handedness	Number of Students
right	
left	

Years at Current Address	Number of Students
0 or 1	
2	
3	
4	
5	
6 or more	

Use with Lesson 8.11.

Name Date Time

Hidden Treasure Gameboards

Each player uses Grids 1 and 2.

Grid 1: Hide your point here.

Grid 2: Guess other player's point here.

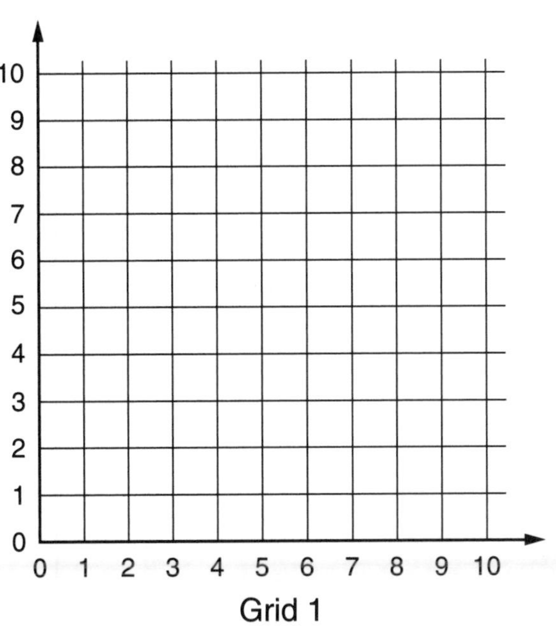

Grid 1

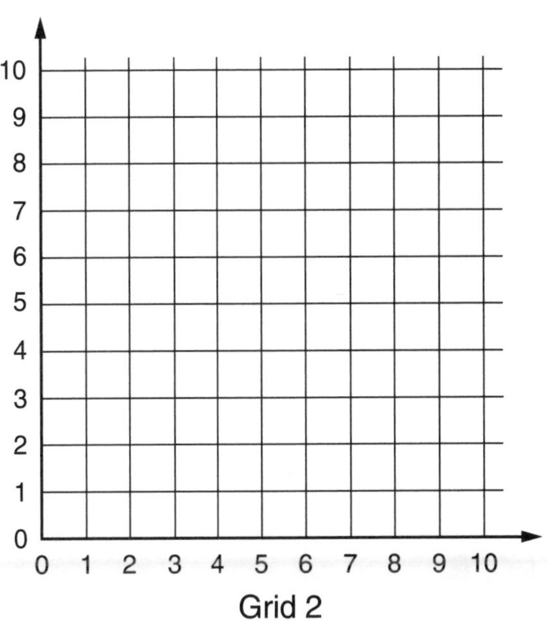

Grid 2

Use Grids 1 and 2 to play another game.

Grid 1: Hide your point here.

Grid 2: Guess other player's point here.

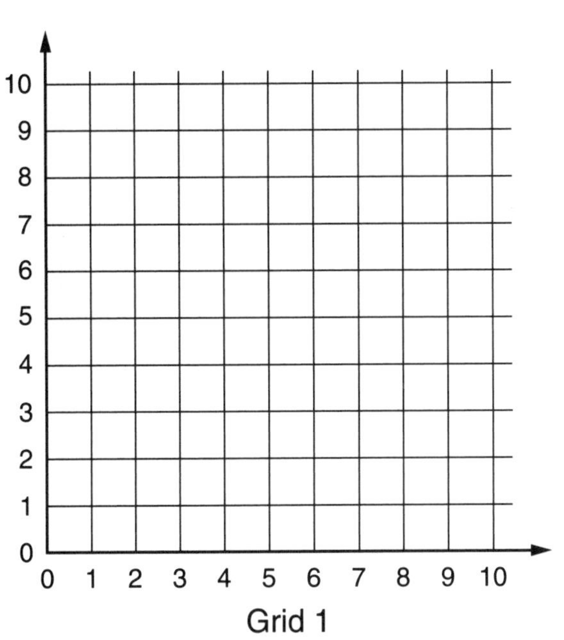

Grid 1

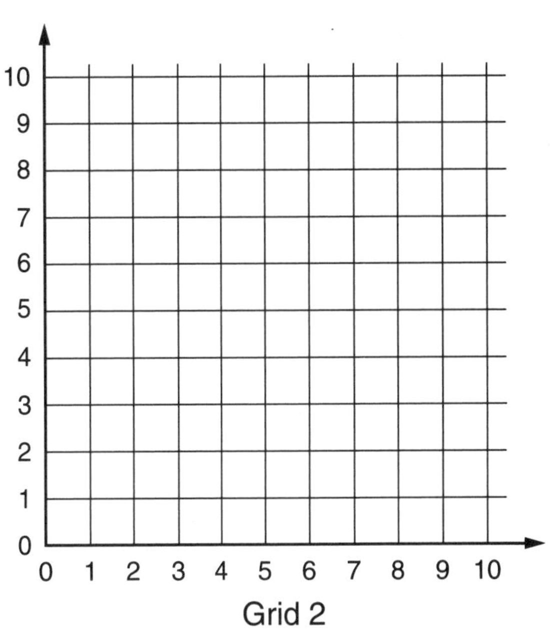

Grid 2

Name Date Time

Grid Paper (1 in.)

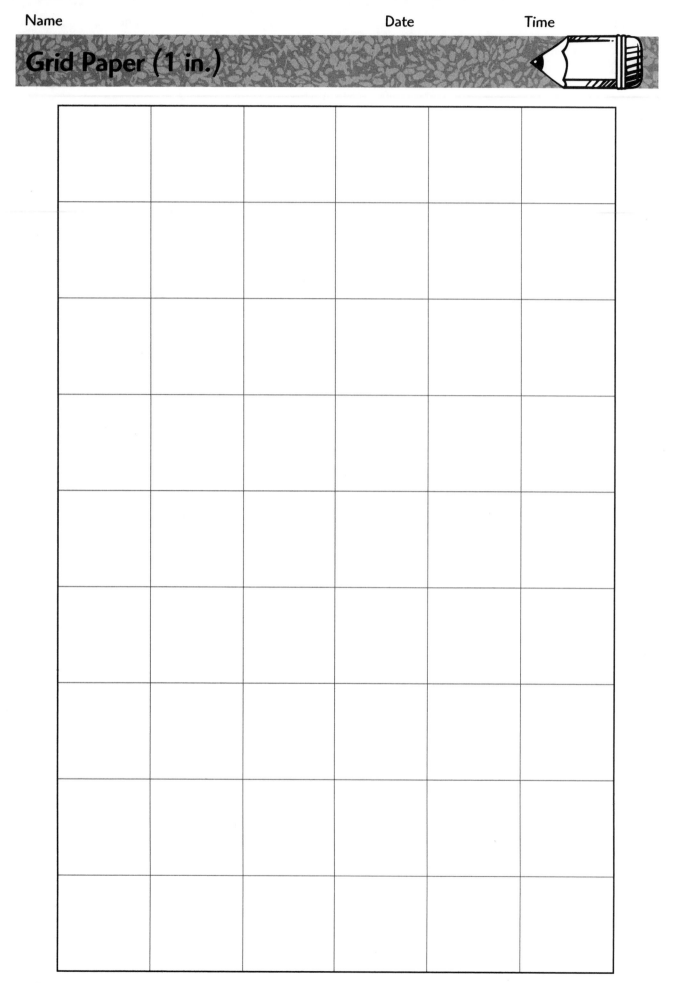

Use with Lesson 9.2.

Name Date Time

Grid Paper (1 cm)

Name Date Time

Plotting a Picture

1. Draw a simple picture that can be formed with straight lines connecting points on the grid. (Use at least 8 points but no more than 14 points.)

2. Record the ordered pairs you have plotted on a separate sheet of paper. Be sure you record your points in the order in which they need to be connected.

3. Give your list of coordinates and a blank grid to your partner and have your partner reproduce your drawing by plotting and connecting the points.

4. Compare your original picture with your partner's copy.

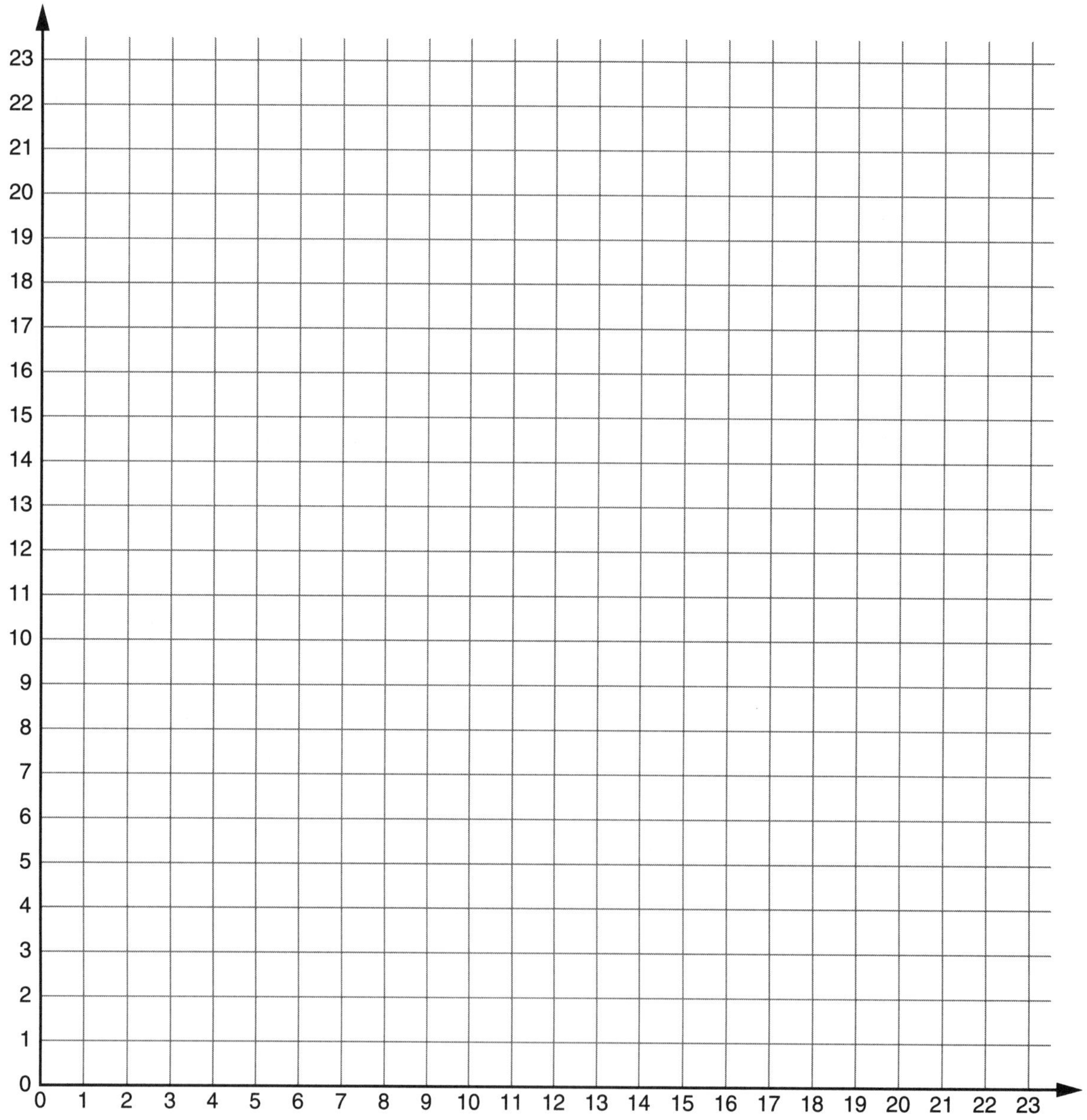

23
22
21
20
19
18
17
16
15
14
13
12
11
10
9
8
7
6
5
4
3
2
1
0

0 1 2 3 4 5 6 7 8 9 10 11 12 13 14 15 16 17 18 19 20 21 22 23

Use with Lesson 9.2.

Name Date Time

Advanced Hidden Treasure Gameboards

Each player uses Grids 1 and 2.

Grid 1: Hide your point here.

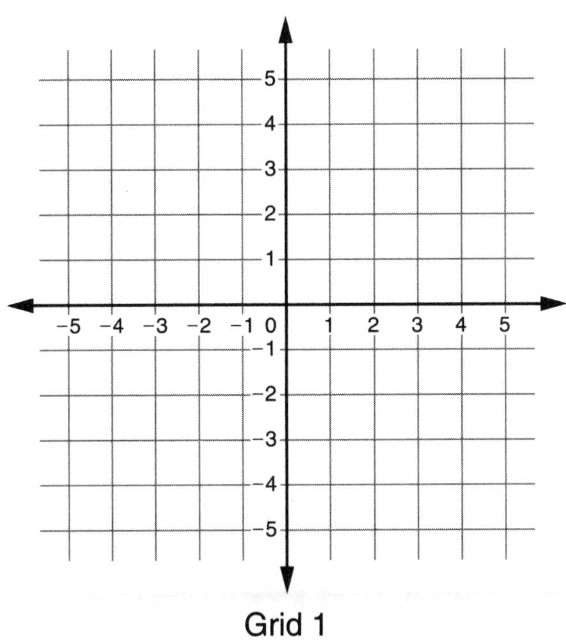

Grid 1

Grid 2: Guess other player's point here.

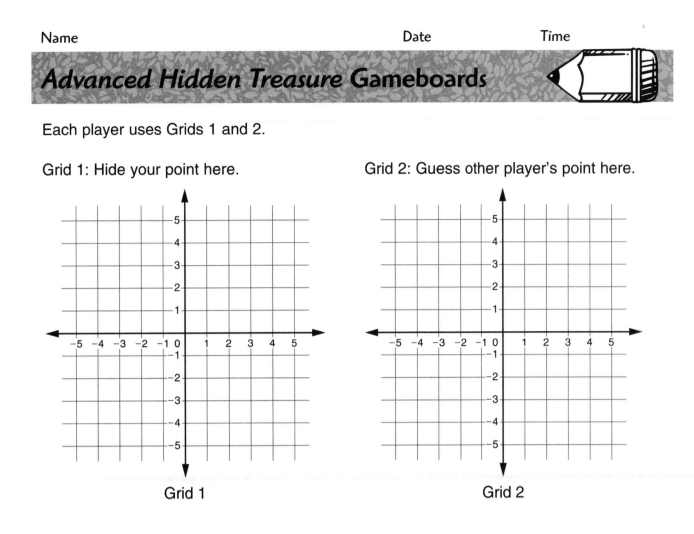

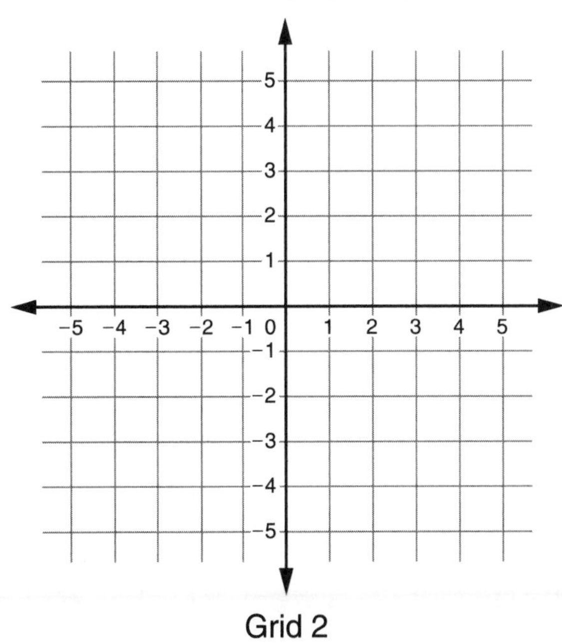

Grid 2

Use Grids 1 and 2 to play another game.

Grid 1: Hide your point here.

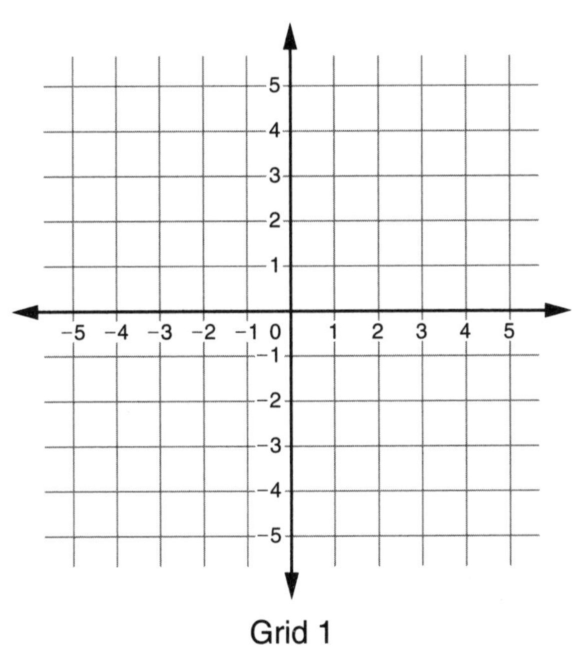

Grid 1

Grid 2: Guess other player's point here.

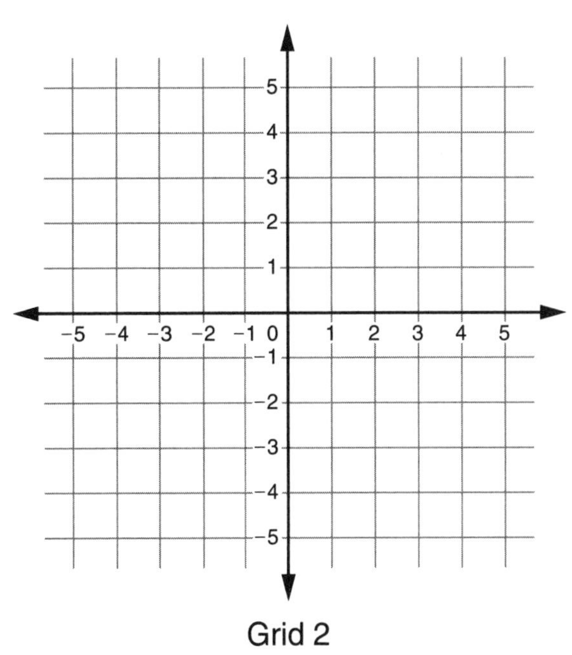

Grid 2

Name Date Time

Reflections on a Coordinate Grid

1. Plot four to eight points in the positive quadrant on *Math Masters,* page 123. Connect the points to make a picture or design. Make a design whose reflection will look distinctly different.

   For example, a rhombus ◇ will look identical when it is reflected, if it is drawn with its lines of symmetry parallel to the axes.

   The reflections of a concave pentagon will look different from the original figure.

2. Use a reflective transparent mirror to draw one reflection directly below the *x*-axis (Design #1), and another directly across the *y*-axis (Design #2).

3. List the ordered pairs for all three drawings in the chart below.

Original Design	**Design #1**	**Design #2**
(_____ , _____)	(_____ , _____)	(_____ , _____)
(_____ , _____)	(_____ , _____)	(_____ , _____)
(_____ , _____)	(_____ , _____)	(_____ , _____)
(_____ , _____)	(_____ , _____)	(_____ , _____)
(_____ , _____)	(_____ , _____)	(_____ , _____)
(_____ , _____)	(_____ , _____)	(_____ , _____)
(_____ , _____)	(_____ , _____)	(_____ , _____)
(_____ , _____)	(_____ , _____)	(_____ , _____)

4. Look at the ordered pairs above. What rule did you use to go from the original design to Design #1?

____

5. What rule did you use to go from the original design to Design #2?

____

Name Date Time

A Four-Quadrant Grid

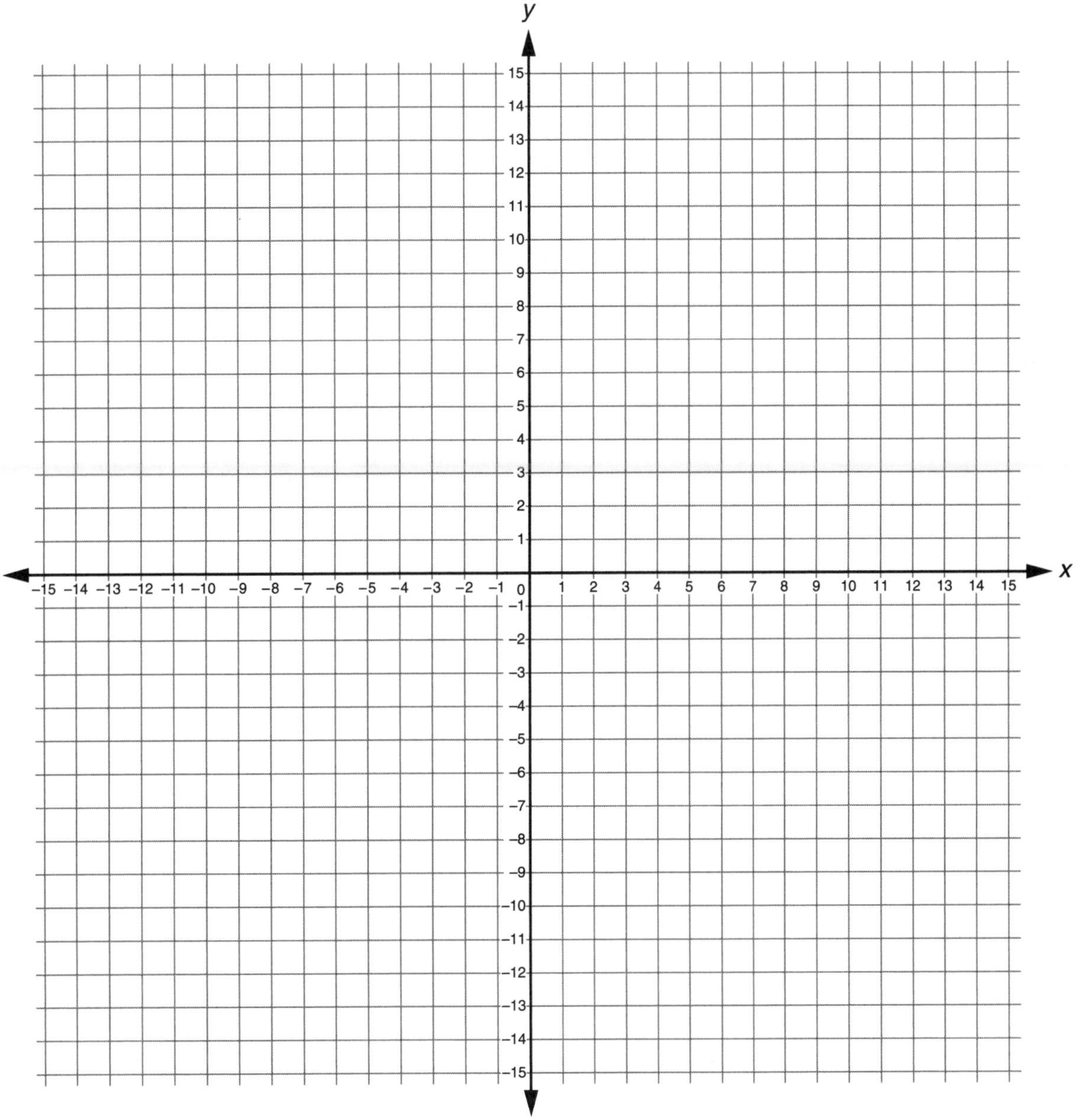

Name Date Time

The Most Common Words

The 32 most commonly used words in the English language are:

a, all, and, are, as, at, be, but, for, had, have, he, him, his, I, in, is, it, not, of, on, one, said, so, that, the, they, to, was, we, with, you.

1. Look in a book, newspaper, or magazine and pick a writing sample that is *exactly* 25 words long. One way is to start at the beginning of a paragraph and count 25 words. Record the source of your sample.

____

2. Make a tally mark for every word in your sample that is on the list above. Some words may occur more than once. Be sure to make a tally mark every time the word occurs. Record the total number of times any of the 32 most common words occur in your sample.

____

The Longest Words

The longest word to be published in a dictionary first appeared in the 1982 supplement to the *Oxford English Dictionary:*

Pneumonoultramicroscopicsilicovolcanoconiosis

It has 45 letters and is defined as "a factitious (made-up) word alleged to mean 'a lung disease caused by the inhalation of very fine silica dust,' but occurring chiefly as an instance of a very long word."

In New Zealand, there is a place whose name is even longer. It has 57 letters:

Taumatawhakatangihangakoauauotamateapokaiwhenvakitanatahu

Source: The Oxford Guide to Word Games

0 CM 1 2 3 4 5 6 7 8 9 10 11 12 13 14 15

Name Date Time

The Most Common Words (cont.)

The diagram at the right represents the 20,000 most commonly used words in the English language. The area of each box in the diagram represents the number of times the words in the box occur, compared to the total.

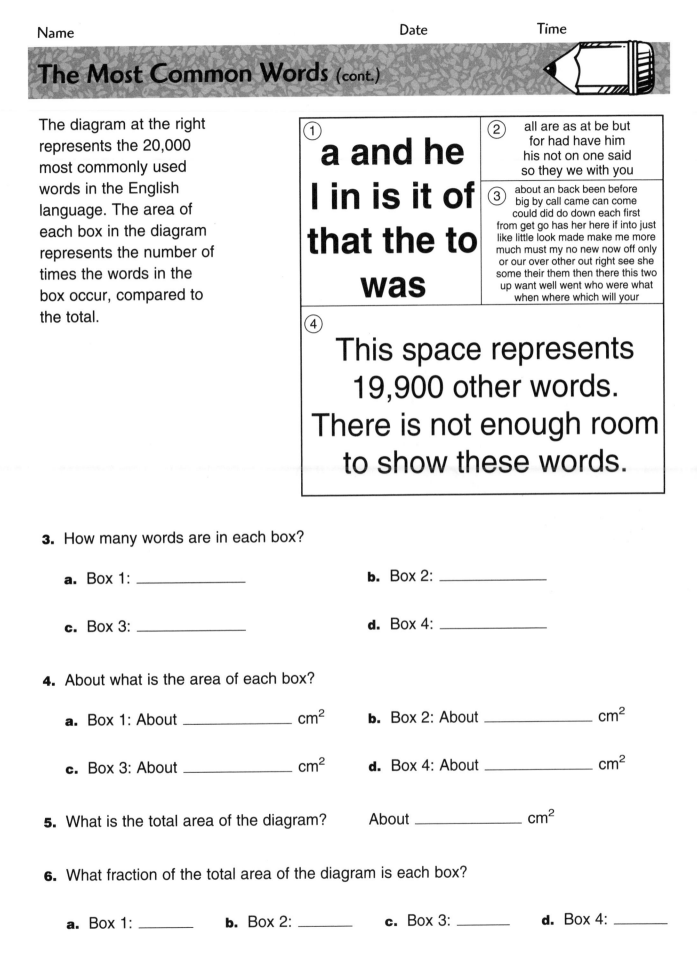

① a and he I in is it of that the to was	② all are as at be but for had have him his not on one said so they we with you ③ about an back been before big by call came can come could did do down each first from get go has her here if into just like little look made make me more much must my no new now off only or our over other out right see she some their them then there this two up want well went who were what when where which will your
④ This space represents 19,900 other words. There is not enough room to show these words.	

3. How many words are in each box?

a. Box 1: ____________ **b.** Box 2: ____________

c. Box 3: ____________ **d.** Box 4: ____________

4. About what is the area of each box?

a. Box 1: About ____________ cm^2 **b.** Box 2: About ____________ cm^2

c. Box 3: About ____________ cm^2 **d.** Box 4: About ____________ cm^2

5. What is the total area of the diagram? About ____________ cm^2

6. What fraction of the total area of the diagram is each box?

a. Box 1: ________ **b.** Box 2: ________ **c.** Box 3: ________ **d.** Box 4: ________

Name Date Time

More Practice with the Rectangle Method

Use the rectangle method to find the area of each triangle and parallelogram below.

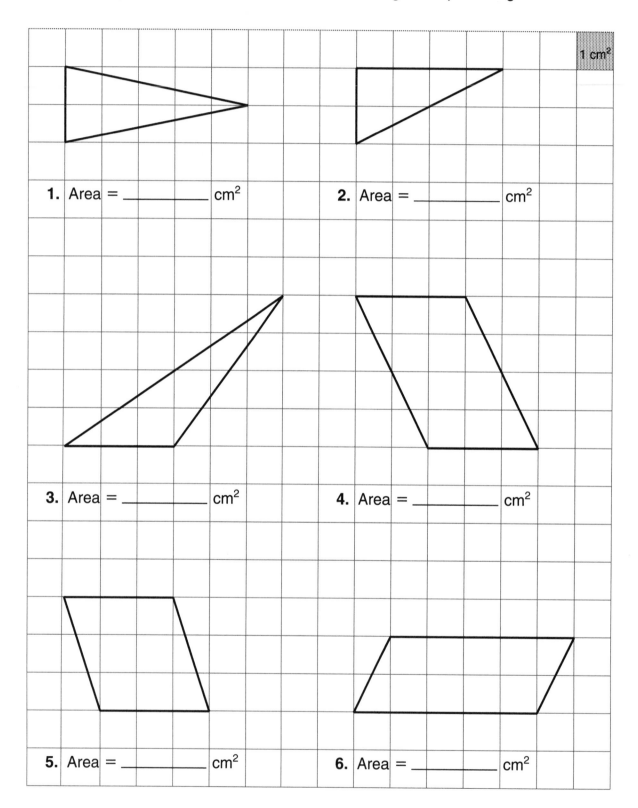

1 cm^2

1. Area = __________ cm^2

2. Area = __________ cm^2

3. Area = __________ cm^2

4. Area = __________ cm^2

5. Area = __________ cm^2

6. Area = __________ cm^2

Name Date Time

Areas of Parallelograms

1. Cut out Parallelogram A on *Math Masters,* page 129. DO NOT cut out the shapes on this page.

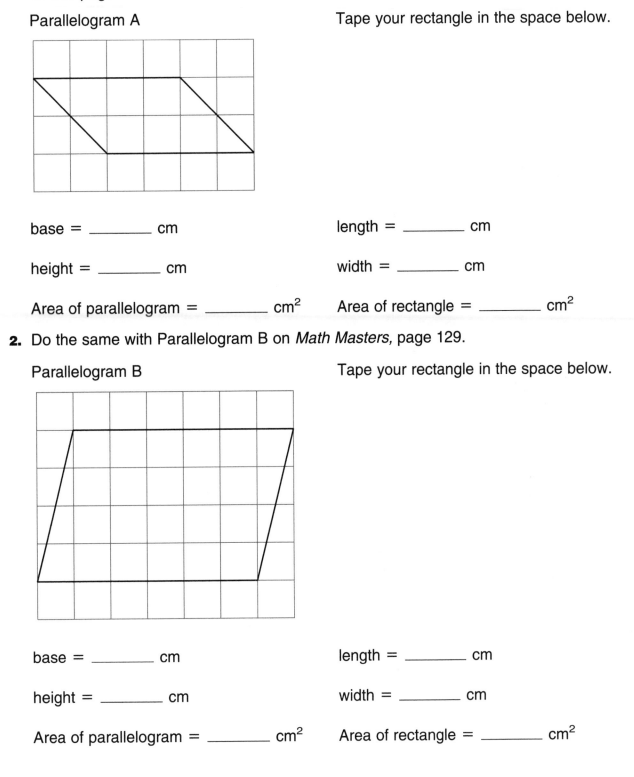

Parallelogram A

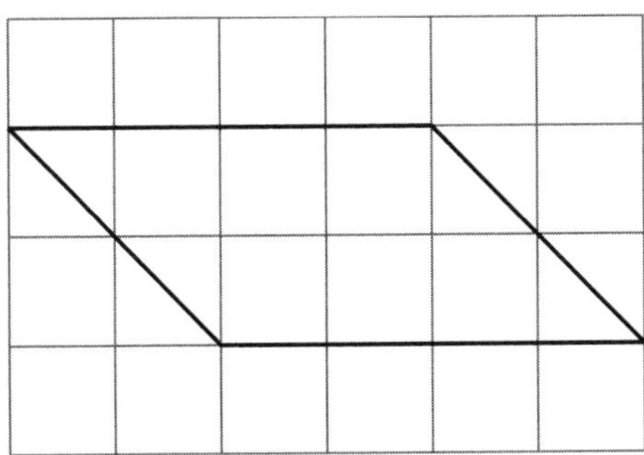

Tape your rectangle in the space below.

base = ________ cm

height = ________ cm

Area of parallelogram = ________ cm^2

length = ________ cm

width = ________ cm

Area of rectangle = ________ cm^2

2. Do the same with Parallelogram B on *Math Masters,* page 129.

Parallelogram B

Tape your rectangle in the space below.

base = ________ cm

height = ________ cm

Area of parallelogram = ________ cm^2

length = ________ cm

width = ________ cm

Area of rectangle = ________ cm^2

3. Write a formula for finding the area of a parallelogram.

____

Name Date Time

Areas of Triangles and Parallelograms

1. Cut out Triangles C and D from *Math Masters,* page 129. DO NOT cut out the shapes below. Tape the two triangles together to form a parallelogram.

Triangle C

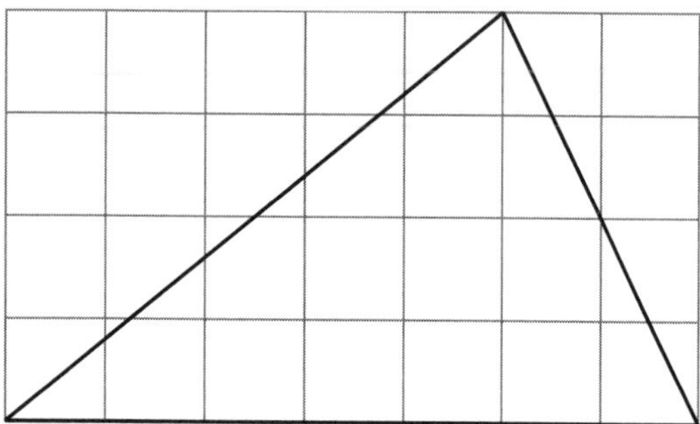

base = ________ cm

height = ________ cm

Area of triangle = ________ cm^2

Tape your parallelogram in this space.

length = ________ cm

height = ________ cm

Area of parallelogram = ________ cm^2

2. Do the same with Triangles E and F.

Triangle E

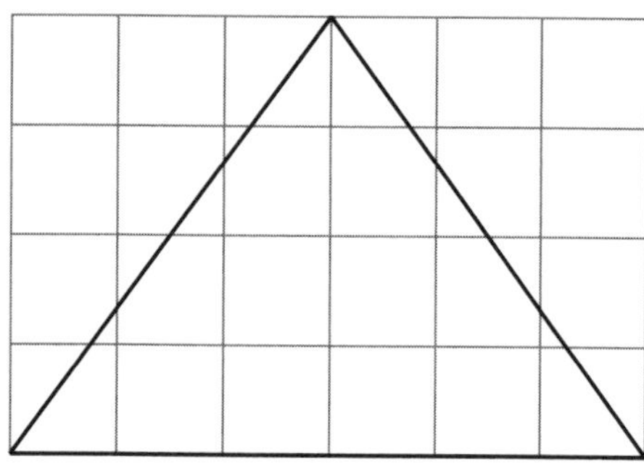

base = ________ cm

height = ________ cm

Area of triangle = ________ cm^2

Tape your parallelogram in this space.

base = ________ cm

height = ________ cm

Area of parallelogram = ________ cm^2

3. Write a formula for finding the area of a triangle.

____

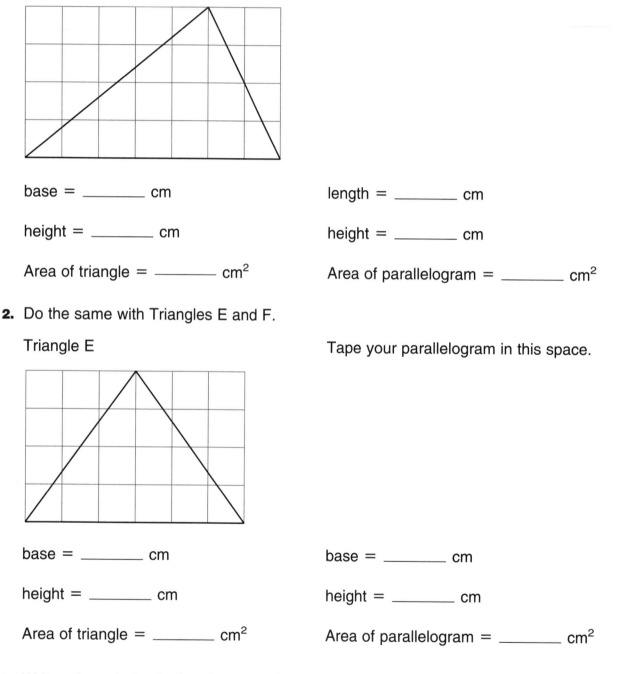

Name Date Time

Areas of Parallelograms and Triangles

Cut out Parallelogram A. (Use the second Parallelogram A if you make a mistake.) Cut it into 2 pieces so that it can be made into a rectangle. Tape the rectangle on *Math Masters,* page 127.

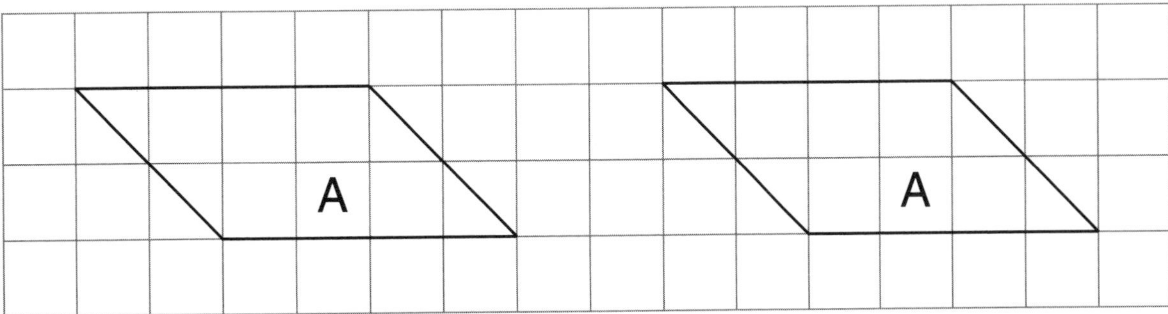

Do the same with Parallelogram B.

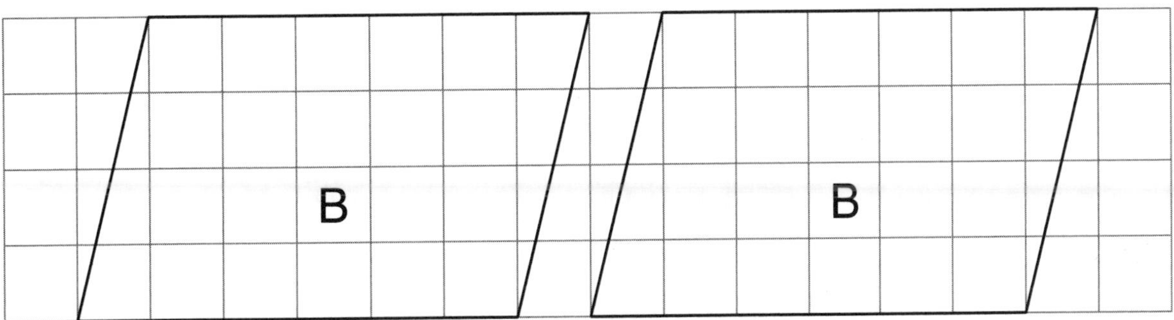

Cut out Triangles C and D. Tape them together at the shaded corners to form a parallelogram. Tape the parallelogram in the space next to Triangle C on *Math Masters,* page 128.

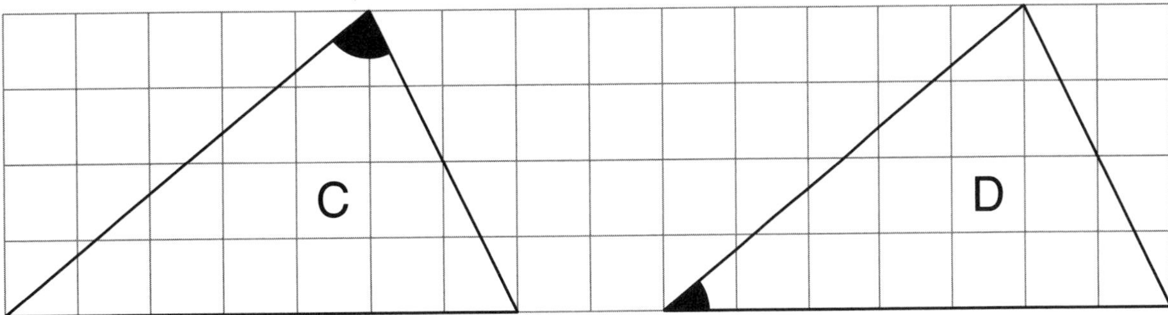

Do the same with the other pair of triangles.

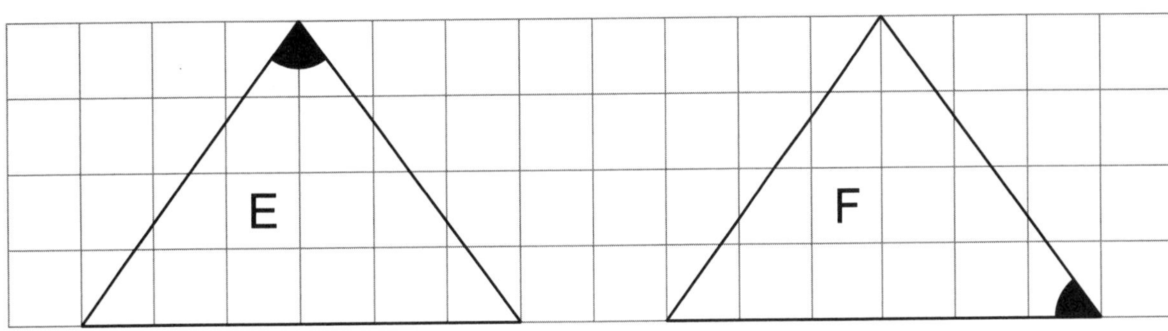

Name Date Time

Calculating Area

1. Determine the area of the shaded path on the grid below.

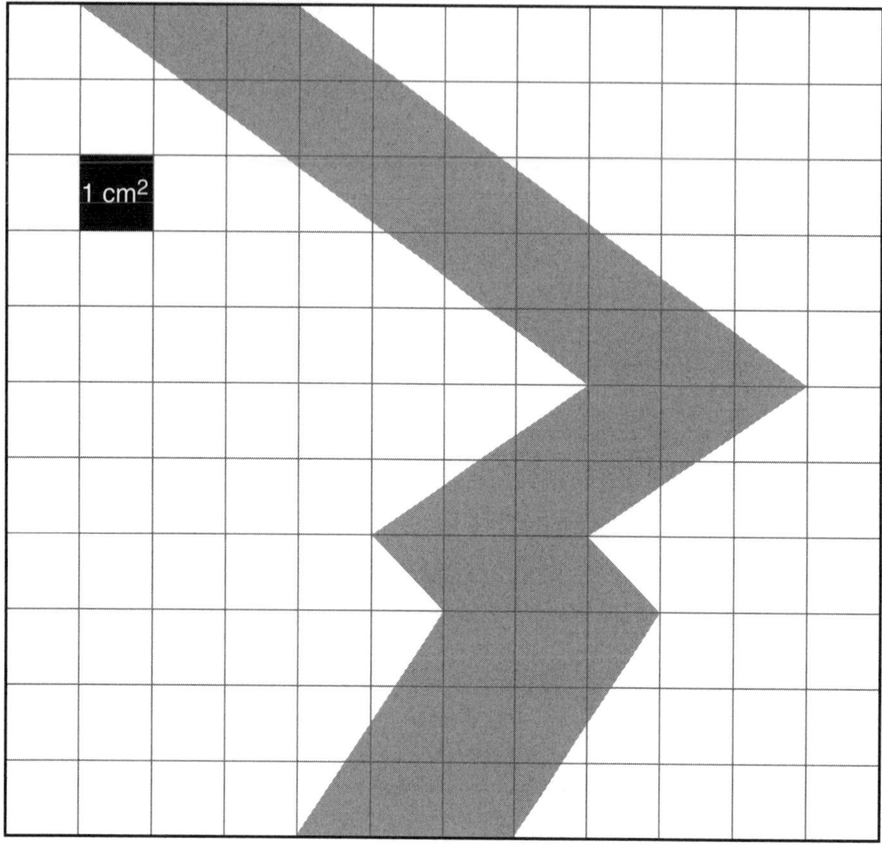

The area of the path is about ________ cm^2.

2. Describe the strategy that you used to calculate the area of the path.

____

____

____

____

____

____

____

____

____

____

Name Date Time

Latitudes

North

0° Latitude (Equator)	10°N	20°N	30°N	40°N
50°N	60°N	70°N		

South

0° Latitude (Equator)	10°S	20°S	30°S	40°S
50°S	60°S	70°S		

In squares for latitude, note that poles (90°N and 90°S) and latitudes 80°N and 80°S are not used.

Name Date Time

Longitudes

0° Longitude (prime meridian)	10°W	20°W	30°W	40°W	50°W
60°W	70°W	80°W	90°W	100°W	110°W
120°W	130°W	140°W	150°W	160°W	170°W
180° Longitude	10°E	20°E	30°E	40°E	50°E
60°E	70°E	80°E	90°E	100°E	110°E
120°E	130°E	140°E	150°E	160°E	170°E

Use with Lesson 9.7.

Name Date Time

Practice with Area Formulas

Area of a triangle: $A = \frac{1}{2} * b * h$
Area of a parallelogram: $A = b * h$

Use a formula to find the area of each figure.

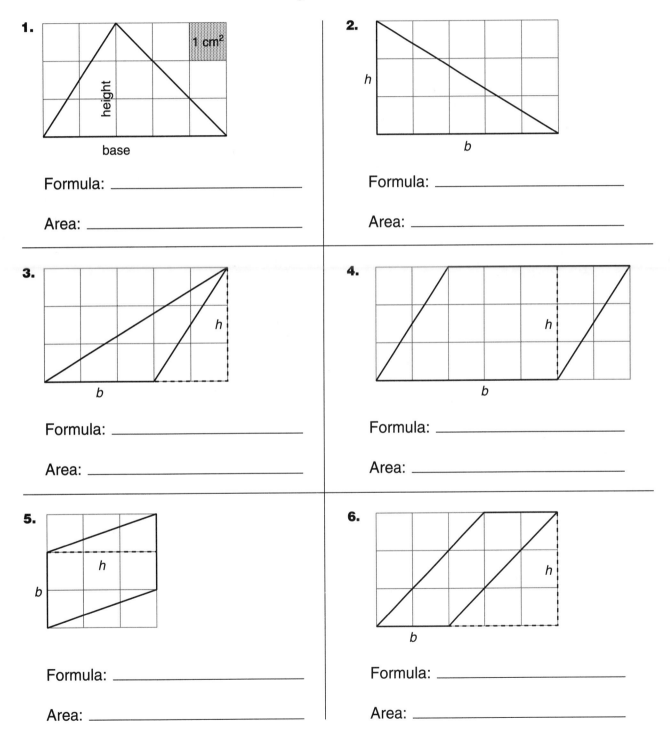

1.

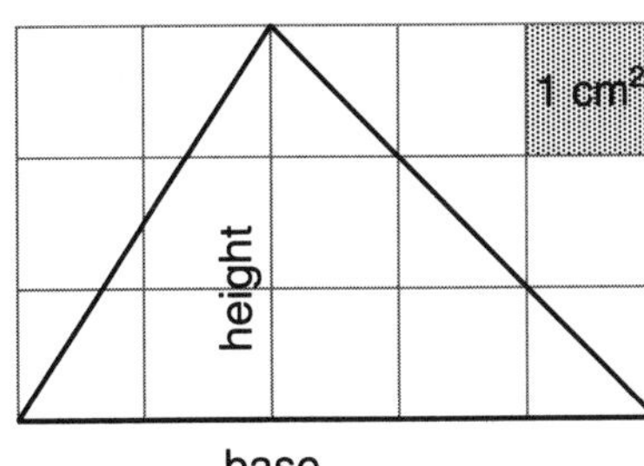

Formula: ____________________

Area: ____________________

2.

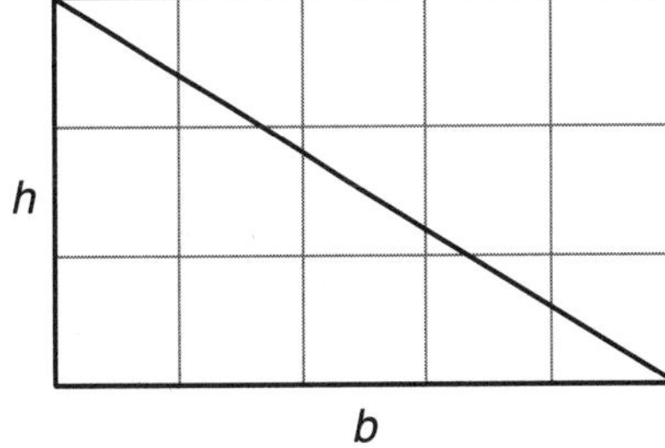

Formula: ____________________

Area: ____________________

3.

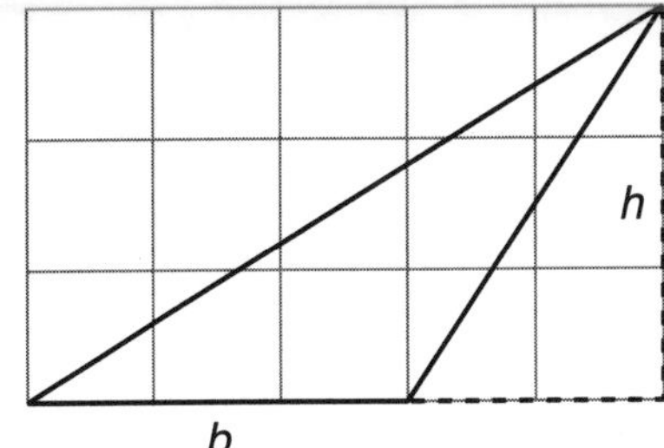

Formula: ____________________

Area: ____________________

4.

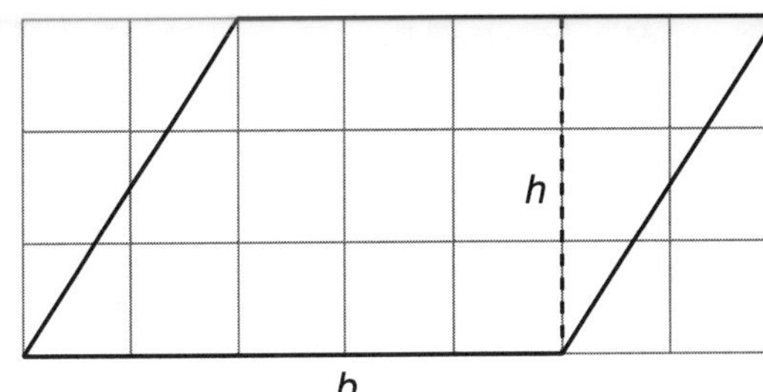

Formula: ____________________

Area: ____________________

5.

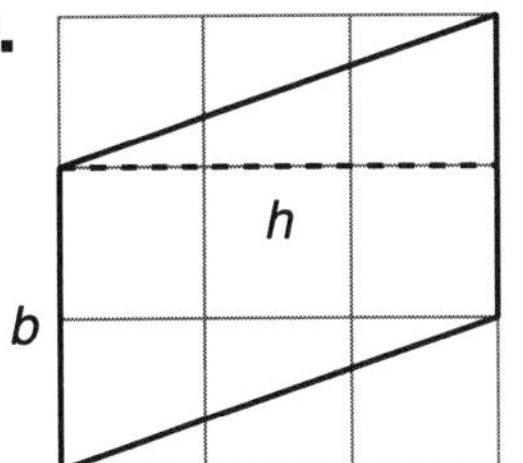

Formula: ____________________

Area: ____________________

6.

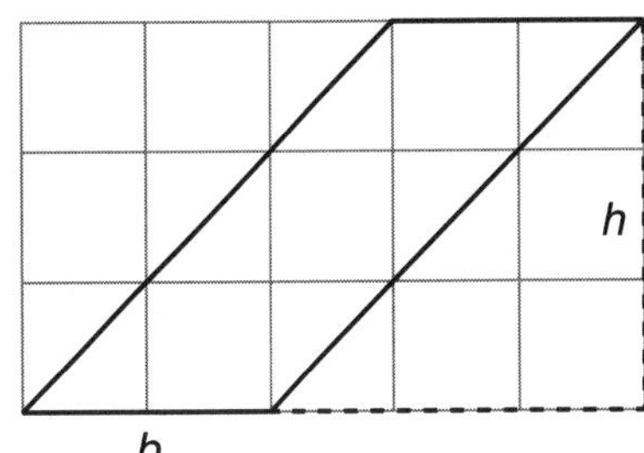

Formula: ____________________

Area: ____________________

Name Date Time

A Piece of Each State

A recent novelty gift offered U.S. citizens the opportunity to own land in each of the 50 states for only $49.95. However, there was a trick. The offer was for a mere *1 square inch* of land in each state.

1. About how much would it cost per square inch for a U.S. citizen to accept this offer?

____

2. What fraction of 1 square yard is 50 square inches? _______________

In China, prices for 50 square inches of land in the United States were much higher. In Guangzhou, the price was about $468, in Beijing $700, and in Shanghai $1,700. When buying this land, many Chinese citizens believed that they would be able to obtain a visa to visit the United States to inspect their property. Unfortunately, this was not true.

3. About how much would it cost per square inch for a Chinese citizen to accept this offer in

a. Guangzhou? _______________

b Beijing? _______________

c. Shanghai? _______________

4. About how much would it cost a Chinese citizen to buy a total of 1 square yard of land in the United States if purchased in

a. Guangzhou? _______________

b. Beijing? _______________

c. Shanghai? _______________

Name Date Time

Triangular Prism Base Template

This template is a pattern for the base of a triangular prism. Place the template on a sheet of foam board. Using a pencil or ballpoint pen, mark the position of the six dots by piercing the template. Remove the template and connect the points with solid or dashed lines, the same as on the template. Cut out the prism along the outer solid line, using a serrated knife or saw, making sure that your cuts are made perpendicular to the base.

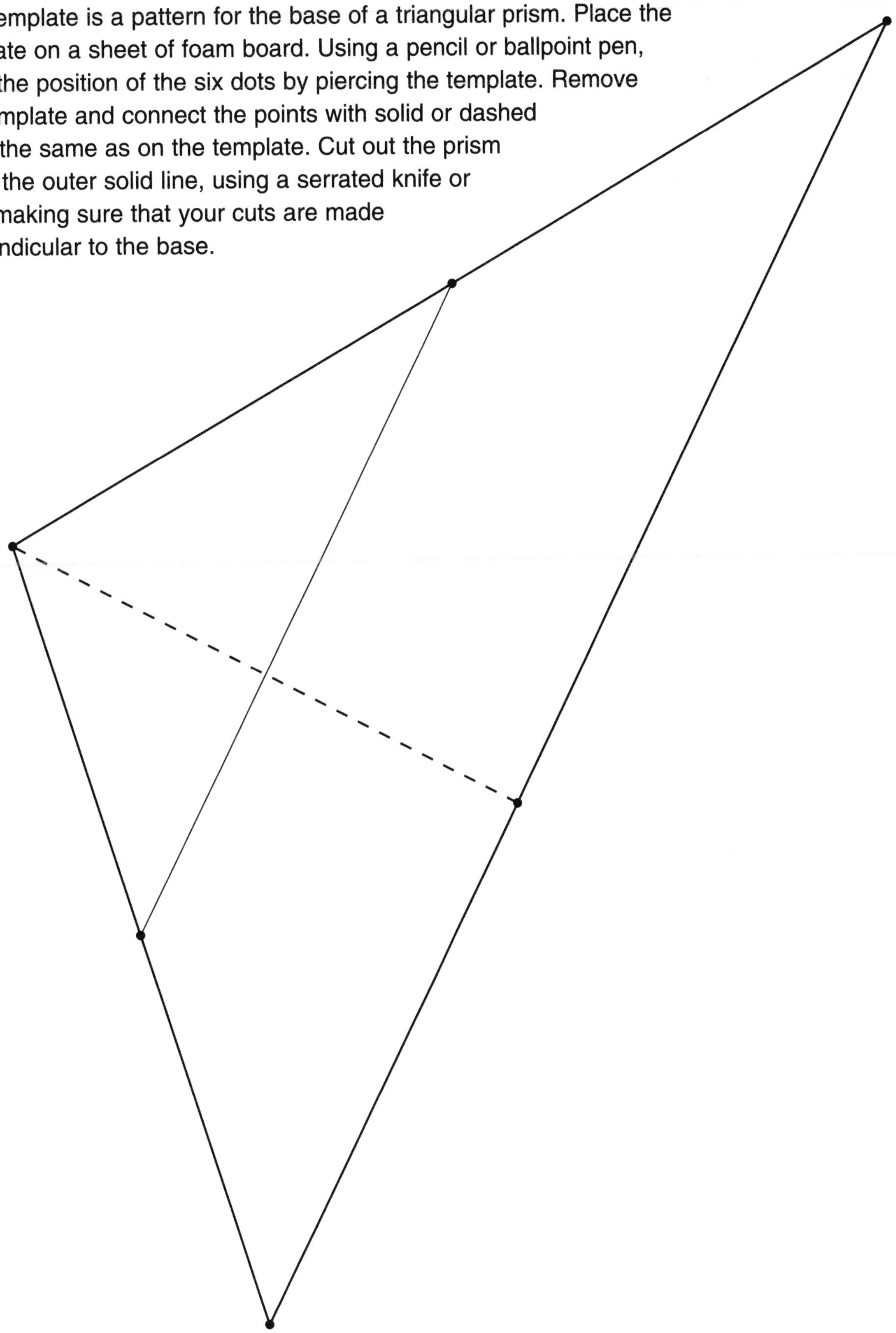

Name Date Time

Parallelogram Prism Base Template

This template is a pattern for the base of a parallelogram prism. Place the template on a sheet of foam board. Using a pencil or ballpoint pen, mark the position of the five dots by piercing the template. Remove the template and connect the points with solid or dashed lines, the same as on the template. Cut out the prism along the solid line, using a serrated knife or saw, making sure that your cuts are made perpendicular to the base.

Use with Lesson 9.9.

Name Date Time

Triangular Prism Template

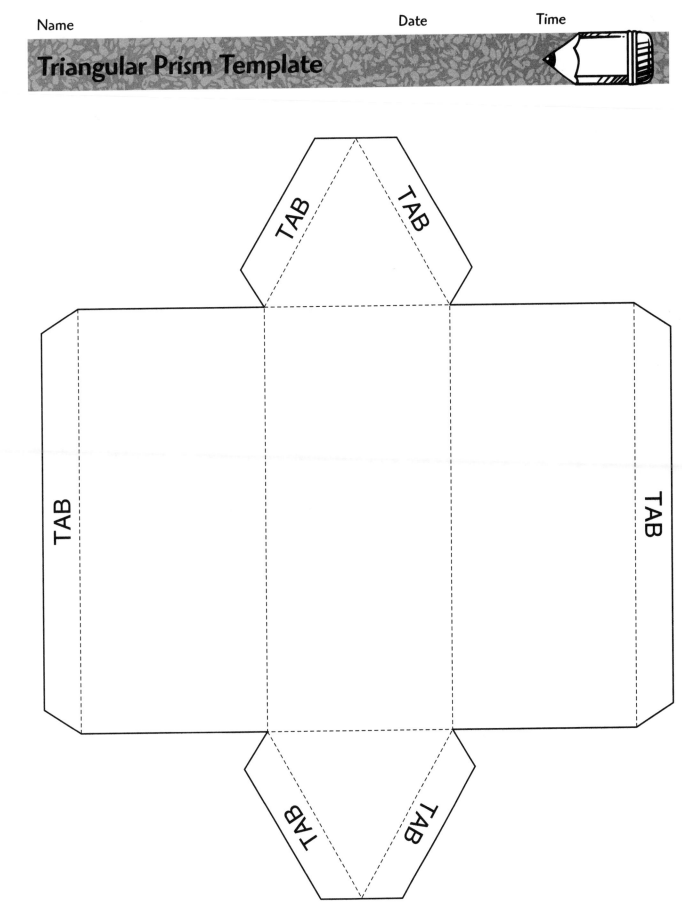

TAB

TAB

TAB

TAB

TAB

TAB

Name Date Time

Plotting a Picture

Draw a simple picture that can be formed with straight lines connecting points on the grid. (Use at least 8 points but no more than 14 points.)

Record the ordered pairs you have plotted on a separate sheet of paper. Be sure you record your points in the order in which they need to be connected.

Give your list of coordinates and a blank grid to your partner and have your partner reproduce your drawing by plotting and connecting the points.

Compare your original picture with your partner's copy.

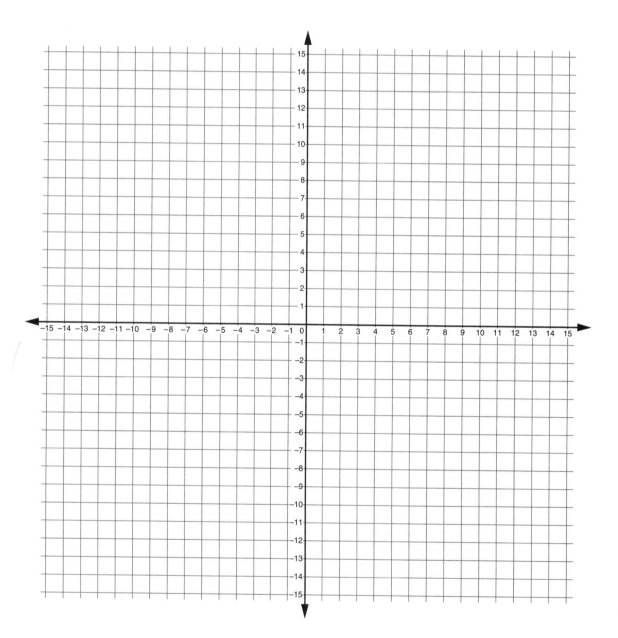

Name Date Time

Pan Balances

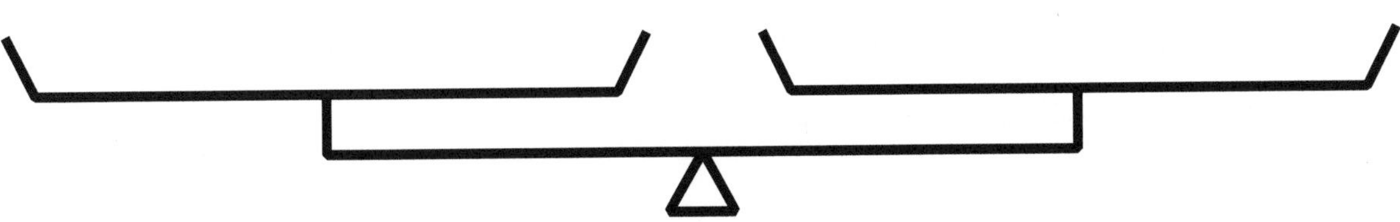

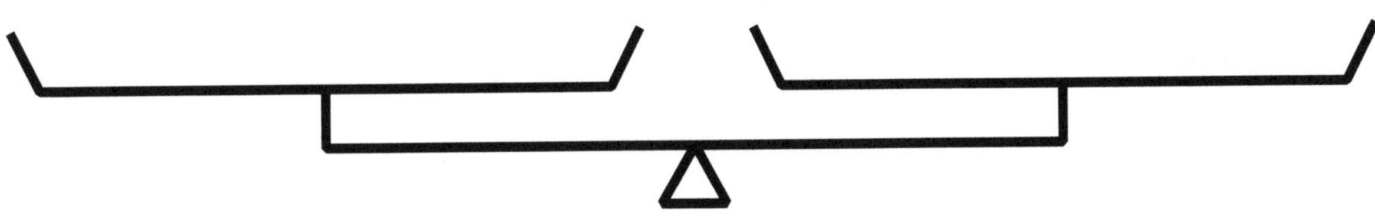

Name Date Time

Penny Weights

The materials out of which a penny is made were changed at the beginning of one of these years: 1981, 1982, or 1983. As a result, the weight of a penny has changed. Your task is to find out in what year the weight of pennies changed.

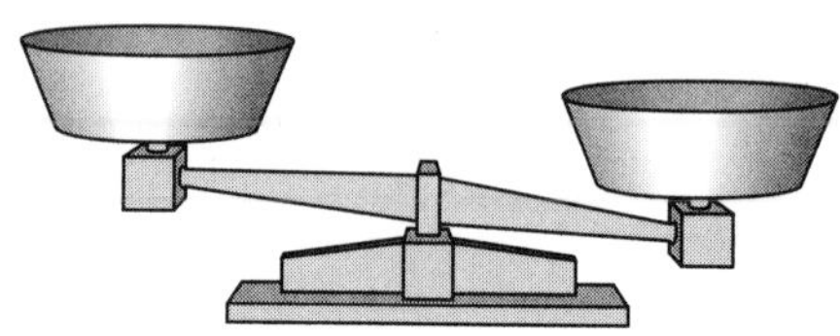

1. Compare 1981 pennies to 1982 pennies.
   Put ten 1981 pennies in one pan and ten 1982 pennies in the other pan.

   Do the pans balance? ________________

2. Return the pennies to their correct containers.
   Put ten 1982 pennies in one pan and ten 1983 pennies in the other pan.

   Do the pans balance? ________________

3. I think that penny weights changed beginning in the year ________________,

   because ____

   ____

4. Why do you think that it is better to compare the weights using 10 pennies for each year rather than only 1 penny for each year? ____

   ____

   ____

   ____

   ____

5. Why do you think they changed the materials out of which a penny is made?

   ____

   ____

You may want to do some research on the Internet to learn more about coins. At the time your journal was printed, the sites below had information about pennies and other coins.
www.usmint.gov/facts/history.cfm
www.usmint.gov/circulating/specifications.cfm

Name ______________________ Date ______________ Time ______________

Pan-Balance Problems

Solve these problems. In each problem, the pans are in perfect balance. The weights of objects, such as triangles, paper clips, and pencils, may be different from problem to problem.

One ______________ weighs

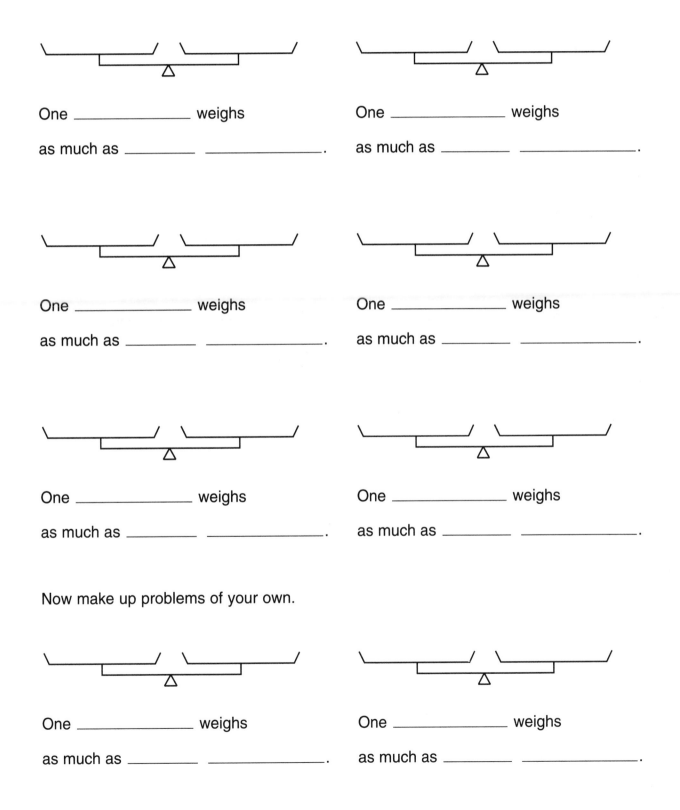

as much as ________ ______________.

One ______________ weighs

as much as ________ ______________.

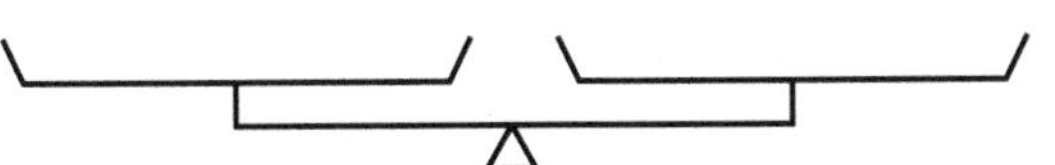

One ______________ weighs

as much as ________ ______________.

One ______________ weighs

as much as ________ ______________.

One ______________ weighs

as much as ________ ______________.

One ______________ weighs

as much as ________ ______________.

Now make up problems of your own.

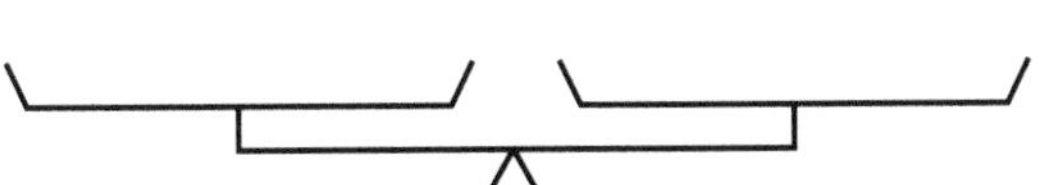

One ______________ weighs

as much as ________ ______________.

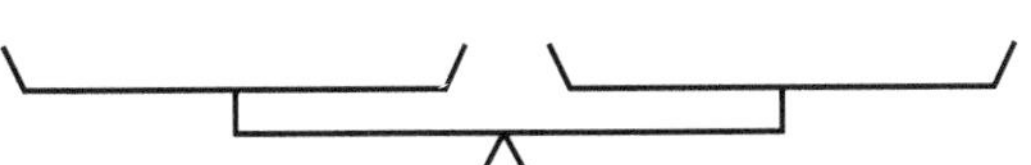

One ______________ weighs

as much as ________ ______________.

Name Date Time

"What's My Rule?"

For each problem, complete the table and find the rule. Add a last table entry of your own.

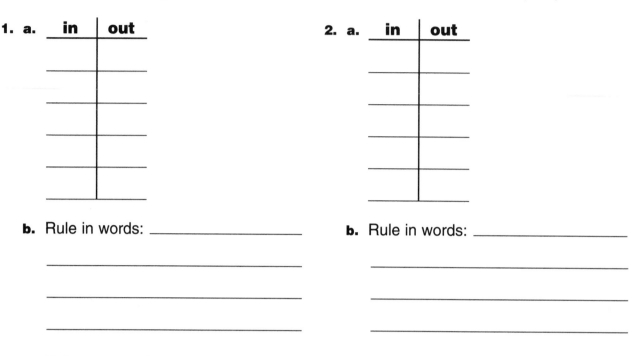

1. a.

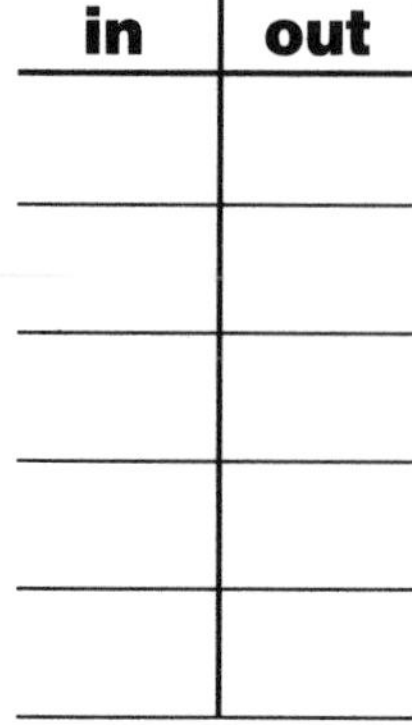

in	out

b. Rule in words: ______________________

____

____

____

c. Rule as a number expression:

____

2. a.

in	out

b. Rule in words: ______________________

____

____

____

c. Rule as a number expression:

____

3. a.

in	out

b. Rule in words: ______________________

____

____

____

c. Rule as a number expression:

____

4. a.

in	out

b. Rule in words: ______________________

____

____

____

c. Rule as a number expression:

____

Name Date Time

Graphing "What's My Rule?" Tables

Graph the "What's My Rule?" tables from Problems 3 and 4 on Study Link 10.4. Record the rule in the space provided.

1. Rule: ______________________

____

____

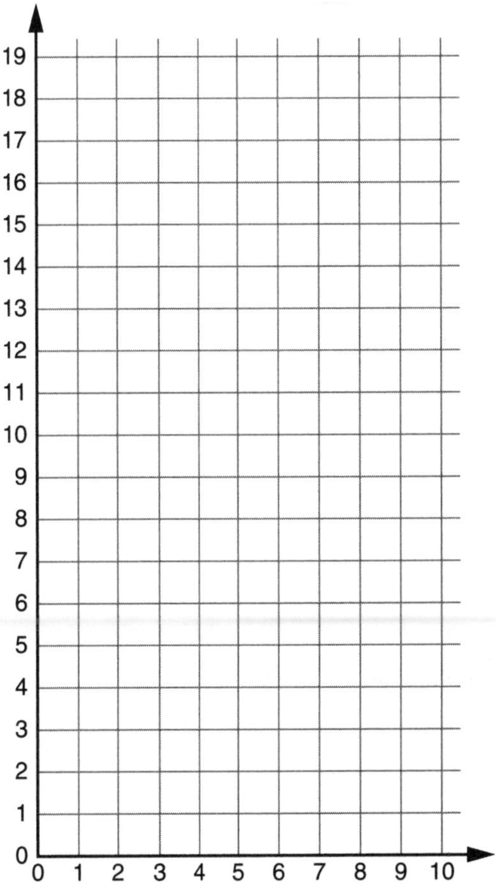

2. Rule: ______________________

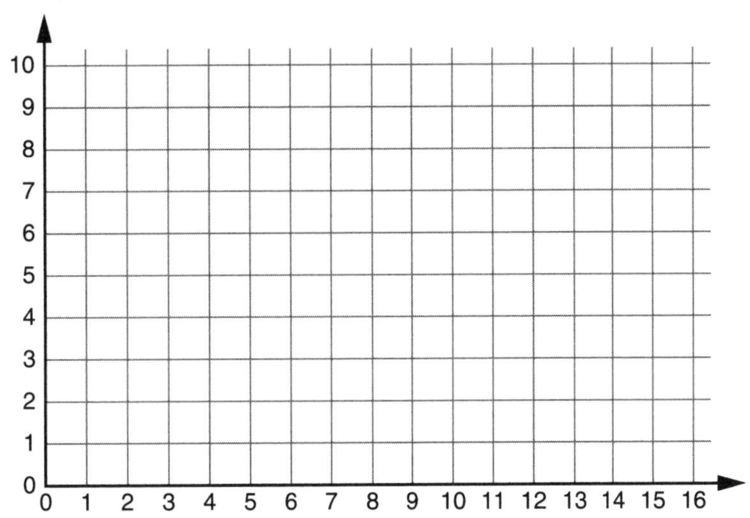

Name Date Time

Graphing "What's My Rule?" Tables (cont.)

Make up a situation for which a rule can be stated. Describe the rule. Then make a table of values and a graph for the situation.

Rule: ______________________________

____

____

____

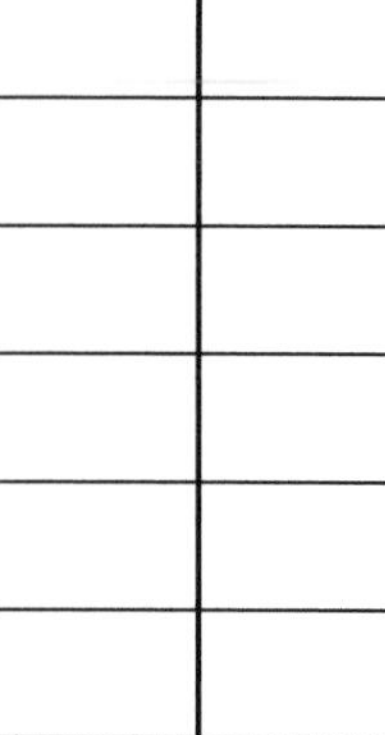

in	out

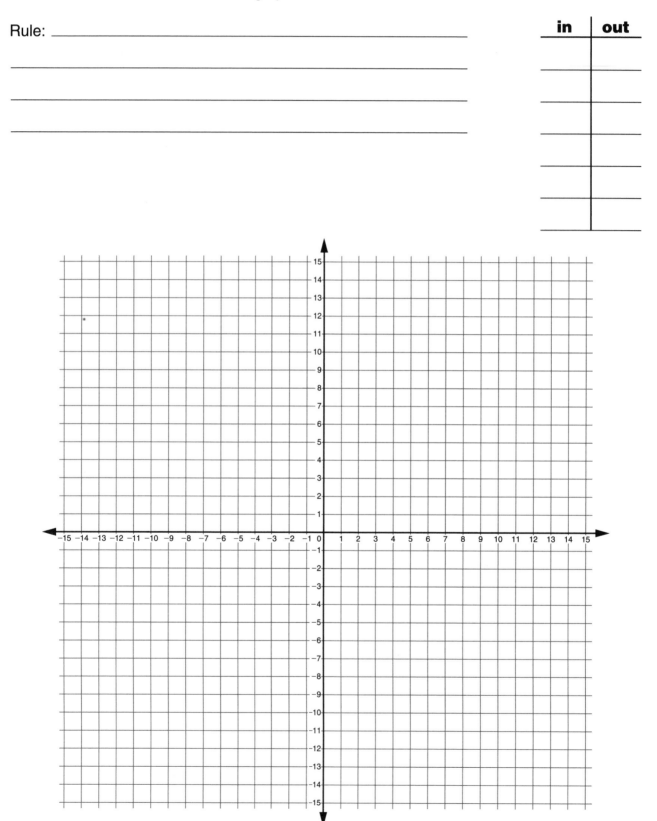

Use with Lesson 10.5.

Name Date Time

Graphs for Seconds and Meters

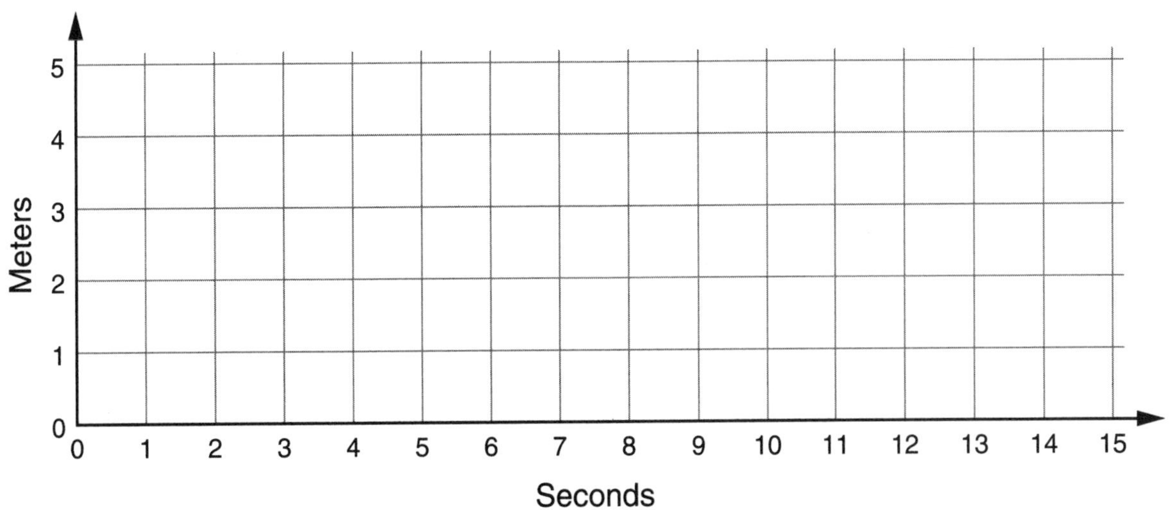

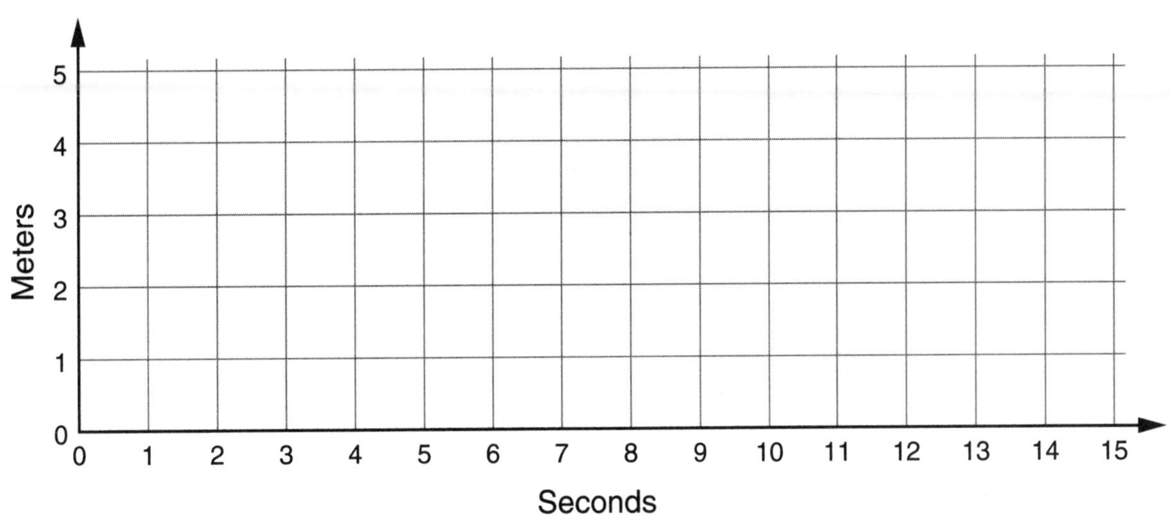

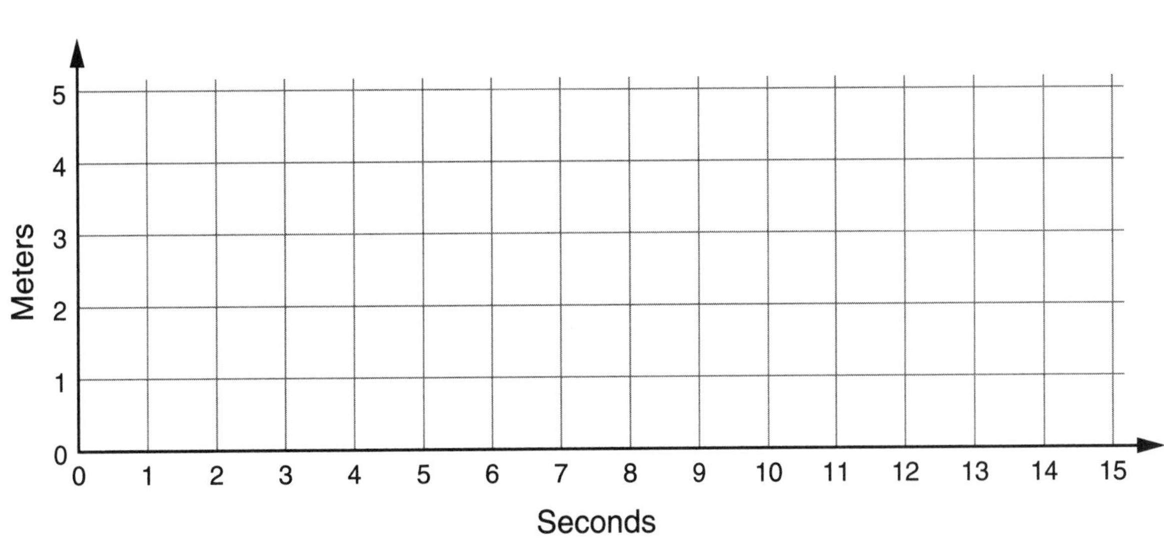

Name Date Time

A Sibling Mystery-Graph

Ms. Jurkowski's students counted their siblings (their brothers and sisters). They counted how many students had 0 siblings (no brothers or sisters), how many had 1 sibling (1 brother or 1 sister), how many had 2 siblings, and so on.

1. Which of the line plots below probably shows Ms. Jurkowski's class's data?

____

Plot A

	X				
	X				
	X				
	X	X			
	X	X			
X	X	X			
X	X	X			
X	X	X	X		
X	X	X	X	X	
X	X	X	X	X	X
0	1	2	3	4	5 or more

Plot B

X					X
X					X
X					X
X					X
X					X
X	X			X	X
X	X			X	X
X	X			X	X
X	X	X	X	X	X
0	1	2	3	4	5 or more

Plot C

X	X	X			X
X	X	X	X	X	X
X	X	X	X	X	X
X	X	X	X	X	X
X	X	X	X	X	X
0	5	10	15	20	25 or more

2. Explain why you chose that line plot. ______________________________

____

____

____

____

3. How many students are in Ms. Jurkowski's class? ________ students

4. About how many siblings do all the students in Ms. Jurkowski's class have? ________ siblings

Use with Lesson 10.7.

Name Date Time

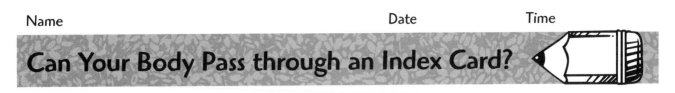

Can Your Body Pass through an Index Card?

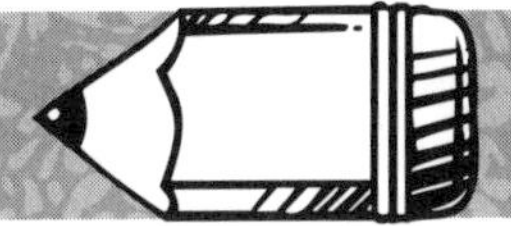

1. Fold a 5-inch by 8-inch index card down the middle "widthwise." (The fold is along the 5-inch width of the card.)

2. Hold the halves of the folded card together. Cut the card as shown by the lines in Diagram A. Some cuts start at the fold and go almost to the edge of the card. Some cuts start at the edge and go almost to the fold. Be sure the first and last cuts start at the fold. Cuts should alternate between starting at the fold and starting at the edge.

3. Open the card. Cut along the fold from *X* to *Y* as shown in Diagram B. Be careful not to cut to the edges of the card.

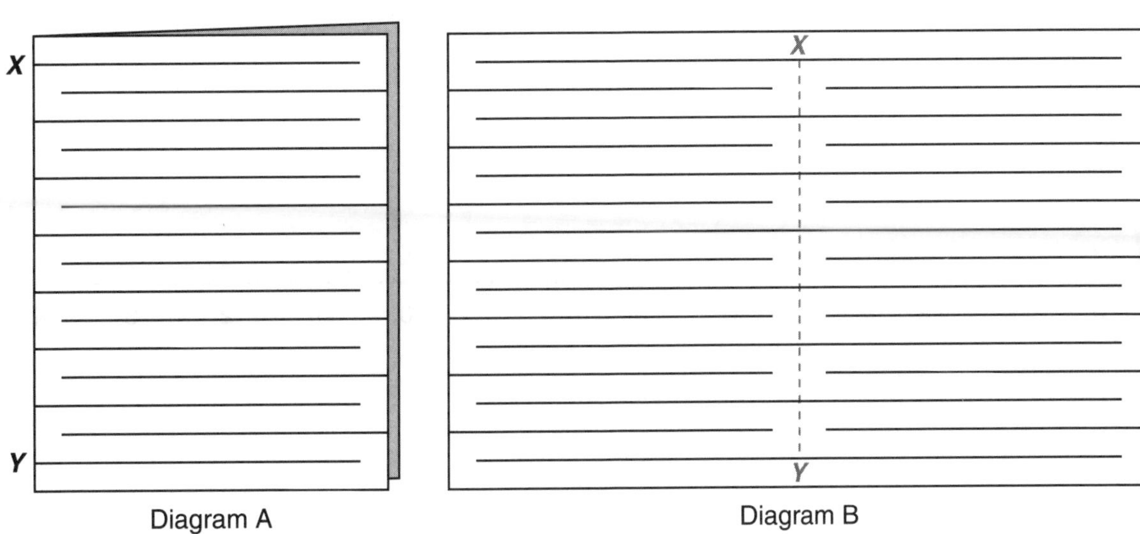

Diagram A

Diagram B

4. Pull the card apart carefully. You'll have a paper ring. Is it large enough for your body to pass through?

Challenge

Use another 5-inch by 8-inch index card. Can you cut out a ring that has a perimeter twice the perimeter of the ring you just made? Explain how you would do it.

____

____

____

Name Date Time

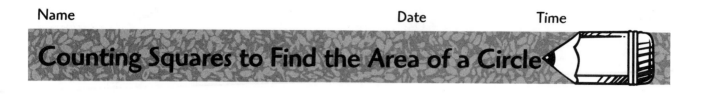

Counting Squares to Find the Area of a Circle

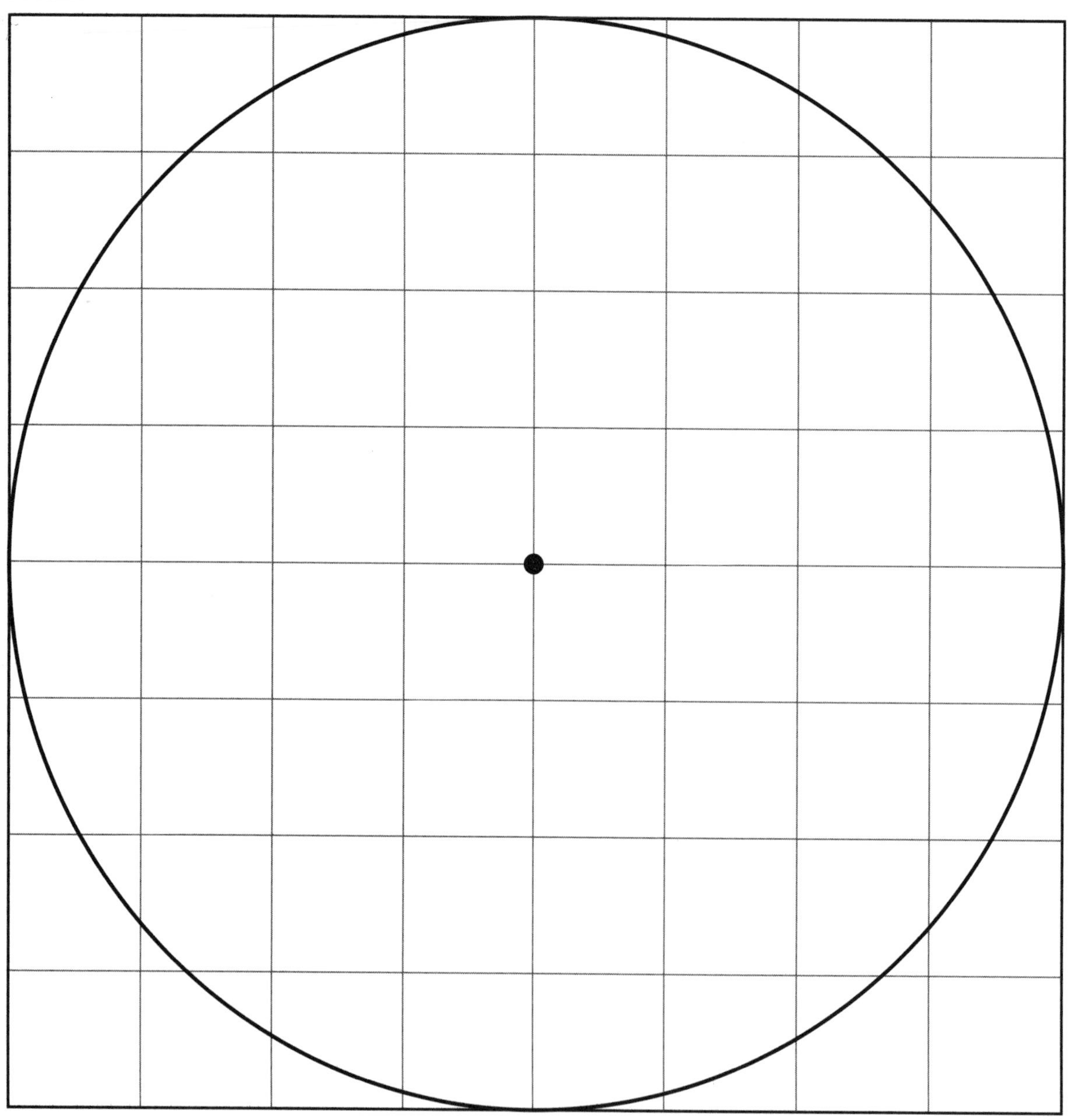

Use with Lesson 10.9.

Name Date Time

More Area and Circumference Problems

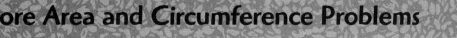

Circle Formulas

Circumference: $C = \pi * d$
Area: $A = \pi * r^2$
where C is the circumference, A is the area of a circle, d is its diameter, and r is its radius.

Measure the diameter of the circle at the right to the nearest centimeter.

1. The diameter of the circle is ______________.

2. The radius of the circle is ______________.

3. The circumference of the circle is ______________.

4. The area of the circle is ______________.

5. Explain the meaning of the word *circumference*. ______________________

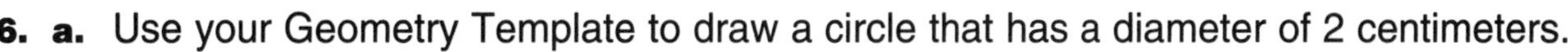

6. a. Use your Geometry Template to draw a circle that has a diameter of 2 centimeters.

b. Find the area of your circle. ______________

c. Find the circumference of your circle. ______________

7. a. Use your Geometry Template to draw a circle that has a radius of $1\frac{1}{2}$ inches.

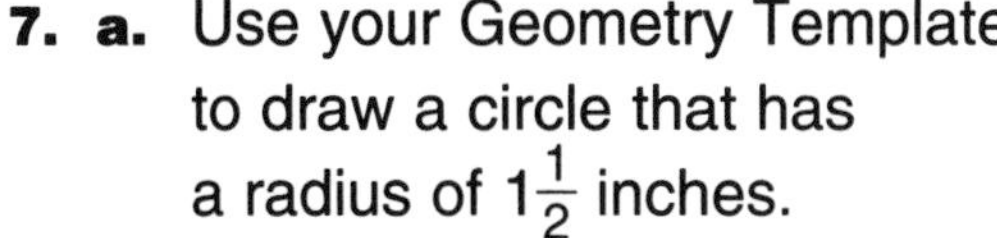

b. Find the area of your circle.

____

c. Find the circumference of your circle. ______________

Name Date Time

Cube Pattern

1. Cut on the solid lines.
2. Fold on the dashed lines.
3. Tape or glue the tabs "inside" or "outside" the figure.

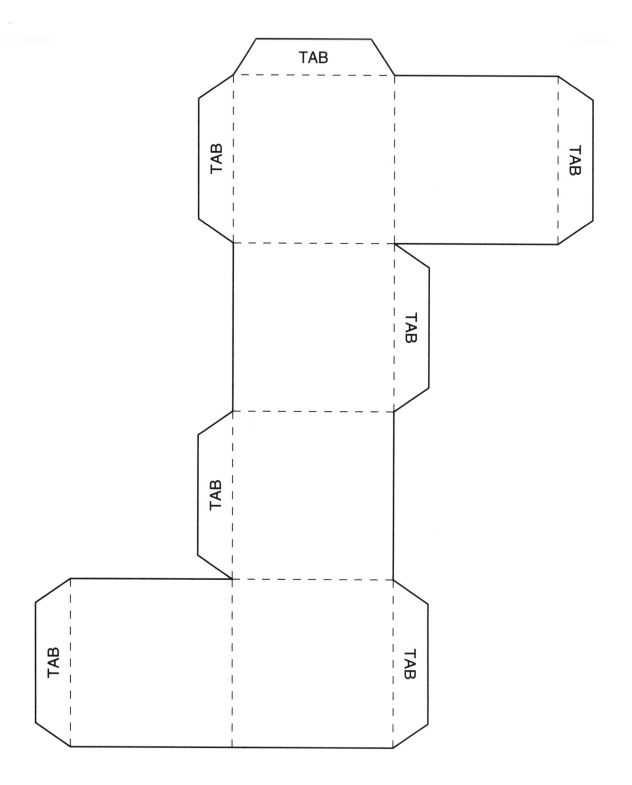

TAB

TAB

TAB

TAB

TAB

TAB

TAB

Name Date Time

Triangular Prism Pattern

1. Cut on the solid lines.
2. Fold on the dashed lines.
3. Tape or glue the tabs "inside" or "outside" the figure.

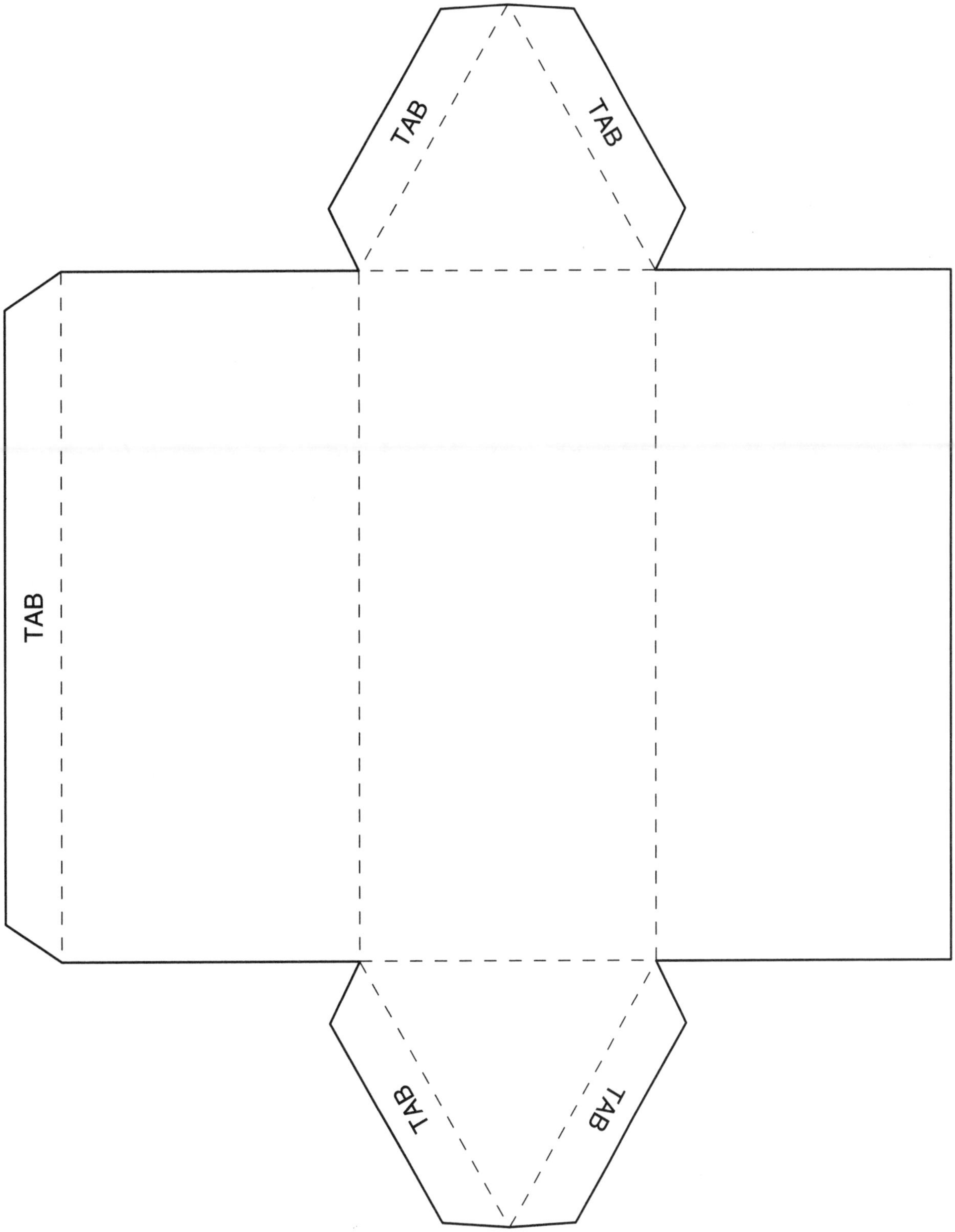

TAB

TAB

TAB

TAB

TAB

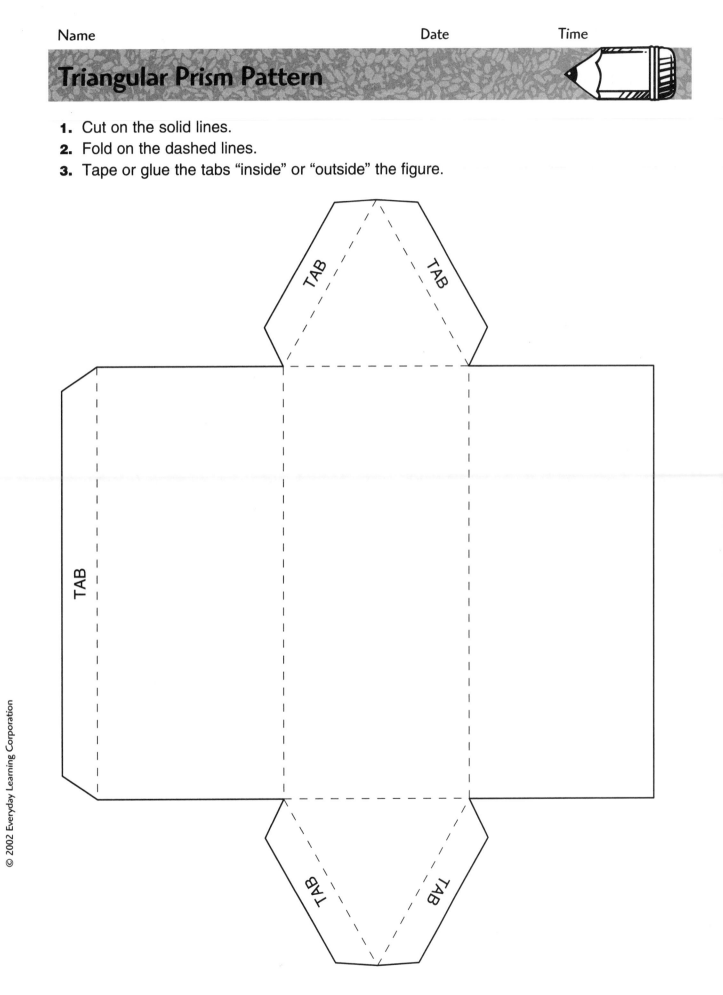

Name Date Time

Triangular Pyramid Pattern

1. Cut on the solid lines.
2. Fold on the dashed lines.
3. Tape or glue the tabs "inside" or "outside" the figure.

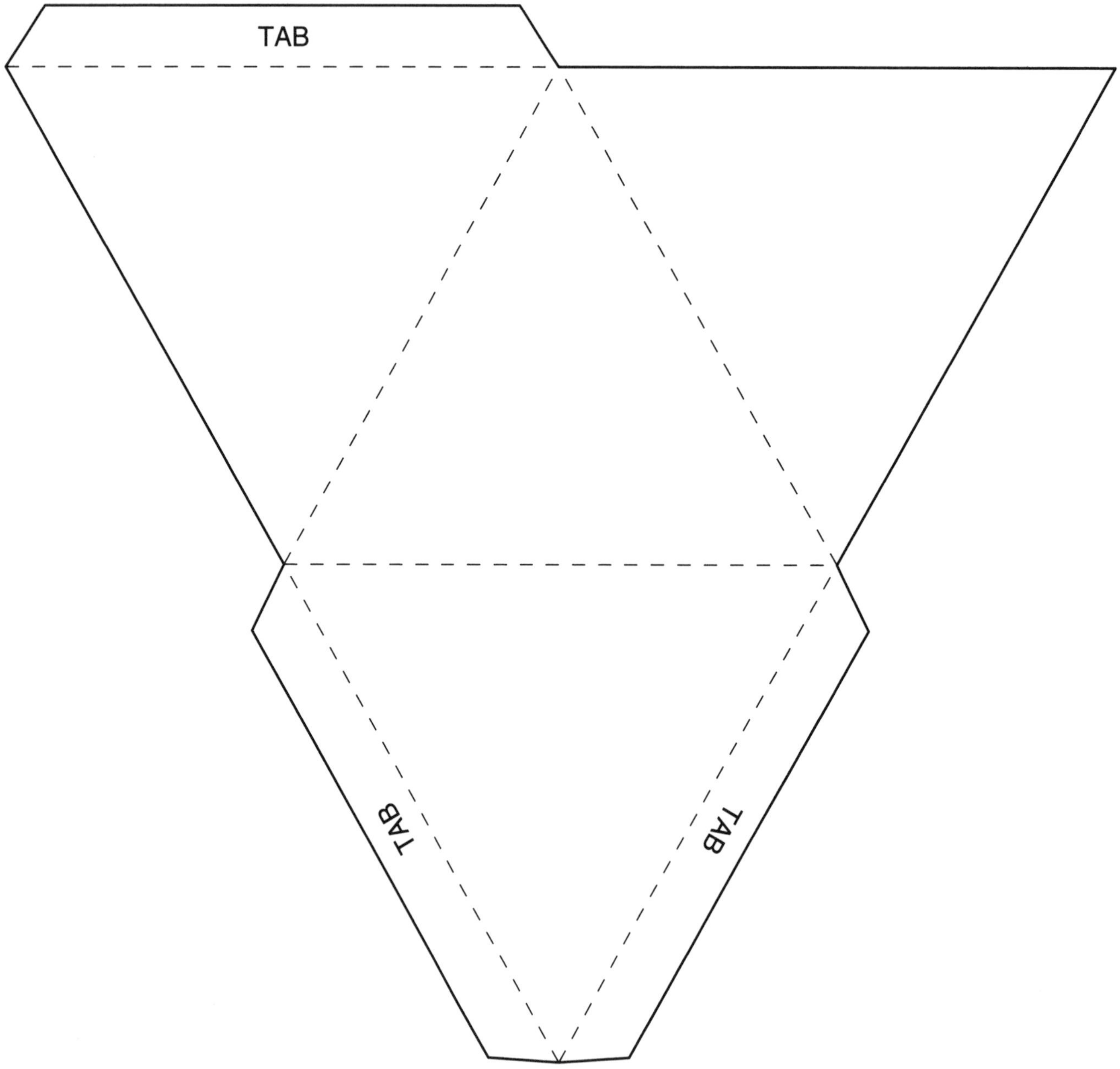

TAB

TAB

TAB

Name Date Time

Square Pyramid Pattern

1. Cut on the solid lines.
2. Fold on the dashed lines.
3. Tape or glue the tabs "inside" or "outside" the figure.

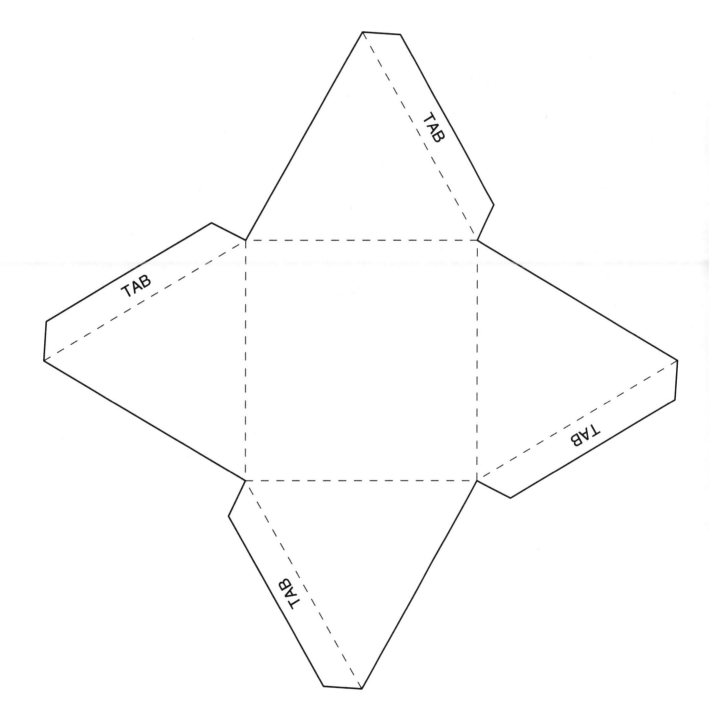

TAB

TAB

TAB

TAB

Name Date Time

Polyhedral Dice and Regular Polyhedrons

A set of polyhedral dice includes the following polyhedrons:

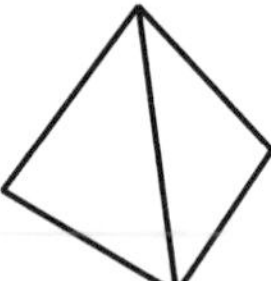

Tetrahedral die

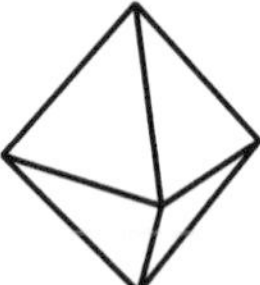

Octahedral die

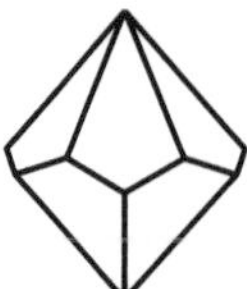

Decahedral die

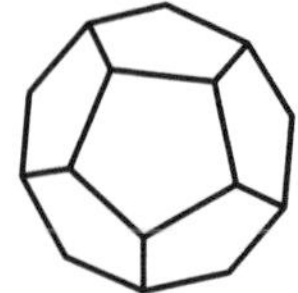

Dodecahedral die

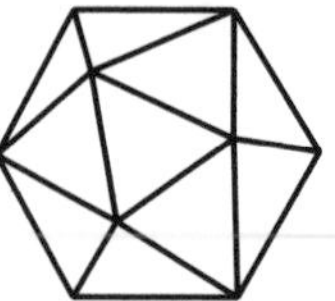

Icosahedral die

Examine the set of polyhedral dice that you have. Answer the following questions:

1. Which of the dice is not a **regular polyhedron?** Why? ______________________

____

2. Which regular polyhedron is missing from the set of polyhedral dice? ____________

3. a. How many faces does an octahedron have? ____________ faces

   b. What shape are the faces? ______________________

4. a. How many faces does a dodecahedron have? ____________ faces

   b. What shape are the faces? ______________________

5. a. How many faces does an icosahedron have? ____________ faces

   b. What shape are the faces? ______________________

6. What makes each of the polyhedral dice "fair"? ______________________

____

____

Name Date Time

Rectangular Prism Pattern

1. Cut on the solid lines.
2. Fold on the dashed lines.
3. Tape or glue the tabs "inside" or "outside" the figure.

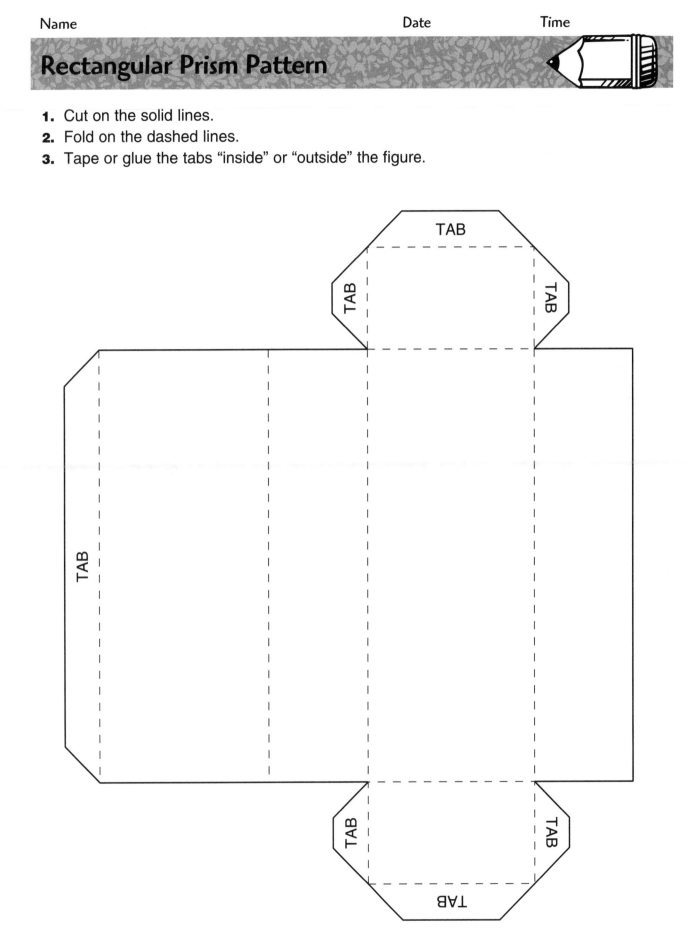

TAB

TAB

TAB

TAB

TAB

TAB

TAB

Name Date Time

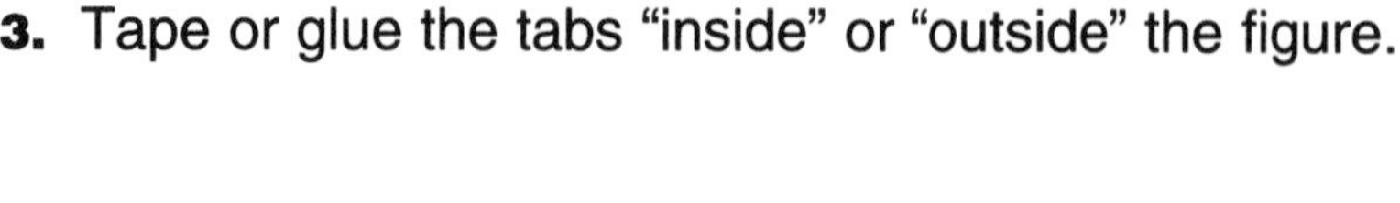

Octahedron Pattern

1. Cut on the solid lines.
2. Fold on the dashed lines.
3. Tape or glue the tabs "inside" or "outside" the figure.

TAB

TAB

TAB

TAB

TAB

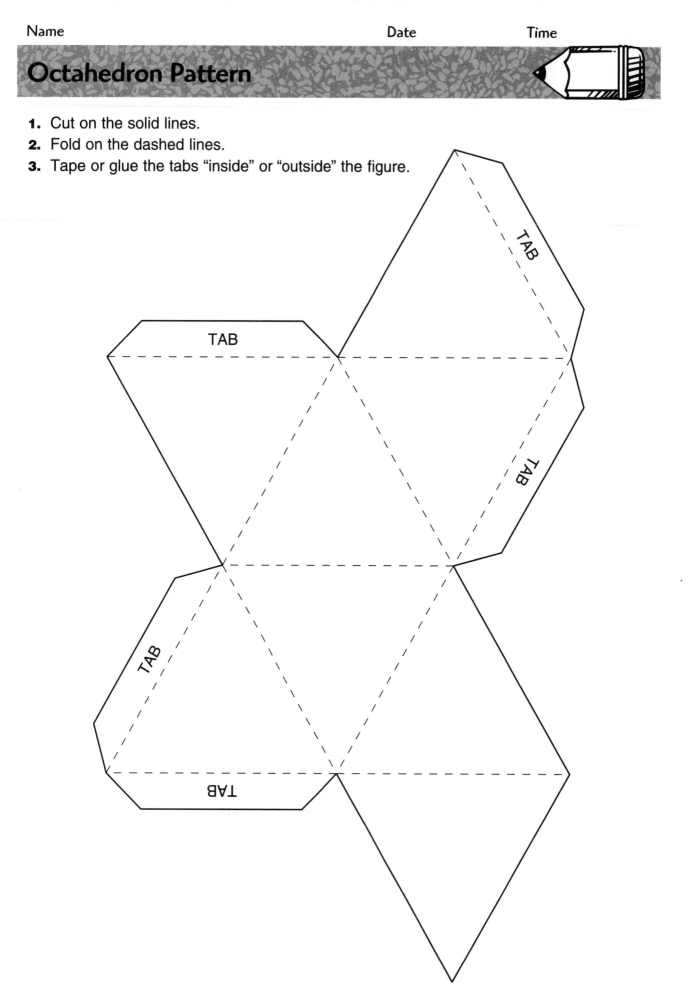

Use with Lesson 11.1.

Name Date Time

Venn Diagram

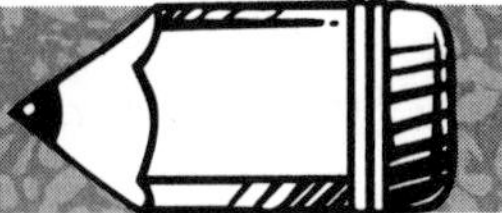

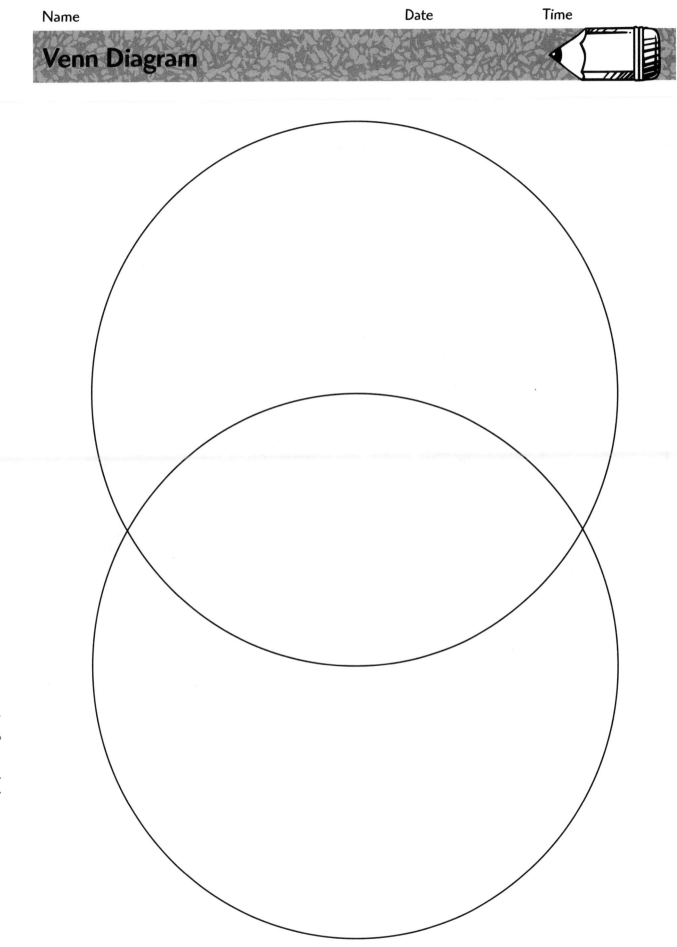

Name Date Time

3-D Shape Sort Shape Cards

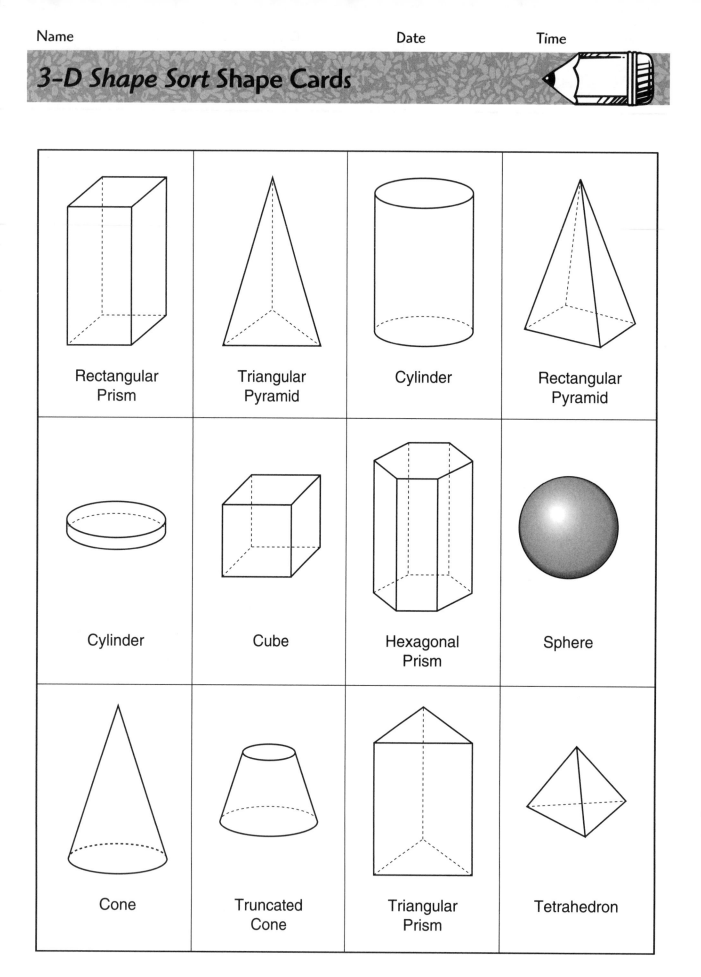

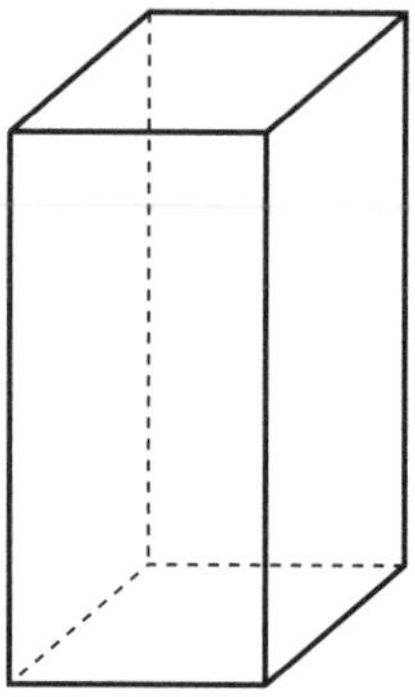

Rectangular Prism	Triangular Pyramid	Cylinder	Rectangular Pyramid
Cylinder	Cube	Hexagonal Prism	Sphere
Cone	Truncated Cone	Triangular Prism	Tetrahedron

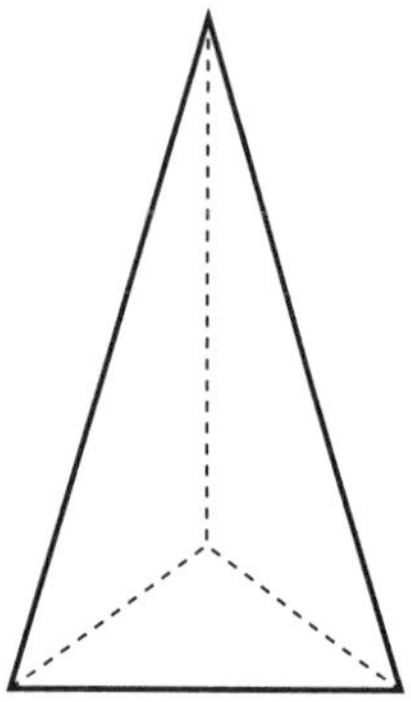

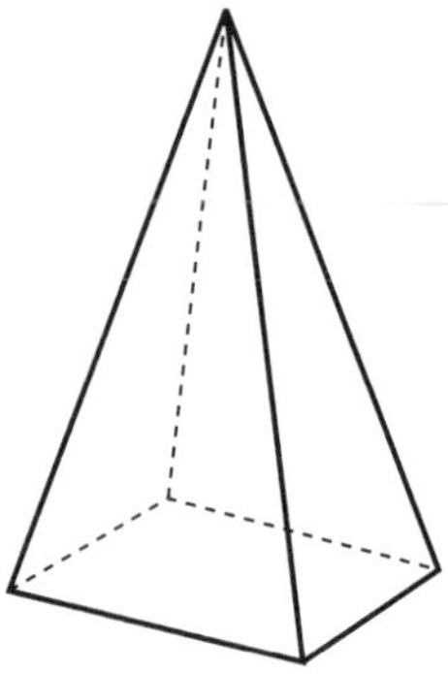

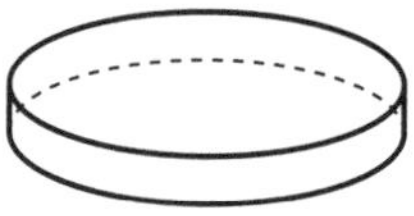

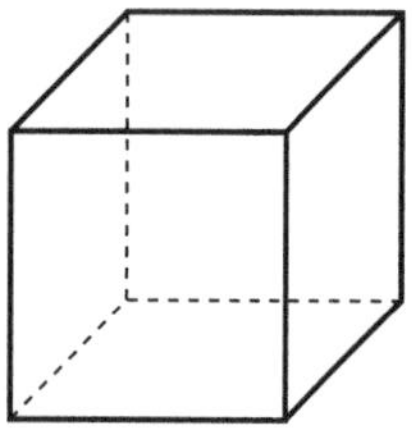

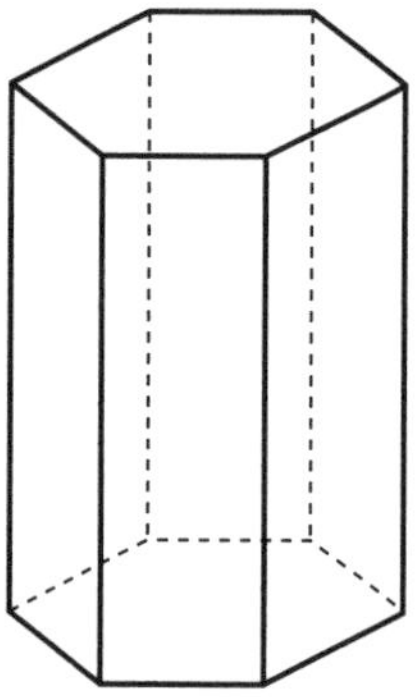

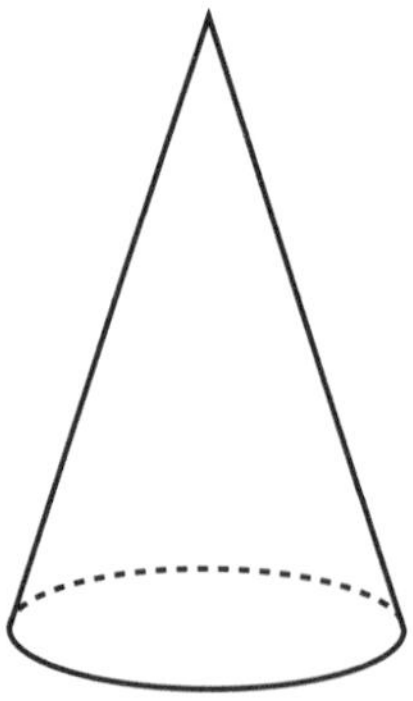

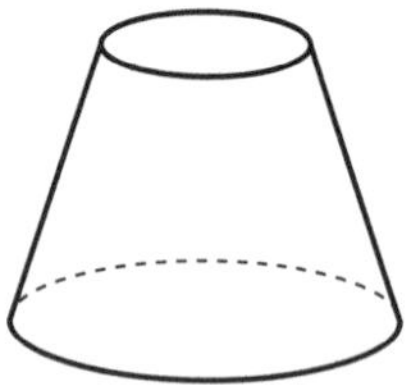

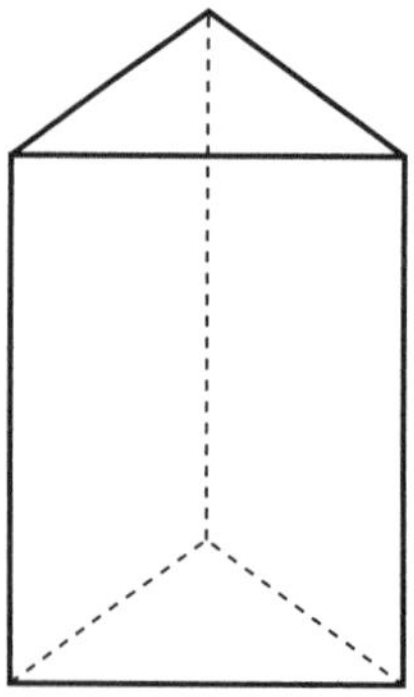

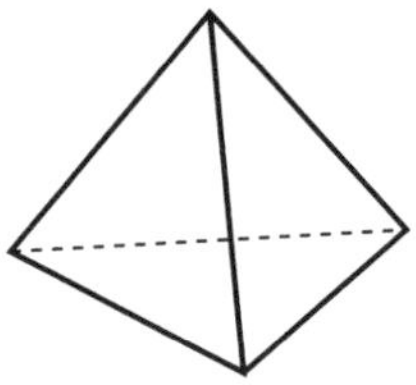

Name Date Time

3-D Shape Sort Property Cards

I have an even number of vertices.	I have no vertices.	I have at least 2 edges that are parallel to each other.	I have an odd number of edges.
One of my vertices is formed by an even number of edges.	I have at least one curved edge.	I have fewer than 6 vertices.	I have at least 2 edges that are perpen-dicular to each other.
All of my surfaces are polygons.	I have at least 1 face (flat surface).	I have at least 1 curved surface.	All of my faces are triangles.
All of my faces are regular polygons.	At least 1 of my faces is a circle.	I have at least 1 pair of faces that are parallel to each other.	**Wild Card:** Pick your own surface property.

Name Date Time

3-D Shape Sort Property Cards (cont.)

Vertex/Edge	Vertex/Edge	Vertex/Edge	Vertex/Edge
Vertex/Edge	Vertex/Edge	Vertex/Edge	Vertex/Edge
Surface	Surface	Surface	Surface
Surface	Surface	Surface	Surface

Name Date Time

Prism and Pyramid Patterns

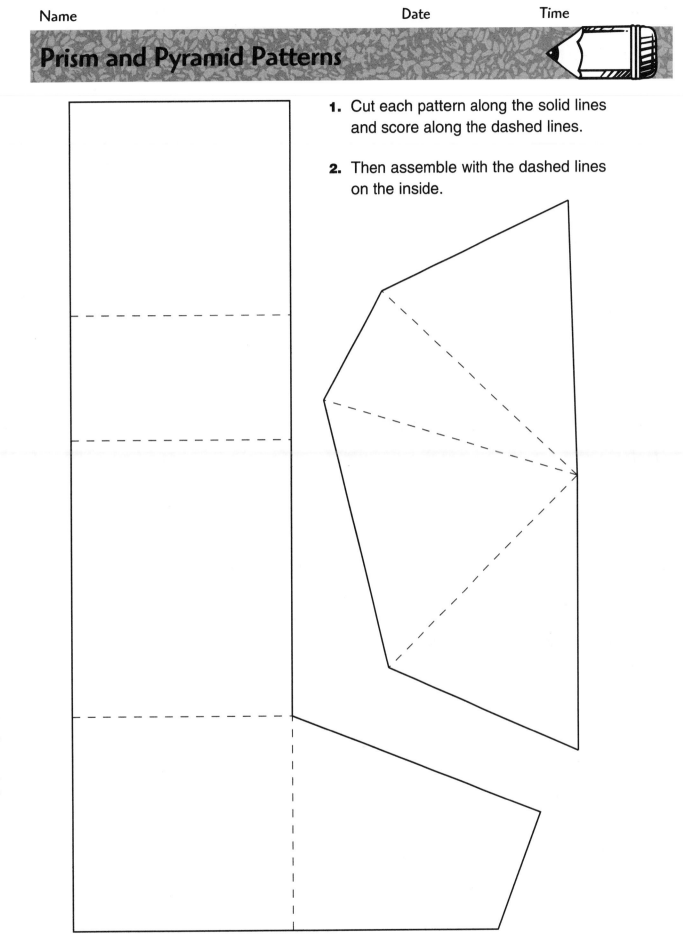

1. Cut each pattern along the solid lines and score along the dashed lines.

2. Then assemble with the dashed lines on the inside.

Name Date Time

Cone Pattern

1. Cut out the pattern.
2. Curl the cone into position, lining up the two heavy black lines and the sets of gray lines.
3. Tape the cone, and then use more tape to seal the seams on the inside and outside.

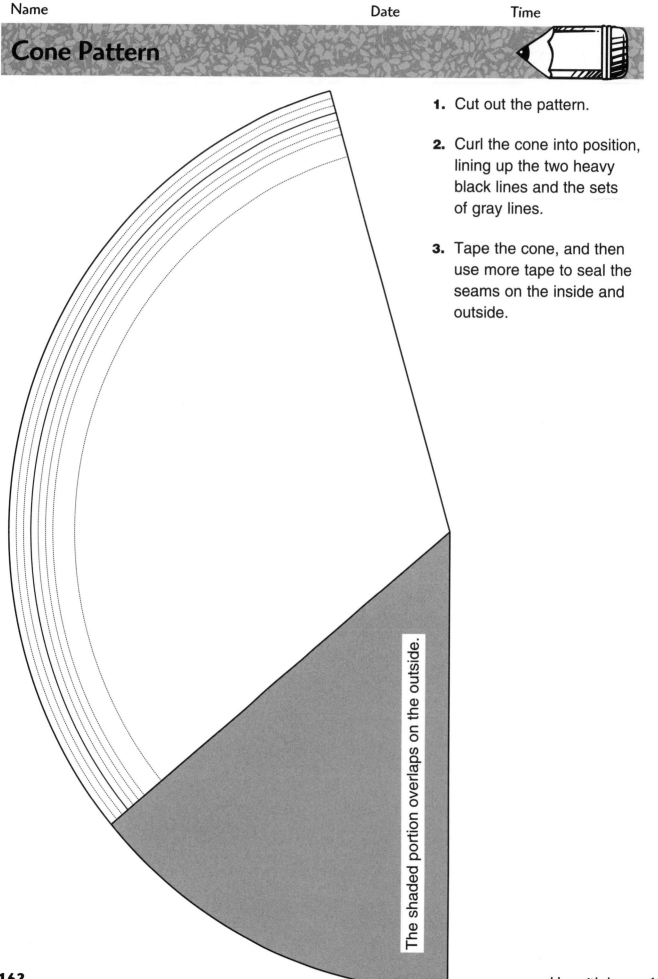

The shaded portion overlaps on the outside.

Name Date Time

More Prism and Pyramid Patterns

1. Cut each pattern along the solid lines and score along the dashed lines.
2. Then assemble with the dashed lines on the inside.

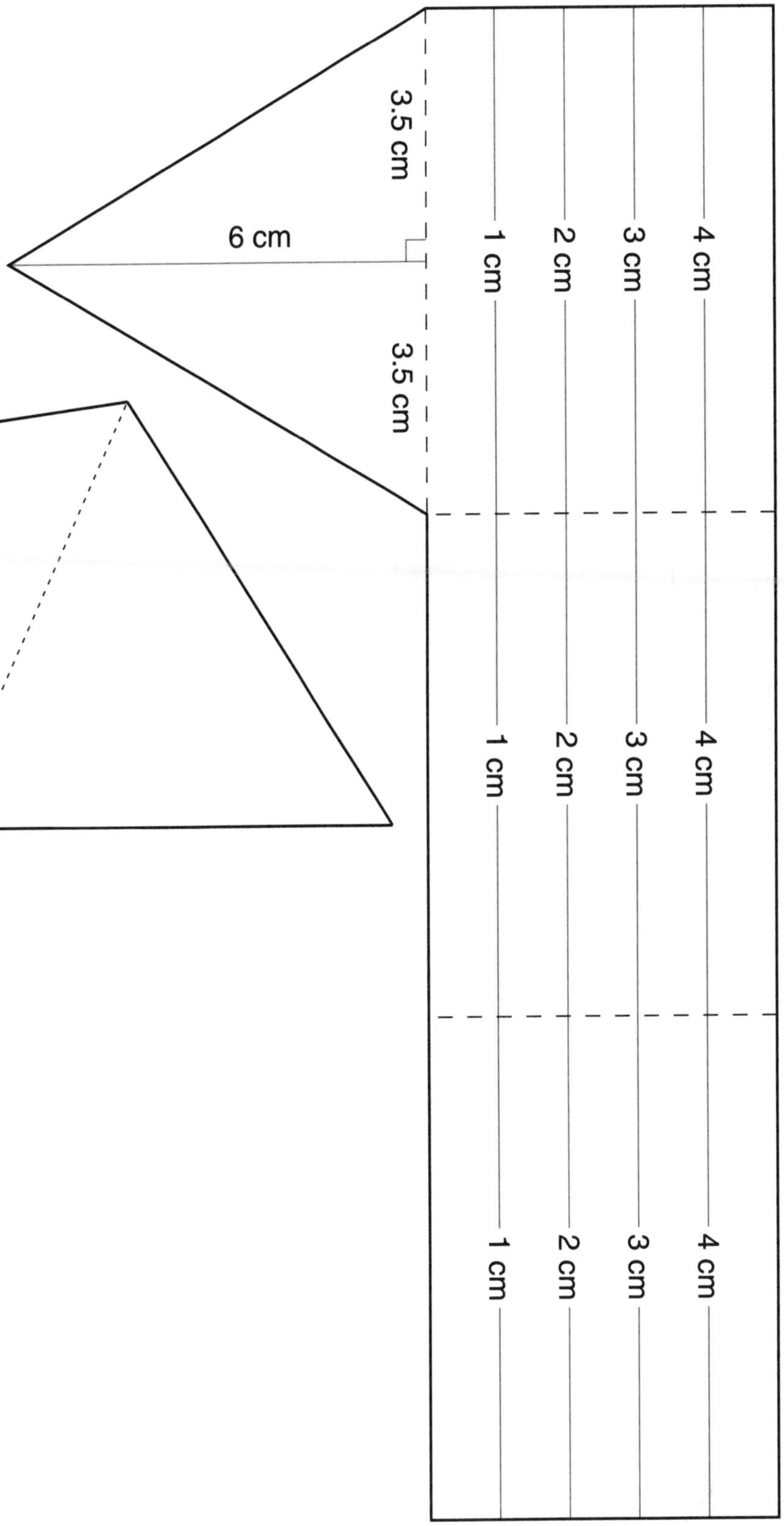

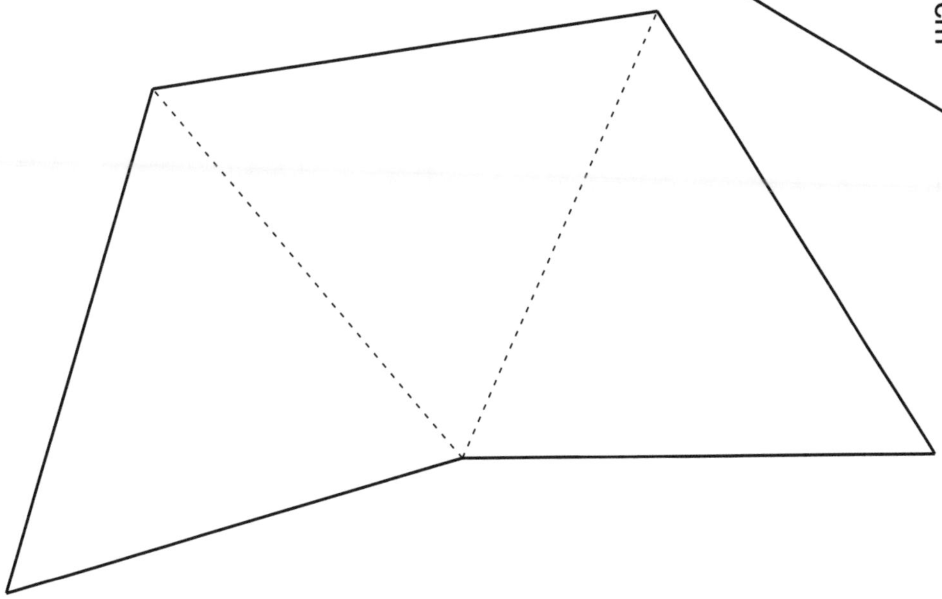

3.5 cm
6 cm
3.5 cm

1 cm 2 cm 3 cm 4 cm
1 cm 2 cm 3 cm 4 cm
1 cm 2 cm 3 cm 4 cm

Name Date Time

More Prism and Pyramid Patterns (cont.)

1. Cut each pattern along the solid lines and score along the dashed lines.
2. Then assemble with the dashed lines on the inside.

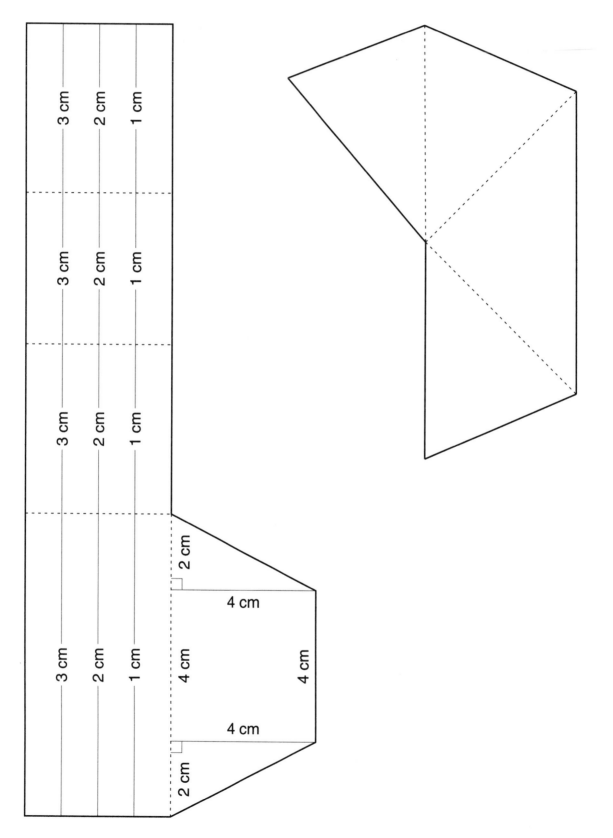

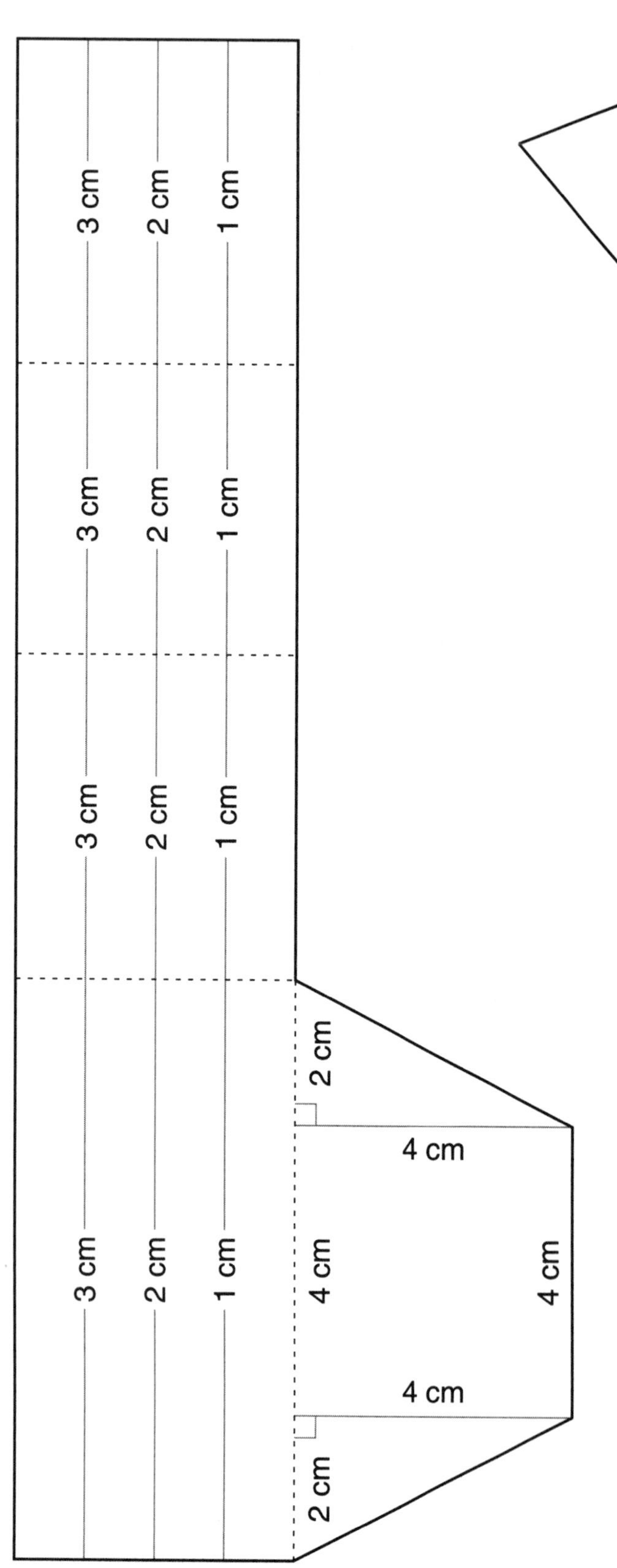

Name Date Time

Volume and Surface Area of Solids

Area of rectangle: $A = l * w$	**Circumference of circle:** $C = \pi * d$
Area of triangle: $A = \frac{1}{2} * b * h$	**Area of circle:** $A = \pi * r^2$
Volume of rectangular prism: $V = l * w * h$	**Volume of cylinder:** $V = \pi * r^2 * h$

Find the volume and the surface area for each figure below. Show your work.

1. Rectangular prism

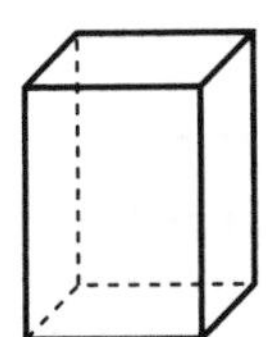

length = ______________

width = ______________

height = ______________

Volume = ______________

Surface area = __________

2. Square pyramid

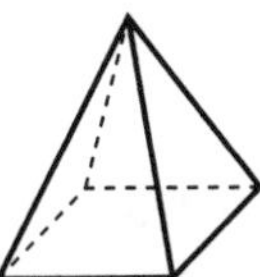

length = ______________

width = ______________

height = ______________

Volume = ______________

Surface area = __________

3. Cylinder

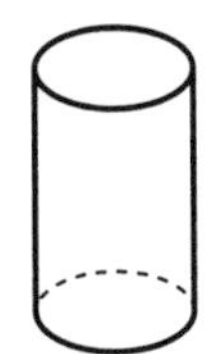

diameter = ______________

height = ______________

Volume = ______________

Surface area = __________

4. Triangular prism

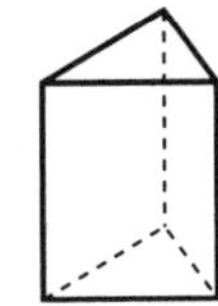

length of base = __________

height of base = __________

height of prism = __________

Volume = ______________

Surface area = __________

Name Date Time

A Surface-Area Investigation

In each problem below, the volume of a rectangular prism is given. Your task is to find the dimensions of the rectangular prism (with that given volume) that has the smallest surface area. To help you, use centimeter cubes to build as many different prisms as possible having the given volume.

Record the dimensions and surface area of each prism you build in the table. Put a star next to the prism with the least surface area.

Do not record prisms with the same surface area. For example, a 2 × 6 × 1 and a 6 × 1 × 2 prism are counted as the same prism, since both have the same surface area.

1.

Dimensions (cm)	Surface Area (sq cm)	Volume (cu cm)
2 × 6 × 1	40	12
		12
		12
		12

2.

Dimensions (cm)	Surface Area (sq cm)	Volume (cu cm)
		24
		24
		24
		24
		24
		24

3. If the volume of the prism is 36 cm^3, try to predict the dimensions that will result in the smallest surface area. Explain how you made your prediction. ______________________

____

____

4. Describe in words or with a number sentence a general rule for finding the surface area of a rectangular prism. ______________________

____

Use with Lesson 11.7.

Name Date Time

Factor Trees and Adding Fractions

1. Make factor trees and write the prime factorization for each number below.

a. 12 **b.** 42 **c.** 32

12 = ________ 42 = ________ 32 = ________

2. Add the following fractions. Use the factor trees above to help you find the least common multiple of the denominators. Use this least common multiple as a common denominator.

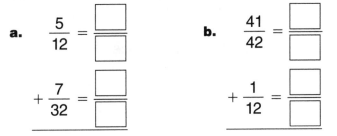

a. $\frac{5}{12} = \frac{\square}{\square}$

$+ \frac{7}{32} = \frac{\square}{\square}$

b. $\frac{41}{42} = \frac{\square}{\square}$

$+ \frac{1}{12} = \frac{\square}{\square}$

3. Use factor trees or some other method to find a common denominator for the fraction pairs below. If you do not use factor trees, explain how you found the least common denominators.

a. $\frac{5}{14}$ and $\frac{2}{21}$ ________

b. $\frac{7}{18}$ and $\frac{16}{36}$ ________

c. $\frac{9}{24}$ and $\frac{21}{64}$ ________

Name Date Time

Spinner Clues

Choosing a Pants Color

There is a 30% chance of choosing blue pants.

There is a $\frac{1}{4}$ chance of choosing black pants.

There is a 0.1 chance of choosing white pants.

There is twice the probability of choosing red pants as there is of choosing white pants.

There is a 15 out of 100 chance of choosing brown pants.

Choosing a Favorite Color

28% of the people said red was their favorite color.

$\frac{1}{3}$ of the people reported that blue was their favorite color.

One-half as many people favored white as favored blue.

0.1 of the people chose brown as their favorite color.

3 out of 25 people named black as their favorite color.

Drawing Colored Chips from a Bag

There is a 1 out of 5 chance of drawing a white chip.

There is a 20% chance of drawing a blue chip.

The probability of drawing black is 0.3.

The chance of drawing a red chip is 15%.

A brown chip is as likely to be drawn as a red chip.

Choosing a Car Color

7 out of 70 people chose white.

25% of the people chose black.

0.15 of the people chose red.

$\frac{4}{12}$ of the people chose blue.

$\frac{1}{6}$ of the people chose brown.

Choosing a Notebook Color

3 out of 20 people favored brown.

20% of the people favored blue.

$\frac{1}{4}$ of the people favored black.

0.3 of the people favored red.

Half as many people favored white as favored blue.

Choosing a Sock Color

1 out of 8 socks sold are red.

$\frac{5}{25}$ of the socks are blue.

$37\frac{1}{2}$% of the socks sold are black.

0.2 of the socks sold are white.

Half as many brown socks are sold as white socks.

Name Date Time

Spinners

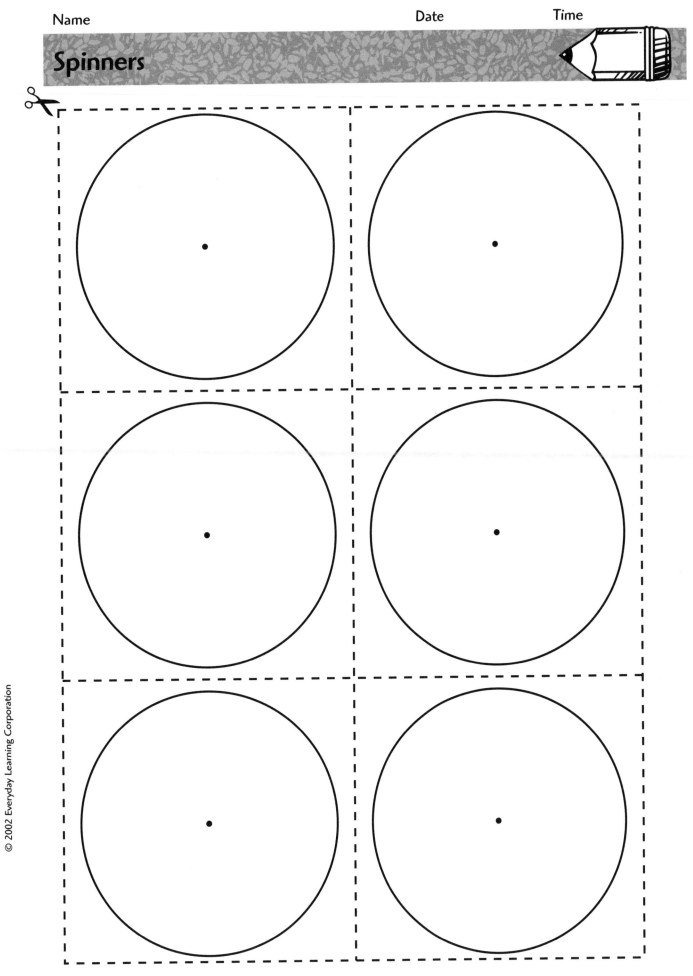

Name Date Time

More Ratios

1. There are 12 children on a bus. In all, there are 50 people on the bus. Express the ratio of children to all people on the bus.

   a. With words: ____________________ people on the bus are children.

   b. With a fraction: ______________ of the people on the bus are children.

   c. With a percent: ______________ of the people on the bus are children.

   d. With a colon: The ratio of children to all people on the bus is ____________________.

2. In Mrs. Horton's fifth grade class, 6 students own a cat. In all, 20 students own pets. Express the ratio of cat owners to all pet owners in the class.

   a. With words: ____________________ pet owners are cat owners.

   b. With a fraction: ____________________ of all pet owners are cat owners.

   c. With a percent: ____________________ of all pet owners are cat owners.

   d. With a colon: The ratio of cat owners to all pet owners is ____________________.

3. In a survey about favorite flavors of ice cream, 8 people said they liked chocolate ice cream best. A total of 24 people were surveyed. Express the ratio of people who chose chocolate ice cream as their favorite to all the people surveyed.

   a. With words: ____________________ people surveyed prefer chocolate.

   b. With a fraction: ____________________ of the people surveyed prefer chocolate.

   c. With a percent: ____________________ of the people surveyed prefer chocolate.

   d. With a colon: The ratio of people who prefer chocolate to all the people surveyed is ____________________.

Name Date Time

Imagining 10 Times More or 10 Times Less

On a separate sheet of paper, write a story about what your life might be like if suddenly—

- everything became 10 times larger or 10 times more.

OR

- everything became 10 times smaller or 10 times less.

Use your imagination, but be specific. Give counts and measurements. Compare the way things are now with the way they would change. Give at least five examples of how things would be different.

Example If everything were 10 times less, I could get to school in 2 minutes instead of the 20 minutes it takes me now. There would be only 3 people on the bus instead of the usual 30. My lunch would cost 30 cents instead of $3.00.

Name Date Time

Imagining 10 Times More or 10 Times Less

On a separate sheet of paper, write a story about what your life might be like if suddenly—

- everything became 10 times larger or 10 times more.

OR

- everything became 10 times smaller or 10 times less.

Use your imagination, but be specific. Give counts and measurements. Compare the way things are now with the way they would change. Give at least five examples of how things would be different.

Example If everything were 10 times less, I could get to school in 2 minutes instead of the 20 minutes it takes me now. There would be only 3 people on the bus instead of the usual 30. My lunch would cost 30 cents instead of $3.00.

Name Date Time

Ratios

Solve the following ratio problems. Use the square tiles you cut out from *Math Journal 2,* Activity Sheet 8 to help you.

1. Place 20 tiles on your desk so that 3 out of 4 tiles are white and the rest are shaded.

How many tiles are white? ______________

How many tiles are shaded? ______________

2. Place 25 tiles on your desk so that 3 out of 5 tiles are white and the rest are shaded.

How many tiles are white? ______________

How many tiles are shaded? ______________

3. Place 4 white tiles on your desk. Add some tiles so that 1 out of 5 tiles is white and the rest are shaded. How many tiles are there in all? ______________

4. Place 9 white tiles on your desk. Add some tiles so that 3 out of 8 tiles are white and the rest are shaded. How many tiles are there in all? ______________

5. Imagine 28 tiles. If 4 out of 7 are white, how many are white? ______________

6. Imagine 24 tiles. If 5 out of 6 are white, how many are white? ______________

7. Place 18 tiles on your desk so that 6 are white and the rest are shaded.

One out of ______________ tiles is white.

8. Place 30 tiles on your desk so that 20 are white and the rest are shaded.

Out of 3 tiles, ______________ are white.

Use with Lesson 12.4.

Name Date Time

Permission Slip

In math class, we plan to examine the effect of exercise on heart rate. Students will find their heart rates after stepping up on and down from a chair 5, 10, 15, 20, and 25 times.

Although the activity is not especially strenuous, we ask that you complete and return this form giving permission for your child's participation.

The data we collect will be used to teach graphing and other statistical skills.

I give permission for ______________________ to participate in the heart-rate activity described above.

Signature ______________________ Date ____________

Name Date Time

Permission Slip

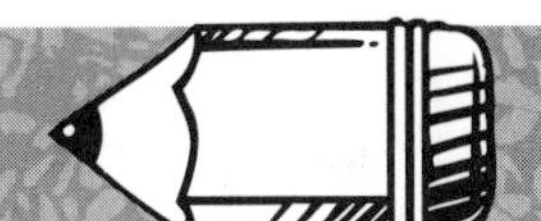

© 2002 Everyday Learning Corporation

In math class, we plan to examine the effect of exercise on heart rate. Students will find their heart rates after stepping up on and down from a chair 5, 10, 15, 20, and 25 times.

Although the activity is not especially strenuous, we ask that you complete and return this form giving permission for your child's participation.

The data we collect will be used to teach graphing and other statistical skills.

I give permission for ______________________ to participate in the heart-rate activity described above.

Signature ______________________ Date ____________

Name Date Time

Permission Slip

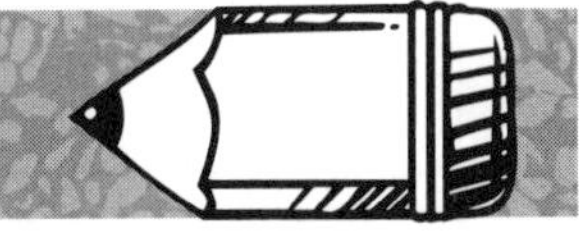

© 2002 Everyday Learning Corporation

In math class, we plan to examine the effect of exercise on heart rate. Students will find their heart rates after stepping up on and down from a chair 5, 10, 15, 20, and 25 times.

Although the activity is not especially strenuous, we ask that you complete and return this form giving permission for your child's participation.

The data we collect will be used to teach graphing and other statistical skills.

I give permission for ______________________ to participate in the heart-rate activity described above.

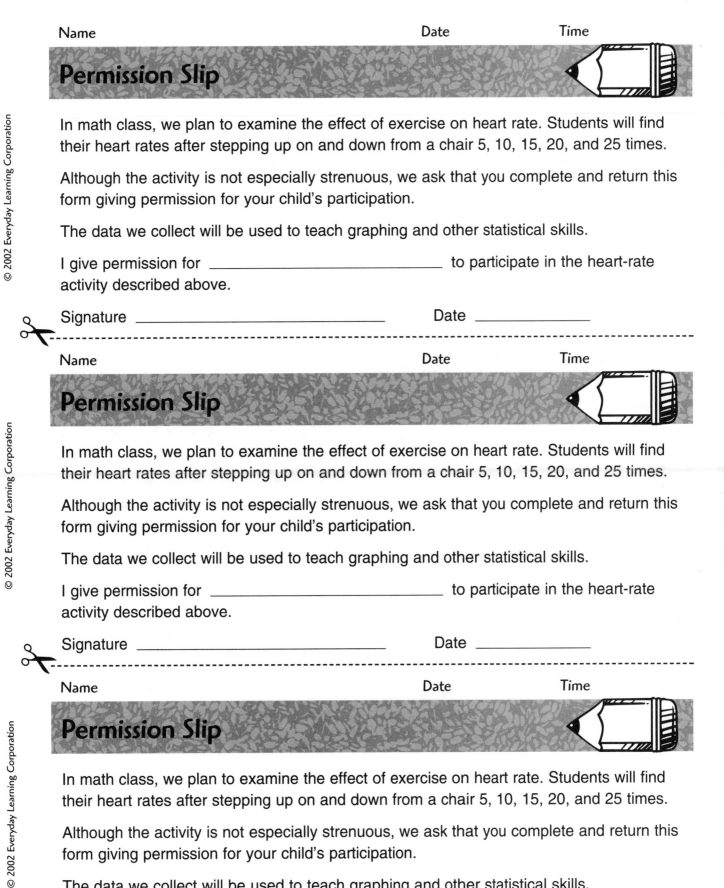

Signature ______________________ Date ____________

Name Date Time

Spoon Scramble Cards

$\frac{1}{4}$ of 24	$\frac{3}{4} * 8$	50% of 12	0.10 * 60
$\frac{1}{3}$ of 21	$3\frac{1}{2} * 2$	25% of 28	0.10 * 70
$\frac{1}{5}$ of 40	$2 * \frac{16}{4}$	1% of 800	0.10 * 80
$\frac{3}{4}$ of 12	$4\frac{1}{2} * 2$	25% of 36	0.10 * 90

Name Date Time

The Search for Prime Numbers

You probably know the following definitions of prime and composite numbers:

> A **prime number** is a whole number that has exactly two **factors.** The factors are 1 and the number itself. For example, 7 is a prime number because its only factors are 1 and 7. A prime number is divisible only by 1 and itself.
>
> A **composite number** is a whole number that has more than two factors. For example, 10 is a composite number because it has four factors: 1, 2, 5, and 10. A composite number is divisible by at least three whole numbers.

The number 1 is neither prime nor composite.

For centuries, mathematicians have been interested in prime and composite numbers because they are the building blocks of whole numbers. They have found that every composite number can be written as the product of prime numbers. For example, 18 can be written as 2 * 3 * 3.

Around 300 B.C., the Greek mathematician Euclid (yoo´ klid) proved that there is no largest prime number. No matter how large a prime number you find, there will always be prime numbers that are larger. Ever since then, people have been searching for more and more prime numbers. In 1893, a mathematician was able to show that there are over 50 million prime numbers between the numbers 1 and 1 billion.

The Greek mathematician Eratosthenes (ĕr′ə-tŏs′thə-nēz′), who lived around 200 B.C., devised a simple method for finding prime numbers. His strategy was based on the fact that every **multiple of a number** is divisible by that number. For example, the numbers 2, 4, 6, 8, and 10 are all multiples of 2, and each of these numbers is divisible by 2. Here is another way to say it: A whole number is a factor of every one of its multiples. For example, 2 is a factor of 2, 4, 6, 8, and 10. The number 2 has only one other factor, the number 1, so 2 is a prime number. All other multiples of 2 are composite numbers.

Eratosthenes' method is called the **Sieve of Eratosthenes.** The directions for using the sieve for finding prime numbers are given on *Math Masters,* page 176.

Since the time of Eratosthenes, mathematicians have invented more powerful methods for finding prime numbers. Some methods use formulas. Today, computers are used. The largest prime number known when this book went to press had 2,098,960 digits. If that number were printed in a book with pages the same size as this page, in the same size type, it would be about 300 pages long.

Name Date Time

The Sieve of Eratosthenes

Follow the directions below for *Math Masters,* page 177. When you have finished, you will have crossed out in the grid every number from 1 to 100 that is not a prime number.

1. Since 1 is not a prime number, cross it out.
2. Circle 2 with a colored marker or crayon. Then count by 2, crossing out all multiples of 2, that is, 4, 6, 8, 10, and so on.
3. Circle 3 with a different colored marker or crayon. Cross out every third number after 3 (6, 9, 12, and so on). If a number is already crossed out, make a mark in a corner of the box. The numbers you have crossed out or marked are multiples of 3.
4. Skip 4, since it is already crossed out, and go on to 5. Use a new color to circle 5 and cross out multiples of 5.
5. Continue. Start each time by circling the next number that is not crossed out. Cross out all multiples of that number. If a number is already crossed out, make a mark in a corner of the box. Use a different color for each new set of multiples.
6. Stop when there are no more numbers to be circled or crossed out. The circled numbers are the prime numbers from 1 to 100.

Squaring Magic

The square of 13 is 169. Reverse 169 and you get 961. The square root of 961 is 31, which, when reversed, gets you back to 13.

Can you find any other number that will do this?

Name Date Time

The Sieve of Eratosthenes (cont.)

1	2	3	4	5	6	7	8	9	10
11	12	13	14	15	16	17	18	19	20
21	22	23	24	25	26	27	28	29	30
31	32	33	34	35	36	37	38	39	40
41	42	43	44	45	46	47	48	49	50
51	52	53	54	55	56	57	58	59	60
61	62	63	64	65	66	67	68	69	70
71	72	73	74	75	76	77	78	79	80
81	82	83	84	85	86	87	88	89	90
91	92	93	94	95	96	97	98	99	100

Name Date Time

The Sieve of Eratosthenes (cont.)

1. List all the prime numbers from 1 to 100.

____

____

2. What are the crossed-out numbers greater than 1 called?

____

3. Notice that 6 is a multiple of both 2 and 3. Find two other numbers that are multiples of both 2 and 3.

____

4. Find a number that is a multiple of 2, 3, and 5. (*Hint:* Look at the colors.)

____

5. Find a number that is a multiple of 2, 3, 4, and 5. ______________

6. Choose any crossed-out number between 50 and 60. List all of its factors.

____

7. List the crossed-out numbers that have no marks in the corners of their boxes.

____

8. Find a pair of consecutive prime numbers. ______________

   Are there any others? __________ If yes, list them.

____

9. The numbers 3 and 5 are called **twin primes** because they are separated by just one composite number. List all the other twin primes from 1 to 100.

____

____

10. Why do you think this grid is called a sieve?

____

____

____

Use with Project 1.

Name Date Time

The Sieve of Eratosthenes (cont.)

101	102	103	104	105	106	107	108	109	100
111	112	113	114	115	116	117	118	119	120
121	122	123	124	125	126	127	128	129	130
131	132	133	134	135	136	137	138	139	140
141	142	143	144	145	146	147	148	149	150
151	152	153	154	155	156	157	158	159	160
161	162	163	164	165	166	167	168	169	170
171	172	173	174	175	176	177	178	179	180
181	182	183	184	185	186	187	188	189	190
191	192	193	194	195	196	197	198	199	200

Name Date Time

Deficient, Abundant, and Perfect Numbers

A **factor** of a whole number *N* is any whole number that can be multiplied by a whole number to give *N* as the product. For example, 5 is a factor of 30 because $6 * 5 = 30$. Also, 6 is a factor of 30. Every whole number has itself and 1 as factors.

A **proper factor** of a whole number is any factor of that number except the number itself. For example, the *factors* of 10 are 1, 2, 5, and 10. The *proper factors* of 10 are 1, 2, and 5.

A whole number is a **deficient number** if the sum of all its proper factors is less than the number. For example, 10 is a deficient number because the sum of its proper factors is $1 + 2 + 5 = 8$, and 8 is less than 10.

A whole number is an **abundant number** if the sum of all its proper factors is greater than the number. For example, 12 is an abundant number because the sum of its proper factors is $1 + 2 + 3 + 4 + 6 = 16$, and 16 is greater than 12.

A whole number is a **perfect number** if the sum of all its proper factors is equal to the number. For example, 6 is a perfect number because the sum of its proper factors is $1 + 2 + 3 = 6$.

Exploration

List the proper factors of each number from 1 through 50 in the table on *Math Masters,* pages 181 and 182. Then find the sum of the proper factors of each number and record it in the third column of the table. Finally, make a check mark in the appropriate column to show whether the number is deficient, abundant, or perfect.

Divide up the work with the other members of your group. Have partners check each other's work, using factor rainbows. When you are satisfied that all the results are correct, answer the questions on page 182.

Name Date Time

Deficient, Abundant, and Perfect Numbers (cont.)

Number	Proper Factors	Sum of Proper Factors	Deficient	Abundant	Perfect
1		0	✓		
2					
3					
4					
5					
6	1, 2, 3	6			✓
7					
8					
9					
10	1, 2, 5	8	✓		
11					
12	1, 2, 3, 4, 6	16		✓	
13					
14					
15					
16					
17					
18					
19					
20					
21					
22					
23					
24					
25					
26					
27					
28					
29					
30					
31					
32					
33					
34					

Name Date Time

Deficient, Abundant, and Perfect Numbers (cont.)

Number	Proper Factors	Sum of Proper Factors	Deficient	Abundant	Perfect
35					
36					
37					
38					
39					
40					
41					
42					
43					
44					
45					
46					
47					
48					
49					
50					

Source: The Math Teacher's Book of Lists. Englewood Cliffs: Prentice Hall, 1995.

Refer to the results in your table.

1. What are the perfect numbers up to 50? ____________

2. Is there an abundant number that is not an even number? ____________

3. Are all deficient numbers odd numbers? ____________

4. What is the next number greater than 50 for which the sum of its proper factors is 1? ____________

5. The sum of the proper factors of 4 is 1 less than 4. List all the other numbers up through 50 for which the sum of the proper factors is 1 less than the number itself. ____________

6. What do you think is the next number greater than 50 for which the sum of its proper factors is 1 less than the number itself? ____________

Use with Project 2.

Name Date Time

A Perfect-Number Challenge

Perfect numbers become big very quickly. The third perfect number has 3 digits, the fourth has 4 digits, the fifth has 8 digits, the sixth has 10 digits, and the thirty-second has 455,663 digits! In other words, perfect numbers are hard to find.

You can find perfect numbers without having to find the sum of the proper factors of every number. Here is what you do:

1. Complete the pattern of starting numbers in the first column in the table.

2. List the factors of each starting number in the second column.

3. Write the sum of the factors of each starting number in the third column.

4. If the sum of the factors of the starting number is prime, multiply this sum by the starting number. The product is a perfect number. Record it in the last column.

The first perfect number is 6. Try to find the next three perfect numbers.

Starting Number	Factors	Sum of Factors	Perfect Number
2	1, 2	3	6
4			
8			

People have been fascinated by perfect numbers for centuries. The ancient Greeks knew the first four. The fifth perfect number was not found until the year 1456. The search for perfect numbers is now carried out on computers. When this book went to press, 38 perfect numbers had been identified. All the perfect numbers found so far are even numbers.

Name Date Time

An Ancient Multiplication Method

Over 4,000 years ago, the Egyptians developed one of the earliest multiplication methods. This method, with some modifications, was then used by the ancient Greeks, and, in the Middle Ages, by people living in other parts of Europe.

Study the examples of the Egyptian method below. Each problem has been solved by this method of multiplication. Try to figure out how the method works.

13 * 25 = 325	18 * 17 = 306	26 * 31 = 806
✓ 1 25 (1 * 25)	~~1 17~~	~~1 31~~
~~2 50 (2 * 25)~~	✓ 2 34	✓ 2 62
✓ 4 100 (4 * 25)	~~4 68~~	~~4 124~~
✓ 8 200 (8 * 25)	~~8 136~~	✓ 8 248
325 (13 * 25)	✓ 16 272	✓ 16 496
	306	806

Make up a multiplication problem. Then solve it by using the Egyptian method.

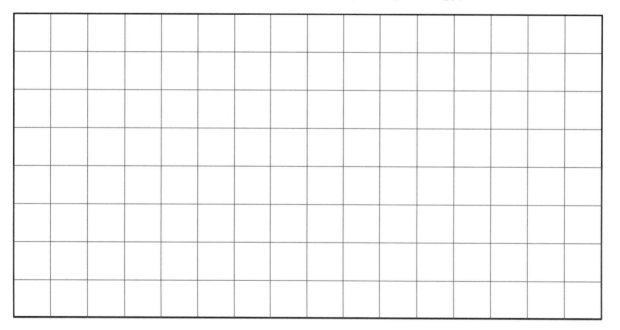

Use with Project 3.

Name Date Time

An Ancient Multiplication Method (cont.)

1. Try to solve these problems using the Egyptian method.

85 * 14 = ______	38 * 43 = ______	45 * 29 = ______

Challenge

2. Here is another ancient multiplication method, based on the Egyptian method. People living in rural areas of Russia, Ethiopia, and the Near East still use this method. See if you can figure out how it works. Then try to complete the problem in the third box, using this method.

13 * 25 = 325	38 * 43 = 1634	45 * 29 = ______
13 25 ~~6 50~~ 3 100 1 200 325	~~38 43~~ 19 86 ~~9 172~~ ~~4 344~~ 2 688 1 1376 1634	45 29 ~~22 58~~ 11 116 5 232 ~~2 464~~ 1 928 ______

Name Date Time

Comparing Multiplication Algorithms

Think about the advantages and disadvantages of each multiplication method that you know. Record your thoughts in the chart below.

Algorithm	Advantages	Disadvantages
Partial Products 43 * 62 60 [40s] = 2400 60 [3s] = 180 2 [40s] = 80 2 [3s] = 6 2666		
Lattice 4 3 2 / 4 , 1 1 / 8 — 6 0 / 8 , 0 / 6 — 2 2, 6, 6, 6		
Egyptian 43 * 62 ✓ 1 62 ✓ 2 124 ~~4 248~~ ✓ 8 496 ~~16 992~~ ✓ 32 1984 2666		

Use with Project 3.

Name Date Time

Old Math

1. The ancient Egyptians used picture symbols, called hieroglyphs, to write numbers. Here is how they might have multiplied 11 ∗ 13 using the algorithm you learned in this project.

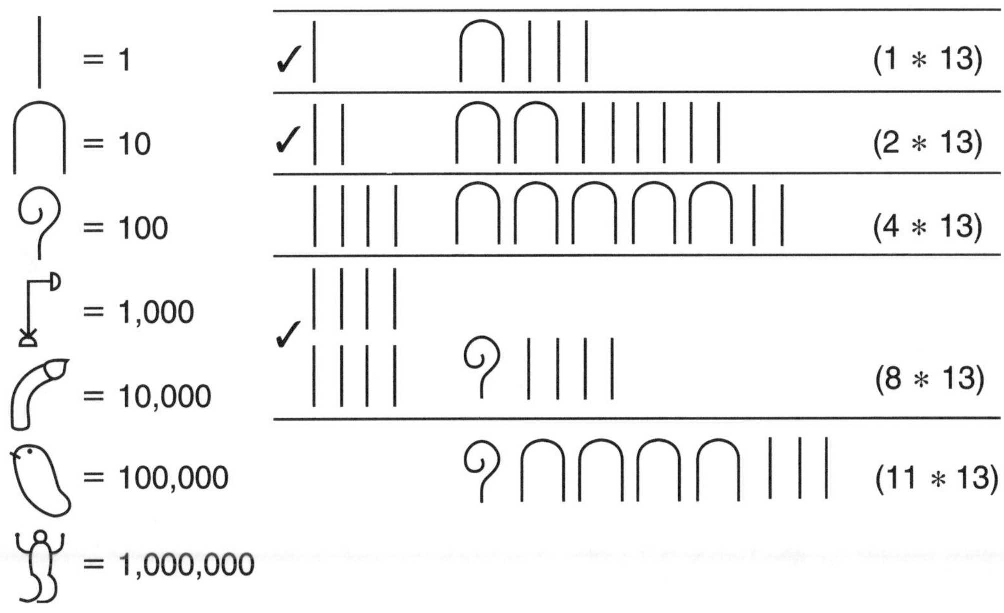

On the back of this sheet, try to multiply 21 ∗ 16 using the Egyptian algorithm and Egyptian numerals.

2. Do you know Roman numerals? They were used in Europe for centuries, until they were replaced by Hindu-Arabic numerals. Today they appear mainly in dates on cornerstones and in copyright notices.

   It is sometimes said that "multiplication with Roman numerals was impossible." Is that true? See whether you can multiply 12 ∗ 15 using Roman numerals and the Egyptian algorithm. Use the back of this sheet.

   Some Roman Numerals

   I = 1 II = 2 III = 3 IV = 4 V = 5 VI = 6 IX = 9 X = 10 XX = 20

   XL = 40 L = 50 LX = 60 C = 100 D = 500 M = 1000

Name Date Time

Computation Trick #1—Super Speedy Addition

Set the Stage: Tell a friend that you have become a whiz at addition. To prove it, you are going to add five 3-digit numbers in your head within seconds.

Props Needed: calculator

Performing the Trick:	***Examples***		
	Trial 1	**Trial 2**	**Trial 3**
1. Ask your friend to jot down a 3-digit number on a piece of paper. Each digit must be different.	493	261	682
2. Ask your friend to write another 3-digit number below the first number. Each digit must be different.	764	503	149
3. One more time. (This is the **"notice me number."**)	175	935	306
4. Now it is your turn. Write a number so that the sum of your number and the first number is 999. (For example, in Trial 1, 493 + 506 = 999.)	506	738	317
5. Write another number so that the sum of this number and the second number is 999. (For example, in Trial 1, 764 + 235 = 999.)	+ 235	+ 496	+ 850
6. Pause a few seconds and give the sum of the five numbers. Have your friend check your super speedy addition on a calculator.	2173	2933	2304

Figure out how to do this trick. How does it work?

____

____

____

____

____

Use with Project 4.

Name Date Time

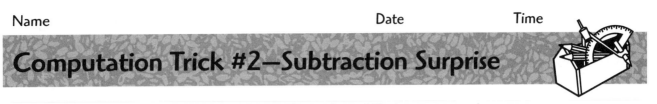

Computation Trick #2—Subtraction Surprise

Set the Stage: Tell a friend that your subtraction skills have soared. You are now able to give the answer to a subtraction problem without ever seeing the problem.

Props Needed: calculator

Performing the Trick:	***Examples***	
	Trial 1	**Trial 2**
1. Ask your friend to **secretly** write a 3-digit number on a piece of paper. Each digit must be different.	135	562
2. Tell your friend to reverse the digits and write the new number below the first number.	531	265
3. Now have your friend use a calculator to subtract the smaller number from the larger number.	531 − 135 396	562 − 265 297
4. Say: "Tell me either the digit in the hundreds place or the digit in the ones place."	"3 in the hundreds place"	"7 in the ones place"
5. Pause a few seconds and give the answer.	396	297

Figure out how to do this trick. How does it work?

____

____

____

____

____

Name Date Time

Computation Trick #3—Crazy Calendar Addition

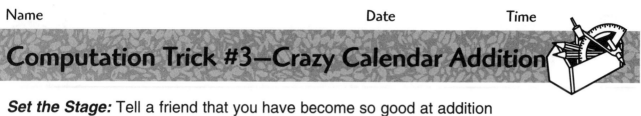

Set the Stage: Tell a friend that you have become so good at addition that you now can tell what an addition problem is by merely looking at the answer.

Props Needed: calculator and a calendar

Performing the Trick:

Examples

Give your friend a calendar.

Sun.	Mon.	Tue.	Wed.	Thu.	Fri.	Sat.
		1	2	3	4	5
6	7	8	9	10	11	12
13	14	15	16	17	18	19
20	21	22	23	24	25	26
27	28	29	30	31		

	Trial 1	**Trial 2**	**Trial 3**
1. Ask your friend to choose a month and to **secretly** circle any three dates that are next to each other, either in a row or in a column.			
2. Now ask your friend to add the three dates on a calculator and to give you the calculator showing the sum in the display.	30	27	39
3. Ask: "Are the three dates you circled in a row or in a column?"	"column"	"row"	"column"
4. Pause a few seconds and give the answer.	3, 10, 17	8, 9, 10	6, 13, 20

Figure out how to do this trick. How does it work?

____

____

____

____

____

Name Date Time

12-Month Calendar

JANUARY

S	M	T	W	T	F	S
1	2	3	4	5	6	7
8	9	10	11	12	13	14
15	16	17	18	19	20	21
22	23	24	25	26	27	28
29	30	31				

FEBRUARY

S	M	T	W	T	F	S
			1	2	3	4
5	6	7	8	9	10	11
12	13	14	15	16	17	18
19	20	21	22	23	24	25
26	27	28				

MARCH

S	M	T	W	T	F	S
			1	2	3	4
5	6	7	8	9	10	11
12	13	14	15	16	17	18
19	20	21	22	23	24	25
26	27	28	29	30	31	

APRIL

S	M	T	W	T	F	S
						1
2	3	4	5	6	7	8
9	10	11	12	13	14	15
16	17	18	19	20	21	22
23	24	25	26	27	28	29
30						

MAY

S	M	T	W	T	F	S
	1	2	3	4	5	6
7	8	9	10	11	12	13
14	15	16	17	18	19	20
21	22	23	24	25	26	27
28	29	30	31			

JUNE

S	M	T	W	T	F	S
				1	2	3
4	5	6	7	8	9	10
11	12	13	14	15	16	17
18	19	20	21	22	23	24
25	26	27	28	29	30	

JULY

S	M	T	W	T	F	S
						1
2	3	4	5	6	7	8
9	10	11	12	13	14	15
16	17	18	19	20	21	22
23	24	25	26	27	28	29
30	31					

AUGUST

S	M	T	W	T	F	S
		1	2	3	4	5
6	7	8	9	10	11	12
13	14	15	16	17	18	19
20	21	22	23	24	25	26
27	28	29	30	31		

SEPTEMBER

S	M	T	W	T	F	S
					1	2
3	4	5	6	7	8	9
10	11	12	13	14	15	16
17	18	19	20	21	22	23
24	25	26	27	28	29	30

OCTOBER

S	M	T	W	T	F	S
1	2	3	4	5	6	7
8	9	10	11	12	13	14
15	16	17	18	19	20	21
22	23	24	25	26	27	28
29	30	31				

NOVEMBER

S	M	T	W	T	F	S
			1	2	3	4
5	6	7	8	9	10	11
12	13	14	15	16	17	18
19	20	21	22	23	24	25
26	27	28	29	30		

DECEMBER

S	M	T	W	T	F	S
					1	2
3	4	5	6	7	8	9
10	11	12	13	14	15	16
17	18	19	20	21	22	23
24	25	26	27	28	29	30
31						

Name Date Time

Computation Trick #1–Super Speedy Addition

Why Does It Work?

All you need to do to solve this addition problem is to look at the "notice me number." Here is why:

Remember that you created two pairs of numbers—each with a sum of 999. These two pairs of numbers add up to 1998 (999 + 999 = 1998). This is 2 short of 2000. The remaining number is the "notice me number." If you subtract 2 from the "notice me number" and add the result to 2000, you will always get the answer!

The final total will always be:

("notice me number" − 2)
+ 2000
____

Example

493	
764	
175	(175 − 2) + 2000
506	
+ 235	
2173	

If you want to do more:

Here are some variations you might want to try. You might use 7 or 9 numbers instead of 5. The trick is done in exactly the same way. However, think about how your formula would change if you did this.

You might also try this with 6-digit numbers. Once again, the procedure is the same but the formula would change.

Record your findings below.

____

____

____

____

____

____

Use with Project 4.

Name Date Time

Computation Trick #2—Subtraction Surprise

Why Does It Work?

The trick is in the way in which you had your classmate create the subtraction problem. There are only 9 possible solutions to a subtraction problem created in that way:

99 198 297 396 495 594 693 792 891

You may have noticed that the digit in the tens place is always 9. And the digits in the hundreds place and the ones place always add up to 9.

For example, if your classmate tells you that the digit in the hundreds place is 4, then you know that the digit in the ones place must be 5, since $4 + 5 = 9$. You know that the digit in the tens place is always 9. Therefore the answer is 495.

What is the answer if your classmate tells you that the digit in the ones place is 9? ____________

If you want to do more:

Will this trick work with a 4-digit number? With a 5-digit number? Describe your findings.

____

____

____

____

____

____

Name Date Time

Computation Trick #3—Crazy Calendar Addition

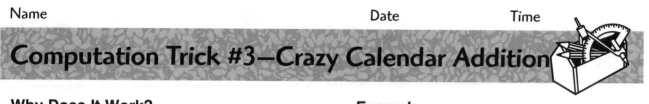

Why Does It Work?

If three numbers are evenly spaced, you can find the middle number by dividing the sum of the numbers by 3.

Example

Sun.	Mon.	Tue.	Wed.	Thu.	Fri.	Sat.
		1	2	3	4	5
6	7	8	9	10	11	12
13	14	15	16	17	18	19
20	21	22	23	24	25	26
27	28	29	30	31		

The numbers in a row and the numbers in a column of a calendar are evenly spaced.

- The numbers in a row are consecutive whole numbers. They are 1 apart.
- The numbers in a column are 7 apart. This is because there are 7 days in a week.

Once you find the middle number by dividing the sum of the numbers by 3, it is easy to find the other two numbers.

- If the three numbers are in a row, then subtract 1 from the middle number to get the first number. Add 1 to the middle number to get the third number.
- If the three numbers are in a column, subtract 7 from the middle number to get the first number. Add 7 to the middle number to get the third number.

If you want to do more:

What would happen if the three dates chosen were on a diagonal? Would the trick still work? Why or why not?

____

____

____

____

____

____

Use with Project 4.

Name Date Time

How Would You Spend $1,000,000?—Emily's Idea

Emily decided that if she had $1,000,000 she would spend it on a fabulous ten-day trip to Florida for her, 19 of her friends, and 4 chaperons—24 people altogether. She thought that this should be a trip that no one would ever forget, and with $1,000,000, she knew that she could make that happen!

Emily began by thinking about all of the things she and her friends might need for their trip. She visited a local department store to find out how much different items cost. She decided to purchase a **vacation wardrobe** for everyone, including the chaperons, at a cost of $50,750. Her next stop was a **sporting goods** store for items such as snorkel gear, swimsuits, and sunglasses. The store clerk calculated that all of her purchases there would cost $24,100.

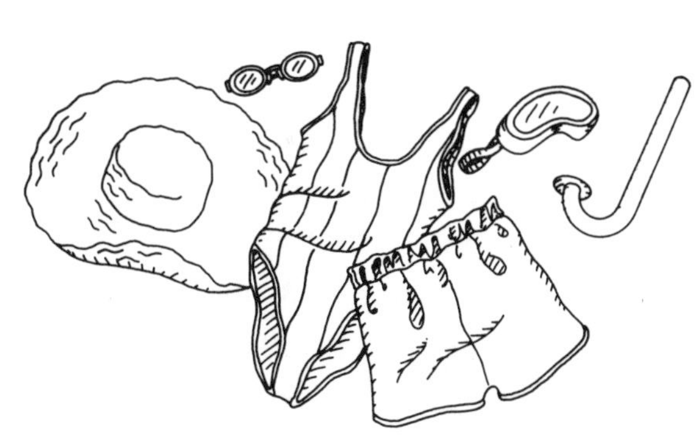

Emily knew that **transportation** to Florida and for getting around while in Florida would be needed. She made a few telephone calls to find out the prices for the transportation. Emily found that when she politely explained her project to people, most of them were willing to help her. After a bit of research, she chartered an airplane for the flight from Chicago to Orlando and back ($54,780). She purchased two stretch limos for use in Florida ($165,160 + $10,000 for gas and two around-the-clock chauffeurs). She also purchased a minivan to take the chaperons and the luggage ($20,700) while in Florida.

Lodging was another consideration. Emily decided that her group would stay at one of the resorts inside the theme park ($33,550). She went to a travel agency to get some information about many of the **activities** that she and her friends might try while they were there. For $177,200, Emily made reservations for several special breakfasts as well as dinner shows, rented a water park for 12 hours, and purchased 10-day passes to the theme park.

Name Date Time

How Would You Spend $1,000,000?

Emily's Idea (cont.)

Emily decided to keep a record of the money she was spending by listing her purchases in major categories. At the right is part of the chart that she began to make.

Major Category	Cost
Vacation Wardrobe	$ 50,750
Sports Equipment	$ 24,100
Transportation	$250,640
Lodging	$ 33,550
Activities	$177,200

Emily also decided that for each category she would keep a detailed record so that she would know exactly how she was spending the $1,000,000.

Here is an example of her record for one category:

Major Category — Vacation Wardrobe			
Item	Quantity	Unit Price	Total Price
Boxer shorts	100	$ 12.50	$ 1,250.00
Socks	200	$ 5.50	$ 1,100.00
Shorts	240	$ 38.00	$ 9,120.00
T-shirts	200	$ 32.00	$ 6,400.00
Long-sleeve shirts	100	$ 36.00	$ 3,600.00
Jeans	100	$ 34.00	$ 3,400.00
Sweatshirts	60	$ 36.00	$ 2,160.00
Flannel shirts	60	$ 38.00	$ 2,280.00
Vests	20	$ 47.50	$ 950.00
Sweaters	40	$ 48.00	$ 1,920.00
Tax			$ 2,570.00
Chaperons' Wardrobe Allotment		$4,000.00 per person	$ 16,000.00
		Total	$50,750.00

These are examples of just a few of the expenses for Emily's amazing trip.

About how much money has Emily spent so far? ________________

About how much money does Emily have left to spend? ________________

Use with Project 5.

Name Date Time

How Would You Spend $1,000,000?

Project Guidelines

Imagine that you have just inherited $1,000,000. One of the conditions for you to receive the money is that you must first investigate, research, and present exactly how you will spend it. The following guidelines must be followed:

Theme The $1,000,000 must be spent carrying out one particular plan.

For example: A plan that would help save the rain forest; a plan to build new parks and playgrounds in your city; a plan for a trip around the world; or a plan to open a ballet studio.

Goal Spend as close to $1,000,000 as possible, but not more than $1,000,000.

Research All of the expenses involved in carrying out the details of your plan must be included.

For example: If you are opening a ballet studio, you must consider how many teachers you will need and how much you will pay them. If you are buying a car, you will need to consider the cost of gas, maintenance, and insurance for the length of time you will own the car.

Accounting Record, in an organized way, exactly how the $1,000,000 will be spent. The purchases needed to carry out your plan should be organized in several major categories. The purchases in each major category must total at least $10,000.

For example: Think about the way in which Emily organized the purchases for her Florida vacation, as described on *Math Masters*, pages 195 and 196.

Display Present the research and accounting for your plan in a report, on a display board, on a posterboard, or in a portfolio. You might even do a video production.

For example: Emily presented her project as a report. In addition to her calculations, she included pictures and sample receipts whenever possible.

Name Date Time

How Would You Spend $1,000,000?—Totals

Accounting Sheet

Totals of Major Categories

Major Category	Cost

Total **$1,000,000**

Use with Project 5.

Name Date Time

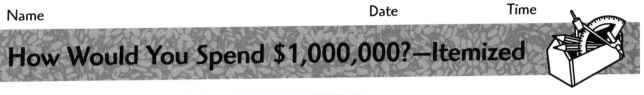

How Would You Spend $1,000,000?—Itemized

Accounting Sheet

A Major Category—Itemized

Category: ______________________________

Item	Quantity	Unit Price	Total Price

Total $ ______________

Name Date Time

How Would You Spend $1,000,000?—Categories

In the table below, list all of your major expense categories and the total amount for each. (Refer to your accounting sheets—*Math Masters,* pages 198 and 199.) Write each amount as a fraction, decimal, and percent of $1,000,000. Round each decimal to the nearest hundredth. Round each percent to the nearest whole percent.

Category	Total $ Spent	Fraction	Decimal	Percent
		$\frac{\quad}{1{,}000{,}000}$		
		$\frac{\quad}{1{,}000{,}000}$		
		$\frac{\quad}{1{,}000{,}000}$		
		$\frac{\quad}{1{,}000{,}000}$		
		$\frac{\quad}{1{,}000{,}000}$		
		$\frac{\quad}{1{,}000{,}000}$		
		$\frac{\quad}{1{,}000{,}000}$		
		$\frac{\quad}{1{,}000{,}000}$		
		$\frac{\quad}{1{,}000{,}000}$		
		$\frac{\quad}{1{,}000{,}000}$		
		$\frac{\quad}{1{,}000{,}000}$		
		$\frac{\quad}{1{,}000{,}000}$		
		$\frac{\quad}{1{,}000{,}000}$		

Use with Project 5.

Name Date Time

How Would You Spend $1,000,000?—Graph

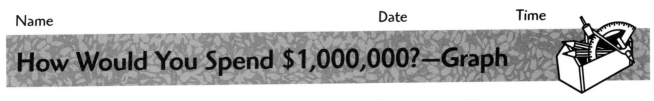

Make a circle graph of your categories for spending $1,000,000. Use your Percent Circle and the information on *Math Masters,* page 200.

Begin by drawing the section for the smallest part of the $1,000,000. Continue with the larger parts. Mark the largest part last. Because of rounding, the percents may not add up to exactly 100%.

Give the graph a title, and label each section.

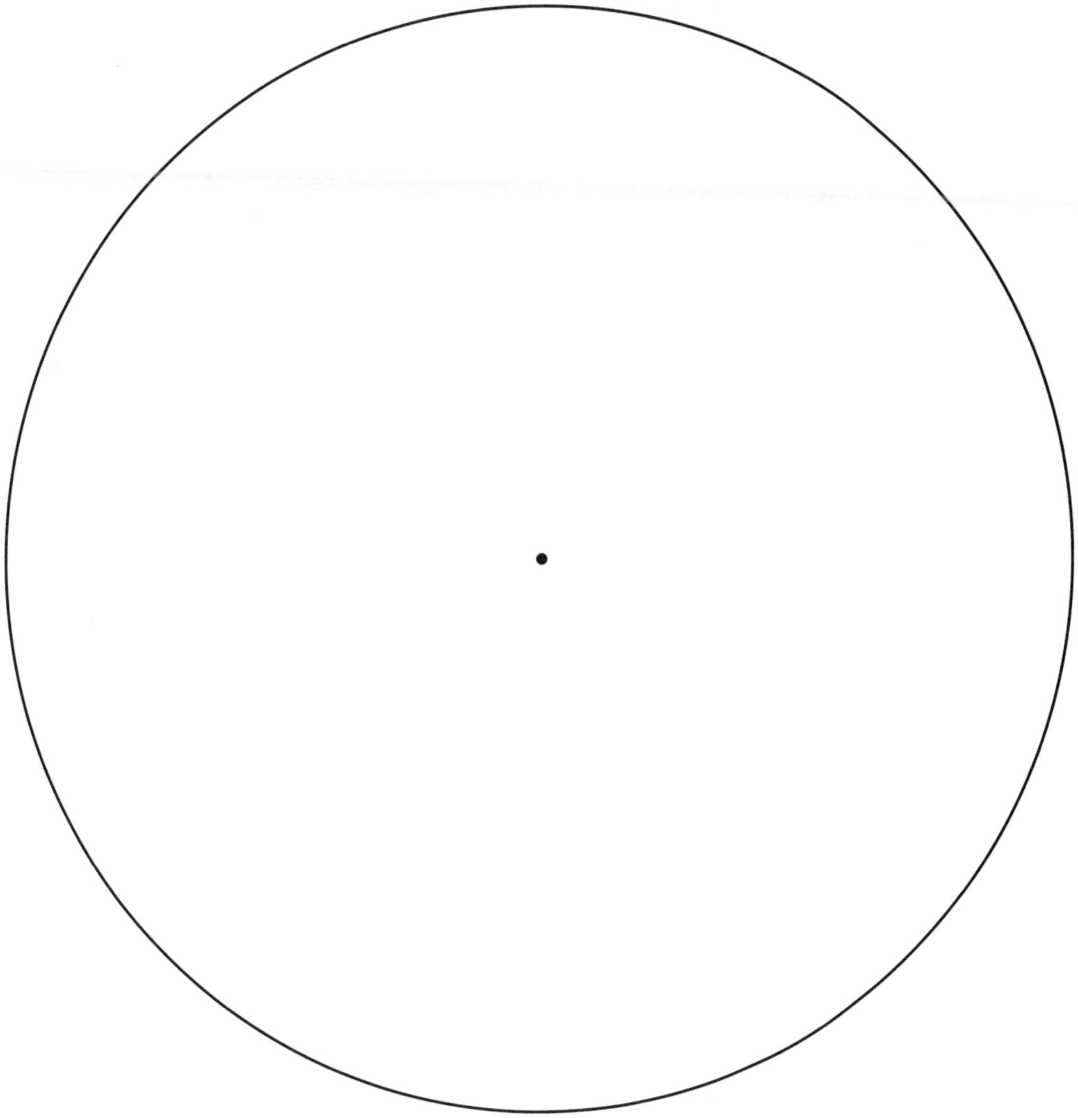

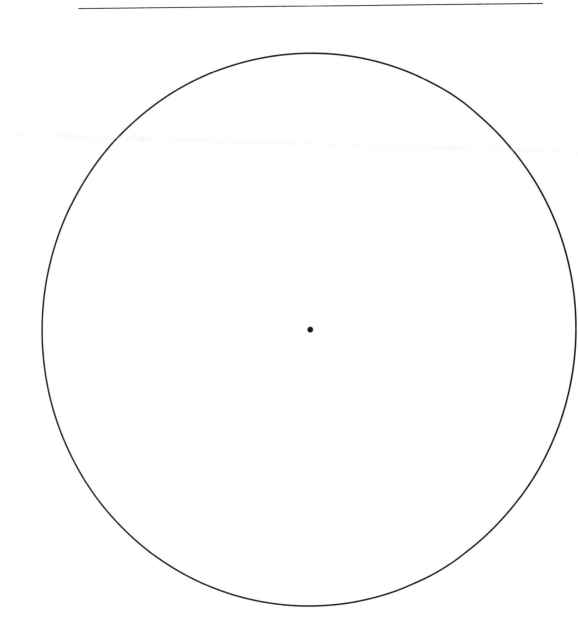

Name Date Time

Playing Areas for Five Contact Sports

Use your calculator to find each playing area.

Scale:

1 mm (drawing) represents 1 ft (actual).

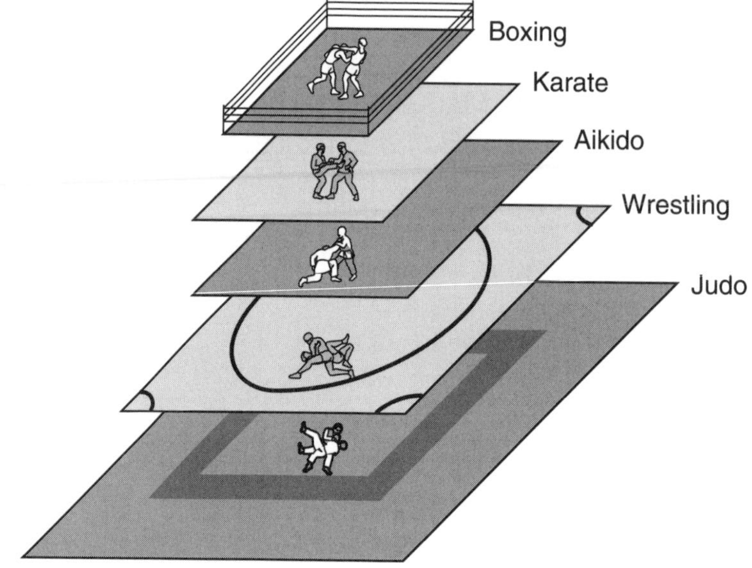

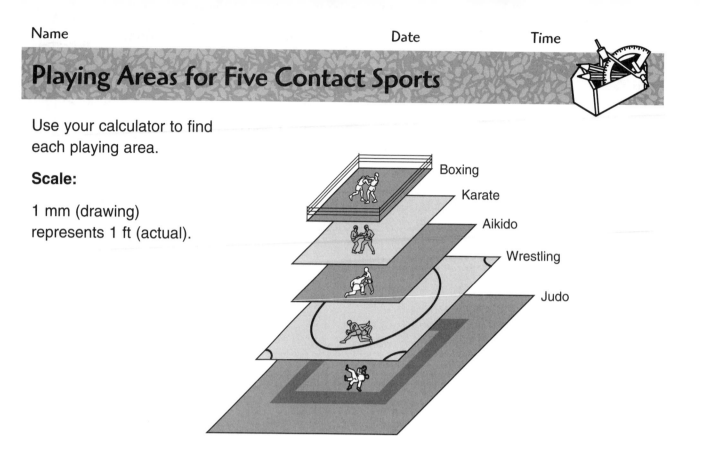

Sport	Dimensions	Playing Area
Boxing	20 ft by 20 ft	ft^2
Karate	26 ft by 26 ft	ft^2
Aikido	29 ft 6 in. by 29 ft 6 in.*	ft^2
Wrestling	39 ft 3 in. by 39 ft 3 in.*	ft^2
Judo	52 ft 6 in. by 52 ft 6 in.*	ft^2

*Calculate with decimals. For example, 29 ft 6 in. is equal to 29.5 ft.

Source: COMPARISONS by the Diagram Group. Reprinted by permission of St. Martin's Press.

Name Date Time

Playing Areas for Other Sports

Use your calculator to find each playing area. Circle "more" or "less" to tell whether each area is more or less than 1 acre.

1 acre = 43,560 square feet

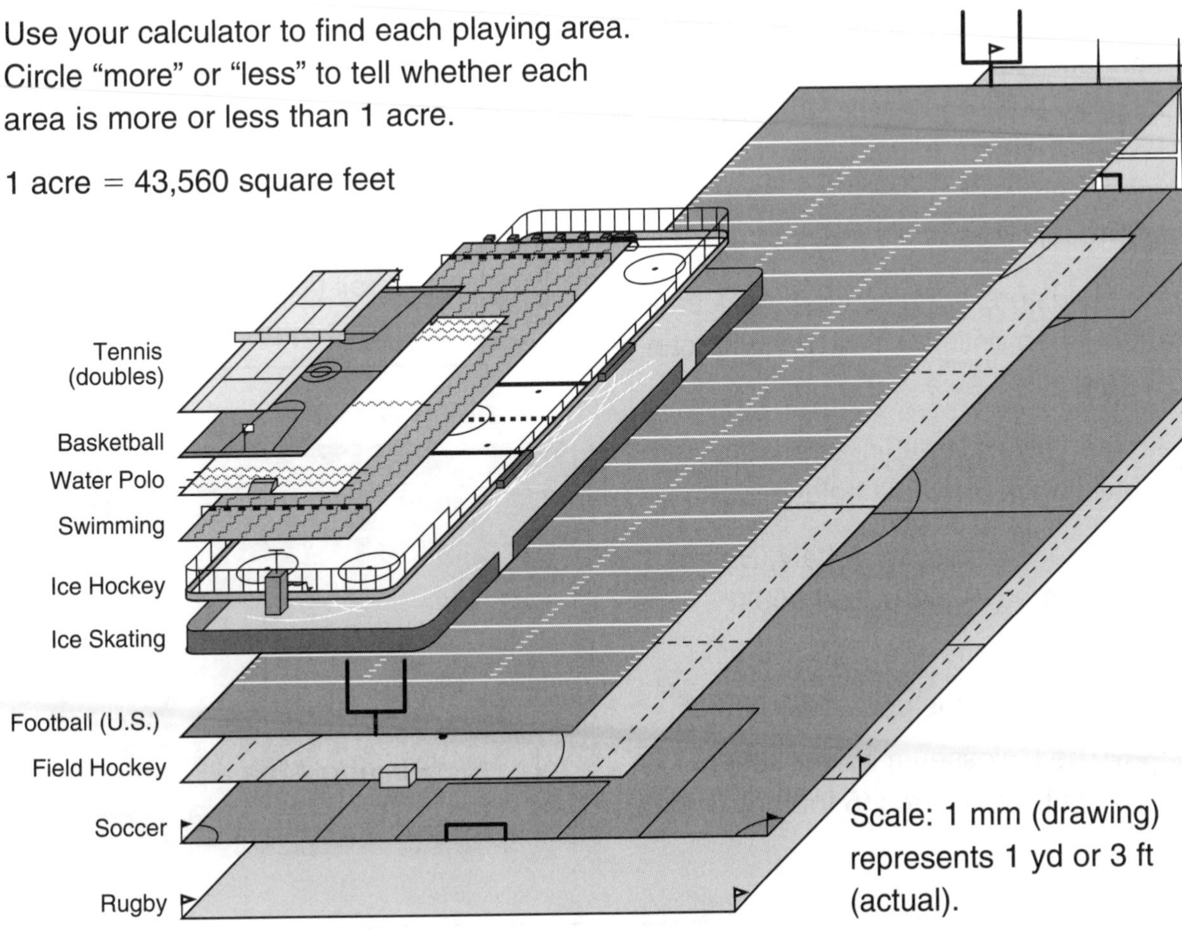

Scale: 1 mm (drawing) represents 1 yd or 3 ft (actual).

Sport	Dimensions	Playing Area	More or Less than 1 Acre?
Tennis (doubles)	78 ft by 36 ft	ft^2	more less
Basketball	94 ft by 50 ft	ft^2	more less
Water Polo	98 ft by 65 ft	ft^2	more less
Swimming	165 ft by 69 ft	ft^2	more less
Ice Hockey	200 ft by 85 ft	ft^2	more less
Ice Skating	200 ft by 100 ft	ft^2	more less
Football (U.S.)	300 ft by 160 ft*	ft^2	more less
Field Hockey	300 ft by 180 ft	ft^2	more less
Soccer	360 ft by 240 ft	ft^2	more less
Rugby	472 ft by 226 ft	ft^2	more less

*Not including end zones

Source: COMPARISONS by the Diagram Group. Reprinted by permission of St. Martin's Press.

Name Date Time

Ground Areas of Famous Large Buildings

The ground areas of buildings, their "footprints," are almost always given in square feet or square meters. Some buildings have very large ground areas. When their areas are given in square feet, the numbers are so large that it is hard to imagine how big the buildings really are.

For large buildings, if you convert the area in square feet to an estimate in acres, you can get a better idea of the size of the building.

Reference

1 acre = 43,560 square feet

For estimating, think of 1 acre as about 50,000 square feet.

A football field (excluding the end zones) is approximately 1 acre.

Estimate the ground area, in acres, of each building in the table below:

Example The Colosseum, in Italy, covers an area of about 250,000 ft^2.

One acre is about 50,000 ft^2.

So 5 acres is about 250,000 ft^2.

The Colosseum covers an area of about 5 acres (5 football fields).

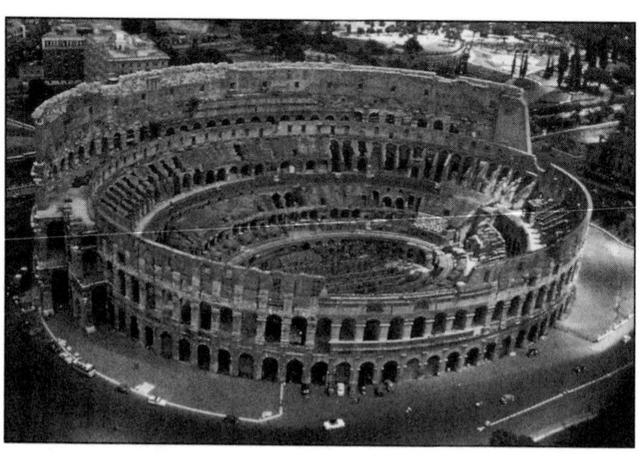

Building	Country	Date Built	Ground Area (ft^2)	Estimated Area (in acres)
Colosseum	Italy	70–224	250,000 ft^2	5 acres
Pyramid of Cheops	Egypt	*c.* 2600 B.C.	571,500 ft^2	______ acres
Chartres Cathedral	France	1194–1514	60,000 ft^2	______ acres
St. Peter's Basilica	Vatican City	1506–1626	392,300 ft^2	______ acres
Taj Mahal	India	1636–1653	78,000 ft^2	______ acres
Pentagon	U.S. (Virginia)	1941–1943	1,263,000 ft^2	______ acres
Ford Parts Center	U.S. (Michigan)	1936	2,800,000 ft^2	______ acres

Use with Project 6.

Name Date Time

Finding Areas with Standard Methods

Finding Areas of Polygons with Standard Methods

Use any method you want to find the area of each polygon below. Record the area in the table on the right. You can use different methods with different figures. If you use any area formulas, remember that *height* is always measured perpendicular to the *base* you choose. Measure *base* and *height* very carefully.

Figure	Area
A	about ________ cm^2
B	about ________ cm^2
C	about ________ cm^2
D	about ________ cm^2
E	about ________ cm^2
F	about ________ cm^2

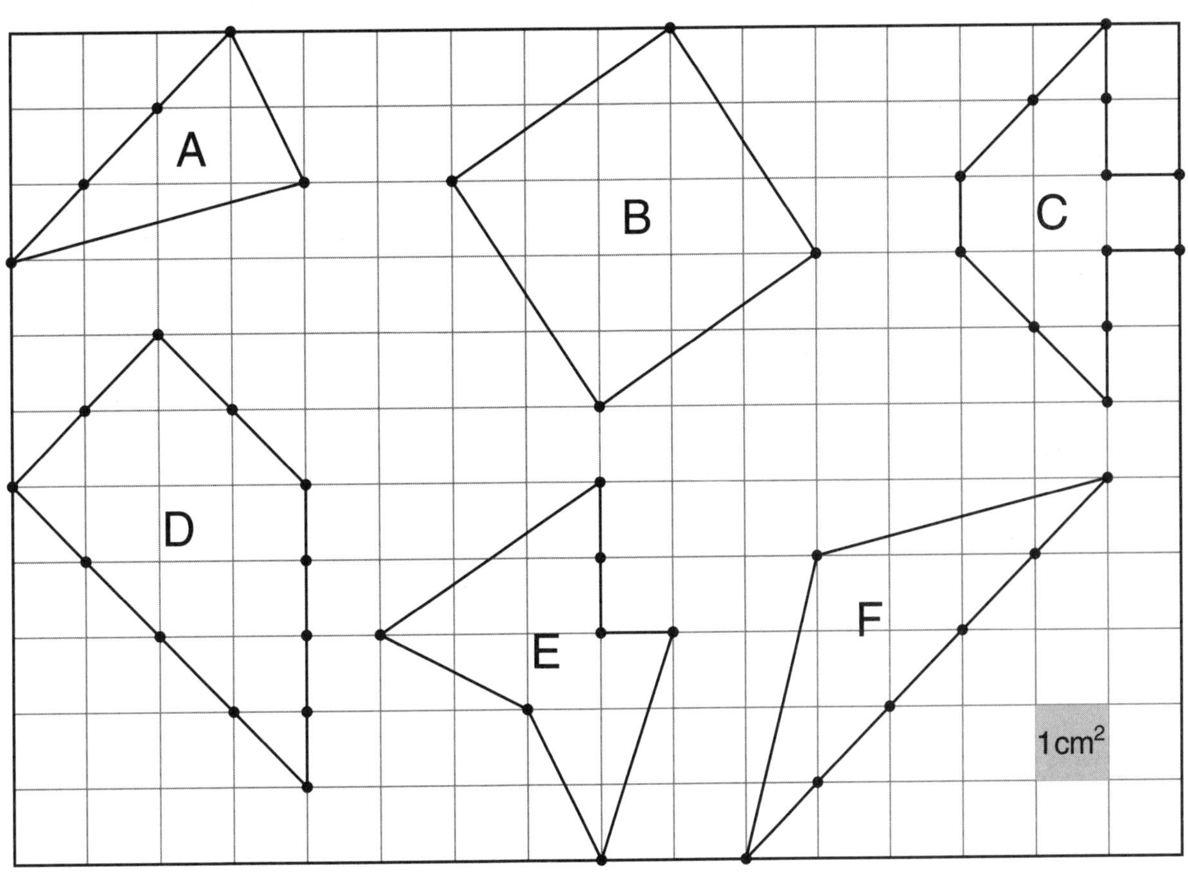

Use with Project 7.

Name Date Time

Finding Areas with Pick's Formula

Read the paragraphs below and then use Pick's Formula to find the areas of the polygons on the previous page. Record them in the table below. Compare them to your results recorded in the table on the previous page. You should expect some differences—measures are always estimates.

Pick's Formula for Finding Polygon Areas by Counting

In 1899 Georg Pick, an Austrian mathematician, discovered a formula for finding the area of a polygon on a square grid (such as graph paper). If a polygon has its vertices at grid points, its area can be found by counting the number of grid points on the polygon *(P)* and the number of grid points in the interior of the polygon *(I)* and then using the formula $A = (\frac{1}{2} * P) + I - 1$. The unit of area is one square on the grid.

For figure B on the previous page, the unit of area is cm^2.

$P = 4$ (grid points on polygon)

$I = 12$ (grid points in interior)

$A = (\frac{1}{2} * P) + I - 1$

$= (\frac{1}{2} * 4) + 12 - 1$

$= 13\ cm^2$

Figure	P	I	Area = $(\frac{1}{2} * P) + I - 1$
A			______ cm^2
B			______ cm^2
C			______ cm^2
D			______ cm^2
E			______ cm^2
F			______ cm^2

Draw two polygons. Be sure that the vertices are at grid points.
Use Pick's Formula to find the areas of the polygons.

1 cm^2

Area: ______________ Area: ______________

Use with Project 7.

Name Date Time

Finding Areas with Pick's Formula (cont.)

You may have found the area of this shaded path in Lesson 9.6.

Now use Pick's Formula to find the area.

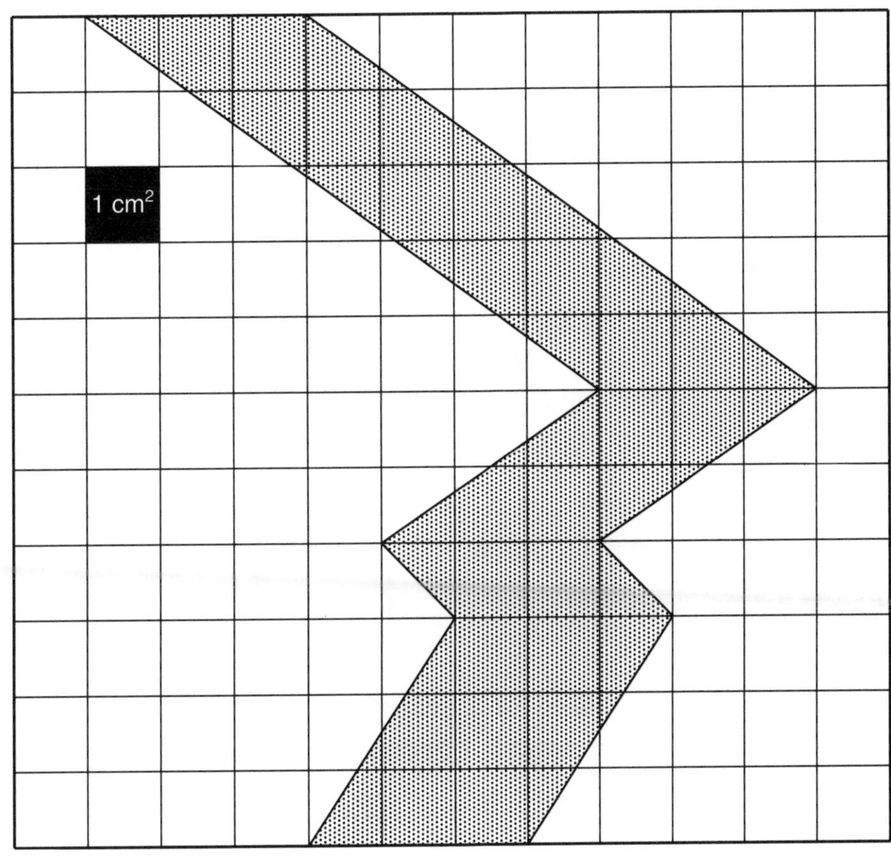

The area of the path is ______________ cm^2.

Do you think Pick's Formula is a good way to find this area? ______________

Explain. ______________

Name Date Time

The Swing Time of Pendulums

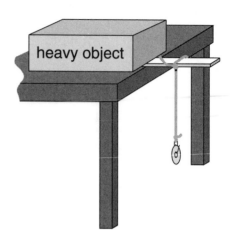

1. Your teacher will demonstrate an experiment with a pendulum that is 50 centimeters long. Record the results below.

   a. It took about __________ seconds for 10 complete swings of the pendulum.

   b. About how much time did it take for 1 swing? Round your answer to the nearest 0.1 second.

   __________ second(s)

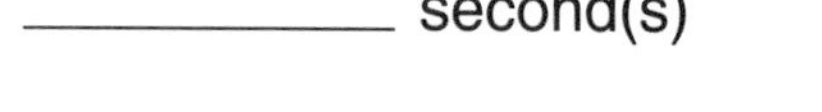

2. Form a pendulum that is 75 centimeters long. Time 10 complete swings of the pendulum. Time the swings to the nearest second.

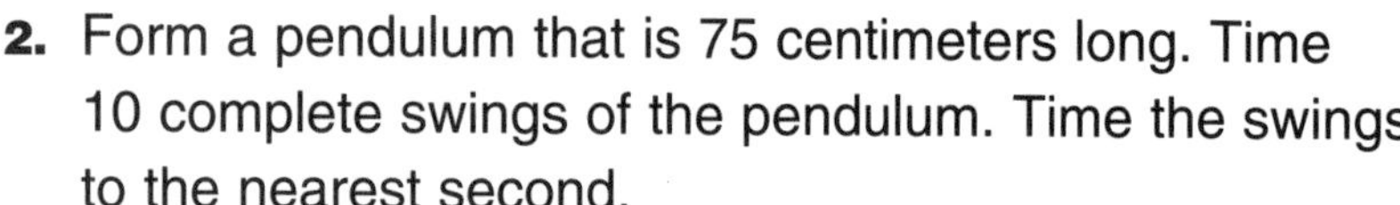

   Practice timing 10 complete swings several times. Then time 10 swings once more, and record the results below.

   a. It took about __________ seconds for 10 complete swings of the pendulum.

   b. About how much time did it take for 1 swing? Round your answer to the nearest 0.1 second. __________ second(s)

3. Record the results for a 50-cm and a 75-cm pendulum in the table at the right.

4. Experiment with different lengths of pendulum string.

   Find the time for 10 complete swings for each of the other pendulum lengths. Time the 10 swings to the nearest 0.1 second. Record your results in the table.

   After collecting your data, divide each of the times by 10 to estimate the time for 1 complete swing. Record your answers in the table, rounded to the nearest 0.1 second.

Length of pendulum	Time for:	
	10 complete swings (to nearest 0.1 sec)	1 complete swing (to nearest 0.1 sec)
5 cm	sec	sec
10 cm	sec	sec
20 cm	sec	sec
30 cm	sec	sec
50 cm	sec	sec
75 cm	sec	sec
100 cm	sec	sec
200 cm	sec	sec

Use with Project 8.

Name Date Time

The Swing Time of Pendulums (cont.)

Wait for instructions from your teacher before drawing the graph in Problem 5.

5. Construct a graph to show the amount of time it took for each length of the pendulum to complete 1 swing.

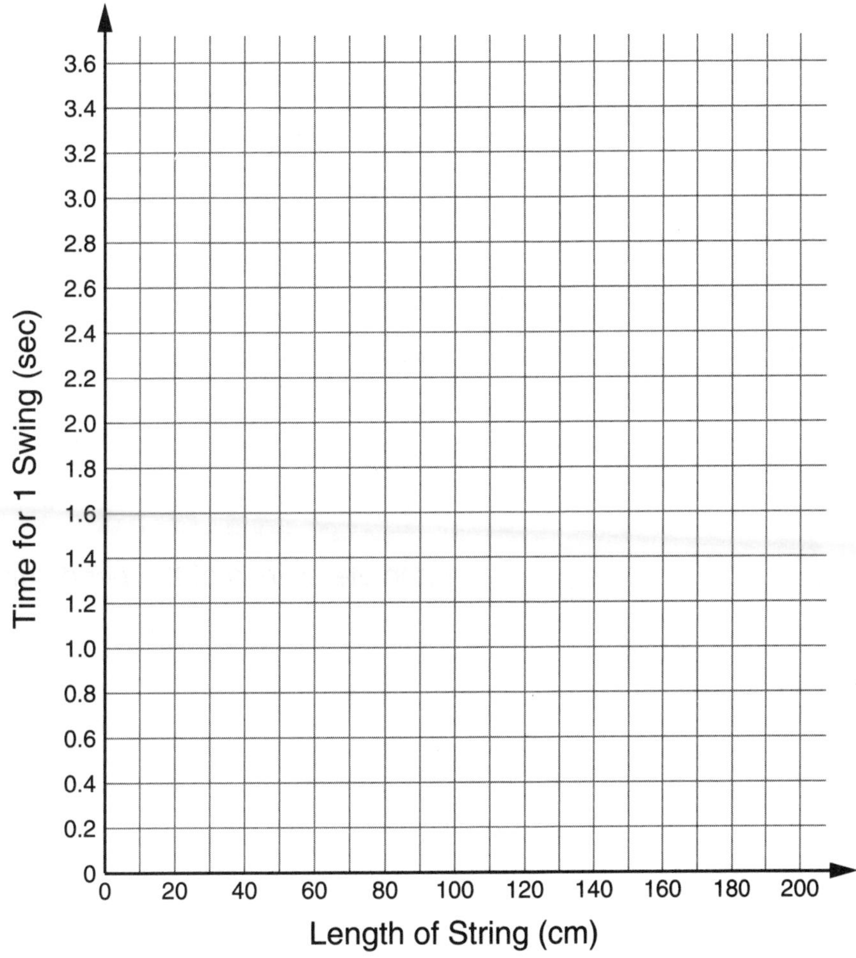

6. Experiment with different arc sizes. The largest arc is formed when the string of the pendulum is in a horizontal position. Does the size of the arc make much of a difference in the amount of time it takes for 10 complete swings?

____

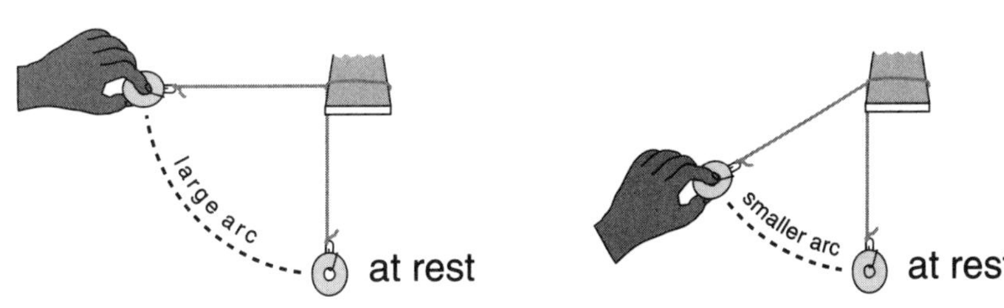

Name Date Time

The Swing Time of Pendulums (cont.)

7. Does the weight of the object at the end of a pendulum affect the time for a complete swing? Using a pendulum with a string 50 cm long, try different numbers of objects to find out if weight makes a difference in the time of the swing.

Length of pendulum	Number of weights (washers or other objects)	Time for 10 swings (to nearest 0.1 sec)	Time for 1 swing (to nearest 0.1 or 0.01 sec)
50 cm	1	sec	sec
50 cm	3	sec	sec
50 cm	5	sec	sec
50 cm	10	sec	sec

My conclusion: It seems that ______________________

____

____

____

____

____

____

____

____

A Long Time?

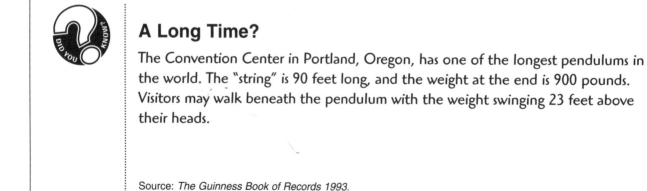

The Convention Center in Portland, Oregon, has one of the longest pendulums in the world. The "string" is 90 feet long, and the weight at the end is 900 pounds. Visitors may walk beneath the pendulum with the weight swinging 23 feet above their heads.

Source: *The Guinness Book of Records 1993.*

Name Date Time

Family Letter

Study Link

Introduction to Fifth Grade Everyday Mathematics

Welcome to *Fifth Grade Everyday Mathematics.* It is part of an elementary school mathematics curriculum developed by the University of Chicago School Mathematics Project. *Everyday Mathematics* offers students a broad background in mathematics.

Several features of the program are described below to help familiarize you with the structure and expectations of *Everyday Mathematics.*

A problem-solving approach based on everyday situations By making connections between their own knowledge and their experiences, both in school and outside of school, students learn basic math skills in meaningful contexts so that the mathematics becomes "real."

Frequent practice of basic skills Instead of practice presented in a single, tedious drill format, students practice basic skills in a variety of more engaging ways. In addition to completing daily review exercises covering a variety of topics, patterning on the number grid, and working with multiplication and division fact families in different formats, students will play games that are specifically designed to develop basic skills.

An instructional approach that revisits concepts regularly To enhance the development of basic skills and concepts, students regularly revisit previously learned concepts and repeatedly practice skills encountered earlier. The lessons are designed to take advantage of previously learned concepts and skills and to build on them throughout the year instead of treating them as isolated bits of knowledge.

A curriculum that explores mathematical content beyond basic arithmetic Mathematics standards around the world indicate that basic arithmetic skills are only the beginning of the mathematical knowledge students will need as they develop critical thinking skills. In addition to basic arithmetic, *Everyday Mathematics* develops concepts and skills in the following topics—numeration; operations and computation; data and chance; geometry; measurement and reference frames; and patterns, functions, and algebra.

Please keep this Family Letter for reference as your child works through Unit 1.

Fifth Grade Everyday Mathematics *emphasizes the following content:*

Numeration Recognizing place value in numerals for whole numbers and decimals, expressing numbers in scientific notation; finding factors of numbers; comparing properties of prime and composite numbers; representing rates and ratios with fraction notation

Operations and Computation Extending whole-number facts with addition, subtraction, multiplication, and division to fractions and decimals; evaluating symbolic expressions

Data and Chance Collecting, organizing, and analyzing data using bar graphs, line graphs, circle graphs, and stem-and-leaf plots

Geometry Investigating angles and rotations; calculating area and volume; drawing to scale; introducing relationships of 2- and 3-dimensional figures; exploring new transformations that affect attributes of geometric shapes

Measurement Using linear, area, capacity, and personal reference measures

Reference Frames Locating items with reference to an origin or zero point; for example, ordinal numbers, times of day, dates, and temperatures

Patterns, Functions, and Algebra Determining divisibility; exploring number patterns; applying formulas to geometric figures; creating number models; working with scientific calculators; squaring and unsquaring numbers; exploring variables in formulas

Everyday Mathematics will provide you with ample opportunities to monitor your child's progress and to participate in your child's mathematics experiences.

Throughout the year, you will receive Family Letters to keep you informed of the mathematical content your child will be studying in each unit. Each letter will include a vocabulary list, suggested Do-Anytime Activities for you and your child, and an answer guide to selected Study Link (homework) activities.

You will enjoy seeing your child's confidence and comprehension soar as he or she connects mathematics to everyday life. We look forward to an exciting year!

Unit 1: Number Theory

During the next 2 or 3 weeks, students will study properties of whole numbers. Unit 1 sets up procedures for review and practice of the multiplication facts. The new material in this unit builds on students' prior work with multiplication and division of whole numbers.

In Unit 1, students will be asked to collect pictures of arrays to form a class Arrays Museum. Pictures may include objects such as floor tiles, windows, and checkerboards. You may want to help your child find pictures to contribute. To practice using arrays with your child at home, use any small objects, such as beans, macaroni, or pennies.

Finally, you may want to help your child memorize the basic multiplication facts found in the multiplication table. You can work together using the Fact Triangles, or you may play *Beat the Calculator, Multiplication Top-It,* or *Baseball Multiplication.* These are games that were introduced in previous grades of *Everyday Mathematics.*

Vocabulary

Important terms in Unit 1:

composite number A whole number that has more than two factors. For example, 4 is a composite number because it has three factors: 1, 2, and 4.

divisible by One whole number is *divisible by* another whole number if there is no remainder when you divide.

exponent The small, raised number in *exponential notation* that tells how many times the base is to be multiplied by itself.

Examples

5^2 ← exponent 5^2 means $5 * 5$, which is 25.

10^3 ← exponent 10^3 means $10 * 10 * 10$, which is 1,000.

2^4 ← exponent 2^4 means $2 * 2 * 2 * 2$, which is 16.

factor One of two or more numbers that are multiplied to give a *product.* The numbers that are multiplied are called *factors.*

$3 * 5 = 15$ (3 and 5: Factors; 15: Product) $15 * 1 = 15$ (15 and 1: Factors; 15: Product)

factor rainbow A way to show factor pairs in a list of all the factors of a number. A factor rainbow can be used to check whether a list of factors is correct.

Factor rainbow for 16: 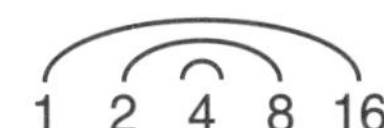

number model A number sentence that models or fits a number story or situation. For example, a number model for the array below would be $4 * 3 = 12$.

prime number A whole number that has exactly two factors: itself and 1. For example, 5 is a prime number because its only factors are 5 and 1.

product The result of mutiplying two numbers, called *factors.*

rectangular array A rectangular arrangement of objects in rows and columns such that each row has the same number of objects and each column has the same number of objects.

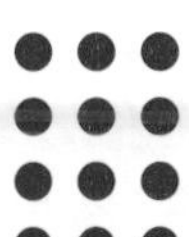

square number A number that is the product of a whole number multiplied by itself. For example, 25 is a square number, because $25 = 5 * 5$.

Building Skills through Games

In Unit 1, your child will practice operations and computation skills by playing the following games. Detailed instructions for each game are in the *Student Reference Book.*

Baseball Multiplication

See *Student Reference Book,* pages 259 and 260

Two players will need 4 regular dice, 4 pennies, and a calculator to play this game. Practicing the multiplication facts for 1–12 and strengthening mental arithmetic skills are the goals of *Baseball Multiplication.*

Multiplication Top-It

See *Student Reference Book,* page 295

Multiplication Top-It is another game used to practice the basic multiplication facts. This game requires a deck of cards with 4 each of the numbers 1–10, and can be played by 2–4 players.

Beat the Calculator

See *Student Reference Book,* page 261

This game involves 3 players and requires a calculator and a deck of cards with 4 each of the numbers 1–10. Playing *Beat the Calculator* helps students review basic multiplication facts.

Factor Captor

See *Student Reference Book,* page 271

This is a game for 2 players. Materials needed include a *Factor Captor* Grid, 48 counters the size of a penny, scratch paper, and a calculator. The goal of the game is to strengthen the skill of finding the factors of a number.

As You Help Your Child with Homework

As your child brings assignments home, you may want to go over the instructions together, clarifying them as necessary. The answers listed below will guide you through this unit's Study Links.

Study Link 1.2

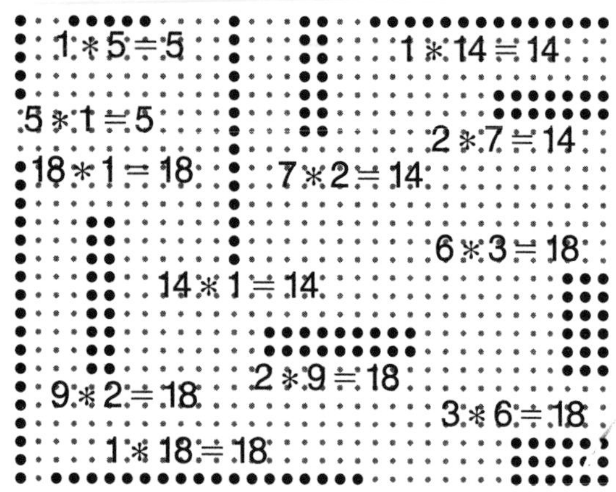

Study Link 1.3

6. 2, 4, 6, 8, 10, 12, 14, 16, 18, 20
7. Even numbers
8. Sample answers: 1, 3, 5, 7, 9, 11, 13, 15, 17, 19
9. Odd numbers

Study Link 1.4

1. 1, 5, 25
2. 1, 2, 4, 7, 14, 28
3. 1, 2, 4, 5, 8, 10, 20, 40
4. 1, 2, 3, 6, 7, 14, 21, 42
5. 1, 2, 3, 4, 6, 8, 12, 16, 24, 48
6. 1, 2, 4, 8, 16, 32, 64
7. 1, 2, 4, 5, 10, 20, 25, 50, 100

Study Link 1.5

1. numbers divisible by 2: 998,876; 5,890; 72,344; 36,540; 1,098
   numbers divisible by 3: 36,540; 861; 33,015; 1,098; 45,369
   numbers divisible by 6: 36,540; 1,098
   numbers divisible by 9: 36,540; 1,098; 45,369
   numbers divisible by 5: 5,890; 36,540; 33,015
   numbers divisible by 10: 5,890; 36,540
2. numbers divisible by 4: 998,876; 72,344; 36,540

Study Link 1.6

2.

Number	Factors	Prime or Composite?
11	1, ⑪	P
18	1, ② ③ 6, 9, 18	C
24	1, ② ③ 4, 6, 8, 12, 24	C
28	1, ② 4, ⑦ 14, 28	C
36	1, ② ③ 4, 6, 9, 12, 18, 36	C
49	1, ⑦ 49	C
50	1, ② ⑤ 10, 25, 50	C
70	1, ② ⑤ ⑦ 10, 14, 35, 70	C
100	1, ② 4, ⑤ 10, 20, 25, 50, 100	C

Study Link 1.7

1. 16 2. 49 3. 6 4. 64 5. 25
6. 81 7. $9 * 4 = 36$ 8. $5 * 5 = 25$
9. a. $5 * 5 = 25$
   b. There are the same number of rows and columns.
10. 13 11. 9 12. 113

Study Link 1.8

1. **64:** 1, 2, 4, 8, 16, 32, 64 2. yes

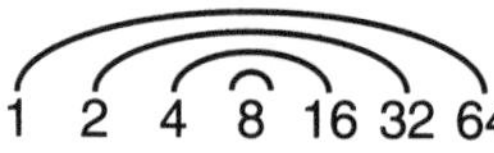

$8^2 = 64$ The square root of 64 is 8.

3. a. 4, 9, 25, 49
   b. They are the squares of prime numbers.

Study Link 1.9

1. a. $10^4 = 10 * 10 * 10 * 10 = 10{,}000$
   b. $7^2 = 7 * 7 = 49$
   c. $20^3 = 20 * 20 * 20 = 8{,}000$
2. a. 11^2 b. 9^3 c. 50^4
3. a. $2 * 3^3 * 5^2 = 2 * 3 * 3 * 3 * 5 * 5 = 1{,}350$
   b. $2^4 * 4^2 = 2 * 2 * 2 * 2 * 4 * 4 = 256$
4. a. $36 = 2 * 2 * 3 * 3 = 2^2 * 3^2$
   b. $40 = 2 * 2 * 2 * 5 = 2^3 * 5$
   c. $90 = 2 * 3 * 3 * 5 = 2 * 3^2 * 5$
5. 4^5

Name Date Time

More Array Play

Study Link 1.2

A **rectangular array** is an arrangement of objects into rows and columns. Each row has the same number of objects and each column has the same number of objects. We can write a multiplication number model to describe a rectangular array.

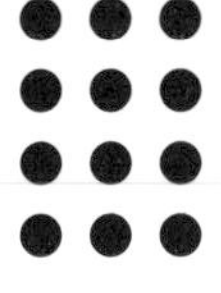

$4 * 3 = 12$

For each number below, use pennies or counters to make as many different arrays as possible. Draw each array on the grid with dots. Write the number model next to each array.

1. 5

2. 14

3. 18

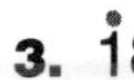

Show each number model below as an array of dots.

4. $2 * 6 = 12$

5. $5 * 4 = 20$

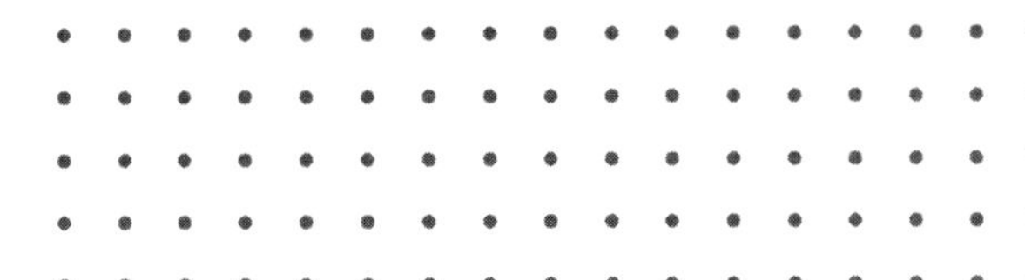

Reminder: Look for examples of arrays and bring them to school.

Name Date Time

Making Dot Arrays

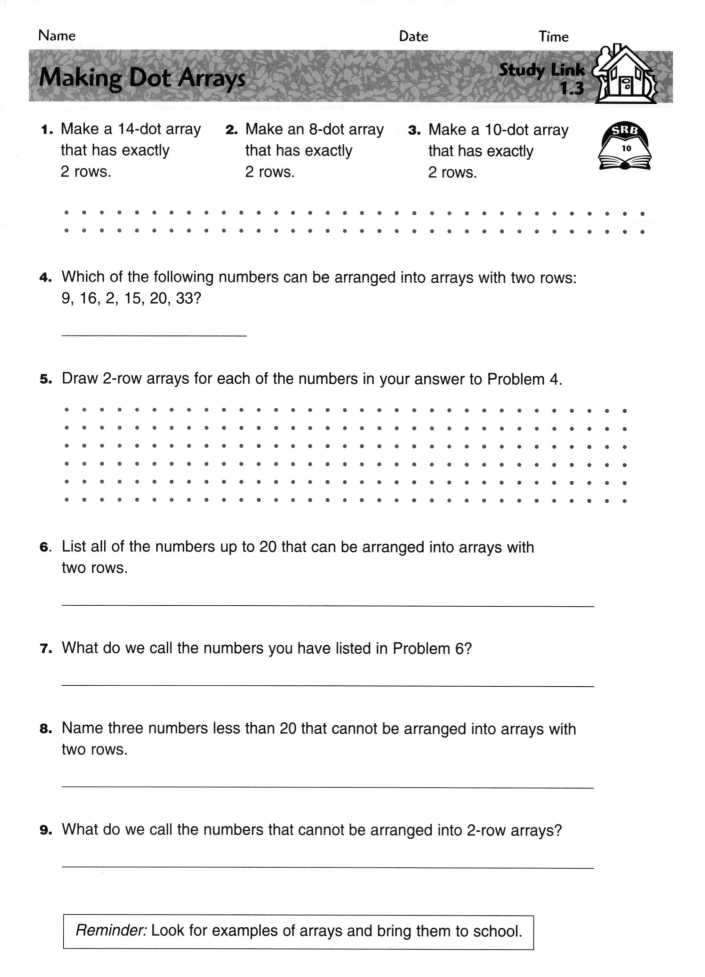

Study Link 1.3

1. Make a 14-dot array that has exactly 2 rows.

2. Make an 8-dot array that has exactly 2 rows.

3. Make a 10-dot array that has exactly 2 rows.

4. Which of the following numbers can be arranged into arrays with two rows: 9, 16, 2, 15, 20, 33?

____

5. Draw 2-row arrays for each of the numbers in your answer to Problem 4.

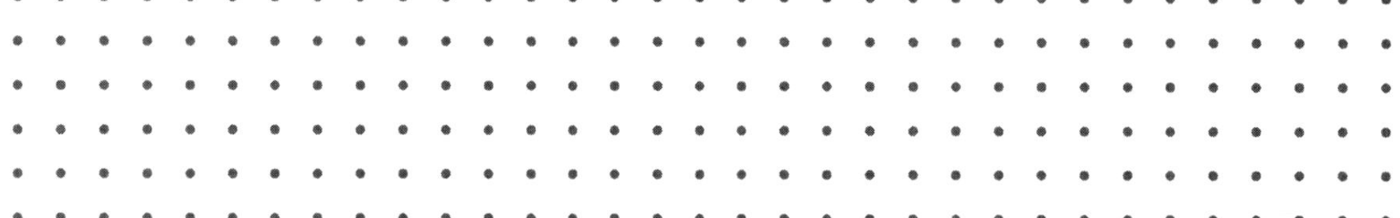

6. List all of the numbers up to 20 that can be arranged into arrays with two rows.

____

7. What do we call the numbers you have listed in Problem 6?

____

8. Name three numbers less than 20 that cannot be arranged into arrays with two rows.

____

9. What do we call the numbers that cannot be arranged into 2-row arrays?

____

Reminder: Look for examples of arrays and bring them to school.

Name Date Time

Factors

Study Link 1.4

To find the factors of a number, ask yourself: Is 1 a factor of the number? Is 2 a factor? Is 3 a factor? Continue with larger numbers. To find all the factors of 15, for example, ask yourself:

SRB 10

	Yes/No	Number Sentence	Factor Pair
Is 1 a factor of 15?	Yes	1 * 15 = 15	1, 15
Is 2 a factor of 15?	No		
Is 3 a factor of 15?	Yes	3 * 5 = 15	3, 5
Is 4 a factor of 15?	No		

You don't need to go any further. Can you tell why?

____

____

____

The factors of 15 are 1, 3, 5, and 15.

List as many factors as you can for each of the numbers below.

1. 25 ______________________________

2. 28 ______________________________

3. 40 ______________________________

4. 42 ______________________________

5. 48 ______________________________

Challenge

6. 64 ______________________________

7. 100 ______________________________

Play *Factor Captor* with someone at home.

Name Date Time

Divisibility Tests

SRB 11

- All even numbers are **divisible by 2.**
- A number is **divisible by 3** if the sum of its digits is divisible by 3.
- A number is **divisible by 6** if it is divisible by both 2 and 3.
- A number is **divisible by 9** if the sum of its digits is divisible by 9.
- A number is **divisible by 10** if it ends in 0.
- A number is **divisible by 5** if it ends in 0 or 5.

1. Use divisibility tests to check whether the following numbers are divisible by 2, 3, 5, 6, 9, or 10.

Number	Divisible ...					
	by 2?	by 3?	by 6?	by 9?	by 5?	by 10?
998,876						
5,890						
72,344						
36,540						
861						
33,015						
1,098						
45,369						
4,009,721						

A number is divisible by 4 if the tens and ones digits form a number that is divisible by 4.

Example 47,8**36** is divisible by 4, because 36 is divisible by 4.

It isn't always easy to tell whether the last two digits form a number that is divisible by 4. A quick way to check is to divide the number by 2, and then divide the result by 2. This is the same as dividing by 4, but it is often easier to do mentally.

Example 5,3**84** is divisible by 4, because 84 / 2 = 42 and 42 / 2 = 21.

Example 9**22** is not divisible by 4, because 22 / 2 = 11, but 11 / 2 = $5\frac{1}{2}$.

Challenge

2. Put a star next to any number in the table that is divisible by 4.

Name Date Time

Prime and Composite Numbers

Study Link 1.6

A **prime number** is a whole number that has exactly two factors—1 and the number itself. A **composite number** is a whole number that has more than two factors.

1. Tell whether the following numbers are **prime** or **composite.**

   a. The number of quarts in a gallon ____________

   b. The number of months in a year ____________

   c. The number of days in a week ____________

   d. The number of sides in a hexagon ____________

   e. The number of sides in a pentagon ____________

2. For each number:
   - list all of its factors
   - tell whether the number is prime or composite
   - circle any of the factors that are prime numbers

Number	Factors	Prime or Composite?
11		
18		
24		
28		
36		
49		
50		
70		
100		

Name Date Time

Exploring Square Numbers

Study Link 1.7

A square number is a number that can be written as the product of a number multiplied by itself. For example, the square number, 9, can be written as 3 * 3.

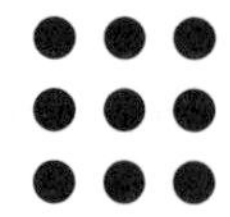

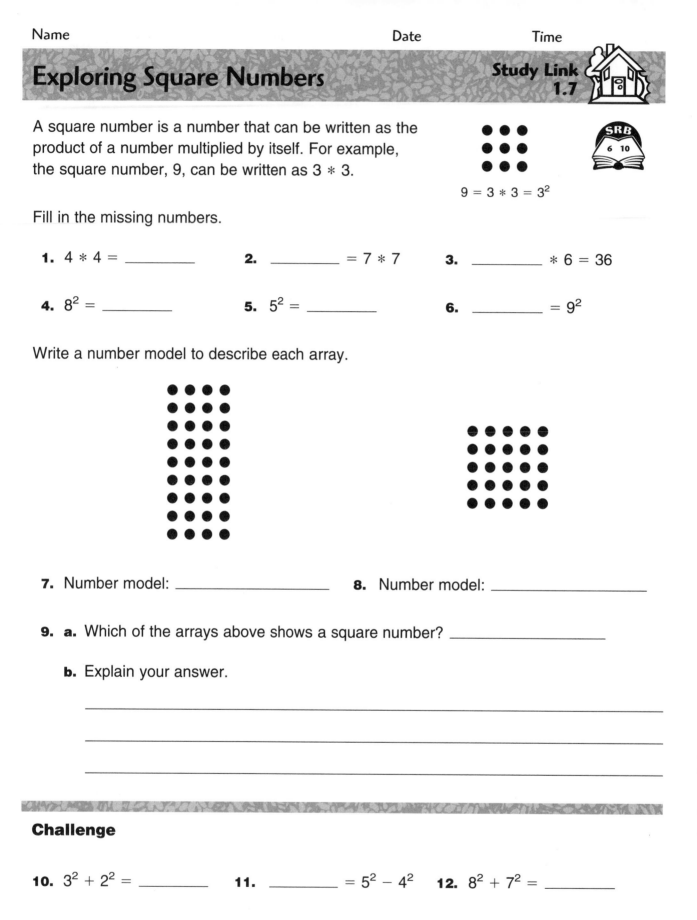

$9 = 3 * 3 = 3^2$

Fill in the missing numbers.

1. $4 * 4 =$ ________ **2.** ________ $= 7 * 7$ **3.** ________ $* 6 = 36$

4. $8^2 =$ ________ **5.** $5^2 =$ ________ **6.** ________ $= 9^2$

Write a number model to describe each array.

7. Number model: ________________ **8.** Number model: ________________

9. a. Which of the arrays above shows a square number? ________________

b. Explain your answer.

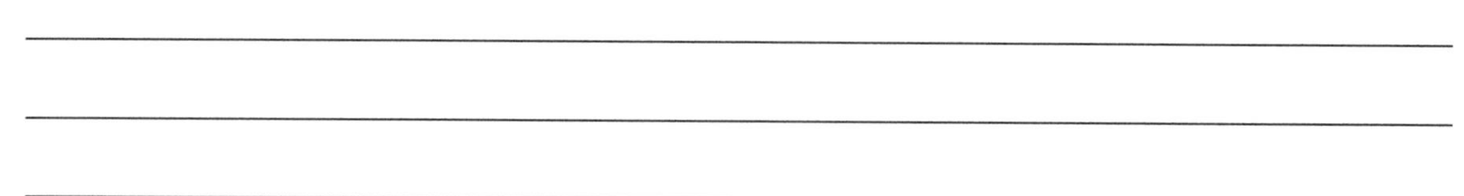

Challenge

10. $3^2 + 2^2 =$ ________ **11.** ________ $= 5^2 - 4^2$ **12.** $8^2 + 7^2 =$ ________

Name Date Time

Factor Rainbows, Squares, and Square Roots

Study Link 1.8

1. List all the factors of each of the square numbers. Make a factor rainbow to check your work. Then fill in the missing numbers. *Reminder:* In a factor rainbow for a number, the product of each connected factor pair should be equal to the number itself. For example, the factor rainbow for the number 16 looks like this:

1 2 4 8 16

$1 * 16 = 16$ $2 * 8 = 16$ $4 * 4 = 16$

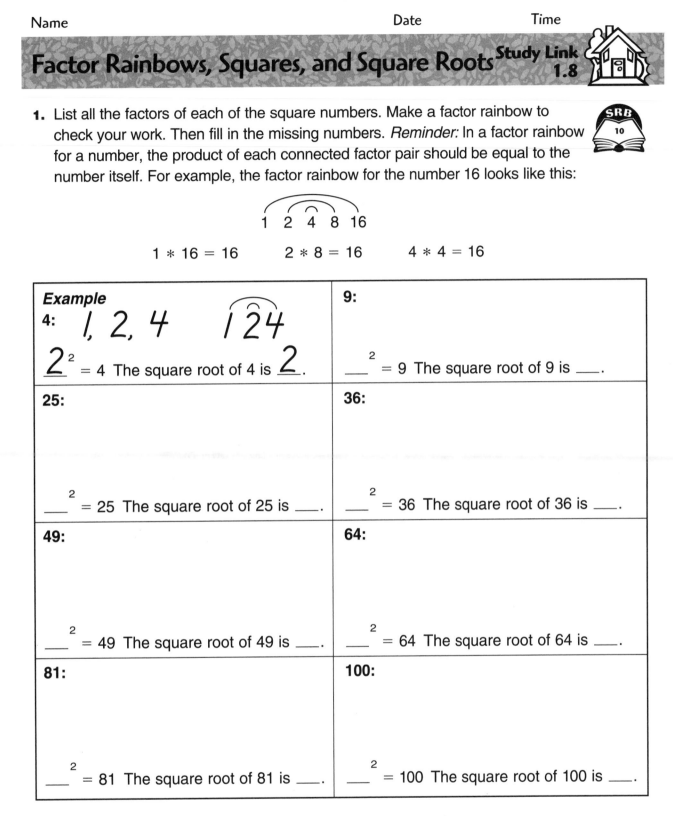

Example **4:** 1, 2, 4 1 2 4 $2^2 = 4$ The square root of 4 is 2.	**9:** $\_\_^2 = 9$ The square root of 9 is __.
25: $\_\_^2 = 25$ The square root of 25 is __.	**36:** $\_\_^2 = 36$ The square root of 36 is __.
49: $\_\_^2 = 49$ The square root of 49 is __.	**64:** $\_\_^2 = 64$ The square root of 64 is __.
81: $\_\_^2 = 81$ The square root of 81 is __.	**100:** $\_\_^2 = 100$ The square root of 100 is __.

2. Do all square numbers have an odd number of factors? ________

Challenge

3. a. Which square numbers in Problem 1 have exactly 3 factors? ________

   b. What do they have in common? ________

Name Date Time

Exponents

Study Link 1.9

SRB 5–7

An **exponent** is a raised number that shows how many times the number to its left is used as a factor.

Examples 5^2 ← exponent 5^2 means $5 * 5$, which is 25.
10^3 ← exponent 10^3 means $10 * 10 * 10$, which is 1,000.
2^4 ← exponent 2^4 means $2 * 2 * 2 * 2$, which is 16.

1. Write each of the following as a factor string. Then find the product.

Example 2^3 = 2∗2∗2 = 8 **a.** 10^4 = ________ = ________

b. 7^2 = ________ = ________ **c.** 20^3 = ________ = ________

2. Write each factor string using an exponent.

Example $6 * 6 * 6 * 6$ = 6^4 **a.** $11 * 11$ = ________

b. $9 * 9 * 9$ = ________ **c.** $50 * 50 * 50 * 50$ = ________

3. Write each of the following as a factor string that does not have any exponents. Then use your calculator to find the product.

Example $2^3 * 3$ = 2∗2∗2∗3 = 24

a. $2 * 3^3 * 5^2$ = ________ = ________

b. $2^4 * 4^2$ = ________ = ________

4. Write the prime factorization of each number. Then write it using exponents.

Example 18 = 2 ∗ 3 ∗ 3 = $2 * 3^2$

a. 36 = ________ = ________

b. 40 = ________ = ________

c. 90 = ________ = ________

Challenge

5. Which is greater, 5^4 or 4^5? ________

Name Date Time

Family Letter

Study Link 1.10

Unit 2: Estimation and Calculation

Computation is an important part of problem solving. Fortunately, we are no longer restricted to paper-and-pencil methods of computation. We can use a calculator to solve lengthy problems, or even a computer program to solve very complex ones. Throughout the year, students will have many opportunities to practice estimation, mental, and paper-and-pencil methods of computation; to use a calculator; and to decide which method is most appropriate for solving a particular problem.

Many of us were taught that there is just one way to do each kind of computation. For example, we may have learned to subtract by "borrowing," without realizing that there are many other methods of subtracting numbers. In Unit 2, students will examine several methods for adding, subtracting, and multiplying whole numbers and decimals. From these exposures to a variety of methods, they will see that there are often several ways to accomplish the same task and achieve the same result. Students are encouraged to solve problems by whatever method they find most comfortable, even if it's one that they themselves may have invented. However, there is one method for each operation that all students will be expected to learn.

The class will also work on the first **Estimation Challenge** of the year. This is a problem for which it is very difficult, time consuming, and perhaps even impossible to find an exact answer. Students work with partners or in small groups to come up with and defend their best estimates. Estimation Challenges will be presented several times during the school year.

Your child will also learn a new game—*Multiplication Bull's-Eye*—which provides practice with estimation. You might want to play this game with your child at home. The rules of the game are found on page 284 in the *Student Reference Book*.

Computation is usually not the first step in the problem-solving process. One must first decide what numerical data is needed to solve the problem and which operations need to be performed. In this unit, your child will continue to develop his or her problem-solving skills with a special focus on writing and solving equations for problems.

Please keep this Family Letter for reference as your child works through Unit 2.

Vocabulary

Important terms in Unit 2:

Estimation Challenge Sometimes your child will be asked to solve a problem for which it is difficult, or even impossible, to find an *exact* answer. Your child will need to make his or her best estimate and then defend it. We call this kind of problem an *Estimation Challenge.*

magnitude estimate A very rough estimate. A magnitude estimate tells whether an answer should be in the tens, hundreds, thousands, and so on.

Example: 56 * 32

Step 1: Round 56 to 60.

Step 2: Round 32 to 30.

60 * 30 = 1,800, so the magnitude estimate for 56 * 32 is in the thousands.

10s	100s	(1,000s)	10,000s

maximum The largest amount; the greatest number in a set of data.

mean The sum of a set of numbers divided by the number of numbers in the set. The mean is often referred to simply as the *average.*

median The middle value in a set of data when the data are listed in order from smallest to largest. If there is an even number of data points, the median is the *mean* of the two middle values.

minimum The smallest amount; the smallest number in a set of data.

partial-sums method A way to add in which sums are computed for each place (ones, tens, hundreds, and so on) separately, and are then added to give the final answer.

	268
	+ 483
1. Add 100s	600
2. Add 10s	140
3. Add 1s	+ 11
4. Add partial sums.	751

Partial-sums algorithm

place value A system that values a digit according to its position in a number. In our system, each place has a value ten times that of the place to its right and one-tenth the value of the place to its left. For example, in the number 456, the 4 is in the hundreds place and has a value of 400.

range The difference between the *maximum* and *minimum* in a set of data.

reaction time The amount of time it takes a person to react to something, such as having a hand squeezed.

trade-first method A subtraction method in which all trades are done before any subtractions are carried out.

100s	10s	1s
	4	12
3	~~5~~	~~2~~
− 1	6	4

Trade 1 ten for 10 ones.

100s	10s	1s
2	14 ~~4~~	12
~~3~~	~~5~~	~~2~~
− 1	6	4
1	8	8

Trade 1 hundred for 10 tens and subtract in each column.

Building Skills through Games

In Unit 2, your child will practice operations and computation skills by playing the following games. Detailed instructions for each game are in the *Student Reference Book.*

Baseball Multiplication

See *Student Reference Book,* pages 259 and 260

Two players need 4 regular dice, 4 pennies, and a calculator to play this game. Practicing the multiplication facts for 1–12 and strengthening mental arithmetic skills are the goals of *Baseball Multiplication.*

Beat the Calculator

See *Student Reference Book,* page 261

This game involves 3 players and requires a calculator and a deck of cards with 4 each of the numbers 1–10. Playing *Beat the Calculator* helps students review basic multiplication facts.

Multiplication Bull's-Eye

See *Student Reference Book,* page 284

Two players need 4 each of the number cards 0–9, a six-sided die, and a calculator to play this game. *Multiplication Bull's Eye* provides practice in estimating products.

Multiplication Wrestling

See *Student Reference Book,* page 285

Two players need 4 of the number cards 0–9 to play this game. *Multiplication Wrestling* provides practice with multiplication of whole numbers.

Do-Anytime Activities

To work with your child on the concepts taught in this unit and in previous units, try these interesting and rewarding activities:

1. Practice extending multiplication facts. Write each set of problems so that your child may recognize a pattern.

Set A	6 * 10	6 * 100	60 * 100
Set B	5 * 10	50 * 10	50 * 100
Set C	10 [7s]	100 [7s]	100 [70s]

2. When your child adds or subtracts multidigit numbers, talk about the strategy that works best. Try not to impose the strategy that works best for you! Here are some problems to try:

   467 + 343 = _______

   894 − 444 = _______

   _______ = 761 + 79

   842 − 59 = _______

3. Write whole numbers and decimals for your child to read, such as 650 *(six hundred fifty)* and 42.5 *(forty-two and five tenths)*. Ask your child to identify digits in various places—thousands place, hundreds place, tens place, ones place, tenths place, hundredths place, thousandths place.

4. You may want to discuss with your child how data are collected in real life. Discuss how the following probability statements might have been obtained.
   - "About 2 out of 3 adults can swim." *(By asking a large number of people if they can swim.)*
   - "There is a chance in 100 that a home will catch on fire during the next year." *(By using fire reports to estimate the number of house fires per year.)*

As You Help Your Child with Homework

As your child brings assignments home, you may want to go over the instructions together, clarifying them as necessary. The answers listed below will guide you through this unit's Study Links.

Study Link 2.1

1. L	**2.** L	**3.** OK	
4. S	**5.** OK	**6.** S	
7. L	**8.** S	**9.** OK	**10.** S

Study Link 2.2

Sample answers are given.

1. The numbers 571 and 261 should be circled.

2. The boxes with the numbers 30, 20, and 7 should have Xs in them.

3. The boxes with the numbers 19 and 23 should have check marks in them.

4. The boxes with the numbers 533 and 125 should have stars in them.

5. The boxes with the numbers 85.2, 20.5, 88.2, and 17.5 should have triangles in them. Since the sum has ".7" in the tenths place, look for numbers with tenths that add to 0.7. 85.2 + 20.5 = 105.7; and 88.2 + 17.5 = 105.7.

6. 4,572 **7.** 4.4 **8.** 246 **9.** 1.918

Study Link 2.3

1. The numbers 451 and 299 should be circled.
2. The boxes with the numbers 100.9 and 75.3 should have Xs in them.
3. Sample answers: The boxes with the numbers 803 and 5,000 should have check marks in them.
4. The boxes with the numbers 17 and 15 should have stars in them.
5. The boxes with the numbers 1,500 and 703 should have triangles in them.
6. The boxes with the numbers 9 and 25 should have smiley faces in them.

7. 61 **8.** 137 **9.** 5.8 **10.** 18.85

Study Link 2.4

2. **a.** 14.08 and 11.85
  b. How much more Julie paid for gas in Chicago than in Iowa
  c. $14.08 - 11.85 = g$
  d. 2.23 **e.** $2.23

4. $27.23 + *s* = $34.98; $7.75

Study Link 2.5

Answers vary for Problems 1–5.

Study Link 2.6

Sample answers are given.

1. Unlikely: 30% Very likely: 80%
Very unlikely: 15% Likely: 70%
Extremely unlikely: 5%

2. 30%: Unlikely 5%: Extremely unlikely
99%: Extremely likely 20%: Very unlikely
80%: Very likely 35%: Unlikely
65%: Likely 45%: 50–50 chance

Study Link 2.7

2. The 1,000s box should be circled.
$10 * 700 = 7,000$

4. The 10,000s box should be circled.
$10 * 6,000 = 60,000$

Study Link 2.8

2. 930; the 100s box should be circled.
4. 21; the 10s box should be circled.
6. 2.26; the 1s box should be circled.

Study Link 2.9

2. 3,100; the 1,000s box should be circled.

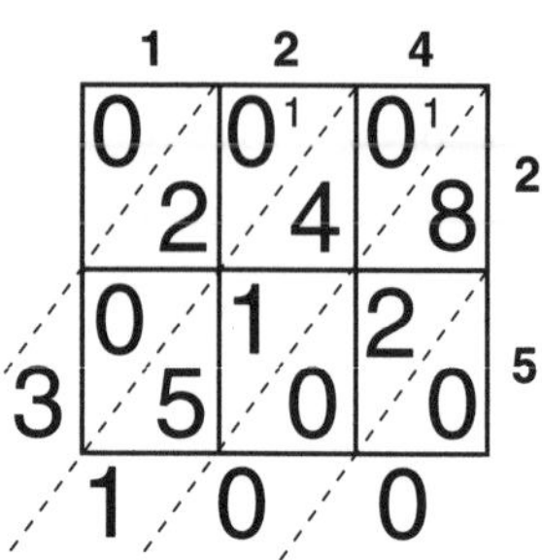

4. 33.372; the 10s box should be circled.

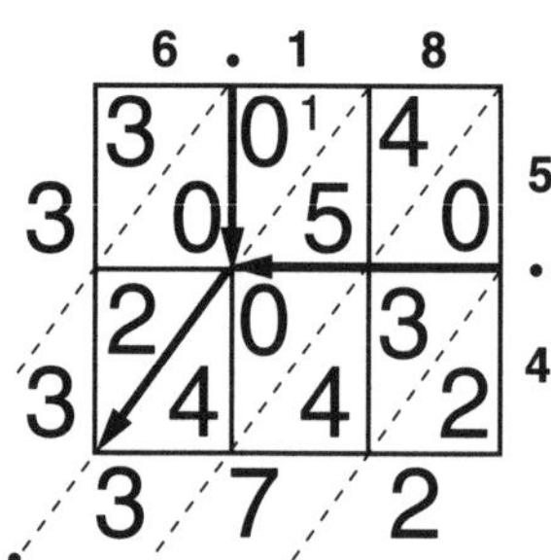

6. 341.61; the 100s box should be circled.

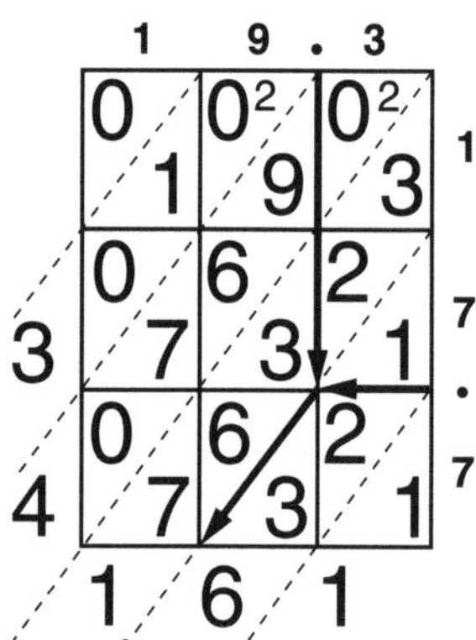

Study Link 2.10

1. **a.** yes **b.** no **c.** more
2. **a.** 350 cups **b.** Sample answer: 18,000 cups
3. About 926,100 quotations

Name Date Time

Estimating Measurements

Study Link 2.1

For each statement below, mark whether the measurement given is

SRB 169 179 186–187

S: too small **OK: reasonable** **L: too large**

_______ **1.** The width of the teacher's desk is 5 yards.

_______ **2.** A paper clip weighs about 3 kilograms.

_______ **3.** The length of an adult's step is about 2 feet.

_______ **4.** The distance between New York City and Los Angeles is about 670 miles.

_______ **5.** The length of a craft stick is about 10 centimeters.

_______ **6.** A full bathtub holds about 50 cups of water.

_______ **7.** The diameter of a penny is about 7 inches.

_______ **8.** It would take about 2.5 minutes to walk a mile.

_______ **9.** The temperature in Chicago during the summer is about 84°F.

_______ **10.** Most people like to drink soft drinks at a temperature of about 0°C.

Name Date Time

Number Hunt

Study Link 2.2

Reminder: A  means *"Do not use a calculator."*

Use the numbers in the following table to answer the questions below. You may not use a number more than once.

19	85.2	533	571
88.2	525	20	17.5
400	261	20.5	125
7	23	901	30

1. Circle two numbers whose sum is 832.

2. Make an X in the boxes containing three numbers whose sum is 57.

3. Make a check mark in the boxes containing two prime numbers whose sum is 42.

4. Make a star in the boxes containing two numbers whose sum is 658.

5. Make a triangle in the boxes containing two numbers whose sum is 105.7. Explain how you found the answer.

____

____

____

Solve Problems 6–9 using any method you want. Show your work in the space below.

6. 3,804 + 768 = __________

7. 2.83 + 1.57 = __________

8. 33 + 148 + 65 = __________

9. 1.055 + 0.863 = __________

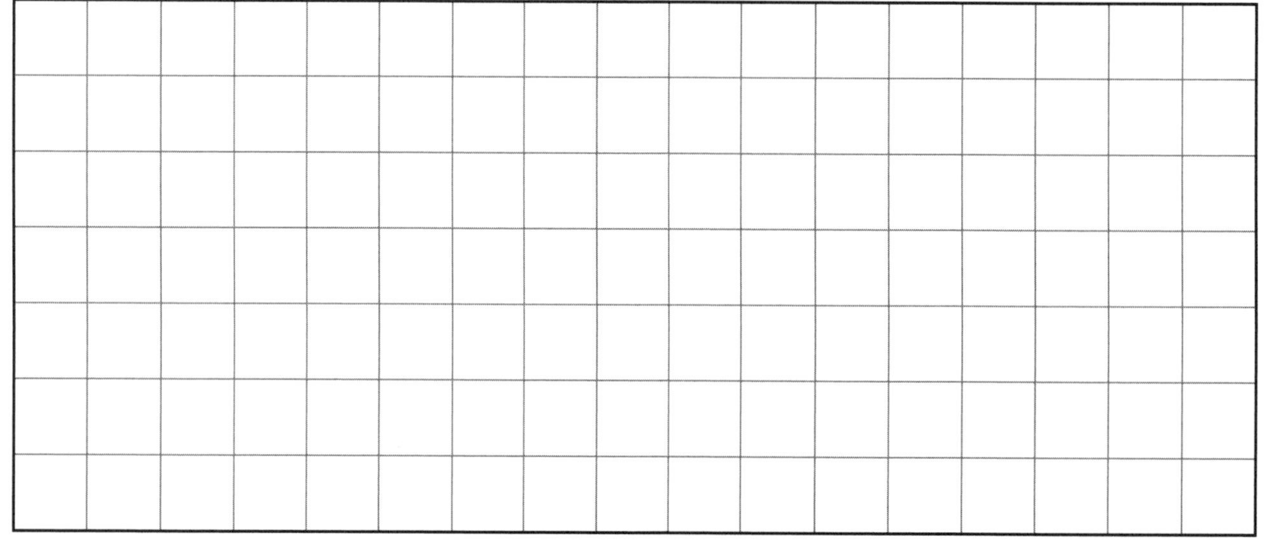

Name Date Time

Another Number Hunt

Study Link 2.3

Use the numbers in the following table to answer the questions below. You may not use a number more than once.

17	15	9	75.03
100.9	803	25	451
1,500	5,000	1	3,096
299	703	75.3	40.03

1. Circle two numbers whose difference is 152.

2. Make an X in the boxes of two numbers whose difference is 25.6.

3. Make a check mark in the boxes of two numbers whose difference is greater than 1,000.

4. Make a star in the boxes of two numbers whose difference is less than 10.

5. Make a triangle in the boxes of two numbers whose difference is equal to the sum of 538 and 259.

6. Make a smiley face in the boxes of two numbers whose difference is equal to 4^2.

Subtract. Show your work in the space below.

7. 247 − 186 = ____________

8. ____________ = 405 − 268

9. 24.5 − 18.7 = ____________

10. ____________ = 62.7 − 43.85

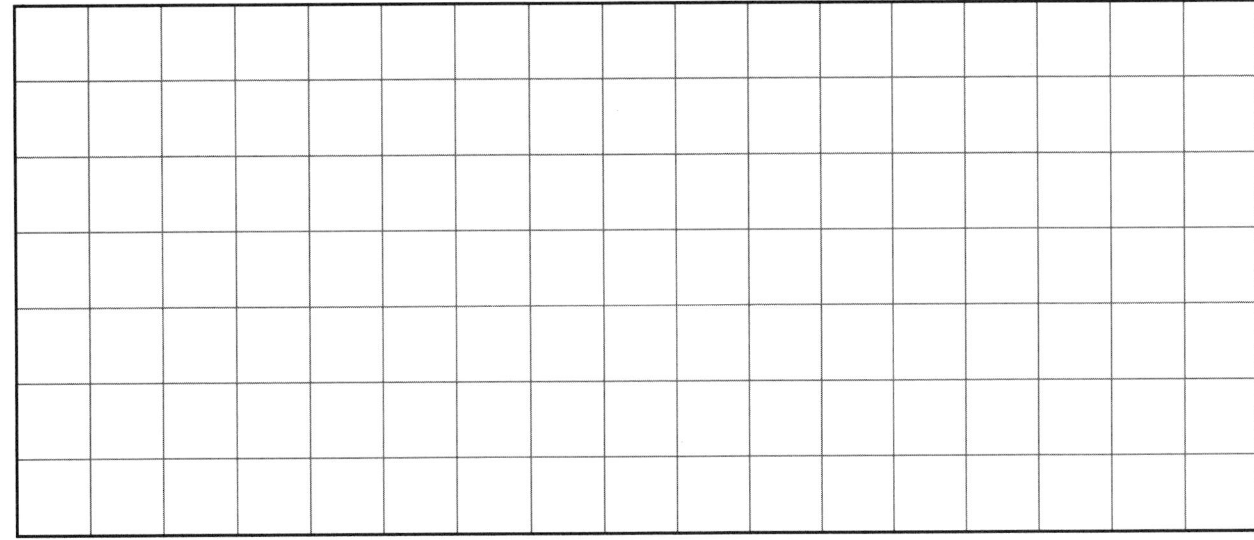

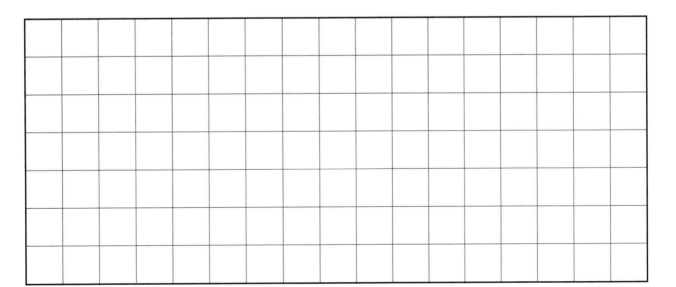

Name Date Time

Open Sentences and Number Stories

Study Link 2.4

For each problem on this page, fill in the blanks and solve the problem.

1. Althea and her brother collect baseball cards. Althea has 148 cards. Her brother has 127 cards. How many cards do they have altogether?

   a. List the numbers needed to solve the problem. ______________________

   b. Describe what you want to find. ______________________

   ____

   c. Open sentence: ______________________

   d. Solution: __________ e. Answer: ______________________ (unit)

2. Julie was driving from Chicago, Illinois, to Topeka, Kansas. Before she started, she filled her tank with 10 gallons of gas. She paid \$14.08. After driving about 305 miles, she stopped for gas in Iowa. Again, she got 10 gallons of gas and paid \$11.85. How much more did she pay for gas in Chicago than in Iowa?

   a. List the numbers needed to solve the problem. ______________________

   b. Describe what you want to find. ______________________

   ____

   c. Open sentence: ______________________

   d. Solution: __________ e. Answer: ______________________

3. Mark paid for his burger and fries with a \$20 bill. His burger cost \$3.89; his fries cost \$1.49. How much change did he receive?

   a. List the numbers needed to solve the problem. ______________________

   b. Describe what you want to find. ______________________

   ____

   c. Open sentence: ______________________

   d. Solution: __________ e. Answer: ______________________

Circle the open sentence that best matches the story. Then solve the problem.

4. Ralph and Adeline saved their money for 6 weeks. Ralph saved \$27.23. Adeline saved \$34.98. How much more did Adeline save than Ralph?

   $\$27.23 + \$34.98 = s$ $6 * s = \$34.98$

   $\$27.23 + s = \$34.98$ $6 + s = \$34.98 - \$27.23$ Answer: __________

Name Date Time

Comparing Reaction Times

Study Link 2.5

Use your Grab-It Gauge. Collect reaction-time data from two people at home. One person should be at least 25 years old.

1.

Person 1	
Left	**Right**

2.

Person 2	
Left	**Right**

3. Median times:

Left hand ________

Right hand ________

4. Median times:

Left hand ________

Right hand ________

5. How do the results for the two people compare to your class data?

____

____

____

____

Name Date Time

How Likely Is Rain?

Study Link 2.6

Many years ago, weather reports described the chances of rain with such phrases as "very likely," "unlikely," and "extremely unlikely." Today, the chances of rain are almost always reported as percents. For example, "There is a 50% chance of rain tonight."

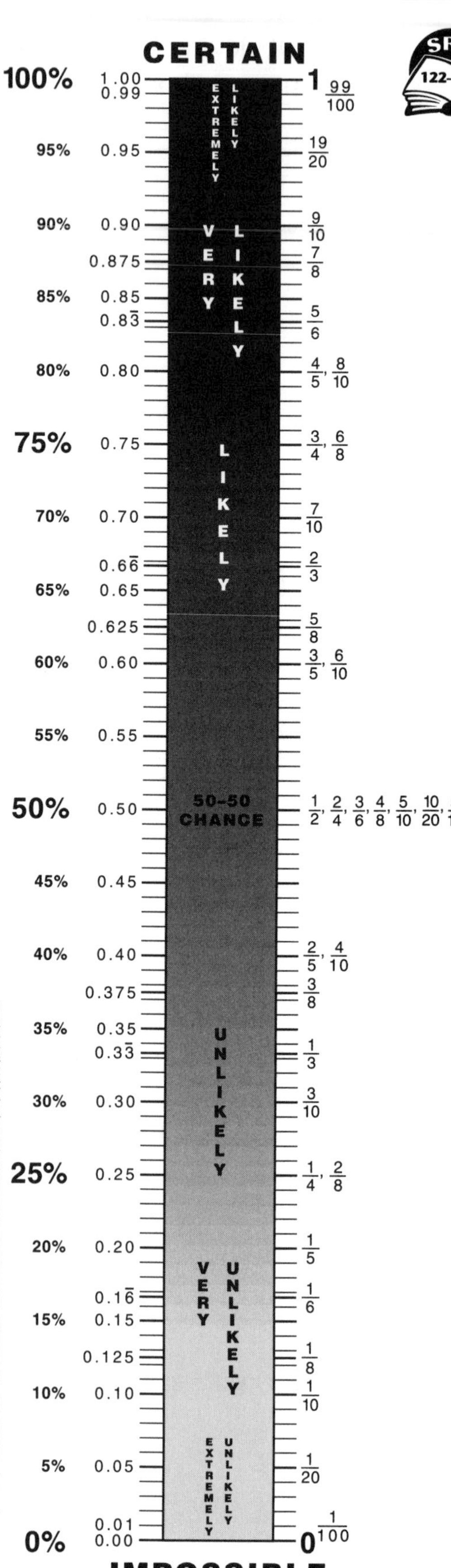

1. Use the Probability Meter Poster to translate phrases into percents.

Phrase	Percent
Unlikely	30%
Very likely	
Very unlikely	
Likely	
Extremely unlikely	

2. Use the Probability Meter Poster to translate percents into phrases.

Percent	Phrase
30%	Unlikely
5%	
99%	
20%	
80%	
35%	
65%	
45%	

Name Date Time

Magnitude Estimates for Products

Study Link 2.7

A **magnitude estimate** is a very rough estimate of the answer to a problem. A magnitude estimate will tell you if the exact answer falls in the tenths, ones, tens, hundreds, thousands, and so on.

For each problem, make a magnitude estimate. Ask yourself: *Is the answer in the tenths, ones, tens, hundreds, thousands, or ten-thousands?* Circle the appropriate box. Do not solve the problems.

Example 18 * 21

10s	(100s)	1,000s	10,000s

20 * 20 = 400

How I estimated

1. 73 * 28

10s	100s	1,000s	10,000s

How I estimated

2. 12 * 708

10s	100s	1,000s	10,000s

How I estimated

3. 98 * 105

10s	100s	1,000s	10,000s

How I estimated

4. 7 * 6,394

10s	100s	1,000s	10,000s

How I estimated

5. 17 * 2.2

10s	100s	1,000s	10,000s

How I estimated

6. 77 * 8.1

0.1s	1s	10s	100s

How I estimated

7. 2.6 * 3.9

0.1s	1s	10s	100s

How I estimated

8. 24.3 * 25.9

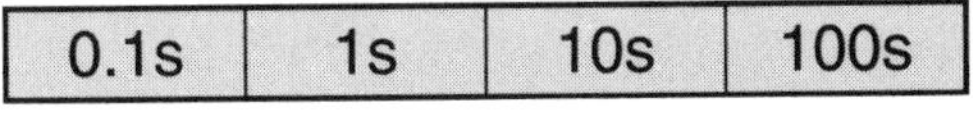

0.1s	1s	10s	100s

How I estimated

9. 0.7 * 0.5

0.1s	1s	10s	100s

How I estimated

Name Date Time

Multiplication of Whole Numbers and Decimals

Study Link 2.8

For each problem:

- Make a magnitude estimate. Circle the appropriate box.
- Solve the problem. Show your work at the right.

1. 8 * 19 = ____________

10s	100s	1,000s	10,000s

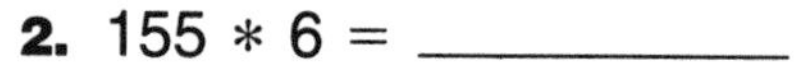

2. 155 * 6 = ____________

10s	100s	1,000s	10,000s

3. 37 * 58 = ____________

10s	100s	1,000s	10,000s

4. 5 * 4.2 = ____________

0.1s	1s	10s	100s

5. 9.3 * 2.8 = ____________

0.1s	1s	10s	100s

6. 11.3 * 0.2 = ____________

0.1s	1s	10s	100s

Use with Lesson 2.8.

Name Date Time

Multiplication by the Lattice Method

Study Link 2.9

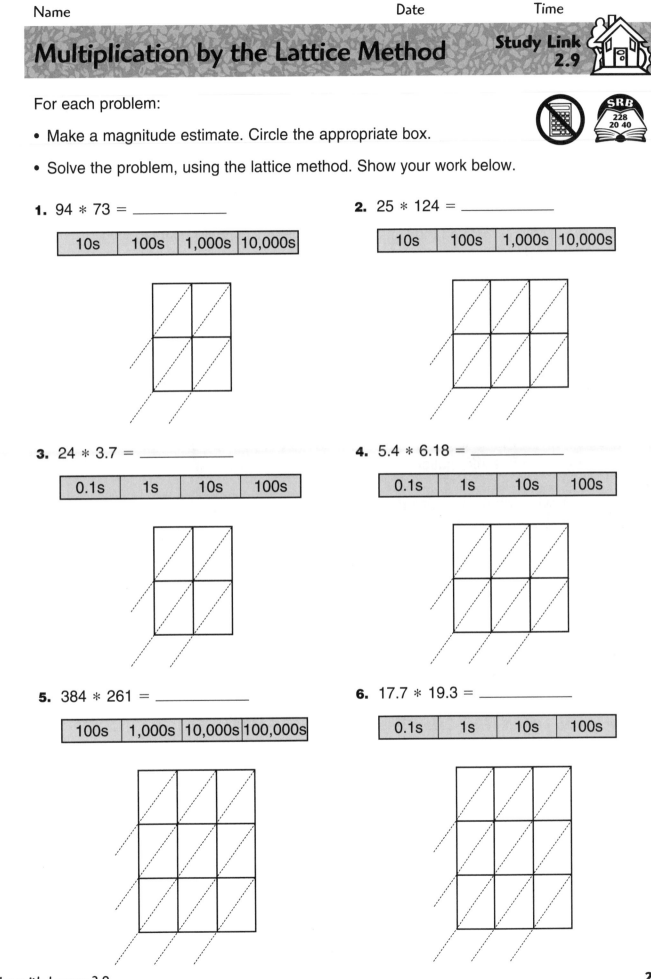

For each problem:

- Make a magnitude estimate. Circle the appropriate box.
- Solve the problem, using the lattice method. Show your work below.

1. 94 * 73 = ____________

10s	100s	1,000s	10,000s

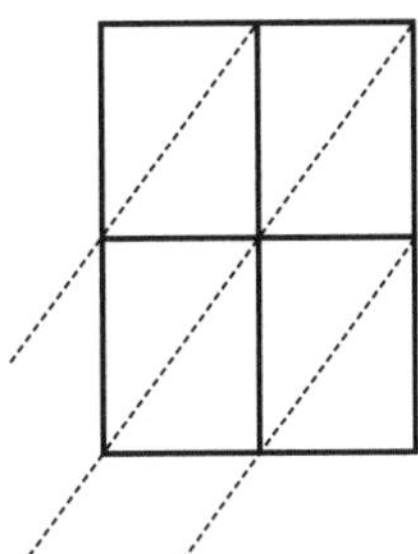

2. 25 * 124 = ____________

10s	100s	1,000s	10,000s

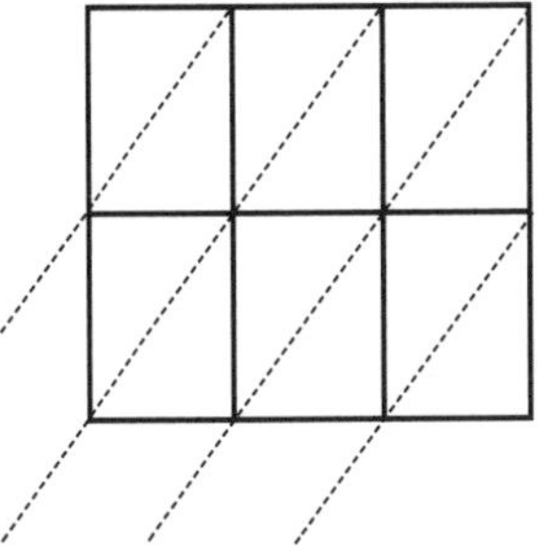

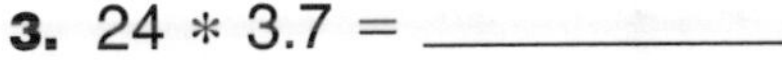

3. 24 * 3.7 = ____________

0.1s	1s	10s	100s

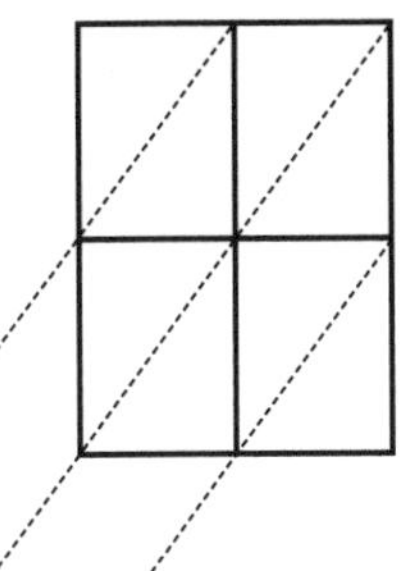

4. 5.4 * 6.18 = ____________

0.1s	1s	10s	100s

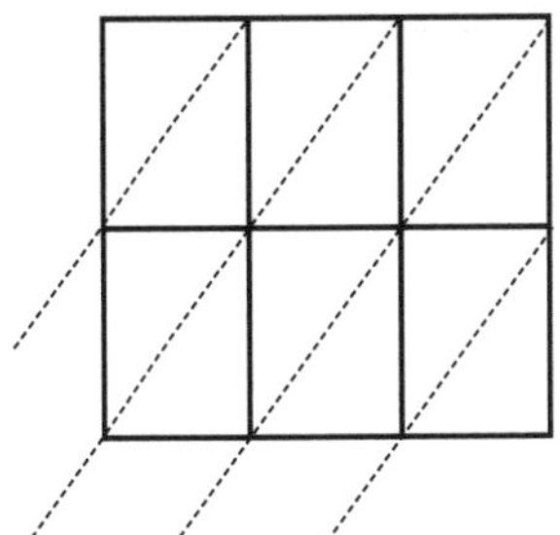

5. 384 * 261 = ____________

100s	1,000s	10,000s	100,000s

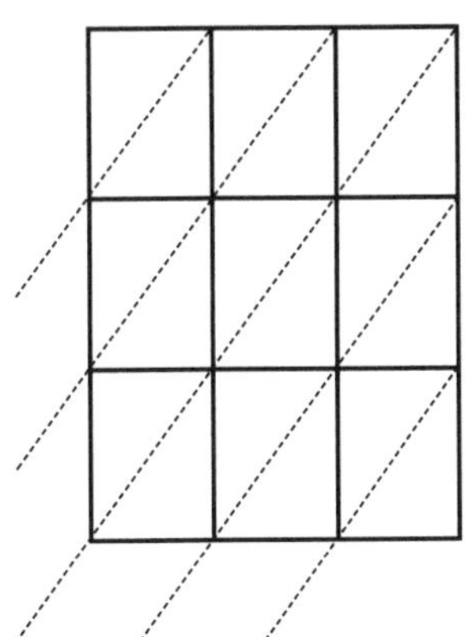

6. 17.7 * 19.3 = ____________

0.1s	1s	10s	100s

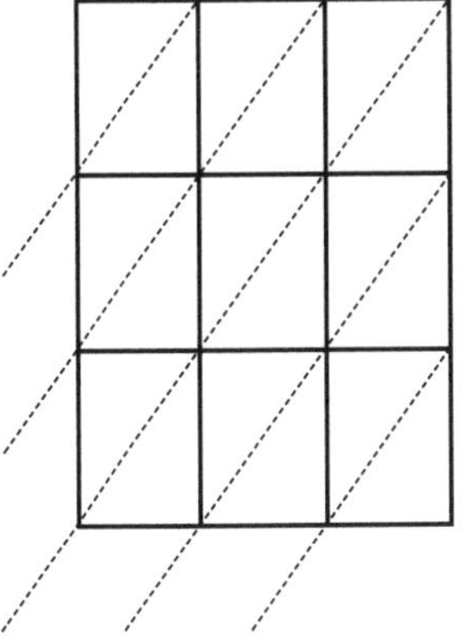

Name Date Time

Estimation

Study Link 2.10

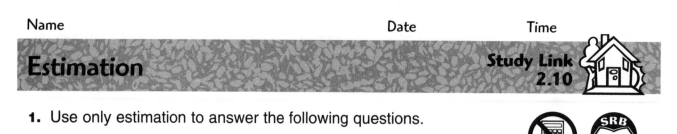

1. Use only estimation to answer the following questions.

   a. Certain varieties of sea horses can move 10.5 inches per minute. Would these sea horses be able to travel 6 yards in 1 hour?

   ____

   b. Orville Wright completed the first successful airplane flight on December 17, 1903. He traveled 120 feet in 12 seconds. If he had been able to stay in the air for a full minute, would he have traveled 1 mile? (*Hint:* 1 mile = 5,280 feet)

   ____

   c. In 1960, the *Triton* became the first submarine to circumnavigate the world. It covered 36,014 miles in 76 days. Is that more or less than 100 miles per day?

   ____

2. It is said that the Aztec king, Montezuma, drank about 50 cups of chocolate a day. Based on this information, answer the following questions.

   a. About how much did he drink per week? ______________________ (unit)

   b. About how much per year? ______________________ (unit)

   Source: The Kids' World Almanac of Records and Facts

Challenge

3. Use paper and pencil to solve the following problem.

   The second edition of the *Oxford English Dictionary* was published, in 20 volumes, in 1989. The dictionary contains about 2,436,600 quotations. There are more quotations from the works of Shakespeare than from any other author—about 33,300. There are about 487,200 from the twentieth century, about 755,300 from the nineteenth century, and about 268,000 from the eighteenth century. About how many quotations are there from before the eighteenth century?

   ______________________ (unit)

Name Date Time

Family Letter

Study Link 2.11

Unit 3: Geometry Explorations and the American Tour

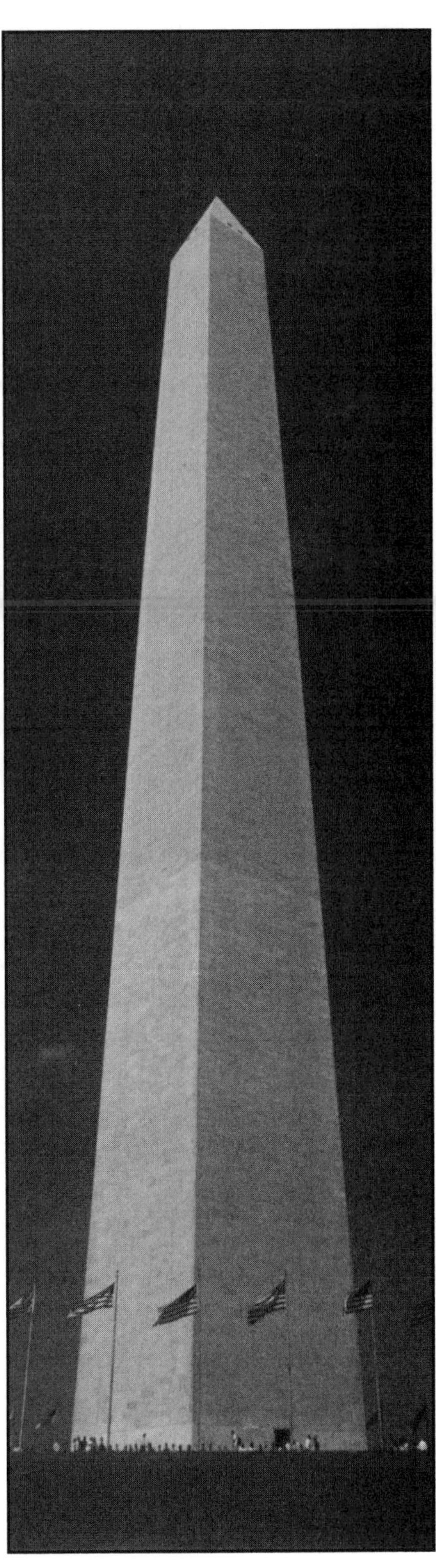

In Unit 3 your child will set out on the American Tour, a yearlong series of mathematical activities that will examine historical, demographic, and environmental features of the United States. The American Tour involves a wide range of mathematical skills, but most important, it seeks to develop your child's ability to read, interpret, critically examine, and use mathematical information presented in text, tables, and graphics. These skills are essential to effective mathematics in our technological age.

Many American Tour activities are based on materials in the American Tour section of the *Student Reference Book.* The American Tour, a cross between an historical atlas and an almanac, contains maps, data, and other information from a wide range of sources, including the U.S. Census Bureau, the National Weather Service, and the National Geographic Society.

Unit 3 also will review some geometry concepts from earlier grades, while introducing and expanding on others. In *Fourth Grade Everyday Mathematics,* students used a compass to construct basic shapes and create geometric designs. In this unit, your child will extend these skills and be introduced to the concept of congruent figures (same size, same shape) by using a compass and a straightedge to copy triangles. Another tool that will be introduced is the Geometry Template, which contains protractors and rulers for measuring, and cutouts for drawing a variety of geometric figures.

Finally, students will be introduced to the mathematics and art of tessellations—patterns of shapes that cover a surface without gaps or overlaps—and will begin to create their own designs.

You may wish to help your child at home by asking questions about information presented in newspaper and magazine tables and graphics. Also, the world is filled with many 2-dimensional and 3-dimensional geometric forms: angles, line segments, curves, cubes, cylinders, spheres, pyramids, and so on. Many wonderful geometric patterns can be seen in nature as well as in the things that people create. It will be helpful for you and your child to look for and talk about geometric shapes throughout the year.

Please keep this Family Letter for reference as your child works through Unit 3.

Vocabulary

Important terms in Unit 3:

acute angle An angle with a measure greater than 0 degrees and less than 90 degrees.

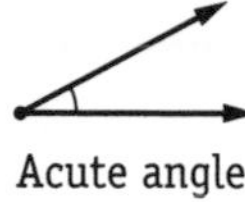

Acute angle

adjacent angles Angles that are next to each other; adjacent angles have a common side, but no other overlap. In the diagram, angles 1 and 2 are adjacent angles. So are angles 2 and 3, angles 3 and 4, and angles 4 and 1.

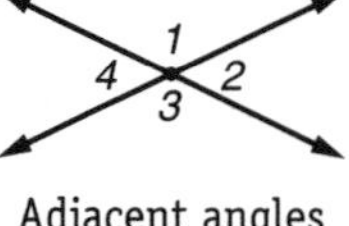

Adjacent angles

congruent Having exactly the same shape and size.

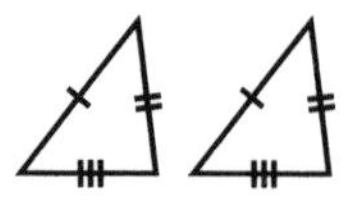

Congruent triangles

diameter A line segment that passes through the center of a circle (or sphere) and has endpoints on the circle (or sphere); also, the length of this line segment. The diameter of a circle or sphere is twice the length of its radius.

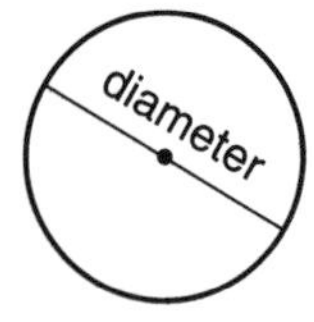

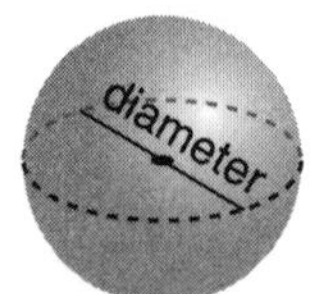

Diameter

equilateral triangle A triangle with all three sides the same length. In an equilateral triangle, all three angles have the same measure.

Equilateral triangles

obtuse angle An angle with a measure greater than 90 degrees and less than 180 degrees.

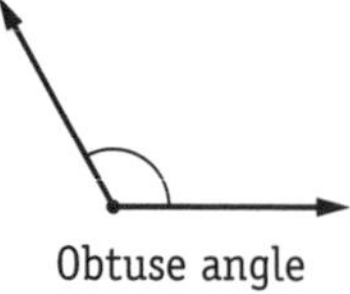

Obtuse angle

radius A line segment from the center of a circle (or sphere) to any point on the circle (or sphere); also, the length of this line segment.

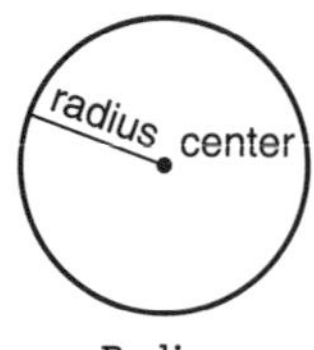

Radius

right angle An angle with a measure of 90 degrees.

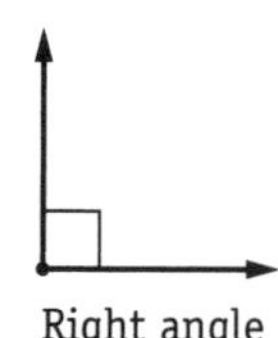

Right angle

tessellation An arrangement of shapes that covers a surface completely without overlaps or gaps. Also called *tiling.*

A tessellation

vertical (or opposite) angles When two lines intersect, the angles that do not share a common side. Vertical angles have equal measures. In the diagram, angles 2 and 4 are a pair of vertical angles. Angles 1 and 3 are another pair of vertical angles.

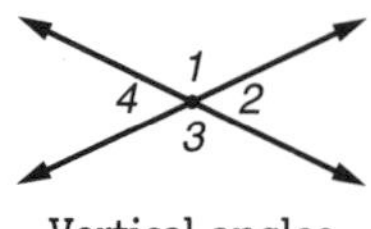

Vertical angles

Use with Lesson 2.11.

Building Skills through Games

In Unit 3, your child will practice geometry skills by playing the following games. For detailed instructions, see the *Student Reference Book.*

Angle Tangle See *Student Reference Book,* page 258
Two players will need a protractor and a straightedge to play this game. Playing *Angle Tangle* gives students practice in drawing and measuring angles.

Polygon Capture See *Student Reference Book,* page 289
This game uses 16 polygons and 16 Property Cards, and is played by partners or 2 teams each with 2 players. *Polygon Capture* gives students practice in identifying properties of polygons related to sides and angles.

Do-Anytime Activities

To work with your child on the concepts taught in this unit and in previous units, try these interesting and rewarding activities:

1. Together, read the book *A Cloak for the Dreamer* by Marilyn Burns.
2. When you are at home or at a store, ask your child to identify different types of polygons such as triangles, squares, pentagons, and hexagons.
3. Visit the Web site for the U.S. Bureau of the Census at http://www.census.gov/. Have your child write three interesting pieces of information that he or she learned from the Web site.
4. Look for examples of bar graphs in newspapers or magazines. Ask your child to explain the information shown by a graph.

As You Help Your Child with Homework

As your child brings assignments home, you may want to go over the instructions together, clarifying them as necessary. The answers listed below and on the next page will guide you through this unit's Study Links.

Study Link 3.1

1. Sample answer: The more years of school completed, the higher the median income.
2. Answers vary.
3. Answers vary.

Study Link 3.2

1. Look before you leap.
2. 5,472,000
3. Saying H
4. Answers vary.
5. Answer vary; Sample answer: The numbers are from a sample, not a census. They have been rounded to the nearest 1,000.
6. **a.** 250,000,000 **b.** 55%

Study Link 3.3

1. 60°; 90°; 60° **2.** 120°; 60°; 60°

3. 90°; 135°; 135° **4.** 30°; 75°

Study Link 3.4

1. 70° **2.** 50° **3.** 110° **4.** 130°

5. 60° **6.** 180° **7.** 120° **8.** 90°

9. 50° **10.** 150° **11.** 170° **12.** 260°

Study Link 3.5

1. acute; 12°

2. acute; 65°

3. obtuse; 103°

4. Sample answer: Angle *D* and angle *E*

5. Sample answer: Angle *D* and angle *F*

6. Sample answer: Angle *D* and angle *F*

7. **a.** 110°

b. Angle *F* and angle *D* are vertical (or opposite) angles; vertical angles are equal in measure.

Study Link 3.6

1. scalene **2.** isosceles

3. isosceles; right **4.** equilateral; isosceles

5. Objects and types of angles vary. **6.** 60°; 60°; 60°

7. Sample answer: 6 angles with the same measure as ∠*A* fit around a point. Since a circle has 360°, and the angles in an equilateral triangle are equal, each angle measures 360 / 6, or 60°.

Study Link 3.7

Sample answers are given for Problems 1–5.

1. 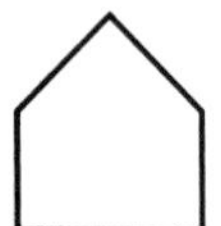 The pentagon is the only shape that is not regular.

2.  The chevron is the only shape that is not convex.

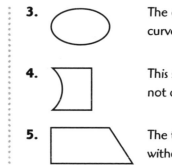

3. The oval is the only shape that is curved.

4. This shape is the only one that is not convex.

5. The trapezoid is the only shape without two pairs of parallel sides.

Study Link 3.8

1.–3. Samples of tessellations vary.

Study Link 3.9

1. Sample answer: Draw a line between two of the vertices to create two triangles. Since the sum of the angles in each triangle is 180°, the sum of the angles in a quadrangle is 360°.

2. 360°

3. **a.–b.**

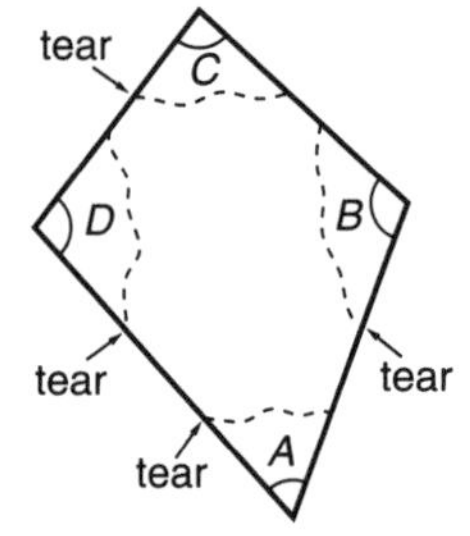

c.–d.

Study Link 3.10

1. Sample answers are given.

a. **b.**  **c.** **d.** 

2.

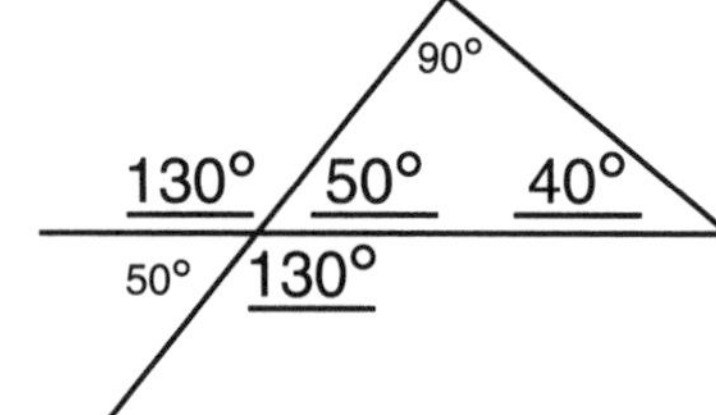

3. **a.** 2 **b.** 70° **c.** 360° **d.** trapezoid

Name Date Time

Education and Earnings

Study Link 3.1

The table below contains information from surveys by the U.S. Census Bureau. The information describes Householders who were at least 25 years old. A *Householder* is the person in whose name a home is owned or rented. If a house is owned jointly by a husband and wife, the Householder could be either the husband or the wife.

	1990			1980		
Years of School Completed	**Number of Householders (thousands)**	**Percent of House-holders**	**Median Income**	**Number of House-holders (thousands)**	**Percent of House-holders**	**Median Income**
Elementary (less than 9 years)	10,146	11%	$13,523	14,012	18%	$ 8,875
High School (1–3 years)	10,007	11%	$18,191	10,547	14%	$13,213
High School (4 years)	32,043	36%	$28,744	25,454	34%	$19,638
College (1–3 years)	16,451	19%	$35,724	11,480	15%	$21,740
College (4 years)	11,443	13%	$47,083	7,862	10%	$27,339
College (5 or more years)	9,269	10%	$54,636	6,661	9%	$30,684
Total	89,359	100%	$30,757	76,016	100%	$18,383

Source: March Current Population Survey, prepared by Income Statistics Branch/HHES Division U.S. Bureau of the Census

Use the table to answer the following questions.

1. Describe the relationship between number of years of education and income.

____

____

2. In which year do you think a higher percentage of Householders were high school graduates—1990 or 2000? Explain your answer.

____

____

____

3. On the back of this page, write one question that can be answered using the information in the table.

Name Date Time

An Unofficial Census

Study Link 3.2

In 1991, author Tom Heymann took an unofficial U.S. census. The table shows how many people believed various common sayings, based on the sample of the population that he surveyed.

	Saying	Number Who Believe Saying Is True
A	Look before you leap.	175,104,000
B	The grass is always greener on the other side of the fence.	69,312,000
C	Haste makes waste.	153,216,000
D	Beauty is only skin deep.	149,568,000
E	Don't cry over spilled milk.	160,512,000
F	The early bird catches the worm.	136,800,000
G	A penny saved is a penny earned.	155,040,000
H	Don't count your chickens before they hatch.	169,632,000

Source: The Unofficial U.S. Census by Tom Heymann. Ballantine Books, 1991

1. Which saying had the largest number of believers?

   ____

2. How many more people believed Saying E than Saying G? ______________

3. Which saying had about 100 million more believers than Saying B? ______________

4. Choose one of the expressions and tell what it means in your own words.

   ____

5. Why do you think the numbers in the table all have zeros in the ones, tens, and hundreds place? ______________________________

   ____

Challenge

6. **a.** About $\frac{7}{10}$ of the U.S. population in 1991 believed Saying A to be true. What was the total population? ______________

   b. About what percent of the total population believed Saying F to be true? (Use your calculator. Round to the nearest whole percent.) ______________

Name Date Time

Finding Angle Measures

Study Link 3.3

Figure out the angle measures for the labeled angles in the patterns below. Remember that there are 360° in a circle and 180° in a straight line. Use the Geometry Template or cut out the shapes at the bottom of this page to help you. Do not use a protractor.

1.

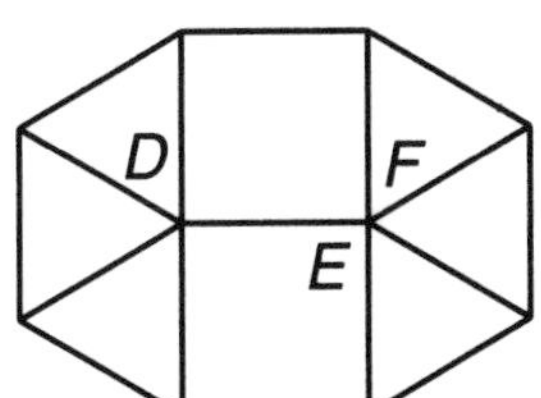

m∠D = ________°

m∠E = ________°

m∠F = ________°

2.

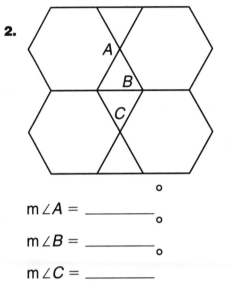

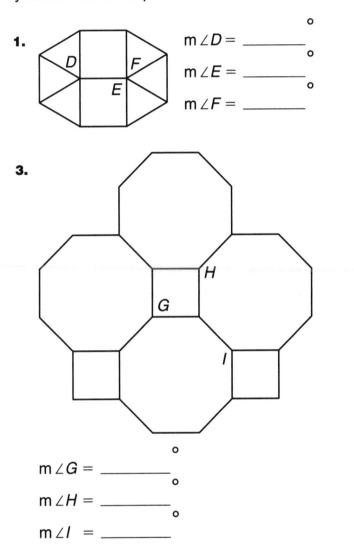

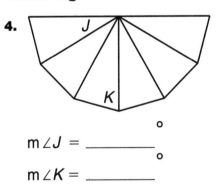

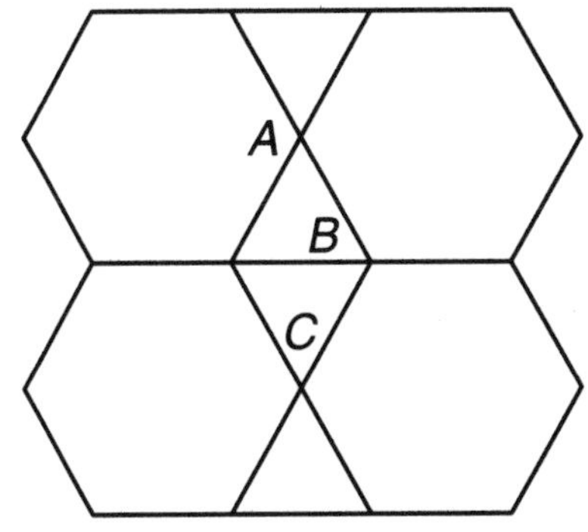

m∠A = ________°

m∠B = ________°

m∠C = ________°

3.

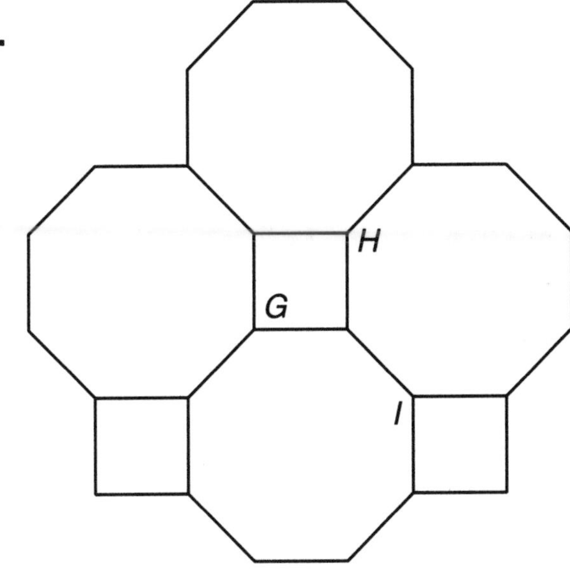

m∠G = ________°

m∠H = ________°

m∠I = ________°

On the back of this page, explain how you found the measure of ∠I.

Challenge

4.

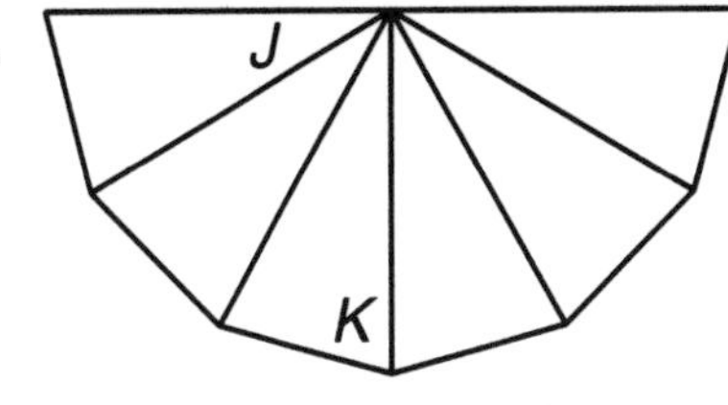

m∠J = ________°

m∠K = ________°

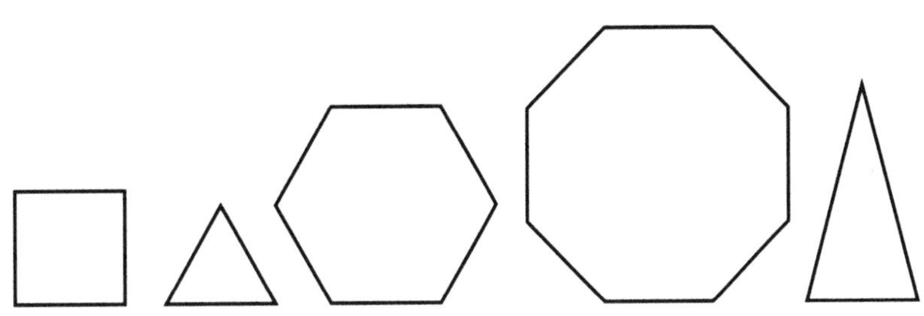

Name Date Time

Angle Measures

Study Link 3.4

SRB 188 189

Find the approximate measure of each angle at the right.

1. measure of ∠*CAT* = ________°

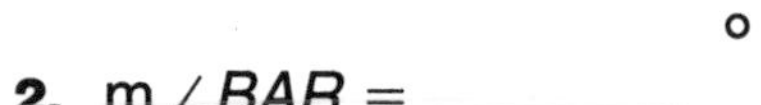

2. m ∠*BAR* = ________°
3. m ∠*RAT* = ________°
4. m ∠*CAB* = ________°
5. m ∠*BAT* = ________°
6. m ∠*CAR* = ________°

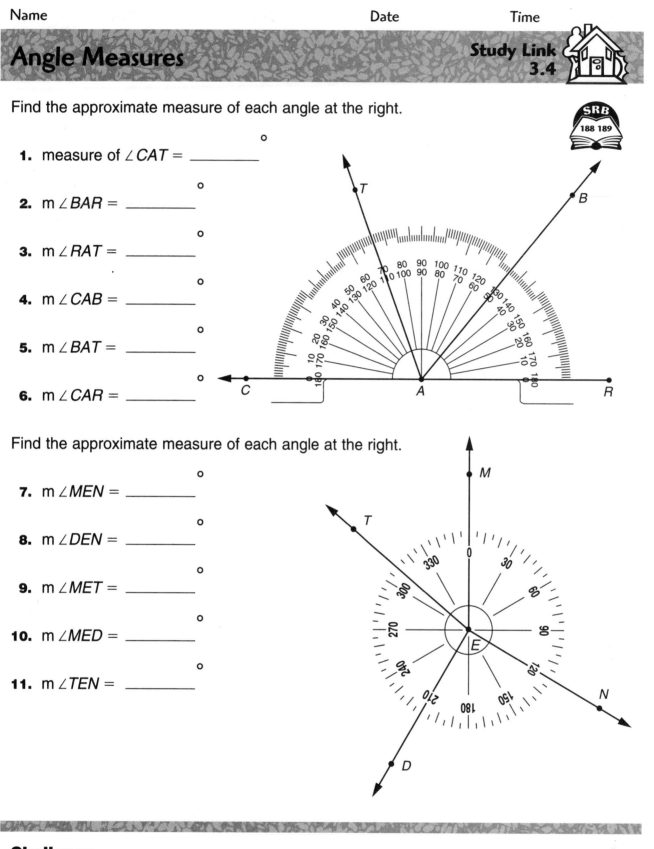

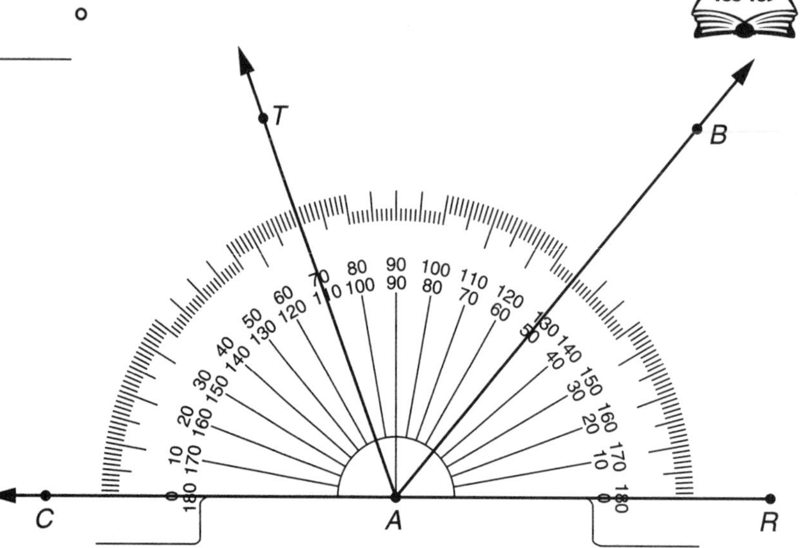

Find the approximate measure of each angle at the right.

7. m ∠*MEN* = ________°
8. m ∠*DEN* = ________°
9. m ∠*MET* = ________°
10. m ∠*MED* = ________°
11. m ∠*TEN* = ________°

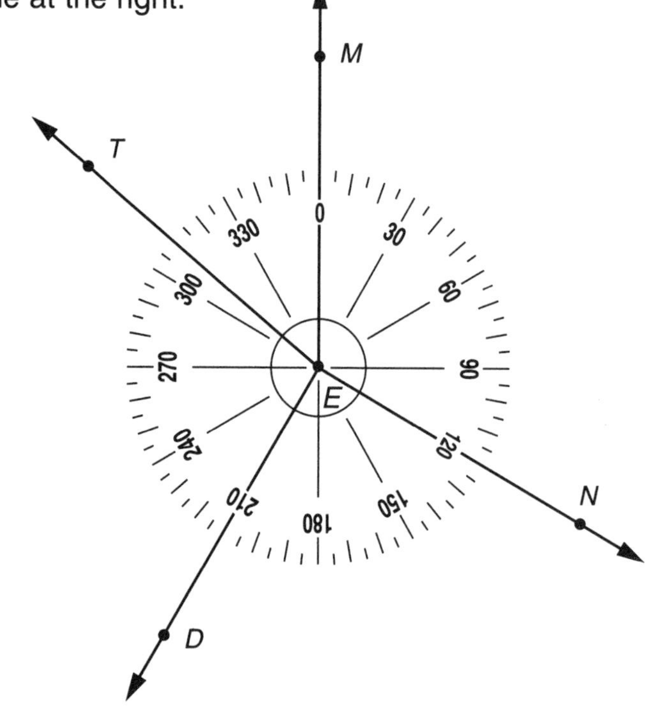

Challenge

12. measure of the reflex angle *TED* = ________°

Name Date Time

Angles in Figures

Study Link 3.5

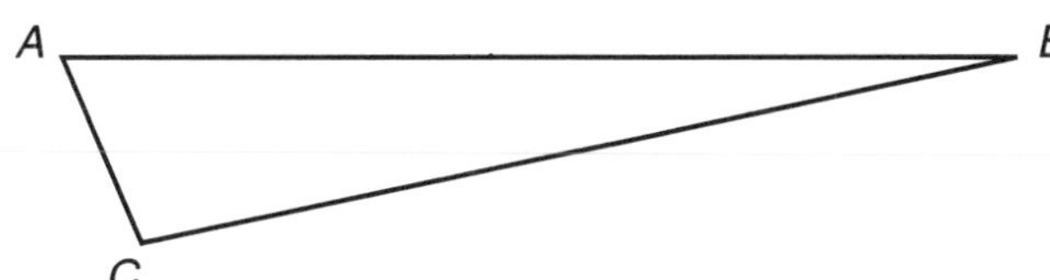

Circle *acute, right,* or *obtuse* for each angle in triangle *ABC*.
Then measure each angle.

1. $\angle ABC$ acute right obtuse m $\angle ABC$ = ________ °

2. $\angle CAB$ acute right obtuse m $\angle CAB$ = ________ °

3. $\angle BCA$ acute right obtuse m $\angle BCA$ = ________ °

Use the figure at the right to do Problems 4–6.

4. Name a pair of adjacent angles.

__________ and __________

5. Name a pair of vertical angles.

__________ and __________

6. Name a pair of opposite angles.

__________ and __________

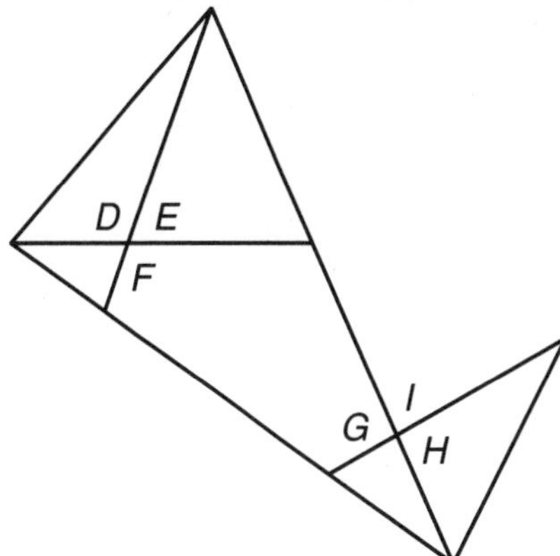

Challenge

7. a. The measure of $\angle F$ is 110°. What is the measure of $\angle D$? ________ °

b. Explain how you know.

____

____

Name Date Time

Triangle and Angle Review

Study Link 3.6

For each triangle below, fill in the ovals for all of the names that apply.

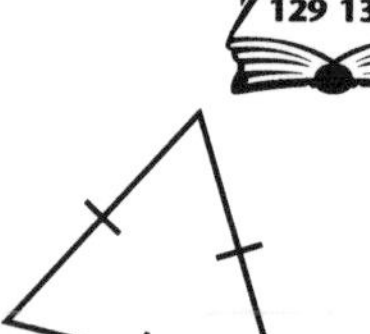

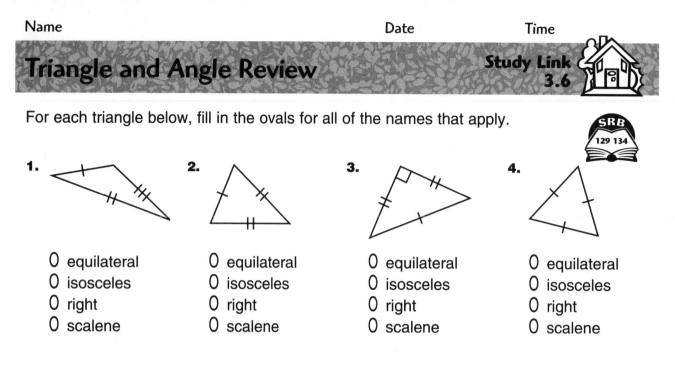

1. 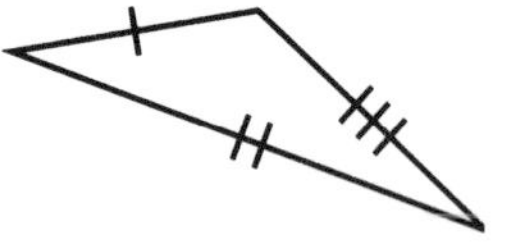

O equilateral
O isosceles
O right
O scalene

2. 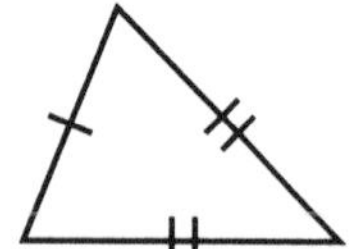

O equilateral
O isosceles
O right
O scalene

3.

O equilateral
O isosceles
O right
O scalene

4.

O equilateral
O isosceles
O right
O scalene

5. On the back of this page, draw three angles of different sizes that you find at home. (For example, you could trace one corner of a book.) For each angle, name the object that has the angle. Then use words from the Word Bank to name each angle.

a. Object ____________________

Type of angle ____________________

b. Object ____________________

Type of angle ____________________

c. Object ____________________

Type of angle ____________________

Word Bank		
acute	obtuse	right
adjacent	reflex	straight

Challenge

6. Use what you know about equilateral triangles and the degree measure of a circle or a straight angle. What is the measure of each angle in equilateral triangle *ABC*?

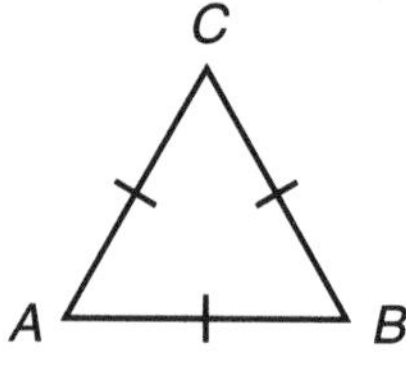

m∠*A* = ________ °   m∠*B* = ________ °   m∠*C* = ________ °

7. Explain how you found your answer to Problem 6. ____________________

____

____

____

Use with Lesson 3.6.

Name Date Time

Odd Shape Out

Study Link 3.7

In each set of shapes, there is one shape that doesn't belong. Cross out that shape and tell why it doesn't belong. (There may be more than one possible reason. What's important is having a good reason for crossing out a shape.)

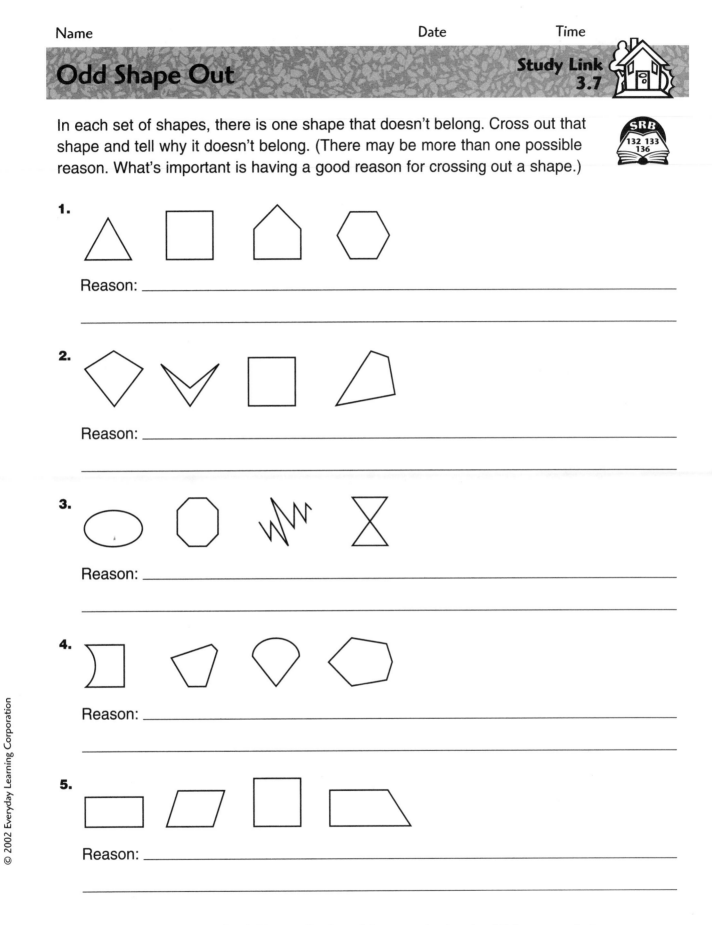

1. 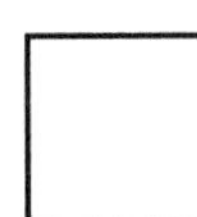  

Reason: ______________________________

____

2. 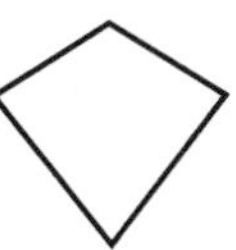   

Reason: ______________________________

____

3. 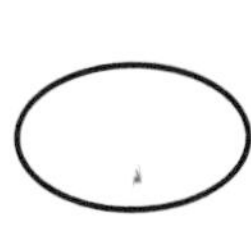   

Reason: ______________________________

____

4. 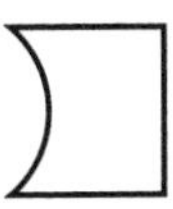 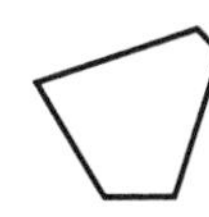  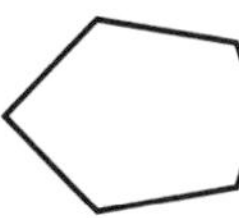

Reason: ______________________________

____

5. 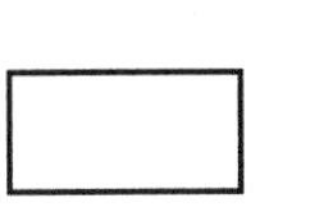 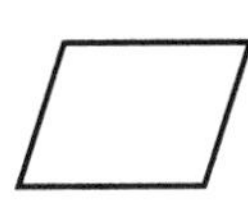  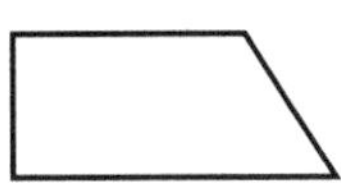

Reason: ______________________________

____

6. Make up your own "Odd Shape Out" problem on the back of this page. Ask a friend or family member to solve it.

Name Date Time

Tessellation Museum

Study Link 3.8

A **tessellation** is an arrangement of repeated, closed shapes that completely cover a surface, without overlaps or gaps. Sometimes only one shape is used in a tessellation. Sometimes two or more shapes are used.

SRB 150 151

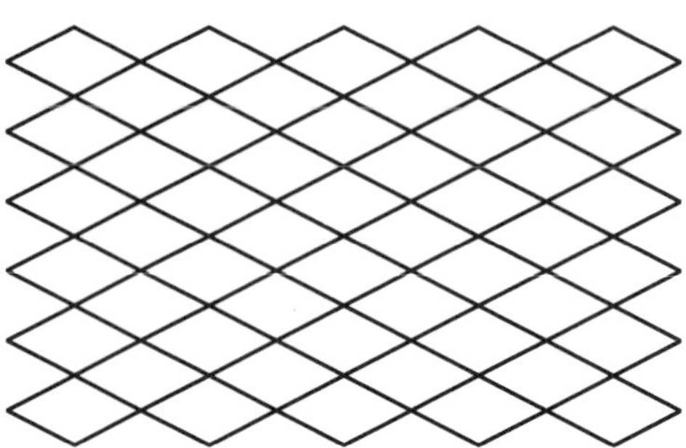

1. Collect tessellations. Look in newspapers and magazines. Ask people at home to help you find examples.

2. Ask an adult if you may cut out the tessellations. Tape your tessellations onto this page in the space below.

3. If you can't find tessellations in newspapers or magazines, look around your home at furniture, wallpaper, tablecloths, or clothing. In the space below, sketch the tessellations you find.

Name Date Time

Sums of Angle Measures

Study Link 3.9

1. Describe one way to find the sum of the angles in a quadrangle without using a protractor. You may want to use the quadrangle at the right to illustrate your explanation.

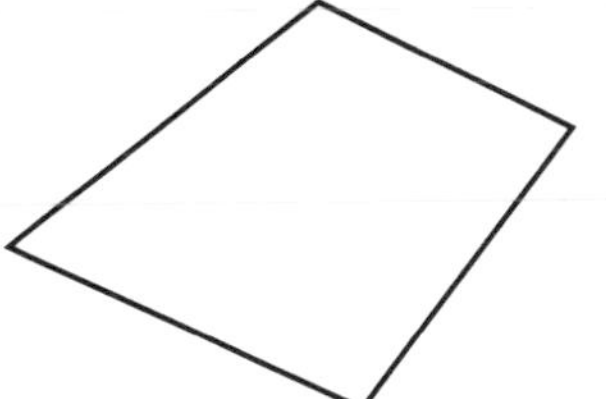

____

____

____

____

____

2. The sum of the angles in a quadrangle is ________°.

3. Do the following to check your answer to Problem 2.

   a. With a straightedge, draw a large quadrangle on a separate sheet of paper.

   b. Draw an arc in each angle.

   c. Cut out the quadrangle and tear off part of each angle.

   d. Tape or glue the angles onto the back of this page so that the angles touch but do not overlap.

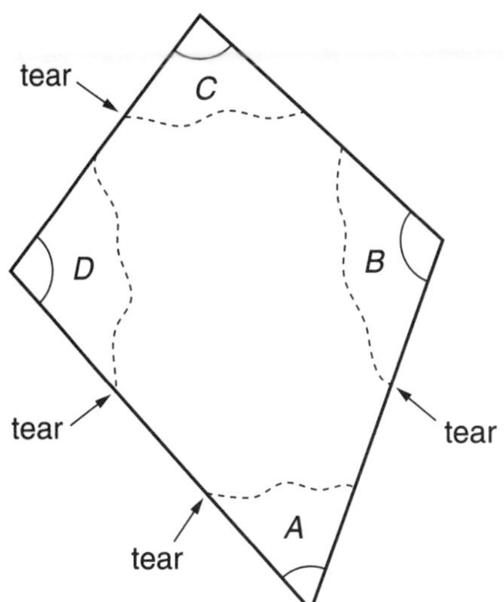

Name Date Time

Polygons and Their Measures

Study Link 3.10

1. Draw each of the following figures.

a. a polygon

b. a triangle with no equal sides

c. a quadrangle with one right angle

d. a quadrangle with no pairs of parallel sides

2. Without using a protractor, record the missing angle measurements in the figure below.

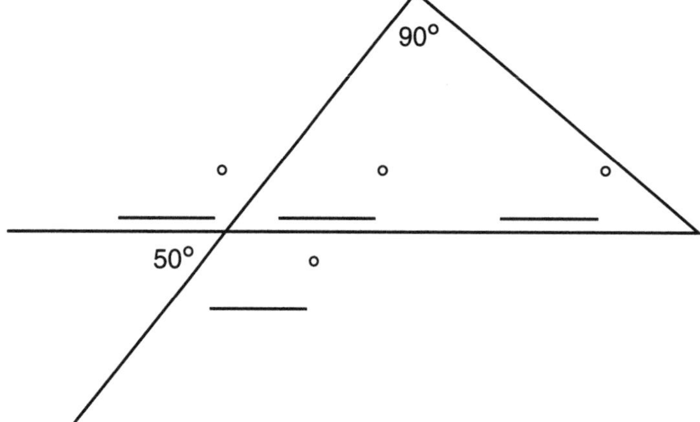

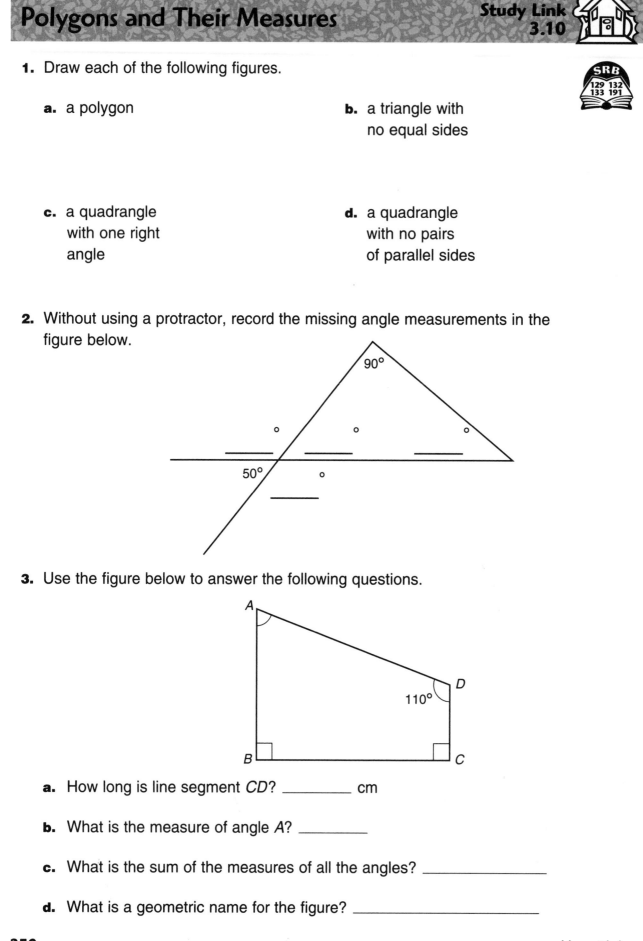

3. Use the figure below to answer the following questions.

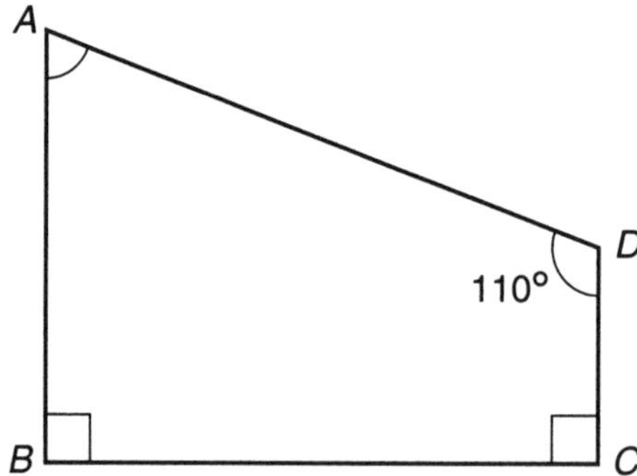

a. How long is line segment *CD*? ________ cm

b. What is the measure of angle *A*? ________

c. What is the sum of the measures of all the angles? ________________

d. What is a geometric name for the figure? ________________________

Name Date Time

Family Letter

Study Link 3.11

Unit 4: Division

Unit 4 begins with a review of division facts and the relation between division and multiplication. Emphasis is on fact families—a person who knows that $4 * 5 = 20$ also knows the related facts $5 * 4 = 20$, $20 \div 4 = 5$, and $20 \div 5 = 4$.

These notations for division are equivalent:

$12\overline{)246}$	$246 \div 12$
246 / 12	$\frac{246}{12}$

We will develop strategies for dividing mentally. Challenge your child to a game of *Division Dash* to assist in practicing mental division. Rules are in the *Student Reference Book,* page 267.

In *Fourth Grade Everyday Mathematics,* students were introduced to a method of long division called the partial-quotients division algorithm. This algorithm is easier to learn and apply than the traditional long division method. It relies on "easy" multiplication, and it can be quickly employed by students who struggle with traditional computation.

In this method, a series of partial answers (partial quotients) are obtained, and then added to get the final answer (the quotient). After your child has worked with this method, you might ask him or her to explain the example below:

```
12)158 |
 - 120 | 10
    38 |
 -  36 |_ 3
     2   13
     ↑    ↑
Remainder  Quotient
```

In the coming unit, we will review the partial-quotients division algorithm and extend it to decimals.

Your child will have many opportunities to practice using this division algorithm—as well as others, if he or she wishes. The partial-quotients division algorithm, and another method called column division, are described in the *Student Reference Book.*

When we solve division number stories, special attention will be placed on interpreting the remainder in division.

The American Tour will continue as the class measures distances on maps and uses map scales to convert the map distances to real-world distances between cities, lengths of rivers, and so on.

Please keep this Family Letter for reference as your child works through Unit 4.

Vocabulary

Important terms in Unit 4:

dividend In division, the number that is being divided. For example, in $35 \div 5 = 7$, the dividend is 35.

division Division is used to find how a total can be separated into a number of groups, or into groups of equal size.

divisor In division, the number that divides another number. For example, in $35 \div 5 = 7$, the divisor is 5.

magnitude estimate A very rough estimate. A magnitude estimate tells whether an answer should be in the tens, hundreds, thousands, millions, and so on.

map legend or key A diagram that explains the symbols, markings, and colors on a map.

map scale A tool that helps you estimate real distances between places shown on a map by relating distances on the map to distances in the real world. For example, a map scale may show that one inch on a map represents 100 miles in the real world.

number sentence A sentence made up of at least two numbers or expressions and a single relation symbol ($=$, $<$, $>$, $\neq$, $\leq$, or $\geq$). For example, $5 + 5 = 10$ is a number sentence. Number sentences usually contain at least one operation symbol. They may also have grouping symbols, such as parentheses. If a number sentence contains one or more variables, it is called an *open sentence.*

open sentence A *number sentence* in which one or more *variables* hold the places of missing numbers. For example, $x + 3 = 5$ is an open sentence.

quotient The result of dividing one number by another number. For example, in $35 \div 5 = 7$, the quotient is 7.

remainder The amount left over when dividing one number by another number. For example, if 38 books are divided into 5 equal piles, there will be 7 books in each pile, with 3 books left over; the remainder is 3. We may write $38 \div 5 \rightarrow 7$ R3, where R3 stands for the remainder.

variable A letter or other symbol that represents a number. A variable can represent one specific number or it can stand for many different numbers.

Do-Anytime Activities

To work with your child on the concepts taught in this unit and in previous units, try these interesting and rewarding activities:

1. Provide your child with opportunities to look at maps from various parts of the country. Ask him or her to explain the map legend and map scale, and to find the distances between two cities or places of interest.

2. Read the book *A Remainder of One* by Elinor J. Pinczes.

3. Play *Division Dash, First to 100,* or *Algebra Election* as described in the *Student Reference Book.*

4. Ask your child to write number stories that can be solved using division. Help your child solve those problems, and then identify how the quotient and remainder are used to answer the question in the number story.

Building Skills through Games

In Unit 4, your child will practice division as well as other skills by playing the following games. For detailed instructions, see the *Student Reference Book.*

Division Dash

See *Student Reference Book,* page 267

This is a game for one or two players. Each player will need a calculator. Playing *Division Dash* helps students practice division and mental calculation.

First to 100

See *Student Reference Book,* page 273

This is a game for two to four players and requires 32 Problem Cards and a pair of six-sided dice. Players answer questions after substituting numbers for the variable on Problem Cards. The questions offer practice on a variety of mathematical topics.

Algebra Election

See *Student Reference Book,* pages 256 and 257

This game is similar to *First to 100,* and uses the same 32 Problem Cards. Players will also need several pennies, 1 six-sided die, a calculator, and a gameboard called the Electoral Vote Map. The game rules model election of a president by winning sufficient electoral votes.

As You Help Your Child with Homework

As your child brings assignments home, you may want to go over the instructions together, clarifying them as necessary. The answers listed below will guide you through this unit's Study Links.

Study Link 4.1

1. 5 times taller
2. 50 students
3. 8 hours
4. 2 gallons
5. 2,000 miles
6. 3 weeks
7. 5 pounds

Study Link 4.2

1. 71
2. 53
3. 82 R22
4. 83

Study Link 4.3

1. a. About 1 mile b. About $1\frac{1}{2}$ miles
2. a. Snakey Lane b. About 2 miles
3. About $4\frac{1}{2}$ miles
4. 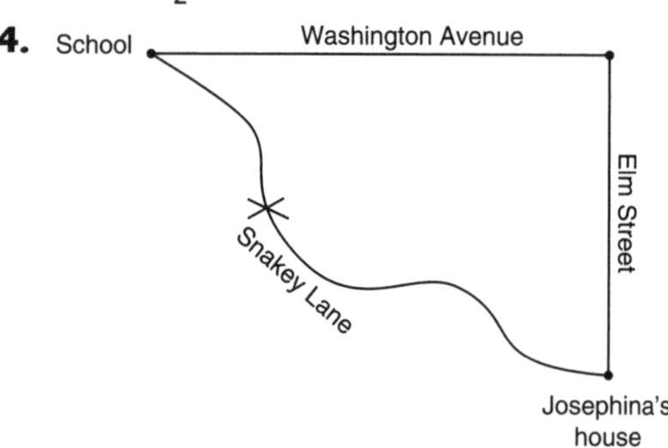

Sample answer: Since Josephina's father was walking twice as fast as Josephina, I marked a spot so that the distance from Josephina's house to the X was twice as long as the distance between school and the X.

Study Link 4.4

Estimates vary. Sample estimates are given for Problems 1–6.

1. The 10s box should be circled; 60 ÷ 6 = 10; 13.1
2. The 100s box should be circled; 300 ÷ 3 = 100; 129
3. The 1s box should be circled; 30 ÷ 10 = 3; $3.69
4. The 10s box should be circled; 800 ÷ 40 = 20; 23
5. The 100s box should be circled; 1,000 ÷ 5 = 200; 169
6. The 1s should be circled; 18 ÷ 9 = 2; 1.76

Study Link 4.5

1. $6.25; Reported it as a fraction or decimal; Sample answer: $50.00 divided by 8 games is $6.00 per game with $2.00 left over. $2.00 divided by 8 games is $0.25 per game. $6.00 + $0.25 = $6.25
2. 7; Ignored it; Sample answer: 7 pizzas cost $56.00. The remaining $4.00 is not enough to buy another pizza, and is ignored.

Study Link 4.6

1. 49 2. 780 3. 610

Answers vary for Problems 4–11.

Name Date Time

Uses of Division

Study Link 4.1

Use what you know about division facts to solve the following problems. (Think: *How many of these are in that?*) Include units in your answers when appropriate.

1. Fifteen-year-old oak trees are often about 25 feet tall. Rose, a 15-year-old girl, is about 5 feet tall. How many times taller are the trees than Rose? ______________

2. The job of interviewing 500 students in a school is to be divided equally among 10 interviewers. How many students should each interviewer talk to? ______________

3. At an average speed of 50 miles per hour, about how long will a 400-mile trip take? ______________

4. A summer camp serves 180 gallons of milk per month to 90 campers. About how much milk, on average, does each camper drink per month? ______________

5. The diameter of Earth is about 4 times the diameter of the Moon. Earth's diameter is about 8,000 miles. What is the approximate diameter of the Moon? ______________

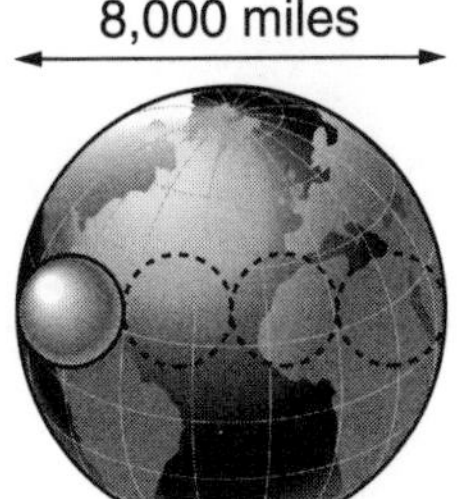

Challenge

Problems 6 and 7 were given to eighth graders on a test used to measure the progress of students in the United States. See how well you can do.

6. Jill needs to earn \$45 for a class trip. She earns \$2 each day on Mondays, Tuesdays, and Wednesdays. She earns \$3 each day on Thursdays, Fridays, and Saturdays. She does not work on Sundays. How many weeks will it take her to earn \$45? ______________

7. The weight of an object on the Moon would be $\frac{1}{6}$ of its weight on Earth. An object that weighs 30 pounds on Earth would weigh how many pounds on the Moon? ______________

Problem 6 was solved correctly by 59% of the eighth graders who tried it. Problem 7 was solved correctly by 49%.

Name Date Time

Division

Study Link 4.2

Here is an example of division using the partial-quotients algorithm.

8)185		How many 8s are in 185? At least 10.
− 80	10	The first partial quotient. 10 ∗ 8 = 80
105		Subtract. At least 10 [8s] are left.
− 80	10	The second partial quotient. 10 ∗ 8 = 80
25		Subtract. At least 3 [8s] are left.
− 24	3	The third partial quotient. 3 ∗ 8 = 24
1	23	Subtract. Add partial quotients: 10 + 10 + 3 = 23
↑	↑	
Remainder	**Quotient**	**Answer: 23 R1**

Solve.

1. 639 ÷ 9 Answer: ______________

2. 954 ÷ 18 Answer: ______________

3. 1,990 / 24 Answer: ______________

4. Robert is making a photo album. 6 photos fit on a page. How many pages will he need for 497 photos? ___________ pages

Use with Lesson 4.2.

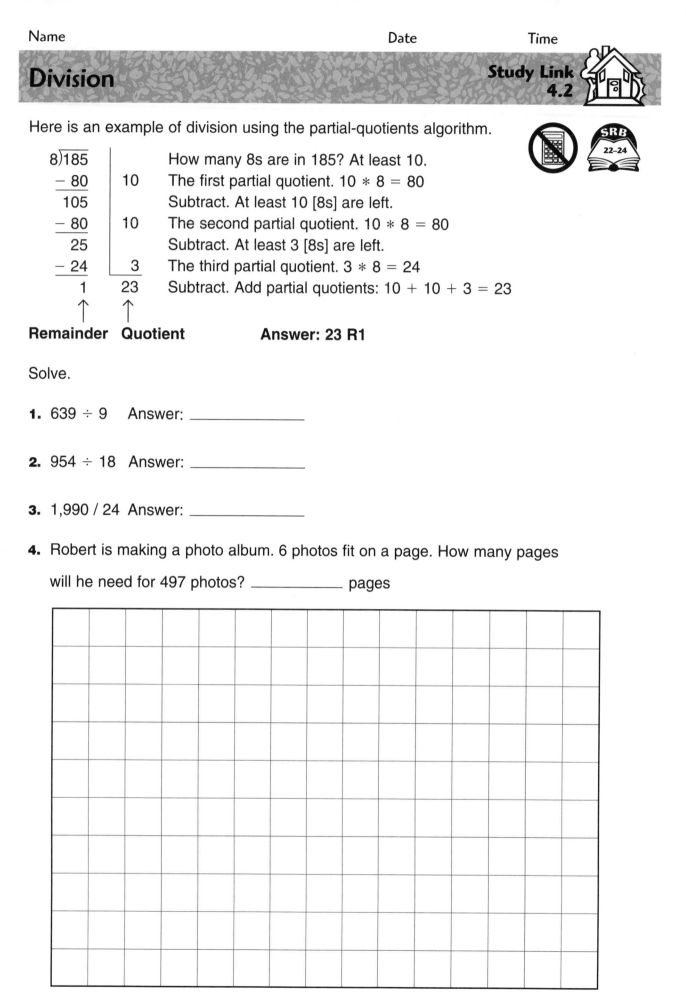

Name Date Time

Distance to School

Study Link 4.3

There are two ways to go from Josephina's house to school. She can take Elm Street and then Washington Avenue. She can also take Snakey Lane.

Use the map and scale below to answer the questions.

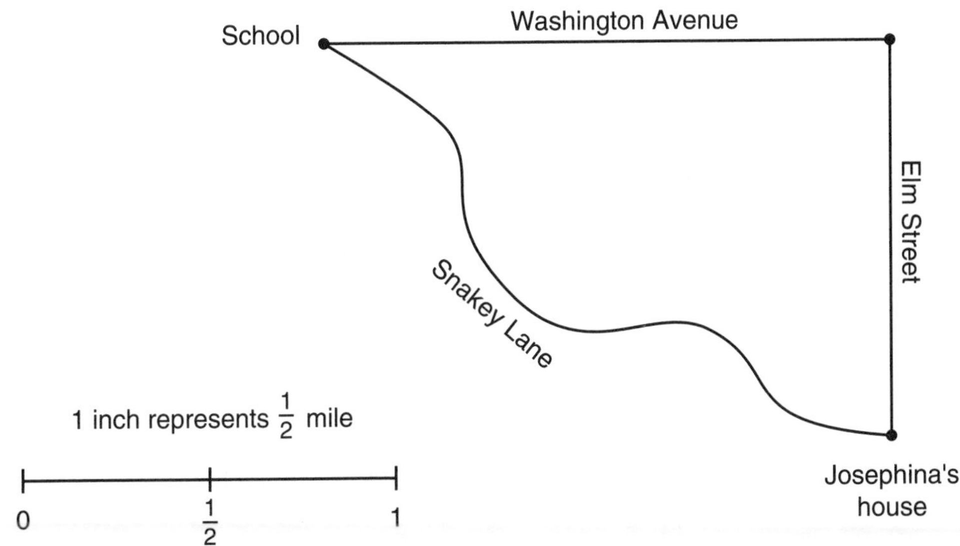

1. Josephina started walking from home to school along Elm Street.

a. How far would Josephina walk before she turned onto Washington Avenue? __________

b. How far would she be from school when she turned the corner? __________

2. a. If Josephina wanted to take the shortest route to school, which road(s) should she take? __________

b. What is this distance? __________

3. Josephina's father jogged from home to the school along Snakey Lane. He jogged back home along Washington Avenue and Elm Street. About how far did he jog in all? __________

4. Josephina left school and walked down Snakey Lane. Her father left home at the same time and walked up Snakey Lane. If her father was walking twice as fast as Josephina, where did they meet? Put a mark on the road where they met. On the back of this page, explain how you found your answer.

Name Date Time

Estimate and Calculate Quotients

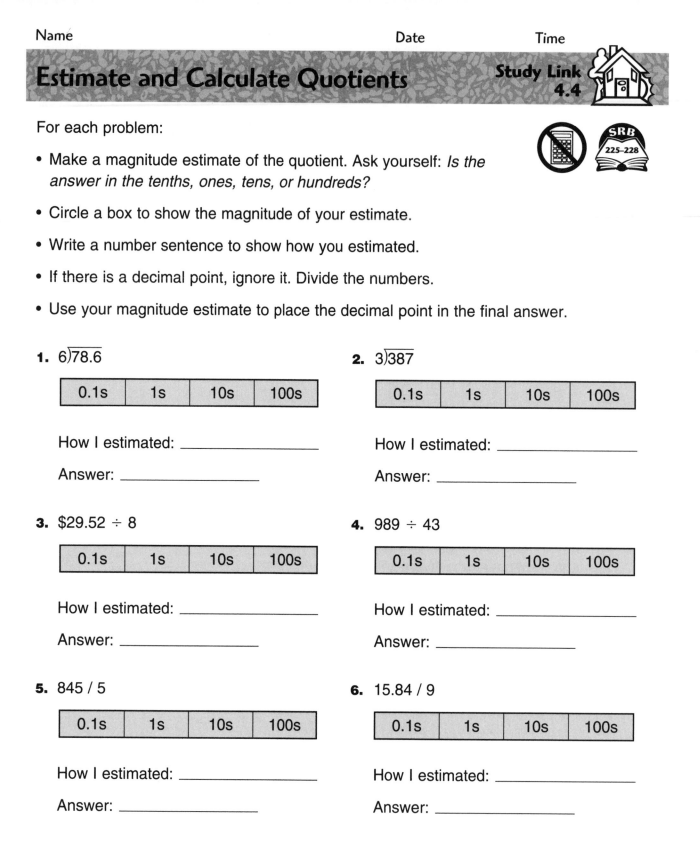

Study Link 4.4

For each problem:

- Make a magnitude estimate of the quotient. Ask yourself: *Is the answer in the tenths, ones, tens, or hundreds?*
- Circle a box to show the magnitude of your estimate.
- Write a number sentence to show how you estimated.
- If there is a decimal point, ignore it. Divide the numbers.
- Use your magnitude estimate to place the decimal point in the final answer.

1. $6\overline{)78.6}$

0.1s	1s	10s	100s

How I estimated: ____________

Answer: ____________

2. $3\overline{)387}$

0.1s	1s	10s	100s

How I estimated: ____________

Answer: ____________

3. $29.52 ÷ 8

0.1s	1s	10s	100s

How I estimated: ____________

Answer: ____________

4. 989 ÷ 43

0.1s	1s	10s	100s

How I estimated: ____________

Answer: ____________

5. 845 / 5

0.1s	1s	10s	100s

How I estimated: ____________

Answer: ____________

6. 15.84 / 9

0.1s	1s	10s	100s

How I estimated: ____________

Answer: ____________

Name Date Time

Division Number Stories with Remainders

Study Link 4.5

For each number story:

- Draw a picture and write a number sentence if you want.
- Use a division algorithm to solve the problem.
- Decide what to do about the remainder.
- Explain why you treated the remainder the way you did.

Example

You need to set up benches for a play. Each bench can seat 7 people. You expect 66 people to attend. How many benches do you need? 10 benches

What did you do about the remainder? Circle the answer.

Ignored it. Reported it as a fraction or decimal. (Rounded the answer up.)

Why? *9 benches seat 63 people. One more bench is needed for 3 remaining people.*

1. It costs \$50.00 to be a member of a soccer team. The team plays 8 games during the season. What is the cost per game? \$________

What did you do about the remainder? Circle the answer.

Ignored it. Reported it as a fraction or decimal. Rounded the answer up.

Why? ______________________________

____

2. Lynn is having a party. Pizzas cost \$8.00 each. How many pizzas can she buy with \$60.00? ________ pizzas

What did you do about the remainder? Circle the answer.

Ignored it. Reported it as a fraction or decimal. Rounded the answer up.

Why? ______________________________

____

Name Date Time

Variables

Study Link 4.6

SRB 202

For Problems 1–3:

- Find the value of x in the first number sentence.
- Use this value to complete the second number sentence.

1. x = number of days in a week

$x^2 =$ ________

2. $x = \frac{1}{10}$ of 100

$x * 78 =$ ________

3. x = largest sum possible with 2 six-sided dice

$598 + x =$ ________

4. Count the number of letters in your first name and in your last name.

a. My first name has ________ letters. **b.** My last name has ________ letters.

c. Find the product of these 2 numbers. Product = ________.

Answer the questions in Problems 5–11 by replacing x with the product you found in Problem 4.

5. Is x a prime or a composite number? ____________

6. Is $\frac{x}{30}$ less than 1? ____________

7. Which is larger: $3 * x$ or $x + 100$? ____________

8. What is the median and the range for this set of 3 weights: 30 pounds, 52 pounds, x pounds? ____________

9. There are 200 students at Henry Clissold School. x% speak Spanish. How many students speak Spanish? ____________

10. $(3x + 5) - 7 =$ ____________

11. True or false: $x^2 > 30 * x$ ____________

Name Date Time

Family Letter

Study Link 4.7

Unit 5: Fractions, Decimals, and Percents

The focus of Unit 5 will be on naming numbers as fractions, decimals, and percents. Your child will use pattern blocks to review basic fraction and mixed-number concepts and notations, and will formulate rules for finding equivalent fractions.

In *Fourth Grade Everyday Mathematics,* your child learned to convert easy fractions, such as $\frac{1}{2}$, $\frac{1}{4}$, $\frac{1}{10}$, and $\frac{3}{4}$, to equivalent decimals and percents. For example, $\frac{1}{2}$ can be renamed as 0.5 and as 50%. Your child will now learn (with the help of a calculator) how to rename any fraction as a decimal and as a percent.

In this unit, *Everyday Mathematics* introduces two new games: *Estimation Squeeze,* to practice estimating products; and *Frac-Tac-Toe,* to practice converting fractions to decimals and percents. These games, like others introduced earlier, are used to reduce the tedium that often comes with the drill of arithmetic skills. Your child will look forward to playing these games. Both games use simple materials (calculator, number cards, and pennies or other counters) so that you can play them at home.

Your child will explore historical data about the United States as the American Tour continues. The class will study education information from the past and compare it with current information.

Please keep this Family Letter for reference as your child works through Unit 5.

Vocabulary

Important terms in Unit 5:

bar graph A graph that uses horizontal or vertical bars to represent data.

circle graph A graph in which a circle and its interior are divided into parts to show the parts of a set of data. The whole circle represents the whole set of data.

denominator The number below the line in a fraction. In a fraction where a whole is divided into equal parts, the denominator represents the number of equal parts into which the whole (the ONE or unit) is divided. In the fraction $\frac{a}{b}$, b is the denominator.

equivalent fractions Fractions that have different denominators but name the same amount. For example, $\frac{1}{2}$ and $\frac{4}{8}$ are equivalent fractions.

improper fraction A fraction whose numerator is greater than or equal to its denominator. For example, $\frac{4}{3}$, $\frac{5}{2}$, $\frac{4}{4}$, and $\frac{24}{12}$ are improper fractions. In *Everyday Mathematics,* improper fractions are sometimes called "top-heavy" fractions.

mixed number A number that is written using both a whole number and a fraction. For example, $2\frac{1}{4}$ is a mixed number equal to $2 + \frac{1}{4}$.

numerator The number above the line in a fraction. In a fraction where the whole is divided into a number of equal parts, the numerator represents the number of equal parts that are being considered. In the fraction $\frac{a}{b}$, a is the numerator.

percent (%) Per hundred, or out of a hundred. For example, "48% of the students in the school are boys" means that 48 out of every 100 students in the school are boys.

Percent Circle A tool on the Geometry Template that is used to measure or draw figures that involve percents (such as circle graphs).

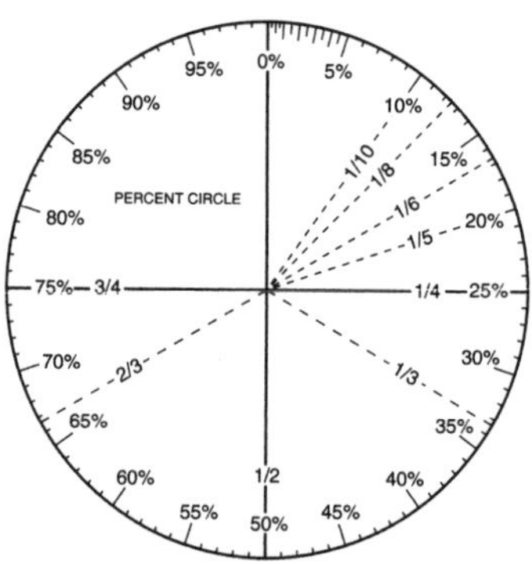

repeating decimal A decimal in which one digit or a group of digits is repeated without end. For example, 0.333... and $0.\overline{147}$ are repeating decimals.

Do-Anytime Activities

To work with your child on the concepts taught in this unit and in previous units, try these interesting and rewarding activities:

1. Help your child find fractions, decimals, and percents in the everyday world—in newspaper advertisements, on measuring tools, in recipes, in the sports section of the newspaper, and so on.
2. Over a period of time, have your child record daily temperatures in the morning and in the evening; and keep track of the temperatures in a chart. Then have your child make a graph from the data. Ask questions about the data. For example, have your child find the differences in temperatures from morning to evening or from one day to the next.
3. Practice using percents in the context of tips. For example, have your child calculate $\frac{1}{10}$ or 10% of amounts of money. Invite your child to find the tip the next time the family goes out for dinner.
4. Ask your child to identify 2-dimensional and 3-dimensional shapes around the house.

Building Skills through Games

In Unit 5, your child will practice operations and computation skills by playing the following games. For detailed instructions, see the *Student Reference Book.*

Multiplication Bull's-Eye See *Student Reference Book*, page 284
Two players use 4 each of the number cards 0–9, a six-sided die, and a calculator to play. This game provides practice in estimating products.

Estimation Squeeze See *Student Reference Book*, page 268
This is a game for two players who use a single calculator. The game provides practice in estimating products.

Frac-Tac-Toe See *Student Reference Book*, pages 274-276
This is a game for two players. Game materials include 4 each of the number cards 0-10, pennies or counters of two colors, a calculator, and a gameboard. The gameboard is a 5-by-5 number grid that resembles a bingo card. Several versions of the gameboard are shown in the *Student Reference Book. Frac-Tac-Toe* helps students practice converting fractions to decimals and percents.

Fraction/Percent Concentration See *Student Reference Book*, page 278
This game provides help in memorizing some of the easy fraction/percent equivalencies. Two or three players use 1 set of *Fraction/Percent Concentration* Tiles and a calculator to play.

As You Help Your Child with Homework

As your child brings assignments home, you may want to go over the instructions together, clarifying them as necessary. The answers listed below will guide you through this unit's Study Links.

Study Link 5.1

1. 9 **2.** 14 **3.** $\frac{4}{5}$

4. $\frac{9}{10}$ **5.** 70 **6.** 16

7. a. 9

b. Sample answer: They have $\frac{3}{8}$ of the distance left to ride. $\frac{1}{8}$ of 24 miles is 3 miles. So $\frac{3}{8}$ of 24 miles is 3 * 3 = 9 miles.

8. a. \$9 **b.** \$15

Study Link 5.2

3. $2\frac{1}{2}$; $\frac{5}{2}$ **4.** $2\frac{4}{6}$, or $2\frac{2}{3}$; $\frac{16}{6}$, or $\frac{8}{3}$

5. $1\frac{2}{3}$; $\frac{5}{3}$ **6.** $2\frac{1}{6}$; $\frac{13}{6}$

7. $2\frac{5}{6}$; $\frac{17}{6}$ **8.** Answers vary.

Study Link 5.3

1. 4 **2.** 12 **3.** 1; 4

4. $\frac{4}{4} = 1$ **5.** $\frac{6}{8} = \frac{3}{4}$ **6.** $\frac{5}{4} = 1\frac{1}{4}$

7. $\frac{9}{8}$, or $1\frac{1}{8}$ cups **8.** $\frac{7}{8}$ inch **9.** Answers vary.

Study Link 5.4

1. $\frac{6}{10}$ **2.** $\frac{15}{18}$ **3.** = **4.** no **5.** no

6. = **7.** = **8.** = **9.** = **10.** no

11. = **12.** no **13.** 6 **14.** 4 **15.** 12

16. 21 **17.** 40 **18.** 2

Study Link 5.5

1. 0.4 **2.** 1.9 **3.** 20.7 **4.** 24.0

5. 60.9 **6.** 160.6 **7.** 181.3 **8.** 296.4

9. 297.9 **10.** 316.0

Study Link 5.6

1. $\frac{7}{10}$; $1\frac{1}{10}$; $2\frac{3}{10}$; $4\frac{9}{10}$

2. 9.5

3. a. $\frac{15}{45}$, or $\frac{1}{3}$ **b.** $0.\overline{3}$ **c.** $\frac{9}{45}$, or $\frac{1}{5}$

d. 0.2 **e.** $\frac{3}{45}$, or $\frac{1}{15}$ **f.** $0.0\overline{6}$

Study Link 5.7

1. a. 2 **b.** 8 **c.** $\frac{2}{8}$, or $\frac{1}{4}$

2. a. 6 **b.** 18 **c.** $\frac{6}{18}$, or $\frac{1}{3}$ **d.** $0.\overline{3}$

3. a. 4 **b.** $\frac{4}{9}$ **c.** $0.\overline{4}$

4. a. 6 **b.** $\frac{6}{22}$, or $\frac{3}{11}$ **c.** $0.\overline{27}$ or 0.27

Study Link 5.8

1. $\frac{3}{4} = 0.75 = 75\%$; $\frac{14}{16} = 0.875 = 88\%$;
$\frac{15}{25} = 0.6 = 60\%$; $\frac{17}{20} = 0.85 = 85\%$;
$\frac{3}{8} = 0.375 = 38\%$

3. $\frac{3}{8}$; $\frac{15}{25}$; $\frac{3}{4}$; $\frac{17}{20}$; $\frac{14}{16}$

4. \$130

5. 10

6. 4; If 80% is 16 words, then 10% is $\frac{1}{8}$ of 16 words, or 2 words. So 100% is 10 * 2, or 20 words. The test had 20 words. Louis missed 20 − 16 = 4 words.

7. \$10,000

Study Link 5.9

2. The circle graph; Sample answer: Because percent means per 100, or out of 100, the graph shows $\frac{33}{100}$ chose blue. If 100 students were in the class, 33 of them would have chosen blue.

3. Bar graph

4. Line graph

Study Link 5.10

1. a. 50% **b.** 15% **c.** 35%

Study Link 5.11

Check your child's circle graph.

Study Link 5.12

1. Jan's recipe calls for $\frac{1}{2}$ cup of flour.

2. Melise scored 84% on her spelling test.

3. Renee had \$0.65 left after buying lunch.

Name Date Time

Parts-and-Whole Fraction Practice

Study Link 5.1

For the following problems, use counters or draw pictures to help you.

SRB 74 75 221

1. If 15 counters are the whole set, how many are $\frac{3}{5}$ of the set?

   ________ counters

2. If 18 counters are the whole set, how many are $\frac{7}{9}$ of the set? ________ counters

3. If 20 counters are the whole set, what fraction of the set is 16 counters? ________

4. If 50 counters are the whole set, what fraction of the set is 45 counters? ________

5. If 35 counters are half of a set, what is the whole set? ________ counters

6. If 12 counters are $\frac{3}{4}$ of a set, what is the whole set? ________ counters

7. Gerald and Michelle went on a 24-mile bike ride. They rode $\frac{1}{4}$ of the distance before stopping. By lunchtime, they rode $\frac{5}{8}$ of the total distance.

   a. How many miles did they have left to ride after lunch? ________ miles

   b. Explain what you did to solve the problem.

   ____

   ____

   ____

Challenge

8. Jen and Heather went to lunch. When the bill came, Jen discovered she had only \$6. Luckily, Heather had enough money to pay the other part, or $\frac{3}{5}$, of the bill.

   a. How much did Heather pay? ________ b. How much was the total bill? ________

   c. Explain how you figured out Heather's portion of the bill.

   ____

   ____

   ____

Name Date Time

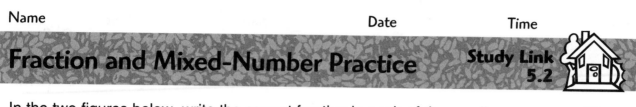

Fraction and Mixed-Number Practice

Study Link 5.2

In the two figures below, write the correct fraction in each of the smaller regions. Check to see that the fractional parts in each figure add up to 1.

1. The whole 6-cm-by-4-cm rectangle is worth 1.

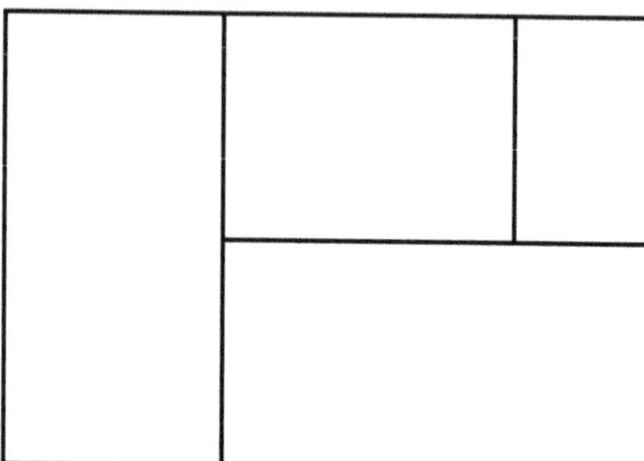

2. The whole square is worth 1.

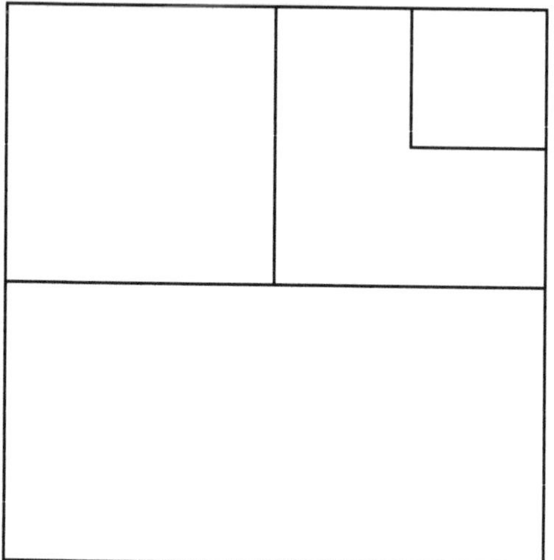

For the problems below, the hexagon is worth 1. Write the mixed-number name and the fraction name shown by each diagram.

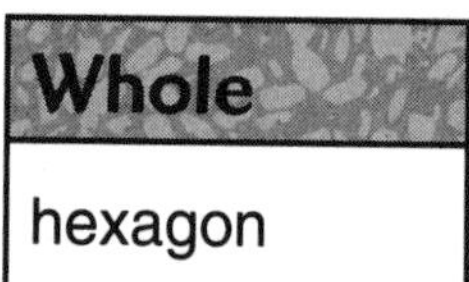

3. Mixed number ____________

Fraction ____________

4. Mixed number ____________

Fraction ____________

5. Mixed number ____________

Fraction ____________

6. Mixed number ____________

Fraction ____________

7. Mixed number ____________

Fraction ____________

8. Make up a mixed-number problem of your own on the back of this page.

Name Date Time

Fraction-Stick Problems

Study Link 5.3

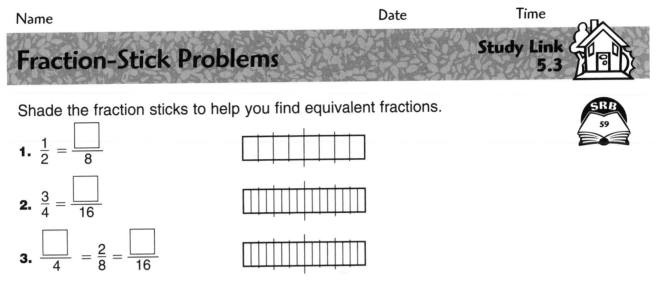

SRB 59

Shade the fraction sticks to help you find equivalent fractions.

1. $\frac{1}{2} = \frac{\square}{8}$ 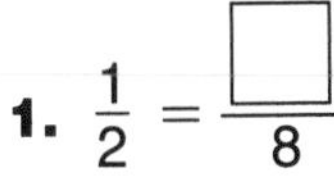

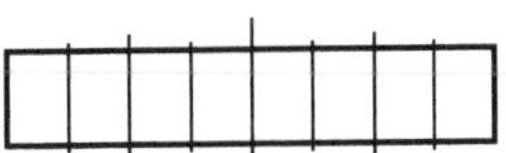

2. $\frac{3}{4} = \frac{\square}{16}$ 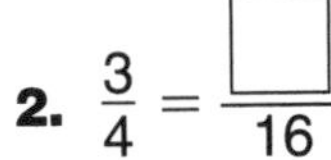

3. $\frac{\square}{4} = \frac{2}{8} = \frac{\square}{16}$

Shade the fraction sticks to help you solve the addition problems.

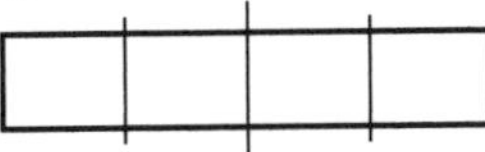

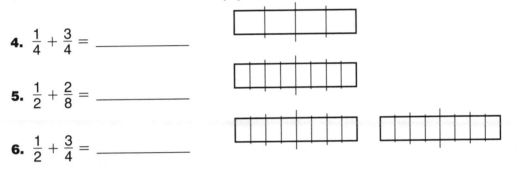

4. $\frac{1}{4} + \frac{3}{4} =$ ________

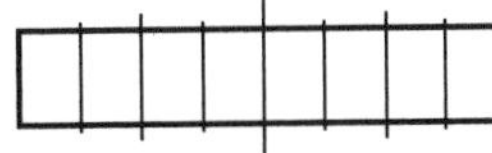

5. $\frac{1}{2} + \frac{2}{8} =$ ________

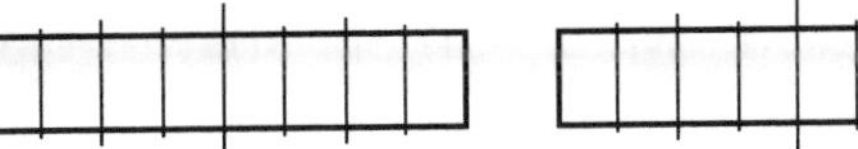

6. $\frac{1}{2} + \frac{3}{4} =$ ________

Shade the fraction sticks to help you solve the fraction number stories.

7. Joe was baking a cake. He added $\frac{3}{4}$ cup of white flour and $\frac{3}{8}$ cup of whole wheat flour. How much flour did he use in all?

________ (unit)

8. Twanda glued together 2 wooden boards. One board was $\frac{3}{8}$-inch thick. The other was $\frac{1}{2}$-inch thick. How thick is the new board?

________ (unit)

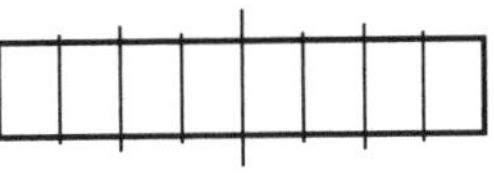

9. On the back of this page, write a number story using fractions. Write a number model to show how you solved it.

Name Date Time

Equivalent Fractions

Study Link 5.4

SRB 59 60

Find equivalent fractions by using the fraction sticks below.

1. Shade $\frac{3}{5}$ of the fraction stick. Draw a horizontal line to split all sections of the stick into two equal parts.

$\frac{3}{5} = \frac{\square}{\square}$

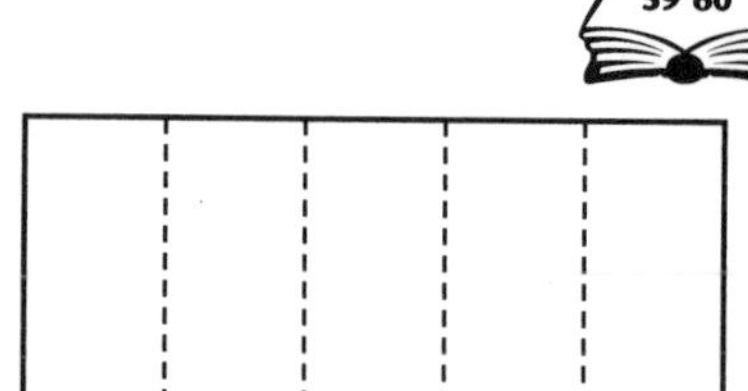

2. Shade $\frac{5}{6}$ of the fraction stick. Draw horizontal lines to split all sections of the stick into three equal parts.

$\frac{5}{6} = \frac{\square}{\square}$

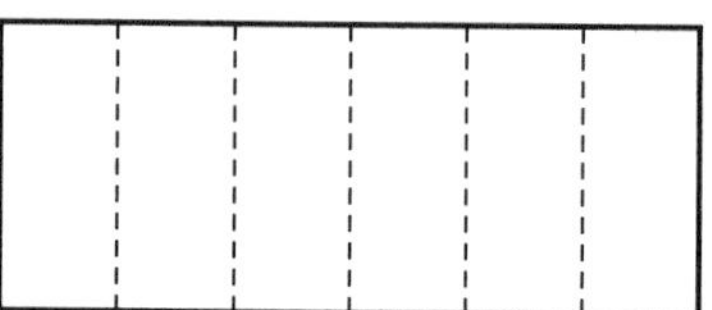

In each of the following:

- If the fractions are equivalent, write = in the answer blank.
- If the fractions are not equivalent, write NO in the answer blank.

3. $\frac{3}{4}$ ______ $\frac{9}{12}$

4. $\frac{3}{10}$ ______ $\frac{1}{5}$

5. $\frac{7}{14}$ ______ $\frac{8}{15}$

6. $\frac{36}{72}$ ______ $\frac{1}{2}$

7. $\frac{7}{12}$ ______ $\frac{21}{36}$

8. $\frac{16}{100}$ ______ $\frac{8}{50}$

9. $\frac{10}{12}$ ______ $\frac{5}{6}$

10. $\frac{9}{16}$ ______ $\frac{45}{48}$

11. $\frac{8}{3}$ ______ $\frac{16}{6}$

12. $\frac{9}{36}$ ______ $\frac{18}{108}$

Fill in the box to complete the equivalent fraction.

13. $\frac{3}{5} = \frac{\square}{10}$

14. $\frac{44}{55} = \frac{\square}{5}$

15. $\frac{35}{60} = \frac{7}{\square}$

16. $\frac{2}{3} = \frac{14}{\square}$

17. $\frac{12}{\square} = \frac{3}{10}$

18. $\frac{\square}{15} = \frac{6}{45}$

Name Date Time

Decimal Numbers

Study Link 5.5

1. Mark each of these numbers on the number line. The first one is done for you.

30.13 30.72 31.05 29.94 30.38

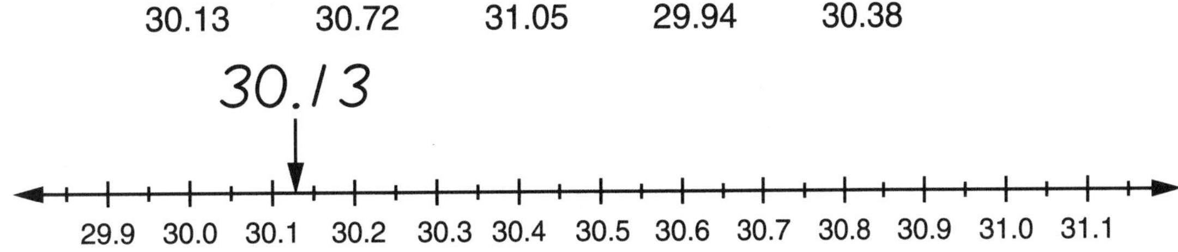

2. Below is a list of the 10 smallest countries in the world. Round the area of each country to the nearest tenth of a square kilometer.

Country	Area in Square Kilometers	Area Rounded to the Nearest Tenth of a Square Kilometer
1. Vatican City	0.44 km^2	_______ km^2
2. Monaco	1.89 km^2	_______ km^2
3. Nauru	20.72 km^2	_______ km^2
4. Tuvalu	23.96 km^2	_______ km^2
5. San Marino	60.87 km^2	_______ km^2
6. Liechtenstein	160.58 km^2	_______ km^2
7. Marshall Islands	181.30 km^2	_______ km^2
8. St. Kitts and Nevis	296.37 km^2	_______ km^2
9. Maldives	297.85 km^2	_______ km^2
10. Malta	315.98 km^2	_______ km^2

Source: Britannica Online

Just a Chip Off the Old Block

In area, the United States is the fourth-largest country in the world, covering about 9,373,000 square kilometers. Rhode Island, the smallest state in the United States, covers about 3,000 square kilometers.

Source: Statistical Abstracts of the United States

Name Date Time

Decimals, Fractions, and Mixed Numbers

Study Link 5.6

1. The five driest inhabited places in the world and the average amount of rain they each receive each year are listed below. Convert each decimal measurement to a fraction or a mixed number.

Location	Average Annual Rainfall Expressed as a Decimal	Average Annual Rainfall Expressed as a Fraction or a Mixed Number
Aswan, Egypt	0.5 mm	$\frac{1}{2}$ mm
Luxor, Egypt	0.7 mm	______ mm
Arica, Chile	1.1 mm	______ mm
Ica, Peru	2.3 mm	______ mm
Antofagasta, Chile	4.9 mm	______ mm

Source: The Top 10 of Everything 2000

2. What is the total average annual rainfall for these 5 locations? ______ mm

3. America's longest place name is

Chargoggagoggmanchauggagoggchaubunagungamaugg.

This name for a lake near Webster, Massachusetts, is 45 letters long. It is a Native American name that means, "You fish on your side, I'll fish on mine, and no one fishes in the middle." Use this word to answer the problems below.

a. What fraction of the word is made up of the letter *g*? ______

b. Write the fraction from Part a as a decimal. ______

c. What fraction of the word is made up of the letter *a*? ______

d. Write the fraction from Part c as a decimal. ______

e. What fraction of the word is made up of the letter *c*? ______

f. Write the fraction from Part e as a decimal. ______

Name Date Time

Champion Tennis Players

The following table shows the number of times through 1999 that each of the following players won the four "Grand Slam" tennis tournaments.

Player	Australian Open	Wimbledon	French Open	U.S. Open	Total
Chris Evert Lloyd	2	3	7	6	18
Monica Seles	4	0	3	2	9
Steffi Graf	4	7	6	5	22
Jimmy Connors	1	2	0	5	8
Pete Sampras	2	6	0	6	14

Source: The World Almanac and Book of Facts 1999

1. a. How many times did Jimmy Connors win Wimbledon? ________

b. What is the total number of times he won the four tournaments listed above? ________

c. What fraction of this total were won at Wimbledon? ________

2. a. How many times did Chris Evert Lloyd win the U.S. Open? ________

b. What is the total number of times she won the four tournaments listed above? ________

c. What fraction of this total were won at the U.S. Open? ________

d. Write the above fraction as a decimal. ________

3. a. How many times has Monica Seles won the Australian Open? ________

b. What fraction is this of her total number of wins for these four tournaments? ________

c. Write the above fraction as a decimal. ________

4. a. How many times has Steffi Graf won the French Open? ________

b. What fraction is this of her total number of wins for these four tournaments? ________

c. Write the above fraction as a decimal. ________

Name Date Time

Percent Problems

Study Link 5.8

1. Convert the following fractions to decimals and percents. Round to the nearest whole percent.

Fraction	Decimal	Percent (rounded to the nearest whole percent)
$\frac{3}{4}$		
$\frac{14}{16}$		
$\frac{15}{25}$		
$\frac{17}{20}$		
$\frac{3}{8}$		

2. On the back of this page, explain how you could find the percent equivalent to $\frac{17}{20}$ without using a calculator.

3. Write the five fractions from Problem 1 in order from least to greatest.

_______ _______ _______ _______ _______

4. Katie spent 50% of her money on shoes for soccer. The shoes cost $65. How much money did Katie start with? _______

5. Tom got 70% correct on a music test. If he got 7 questions correct, how many questions were on the test? _______

6. Louis got 16 words correct on his vocabulary test. This was 80%. How many words did he miss? _______

Explain how you got your answer. _______

____

____

Challenge

7. Lincoln School raised $3,000 for charity. This is 30% of the school's goal. What is Lincoln School's goal? _______

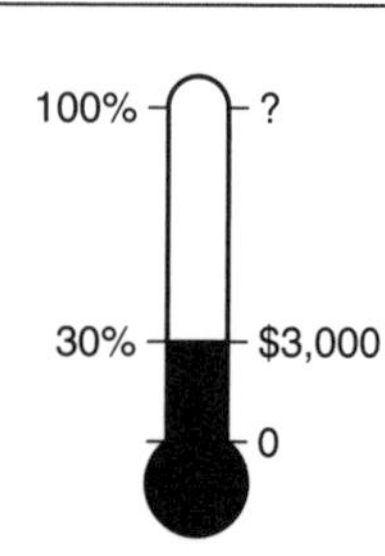

Use with Lesson 5.8.

Name Date Time

Graphs

Study Link 5.9

Brenda's class made a list of their favorite colors. The results were as follows:

Blue 8 Red 7 Yellow 3 Green 2 Other 4

1. Circle each graph that correctly represents the data above. (There may be more than one.)

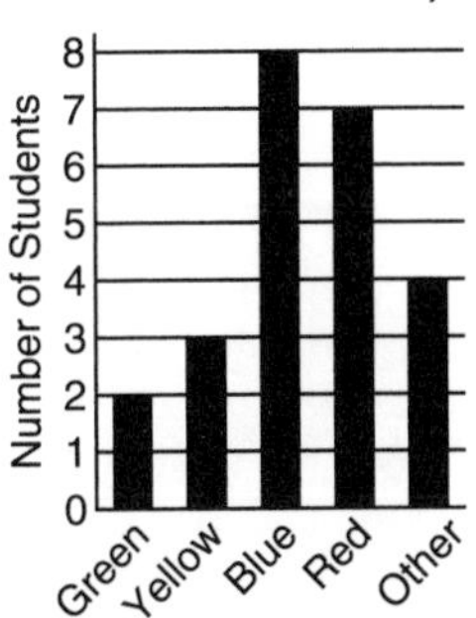

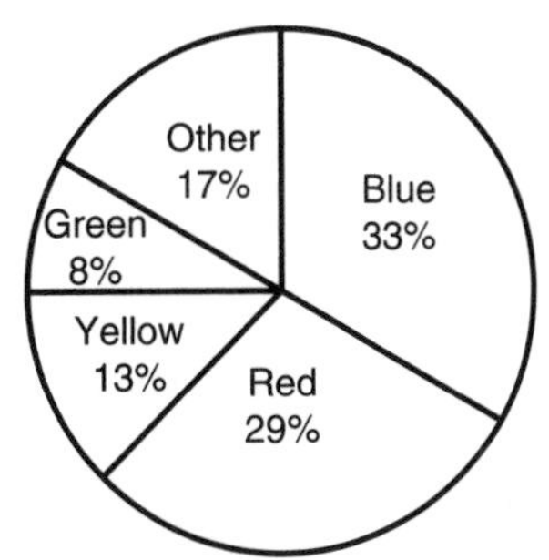

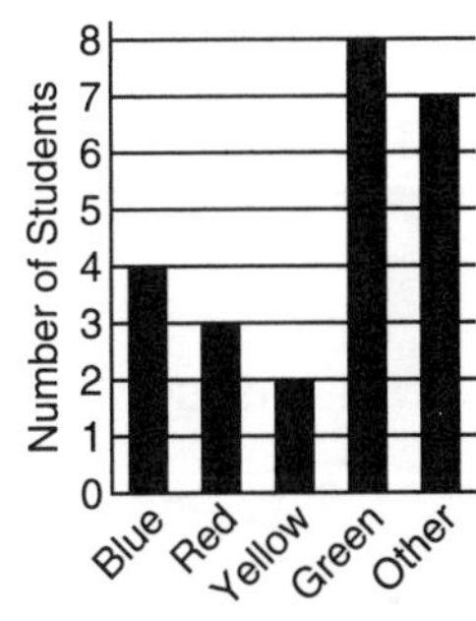

2. Which graph would help you answer the question "What fraction of the students chose blue as their favorite color?" ______

Explain. ______

______

______

Marsha kept track of the low temperatures at the end of May. They were as follows:

May 17	50°F	May 18	63°F	May 19	58°F	May 20	60°F
May 21	65°F	May 22	57°F	May 23	58°F	May 24	65°F
May 25	68°F	May 26	70°F	May 27	66°F	May 28	65°F
May 29	64°F	May 30	68°F	May 31	74°F		

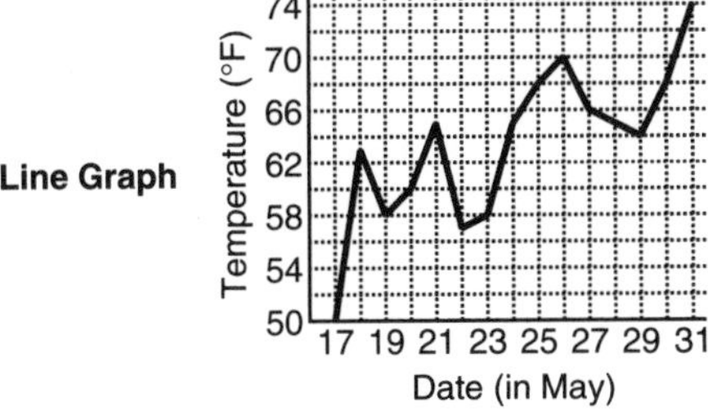

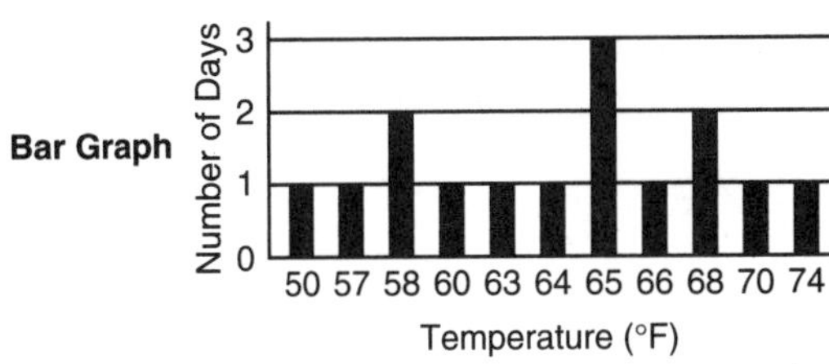

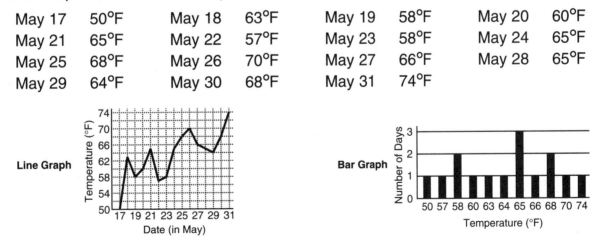

3. Which graph do you think is more helpful for answering the question "On how many days was the low temperature 65°F?" ______

4. Which graph do you think is more helpful for showing trends in the temperature for the last two weeks of May? ______

Name Date Time

Circle Graphs and Collecting Data

Study Link 5.10

Estimating the Size of Pieces in a Circle Graph

SRB 119 120

1. Estimate the percent of the circle for each piece of the graph at the right.

a. A is about ________ of the circle.

b. B is about ________ of the circle.

c. C is about ________ of the circle.

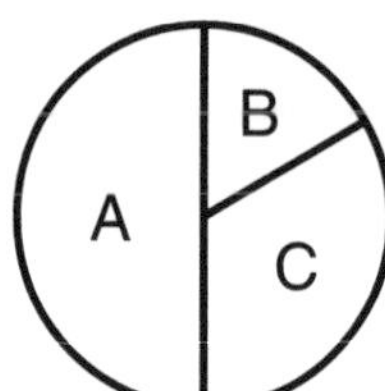

2. Draw a line connecting each data set with the most likely circle graph.

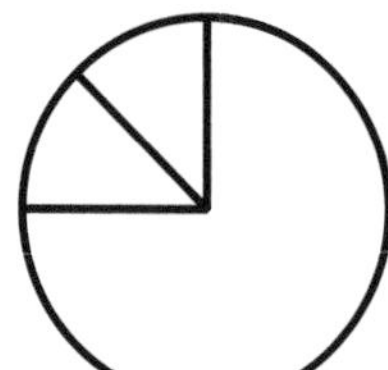

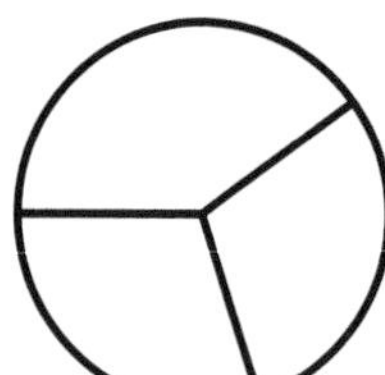

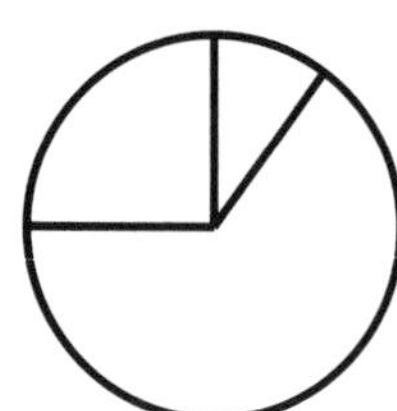

30% of Michel's class walks to school.	25% of Jeannene's toy cars are blue.	$\frac{1}{8}$ of Angelo's pants are jeans.
30% of Michel's class rides the bus.	10% of Jeannene's toy cars are striped.	$\frac{1}{8}$ of Angelo's pants are black dress pants.
40% of Michel's class rides in a car or van.	65% of Jeannene's toy cars are red.	$\frac{3}{4}$ of Angelo's pants are blue dress pants.

Challenge

3. Circle the graph above that you did not use. Write a set of data to match that circle graph.

____

____

Continue on the next page.

Name Date Time

Circle Graphs and Collecting Data (cont.)

The Number of States We've Been In

4. Talk with an adult at home and think of all the states you have ever been in. (Be sure to include the state you're living in.) Look at the map below to help you remember.

Use a pencil or crayon to mark each state you have been in.

Don't count any state that you have flown over in an airplane, unless the plane landed and you left the airport.

5. Count the number of states you have marked.

I have been in ________ states in my lifetime.

6. Now ask the adult to mark the map to show the states he or she has been in, using a different color or mark from yours.

Keep a tally as states are marked.

The adult I interviewed has been in ________ states.

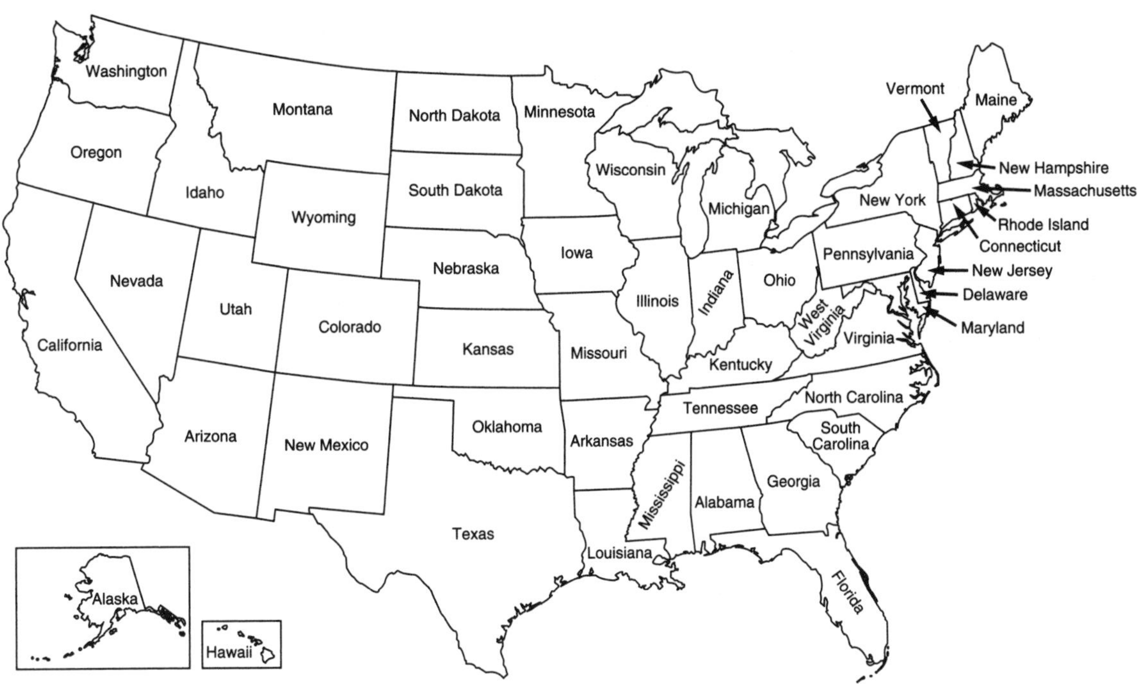

Note: Alaska and Hawaii are not shown to scale.

Student and adult: This data is important for our next mathematics class. Please bring this completed Study Link back to school tomorrow.

Name Date Time

What's in a Landfill?

Study Link 5.11

People who study landfills have estimated the percent of landfill space (volume) taken up by paper, food, plastic, and so on.

Space in landfills taken up by:

Paper	50%
Food and yard waste	13%
Plastic	10%
Metal	6%
Glass	1%
Other waste	20%

> *Think of it this way:*
> For every 100 boxes of garbage hauled to the dump, expect that about 50 boxes could be filled with paper, 6 with metal, 1 with glass, and so on.

Cut out the Percent Circle. Use it to make a circle graph for the data in the table. (Remember to label the graph and give it a title.)

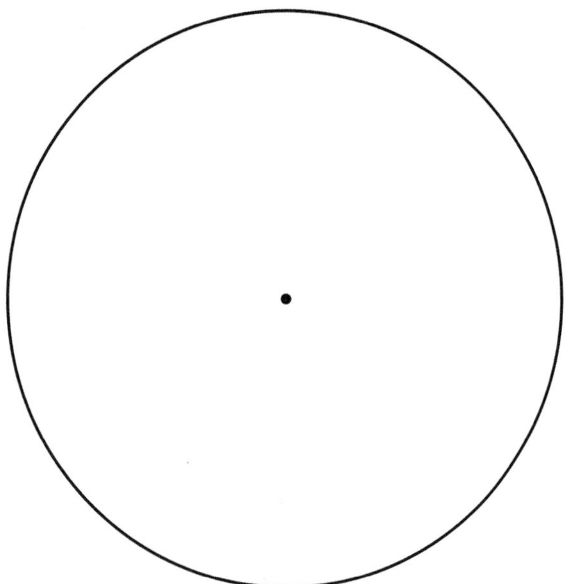

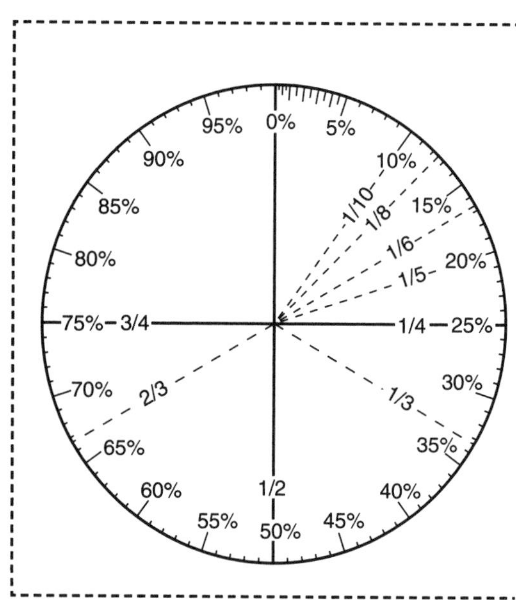

Name Date Time

Fraction Review

Study Link 5.12

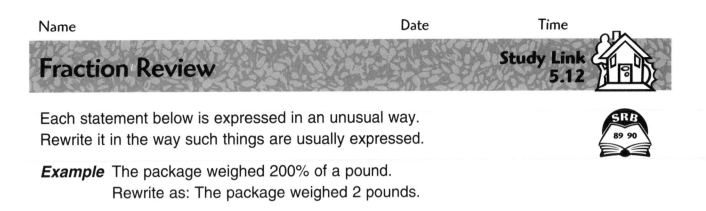

Each statement below is expressed in an unusual way.
Rewrite it in the way such things are usually expressed.

Example The package weighed 200% of a pound.
Rewrite as: The package weighed 2 pounds.

1. Jan's recipe calls for 50% of a cup of flour.

____

2. Melise scored 0.84 on her spelling test.

____

3. Renee had 65% of a dollar left after buying lunch.

____

Fill in the tag on each name-collection box. Cross out the names that do not belong and add 5 names of your own.

4.

$\frac{2}{4}$
$\frac{3}{8}$
0.5
100% − 50%
one-half

5.

$\frac{2}{3}$
one third less than 1
$\frac{5}{6}$
50%
0.23

Name Date Time

Unit 6: Using Data; Addition and Subtraction of Fractions

The authors of *Everyday Mathematics* believe that students should do serious and substantial work with data. Unit 6 provides many activities designed to present and teach relevant data skills and concepts, allowing your child ample opportunities to practice organizing and analyzing the data he or she collects.

The data that your child initially collects will usually consist of an unorganized collection of numbers. After organizing the data using a variety of methods, he or she will study the **landmarks** of the data. The following terms are called landmarks because they show the important features of the data:

- ▷ The **maximum** is the largest data value observed.
- ▷ The **minimum** is the smallest data value observed.
- ▷ The **range** is the difference between the maximum and the minimum.
- ▷ The **mode** is the "most popular" data value—the value observed most often.
- ▷ The **median** is the middle data value observed.
- ▷ The **mean,** commonly known as the "average," is a central value for a set of data.

At the end of the unit, students will have an opportunity to demonstrate their skills in this area by conducting a survey of their peers; gathering and organizing the data; analyzing their results; and writing a summary report.

Your child will continue his or her work with the American Tour by studying a variety of Native American measurements for length and distance based on parts of the body. Students will convert these body measures to personal measures by measuring their fingers, hands, and arms in both metric and U.S. customary units. In addition, your child will learn how to read a variety of contour-type maps, such as climate, precipitation, and growing-seasons maps.

Finally, students will explore addition and subtraction of fractions by using paper slide rules, the familiar clock face, and fraction sticks. They will learn to find common denominators and apply this skill in adding and subtracting fractions with unlike denominators.

Please keep this Family Letter for reference as your child works through Unit 6.

Vocabulary

Important terms in Unit 6:

angle of separation A measure of how far fingers can be spread apart. The figure shows the angle of separation between a person's thumb and first finger.

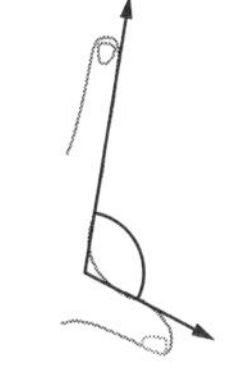

Angle of separation

common denominator Any number except zero that is a multiple of the denominators of two or more fractions. For example, the fractions $\frac{1}{2}$ and $\frac{2}{3}$ have common denominators 6, 12, 18, and so on.

contour line A curve on a map through places where a certain measurement (such as temperature or elevation) is the same. Often, contour lines separate regions that have been colored differently to show a range of conditions.

cubit An ancient unit of length, measured from the point of the elbow to the end of the middle finger. A cubit is about 18 inches.

decennial Occurring or being done every 10 years.

fair game A game in which each player has the same chance of winning. If any player has an advantage or disadvantage (for example, by playing first), then the game is not fair.

fathom A unit used by people who work with boats and ships to measure depths under water and lengths of cables. A fathom is now defined as 6 feet.

great span The distance from the tip of the thumb to the tip of the little finger (pinkie), when the hand is stretched as far as possible.

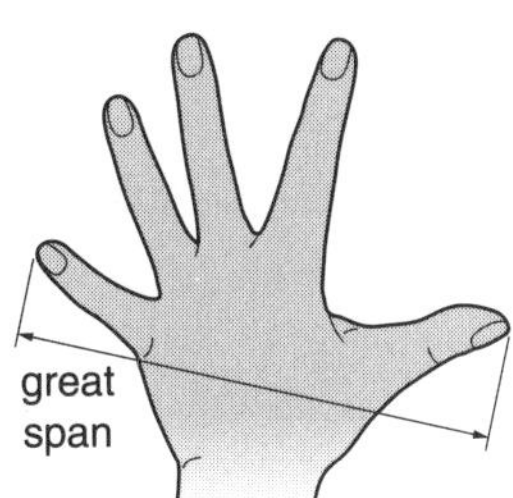

landmark A notable feature of a data set. Landmarks include the *median, mode, maximum, minimum,* and *range.*

line plot A sketch of data in which check marks, Xs, or other marks above a number line show the frequency of each value.

map legend (map key) A diagram that explains the symbols, markings, and colors on a map.

maximum The largest amount; the greatest number in a set of data.

mean The sum of a set of numbers divided by the number of numbers in the set. The mean is often referred to simply as the **average.**

median The middle value in a set of data when the data are listed in order from smallest to largest. If there is an even number of data points, the median is the *mean* of the two middle values.

minimum The smallest amount; the smallest number in a set of data.

mode The value or values that occur most often in a set of data.

normal span The distance from the tip of the thumb to the tip of the first (index) finger of an outstretched hand. Also called *span.*

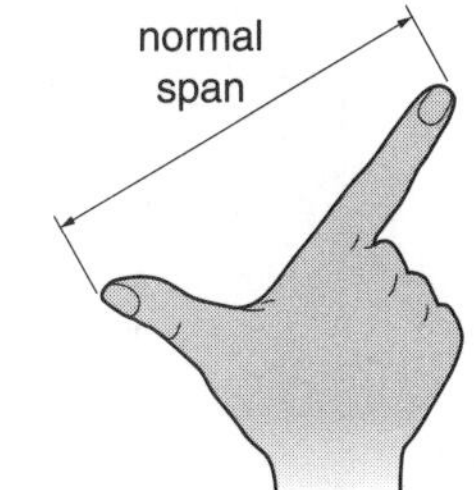

population In data collection, the collection of people or objects that is the focus of the study.

range The difference between the *maximum* and *minimum* in a set of data.

sample A part of a group chosen to represent the whole group.

simplest form A fraction less than 1 is in simplest form if there is no number other than 1 that divides its numerator and denominator evenly. A mixed number is in simplest form if its fractional part is in simplest form.

stem-and-leaf plot A display of data in which digits with larger place values are "stems" and digits with smaller place values are "leaves."

Stems (10s)	Leaves (1s)
2	4 4 5 6 7 7 8
3	1 1 2 2 6 6 6
4	1 1 3 5 8
5	0 2

Stem-and-leaf plot

survey A study that collects data.

Do-Anytime Activities

To work with your child on the concepts taught in this unit and in previous units, try these interesting and rewarding activities:

1. Have your child design and conduct an informal survey. Help him or her collect and organize the data, and then describe the data using data landmarks. Challenge your child to create different ways in which the organized data can be presented.

2. Encourage your child to develop his or her own set of personal measures for both metric and U.S. customary units.

Building Skills through Games

In this unit, your child will work on his or her understanding of angles and the addition and subtraction of fractions by playing the following games. For detailed instructions, see the *Student Reference Book.*

Frac-Tac-Toe See *Student Reference Book,* pages 274–276
This is a game for two players. Game materials include 4 each of the number cards 0–10, pennies or counters of two colors, a calculator, and a gameboard. The gameboard is a 5-by-5 number grid that resembles a bingo card. Several versions of the gameboard are shown in the *Student Reference Book. Frac-Tac-Toe* helps students practice converting fractions to decimals and percents.

Angle Tangle See *Student Reference Book,* page 258
This is a game for two players and requires a protactor, a straight-edge, and paper. The game provides practice with measuring angles and estimating angle measures.

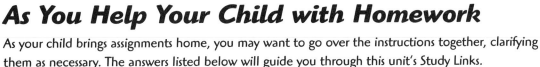

As You Help Your Child with Homework

As your child brings assignments home, you may want to go over the instructions together, clarifying them as necessary. The answers listed below will guide you through this unit's Study Links.

Study Link 6.1

3. a. 59 **b.** 24 **c.** 33
d. 36 **e.** 39.5

Study Link 6.2

1. a.–c. Answers vary.

2. a. cm; ft **b.** ounces; gal; liters
c. m; miles **d.** cm; ft; mm
e. kg; lb; grams

Study Link 6.3

1. 73 **2.** 19 **3.** 53

4. Sample answer: Cross off the highest and lowest values—31 and 73. Continue by crossing off the highest and lowest values remaining. Finally, only the number 53 remains. So 53 is the median.

Study Link 6.4

1. tapes and CDs

2. books and magazines

3. movie tickets

Study Link 6.5

Sample answers given for Problems 1–3.

1. 5, 7, 7, 8, 8, 9, 10, 13, 14, 15, 15, 15, 20

2.

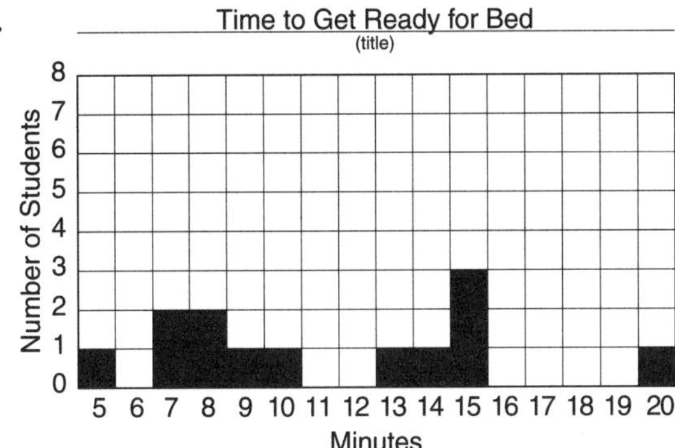

3. The number of minutes it takes to get ready for bed

Study Link 6.6

1. Sample answer: The ages of the oldest people we know
Title: The Oldest People Our Class Knows
Unit: Years

2. a. 77 **b.** 94 **c.** 85 **d.** 85

3. Sample answer: Scores on a science test
Title: Science Test Scores
Unit: % Correct

4. a. 32 **b.** 99 **c.** 66 **d.** 78.5

Study Link 6.7

1. Florida; Arizona

2. Oregon; Washington

3. Answers vary.

4. Utah; Wyoming

Study Link 6.8

1. $\frac{12}{20}$, or $\frac{3}{5}$ **2.** $18\frac{1}{2}$; 9

3. 14; $1\frac{6}{8}$, or $1\frac{3}{4}$ **4.** 7; $\frac{7}{8}$

5. $\frac{7}{8}$ **6.** $2\frac{2}{8}$, or $2\frac{1}{4}$

Study Link 6.9

1. $\frac{22}{15}$, or $1\frac{7}{15}$ **2.** $\frac{1}{18}$

3. $\frac{9}{4}$, or $2\frac{1}{4}$ **4.** 4; $7\frac{3}{4}$

5. $5\frac{5}{6}$

Study Link 6.10

1. $\frac{18}{22} - \frac{11}{22} = \frac{7}{22}$ **2.** $\frac{20}{36} - \frac{9}{36} = \frac{11}{36}$

3. $\frac{21}{30} + \frac{8}{30} = \frac{29}{30}$ **4.** $\frac{21}{30} - \frac{8}{30} = \frac{13}{30}$

5. $\frac{19}{18}$, or $1\frac{1}{18}$ **6.** $\frac{59}{42}$, or $1\frac{17}{42}$

7. $\frac{1}{6}$ **8.** $\frac{3}{4}$

9. $\frac{2}{12}$, or $\frac{1}{6}$ **10.** $\frac{1}{2}$

11. $\frac{1}{3}$ **12.** $\frac{23}{12}$, or $1\frac{11}{12}$

13. $\frac{23}{12}$, or $1\frac{11}{12}$ **14.** $\frac{19}{12}$, or $1\frac{7}{12}$

Name Date Time

The Standing Long Jump

Study Link 6.1

Ms. Perez's physical education class participated in the standing long jump. Following are the results rounded to the nearest inch.

24	35	33	48	33	48	27	35	27	55	43	24
55	33	52	33	29	59	26	59	48	37	42	42

1. Organize these data on the line plot below.

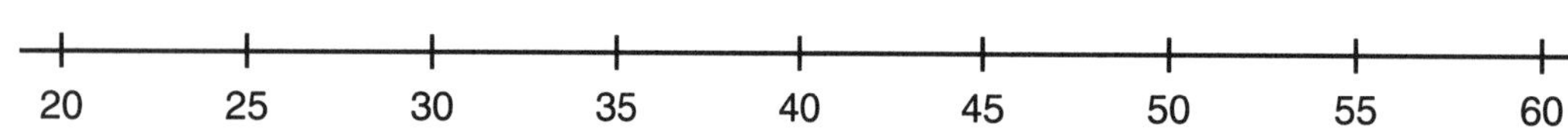

2. Make a bar graph for these data.

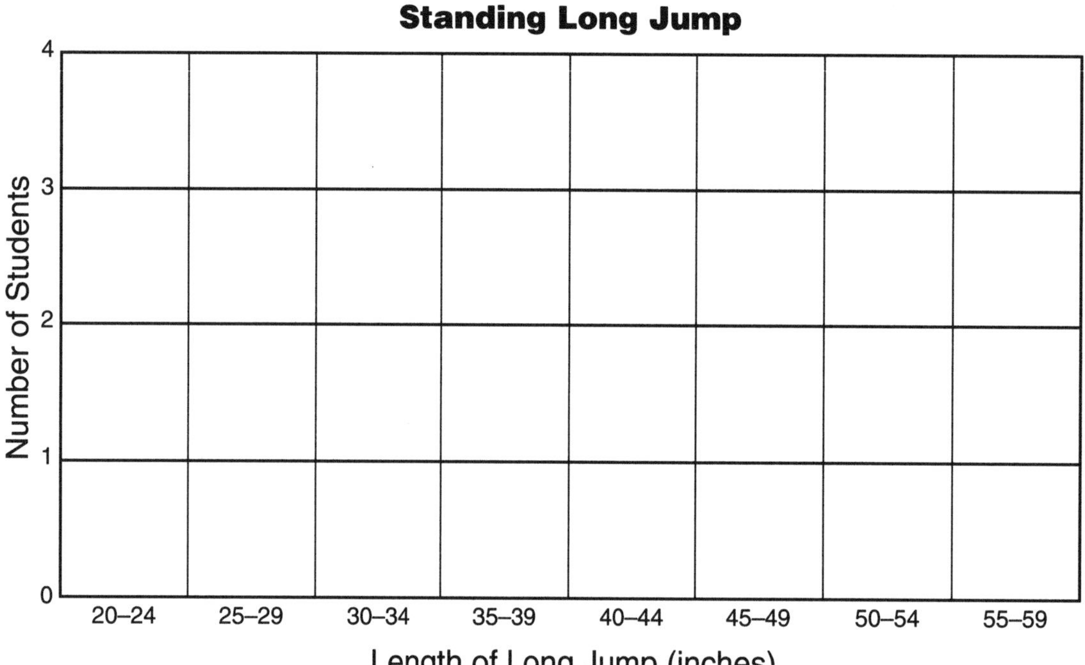

3. Find the following landmarks for the standing long jump data:

a. Maximum (the longest distance a student jumped): ________ in.

b. Minimum (the shortest distance a student jumped): ________ in.

c. Mode: ________ in.

d. Median: ________ in.

e. Mean (average): ________ in. (Use a calculator. Add the distances and divide the sum by the number of jumps. Round to the nearest tenth.)

Name Date Time

Standard and Nonstandard Units

1. Use your body measures to find three objects that are about the size of each measurement below.

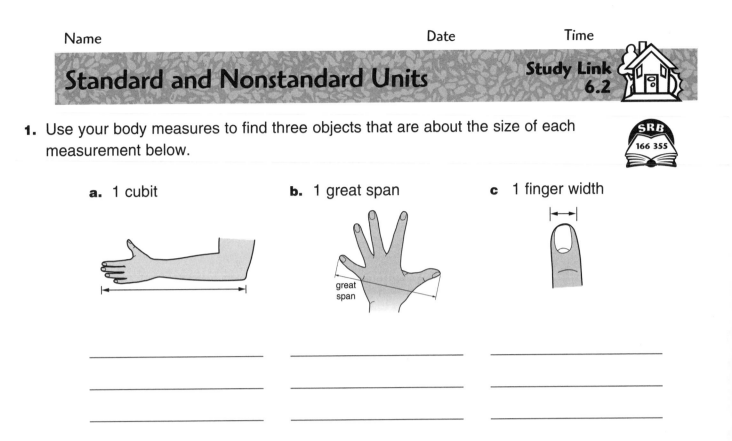

a. 1 cubit

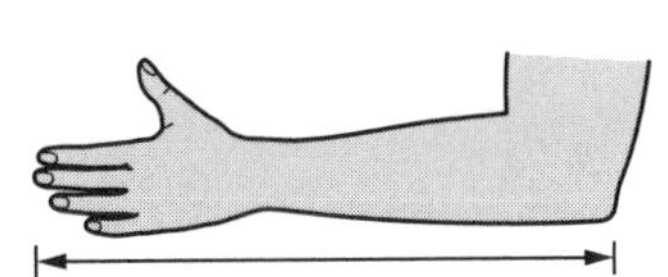

____

____

____

b. 1 great span

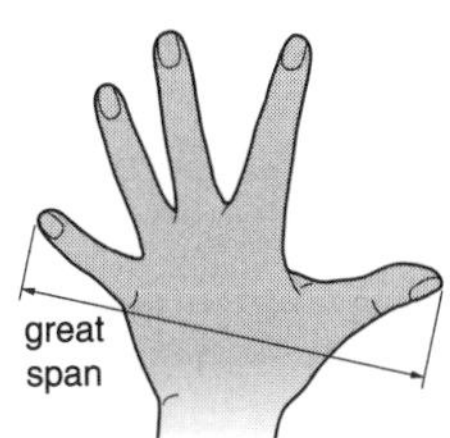

____

____

____

c 1 finger width

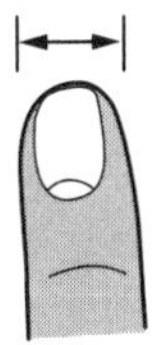

____

____

____

2. For each problem below, mark the unit or units you *could* use to measure the object.

a. Height of your ceiling	O cm	O ft	O lb	O miles
b. Amount of milk in a pitcher	O cm	O ounces	O gal	O liters
c. Depth of the ocean	O m	O ounces	O gal	O miles
d. Length of a bee	O cm	O ft	O mm	O liters
e. Weight of a nickel	O in.	O kg	O lb	O grams

Name Date Time

Reading a Stem-and-Leaf Plot

Study Link 6.3

Use the information below to answer the questions.

SRB 112 113

Randy was growing sunflowers. After eight weeks, he measured the height of his sunflowers, in inches. He recorded the heights in the stem-and-leaf plot below.

Height of Sunflowers (inches)

Stems (10s)	**Leaves** (1s)
3	9 1
4	7 6 9 2 9
5	2 3 3 5 2 8 7 3
6	5 3 4
7	3

1. How tall is the tallest sunflower? ________ in.

   Which landmark is the height of the tallest flower? Circle its name.

   minimum mode maximum mean

2. How many sunflowers did Randy measure? ________ sunflowers

3. What is the mode for his measurements? ________ in.

4. Explain how you would find the median for his measurements.

   ____

   ____

   ____

   ____

Challenge

5. On the back of this page, describe how Randy made his stem-and-leaf plot once he had his measurements.

Name Date Time

How Much Do Students Spend?

Study Link 6.4

A fifth grade class collected data about how much students in the class spent per month on various items. Here are some of the results:

- A median amount of $6 per month was spent for books and magazines.
- A median amount of $10 per month was spent for tapes and CDs.
- A median amount of $8 per month was spent for movie tickets.

The number-line plots below display the data they collected. One plot shows monthly spending for books and magazines. One plot shows monthly spending for tapes and CDs. One plot shows monthly spending for movie tickets.

Match the plots with the items. Which plot is for books and magazines? Which is for tapes and CDs? Which is for movie tickets?

Fill in the correct title for each number-line plot.

1. Spending for: ______________________ in 1 month

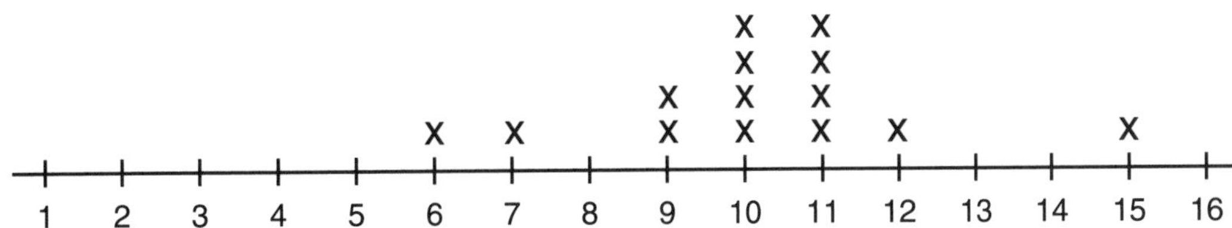

2. Spending for: ______________________ in 1 month

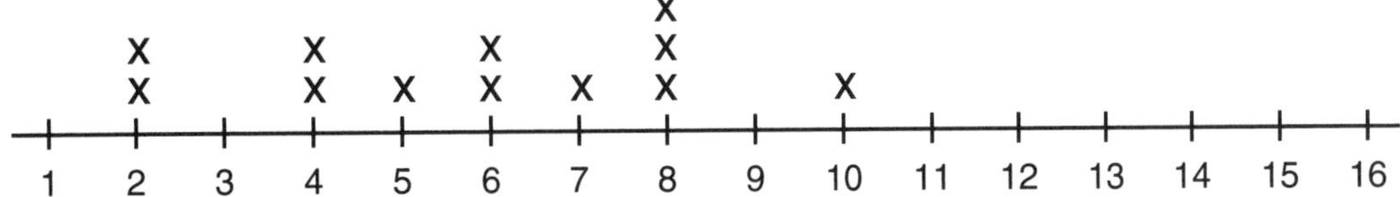

3. Spending for: ______________________ in 1 month

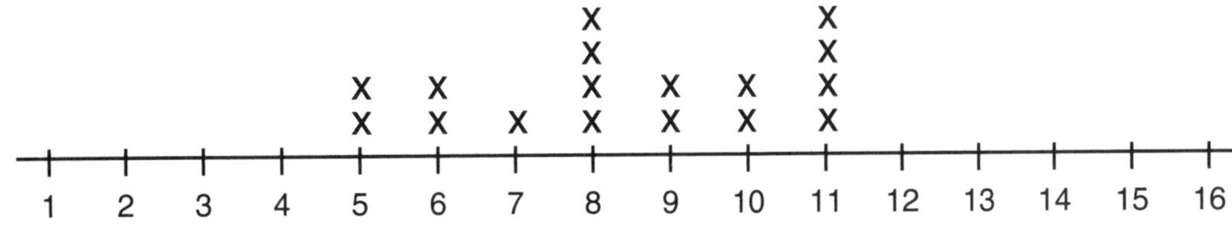

Name Date Time

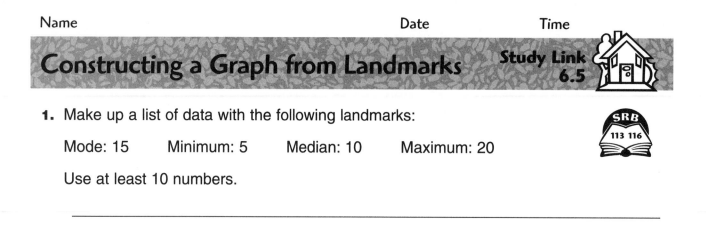

Constructing a Graph from Landmarks

Study Link 6.5

1. Make up a list of data with the following landmarks:

Mode: 15 Minimum: 5 Median: 10 Maximum: 20

Use at least 10 numbers.

____

2. Draw a bar graph to represent your data.

____
(title)

3. Describe a situation in which these data might actually occur.

____

____

____

____

Name Date Time

Data Analysis

Study Link 6.6 

SRB 111–113

1. Describe a situation in which the data in the line plot below might occur. Then give the plot a title and a unit.

____

____

______________________________ (title) __________ (unit)

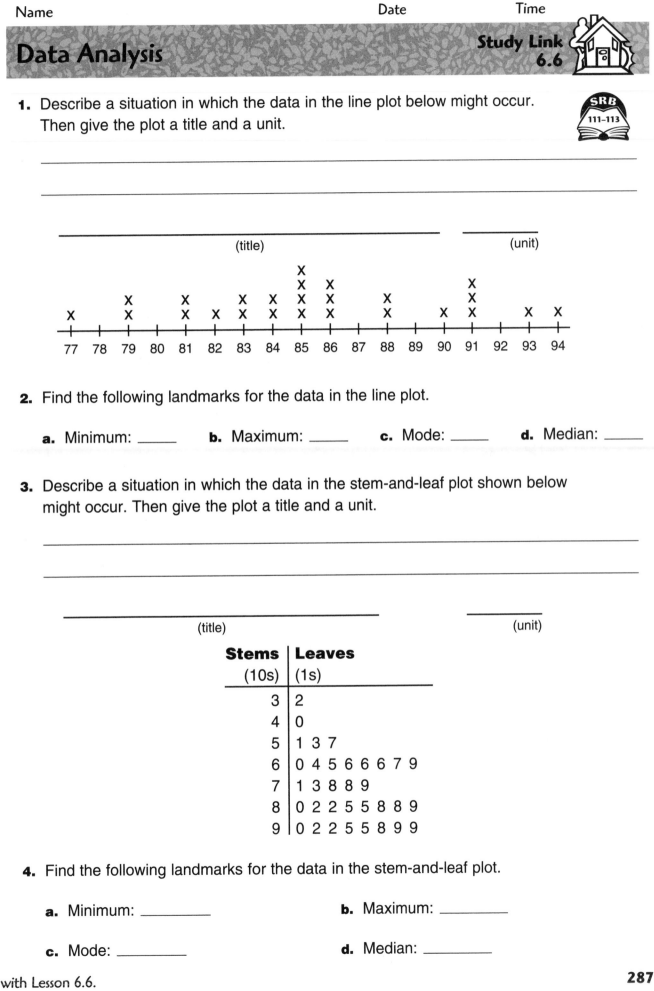

77	78	79	80	81	82	83	84	85	86	87	88	89	90	91	92	93	94
X		X X		X X	X	X X	X X	X X X X	X X X		X X		X	X X X		X	X

2. Find the following landmarks for the data in the line plot.

a. Minimum: _____ **b.** Maximum: _____ **c.** Mode: _____ **d.** Median: _____

3. Describe a situation in which the data in the stem-and-leaf plot shown below might occur. Then give the plot a title and a unit.

____

____

______________________________ (title) __________ (unit)

Stems (10s)	**Leaves** (1s)
3	2
4	0
5	1 3 7
6	0 4 5 6 6 6 7 9
7	1 3 8 8 9
8	0 2 2 5 5 8 8 9
9	0 2 2 5 5 8 9 9

4. Find the following landmarks for the data in the stem-and-leaf plot.

a. Minimum: _________ **b.** Maximum: _________

c. Mode: _________ **d.** Median: _________

Name Date Time

Contour Map

Study Link 6.7

The contour map below shows the approximate percentage of sunny or partly sunny days for the months of December through February.

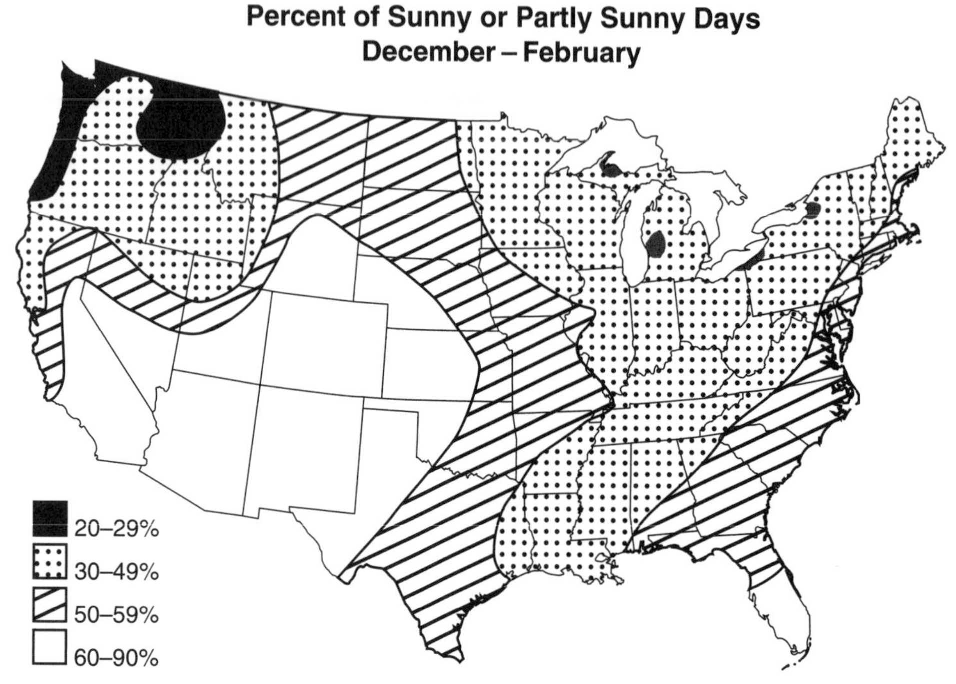

1. States where at least part of the state has sunny days more than 60% of the time between December and February.

   O Washington O Florida O Arizona O New York

2. States that border the Pacific Ocean where, in some part of the state, more than 70% of the days are NOT sunny between December and February.

   O California O Oregon O Montana O Washington

3. On the back of this page, make up your own question about the map. Answer your question.

Challenge

4. States with several regions where the amount of sunshine varies. Part of the state is sunny most of the time, but another part of the state is NOT sunny most of the time.

   O Utah O Ohio O Wyoming O Wisconsin

Name Date Time

Fraction Problems

Study Link 6.8

SRB 63 68 71

1. To maintain their energy during the racing season, professional bicycle racers eat between 6,000 and 8,000 calories per day.

About $\frac{3}{20}$ of these calories come from fat, and about $\frac{5}{20}$ come from protein. The remaining calories come from carbohydrates.

carbohydrates
$\frac{5}{20}$ protein
$\frac{3}{20}$ fat

What fraction of a bicycle racer's calories comes from carbohydrates? __________

2. Study the plan at the right for a small bookcase.

All boards are $\frac{3}{4}$-inch thick.

What is the width of each shelf? __________ inches

If the shelves are evenly spaced, what is the height of the opening for each of the 3 spaces? ________ inches

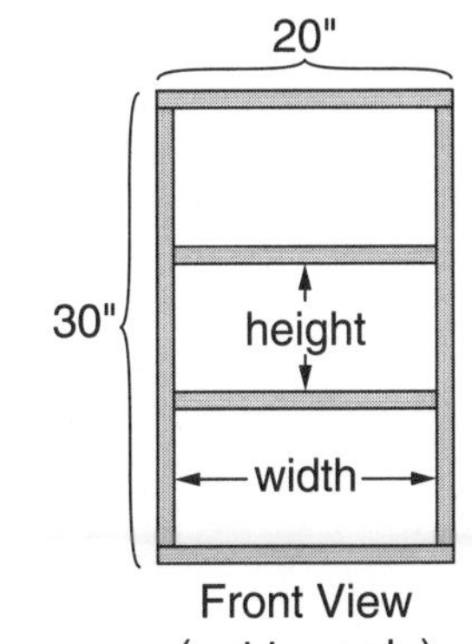

Front View (not to scale)

Each square in the grid at the right represents a city block. Each side of a block is $\frac{1}{8}$ mile long (that is, in this city, there are 8 blocks to each mile).

The distances below are measured along the sides of blocks.

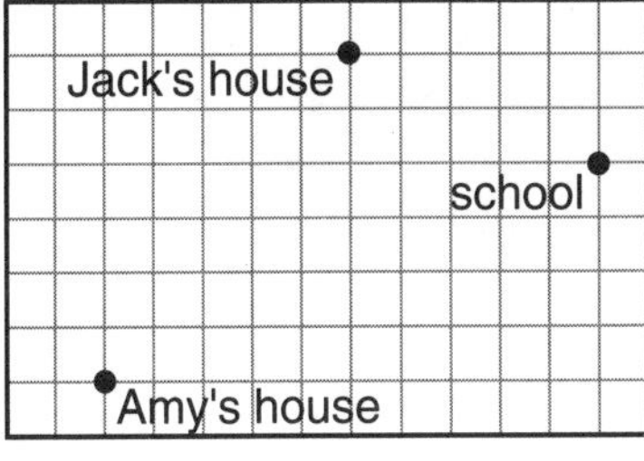

3. The distance from Amy's house to school is

________ blocks, or ________ mile(s).

4. The distance from Jack's house to school is

________ blocks, or ________ mile(s).

5. How much farther from school is Amy's house than Jack's house? ________ mile(s)

6. Amy walks from school to Jack's house and then home.

How far is that? ________ mile(s).

Name Date Time

Adding and Subtracting Fractions

Study Link 6.9

Multiplication Rule

To find a fraction equivalent to a given fraction, multiply both the numerator and the denominator of the fraction by the same number.

$$\frac{a}{b} = \frac{a * n}{b * n}$$

Example 1 $\frac{4}{9} - \frac{1}{3} = ?$

$\frac{1}{3} = \frac{2}{6} = \frac{3}{9} = \frac{4}{12} = \frac{5}{15} = \frac{6}{18} = \ldots$

9 is a common denominator.

$\frac{4}{9} - \frac{1}{3} = \frac{4}{9} - \frac{3}{9} = \frac{1}{9}$

Example 2 $\frac{5}{8} + \frac{2}{5} = ?$

$\frac{5}{8} = \frac{10}{16} = \frac{15}{24} = \frac{20}{32} = \frac{25}{40} = \frac{30}{48} = \ldots$

$\frac{2}{5} = \frac{4}{10} = \frac{6}{15} = \frac{8}{20} = \frac{10}{25} = \frac{12}{30} = \frac{14}{35} = \frac{16}{40} = \frac{18}{45} = \ldots$

Both fractions can be rewritten with the common denominator 40.

$\frac{5}{8} + \frac{2}{5} = \frac{25}{40} + \frac{16}{40} = \frac{41}{40}$ (or $1\frac{1}{40}$)

Find a common denominator. Then add or subtract.

1. $\frac{2}{3} + \frac{4}{5} =$ ________

2. $\frac{8}{9} - \frac{5}{6} =$ ________

3. $\frac{3}{4} + 1\frac{1}{2} =$ ________

4. Lisa was 4 feet $10\frac{1}{2}$ inches tall at the end of fifth grade. During the year, she had grown $2\frac{3}{4}$ inches. How tall was Lisa at the start of fifth grade?

________ feet ________ inches

5. Bill was baking two different kinds of bread. One recipe called for $3\frac{1}{2}$ cups of flour. The other called for $2\frac{1}{3}$ cups of flour. How much flour did Bill need in all?

________ cups

Name Date Time

Fractions

Find a common denominator. Then add or subtract.

1. $\frac{9}{11} - \frac{1}{2} =$ ____________

2. $\frac{5}{9} - \frac{1}{4} =$ ____________

3. $\frac{7}{10} + \frac{4}{15} =$ ____________

4. $\frac{7}{10} - \frac{4}{15} =$ ____________

5. $\frac{3}{2} - \frac{4}{9}$

6. $\frac{5}{6} + \frac{4}{7}$

Write the fraction represented by the shaded part of each fraction stick.

7. ____________

8. ____________

9. ____________

10. ____________

11. ____________

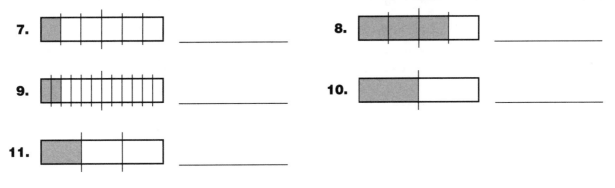

12. The sum of the five fractions in Problems 7–11 is ____________.

Use the information on Elise's shopping list to fill in the blanks below.

13. Elise plans to buy ____________ pounds of meat.

14. She plans to buy ____________ pounds of cheese.

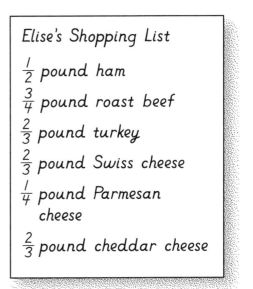

Elise's Shopping List

$\frac{1}{2}$ pound ham

$\frac{3}{4}$ pound roast beef

$\frac{2}{3}$ pound turkey

$\frac{2}{3}$ pound Swiss cheese

$\frac{1}{4}$ pound Parmesan cheese

$\frac{2}{3}$ pound cheddar cheese

Name Date Time

Family Letter

Study Link 6.11

Unit 7: Exponents and Negative Numbers

In this unit, your child will be introduced to exponential and scientific notation as a way of naming very large and very small numbers. These topics will become increasingly important later on, when your child begins work with algebra concepts. If you and your child have enjoyed playing math games in the past, you might want to play *Exponent Ball* during these lessons.

Your child will also review how parentheses are used to make expressions unambiguous and will be introduced to rules that determine in what order the operations in a mathematical expression must be performed.

Finally, your child will investigate why negative numbers were invented and learn to work with positive and negative numbers, using a variety of strategies. For example, your child will use number lines to compare, add, and subtract positive and negative numbers; use a slide rule to add and subtract positive and negative numbers; and use red and black counters to represent positive and negative numbers to model addition and subtraction problems.

The activities with counters are especially instructive. Counters are used to represent an account balance. The red counters (−\$1) represent a debit, the black counters (+\$1), a credit. If there are more red counters than black ones, the account is "in the red;" that is, the balance is negative. On the other hand, if there are more black counters than red ones, the account is "in the black;" that is, the balance is positive. By adding or subtracting red and black counters from an existing account balance, your child can model addition and subtraction of positive and negative numbers. To assist your child, you may want to explain how a checking or savings account works.

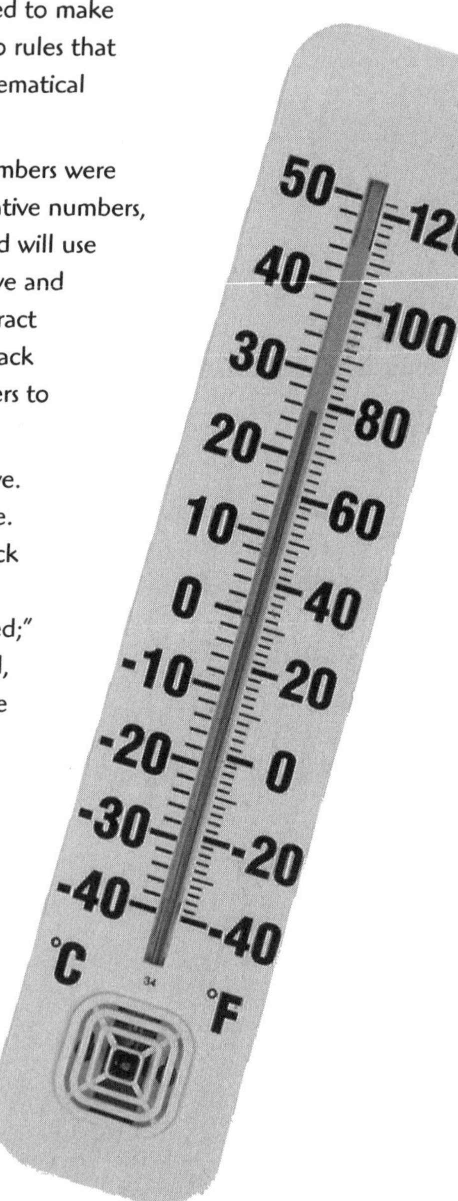

Please keep this Family Letter for reference as your child works through Unit 7.

Use with Lesson 6.11.

Vocabulary

Important terms in Unit 7:

account balance An amount of money that you have or that you owe.

exponential notation A way to show repeated multiplication by the same factor. For example, 2^3 is exponential notation for 2 * 2 * 2.

expression A group of mathematical symbols that represents a number—or can represent a number if values are assigned to any variables in the expression.

"in the black" Having a positive balance; having more money than is owed.

"in the red" Having a negative balance; owing more money than is available.

negative number A number that is less than zero.

nested parentheses Parentheses inside parentheses.

Example

((6 * 4) − 2) / 2 = 11

number-and-word notation A way of writing a large number using a combination of numbers and words. For example, *27 billion* is number-and-word notation for 27,000,000,000.

opposite of a number A number that is the same distance from 0 on the number line as a given number, but on the opposite side of 0. For example, the opposite of +3 is −3; the opposite of −5 is +5.

order of operations Rules that tell in what order to perform operations in arithmetic and algebra. The order of operations is:

1. Do the operations in parentheses first. (Use rules 2–4 inside the parentheses.)
2. Calculate all the expressions with exponents.
3. Multiply and divide in order from left to right.
4. Add and subtract in order from left to right.

parentheses Grouping symbols, ( ), used to tell which parts of an expression should be calculated first.

scientific notation A system for writing numbers in which a number is written as the product of a *power* of 10 and a number that is at least 1 and less than 10. Scientific notation allows you to write big and small numbers with only a few symbols. For example, 4 * 10^{12} is scientific notation for 4,000,000,000,000.

slide rule A tool used to perform calculations.

standard notation The most familiar way of representing whole numbers, integers, and decimals. In standard notation, the value of each digit depends on where the digit is in the number. For example, standard notation for three hundred fifty-six is 356.

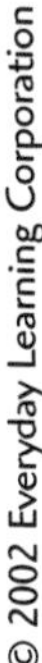

Do-Anytime Activities

To work with your child on the concepts taught in this unit and in previous units, try these interesting and rewarding activities:

1. Have your child pick out a stock from the stock-market pages of a newspaper. Encourage your child to watch the stock over a period of time and to report the change in stock prices daily, using positive and negative numbers.

2. Using the same stock in Activity 1, have your child write the high and low of that stock for each day. After your child has watched the stock over a period of time, have him or her find
   - the *maximum* value observed.
   - the *minimum* value observed.
   - the *range* in values.
   - the *mode,* if there is one.
   - the *median* value observed.

3. Review tessellations with your child. Encourage your child to name the regular tessellations and to draw and name the 8 semiregular tessellations. Challenge your child to create Escher-type translation tessellations. You may want to go to the library first, and show your child examples of Escher's work.

4. Practice finding perimeters of objects and circumferences of circular objects around your home.

Building Skills through Games

In Unit 7, your child will practice operations and computation skills by playing the following games. For detailed instructions, see the *Student Reference Book.*

Name That Number See *Student Reference Book,* page 286
A game for two or three players using the Everything Math Deck or a complete deck of number cards. Playing *Name That Number* helps students review operations with whole numbers.

Scientific-Notation Toss See *Student Reference Book,* page 290
Two players will need 2 six-sided dice to play this game. This game develops skill in converting numbers from scientific notation to standard notation.

Top-It See *Student Reference Book,* page 296
The two versions of this game provide practice in adding and subtracting positive and negative numbers. Two to four players need a complete deck of number cards to play the game.

As You Help Your Child with Homework

As your child brings assignments home, you may want to go over the instructions together, clarifying them as necessary. The answers listed below will guide you through this unit's Study Links.

Study Link 7.1

1. Answers vary. **2.** 1,838,265,625

3. a. yes
b. Sample answer: There are more possible license plates (about 2 billion) than there are vehicles (about 200 million)

4. 1,728 **5.** 6,561

6. 537,824 **7.** 2,985,984

Study Link 7.2

1. billion **2.** 10^3 **3.** trillion

4. 10^6 **5.** thousand; 10^3 **6.** million; 10^6

7. Sample answer: About 17 hours; About 2 years; About 2,000 years; About 2 million years

Study Link 7.3

1. 600; 3 **2.** 6 **3.** 500 million

4. 1 billion **5.** 10 million

Study Link 7.4

1. $2 = (3 * 2) - (4 / 1)$ **2.** $3 = (4 + 3 - 1) / 2$

3. $4 = (3 - 1) + (4 / 2)$ **4.** $5 = (3 + 4 - 2) / 1$

5. $9 = (4 / 1) + 3 + 2$ **6.** $10 = 3 + (4 * 2) - 1$

8. $1 = ((4 + 1) - 3) / 2$ **9.** $6 = (1 + (4 * 2)) - 3$

10. $7 = ((4 * 3) / 2) + 1$

11. $8 = ((3 - 1) * 2) + 4$

Study Link 7.5

1. 34 **2.** 25 **3.** 28 **4.** 30

5. 21 **6.** 28 **7.** false **8.** true

9. true **10.** true **11.** false **12.** true

13. false **14.** true

15. Story 1: $(2 * 8) + 4$; Story 2: $2 * (8 + 4)$

Study Link 7.6

For Problems 1–4, sample answers:

1. 2.6 **2.** 1.58 **3.** −5.5 **4.** −9.8

5. $-1.2, -1, 3.8, 5\frac{1}{4}, 5\frac{3}{8}$

6. $-7, -6, -4\frac{1}{2}, -0.5, 0$

7. F **8.** F **9.** T **10.** T **11.** T

For Problems 12–15, sample answers:

12. $-1 < 1$; T **13.** $-5 = -\frac{500}{100}$; T

14. $-\frac{1}{2} = 2^2 - \frac{1}{2}$; F **15.** $-3 > -1$; F

Study Link 7.7

1. < **2.** > **3.** >

4. > **5.** $2 debt **6.** $5 cash

7. −9 **8.** 22 **9.** −88

10. 70 **11.** 3 **12.** −9,000

Study Link 7.8

1. −41 **2.** 43 **3.** 0 **4.** −8

5. 40 **6.** 20 **7.** −85 **8.** −0.5

9. 3.0 **10.** 2 **11.** (−15) **12.** (−10)

Study Link 7.9

1. < **2.** > **3.** > **4.** >

5. > **6.** > **7.** −5 **8.** −21

9. 4 **10.** −6 **11.** −11 **12.** −26

13. 16 **14.** −4 **15.** T **16.** T

17. $(-2 + 3) * 4 = 4$ **18.** T

19. $-3 + 5 * (2 - (-6)) = 37$

20. $4^2 + ((-3) - (5)) * 2 = 20$ **21.** 10:04 A.M.

Study Link 7.10

1. $-5 - (-58) = 53$ **2.** 10^6 **3.** 10^4

4. 10^5 **5.** 10^9 **6.** 3,000,000 **7.** 20,000

8. 640,000 **9.** 2,600,000 **10.** $8 * 10^6$

11. $7 * 10^9$ **12.** $3 * 10^3$ **13.** $17 * 10^{10}$

14. Number model: $3 * 6 - 5 = 13$;
Answer: 13 containers

15. above; Number model: $-\frac{5}{8} + \frac{6}{8} = \frac{1}{8}$
Answer: $\frac{1}{8}$ inch above

Name Date Time

Counting License Plates

Study Link 7.1

Automobile license plates can include letters, numbers, or a combination of letters and numbers. The letter O is usually not used because it might be confused with the number zero. This leaves 35 different characters.

In many states, license plates consist of 6 characters. There are 35 choices for each character.

A	B	C	D	E	F	G
H	I	J	K	L	M	N
P	Q	R	S	T	U	V
W	X	Y	Z	0	1	2
3	4	5	6	7	8	9

___ ___ ___ ___ ___ ___

35 choices for each character

1. List three possible 6-character license plates.

a. ___ ___ ___ ___ ___ ___

b. ___ ___ ___ ___ ___ ___

c. ___ ___ ___ ___ ___ ___

2. The total number of possible license plates can be found by using 35 as a factor 6 times.

$$35 * 35 * 35 * 35 * 35 * 35, \text{ or } 35^6$$

If your calculator can display up to 10 digits, find 35^6, the number of possible different six-character license plates. __________

Challenge

In 1997, there were 207,754,000 registered motor vehicles in the United States.

3. a. Could every registered motor vehicle in the United States have a different six-character license plate? _____

b. Explain how you found the answer.

____

____

Practice

Use your calculator to write the following numbers in standard notation.

4. $12 * 12 * 12 =$ ________

5. $9 * 9 * 9 * 9 =$ ________

6. $14^5 =$ ________

7. 12 to the sixth power = ________

Name Date Time

Guides for Powers of 10

Study Link 7.2

There are prefixes that name powers of 10. You know some of them from the metric system; for example, *kilo-* in "kilometer" (1,000 meters). It's helpful to memorize the prefixes for every third power of 10 through one trillion.

Memorize the table below. Have a friend quiz you. Then cover the table and try to complete the statements below.

Standard Notation	Number-and-Word Notation	Exponential Notation	Prefix
1,000	1 thousand	10^3	kilo-
1,000,000	1 million	10^6	mega-
1,000,000,000	1 billion	10^9	giga-
1,000,000,000,000	1 trillion	10^{12}	tera-

1. More than 10^9 or one ______________ people live in China.
2. One thousand or $10^{\square}$ feet is a little less than $\frac{1}{5}$ of a mile.
3. Astronomers estimate that there are more than 10^{12} or one ______________ stars in the universe.
4. More than one million or $10^{\square}$ copies of *The New York Times* are sold every day.
5. A kiloton equals one ______________ or $10^{\square}$ metric tons.
6. A megaton equals one ______________ or $10^{\square}$ metric tons.

Challenge

7. How far back in time would you travel if you went back
   a. 10^3 minutes? ______________
   b. 10^6 minutes? ______________
   c. 10^9 minutes? ______________
   d. 10^{12} minutes? ______________

(Remember that a million is 1,000 thousands; a billion is 1,000 millions; and a trillion is 1,000 billions.)

Name Date Time

Interpreting Scientific Notation

Study Link 7.3

SRB 8

Scientific notation is a short way to represent large and small numbers. In scientific notation, a number is written as the product of two factors. One factor is a whole number or decimal. The other factor is a power of 10.

Scientific notation: $4 * 10^4$

Meaning: Multiply 10^4 (10,000) by 4.

$4 * 10^4 = 4 * 10{,}000 = 40{,}000$

Scientific notation: $6 * 10^6$

Meaning: Multiply 10^6 (1,000,000) by 6.

$6 * 10^6 = 6 * 1{,}000{,}000 = 6{,}000{,}000$

Guides for Powers of 10	
10^3	one thousand
10^6	one million
10^9	one billion
10^{12}	one trillion

Complete the following statements.

1. The area of Alaska is about $6 * 10^5$ or ________ thousand square miles.

The area of the "lower 48" states is about $3 * 10^6$ or ________ million square miles.

2. There are about $6 * 10^9$ or ________ billion people in the world.

3. It is estimated that about $5 * 10^8$ or ____________________ people speak English as their first or second language.

4. The language spoken by the greatest number of people is Chinese.

More than $1 * 10^9$ or ____________________ people speak Chinese.

5. It is estimated that the most popular television shows in the United States are watched by at least one person in

each of $1 * 10^7$ or ____________________ households.

Source: The World Almanac and Book of Facts, 2000

Name Date Time

Different Ways to Write 1 through 10

Study Link 7.4

Make each sentence true by inserting parentheses.

1. 2 = 3 * 2 − 4 / 1 **2.** 3 = 4 + 3 − 1 / 2 **3.** 4 = 3 − 1 + 4 / 2

4. 5 = 3 + 4 − 2 / 1 **5.** 9 = 4 / 1 + 3 + 2 **6.** 10 = 3 + 4 * 2 − 1

7. Write seven different names for the number 8. Use only numbers less than 10, and use at least three different operations in each name. Use parentheses.

8

Problem 12 tells how to fill in the last 2 names.

Challenge

Make each sentence true by inserting parentheses. You will need at least two pairs of parentheses for each sentence. (*Reminder:* When you have a pair of parentheses inside another pair, the parentheses are called **nested parentheses.**)

Example 8 = 5 * 6 + 2 / 4

Answer 8 = ((5 * 6) + 2) / 4

8. 1 = 4 + 1 − 3 / 2 **9.** 6 = 1 + 4 * 2 − 3

10. 7 = 4 * 3 / 2 + 1 **11.** 8 = 3 − 1 * 2 + 4

12. Add two names to your name-collection box in Problem 7. Use nested parentheses in your expressions.

Name Date Time

Order of Operations

Study Link 7.5

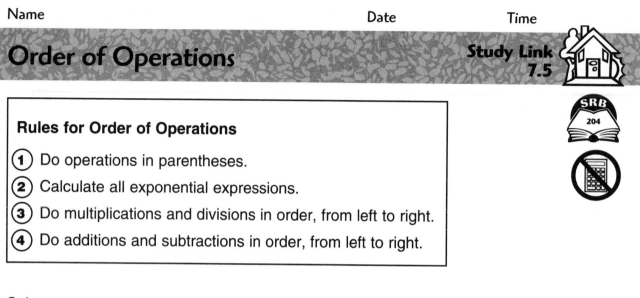

Rules for Order of Operations

1. Do operations in parentheses.
2. Calculate all exponential expressions.
3. Do multiplications and divisions in order, from left to right.
4. Do additions and subtractions in order, from left to right.

Solve.

1. $4 + 5 * 6 =$ ________

2. $(2 + 3)^2 =$ ________

3. $12 * 2 + 8 \div 2 =$ ________

4. $115 - 10^2 + 3 * 5 =$ ________

5. $6 * (3 + 2^2) \div 2 =$ ________

6. $7 + 9 * 7 \div 3 =$ ________

Write true or false for each number sentence. Follow the rules of order of operations.

7. $3 + 4 * 5 = 35$ ________

8. $(3 + 4) * 5 = 35$ ________

9. $0 = 3 * 4 - 12$ ________

10. $0 = (3 * 4) - 12$ ________

11. $36 = 12 - 3 * 4$ ________

12. $36 = (12 - 3) * 4$ ________

13. $8 \div 2 + 6 = 1$ ________

14. $8 \div (2 + 6) = 1$ ________

15. Match each story with the expression that fits it.

Story 1

Marlene and her friend Mandy each had eight pencils. They bought four more pencils.

Story 2

Marlene bought 2 eight-packs of pencils. Four free pencils came with each pack.

Number of pencils in all:

$(2 * 8) + 4$

$2 * (8 + 4)$

Name Date Time

Greater Than or Less Than?

Study Link 7.6

Name a number between each pair of numbers.

1. 2 and 3 ________

2. 1.5 and 2 ________

3. -5 and -6 ________

4. -9.5 and -10 ________

Order each set of numbers from *least* to *greatest.*

5. $5\frac{1}{4}$, 3.8, -1.2, -1, $5\frac{3}{8}$ ________________

6. -6, $-4\frac{1}{2}$, -0.5, -7, 0 ________________

True or false? Write T for true and F for false.

7. $-6 > 5$ ______

8. $5\frac{1}{2} < 5\frac{3}{6}$ ______

9. $-2.5 > -3.5$ ______

10. $-4 < 0$ ______

11. 7 is greater than -7 ______

Write two true number sentences and two false number sentences. In each sentence, use at least one negative number and one of the symbols $>$, $<$, or $=$. Label each sentence T or F.

12. ________________ ______

13. ________________ ______

14. ________________ ______

15. ________________ ______

Name Date Time

Positive and Negative Numbers

Study Link 7.7

SRB 92–94 208

Write $<$ or $>$.

1. -7 ________ 6

2. 0.01 ________ -32

3. 8.5 ________ -10^3

4. $-\frac{3}{4}$ ________ -1.6

Find the account balance. $\boxed{+}$ = \$1 cash. $\boxed{-}$ = \$1 debt.

5. Balance = \$ ______________

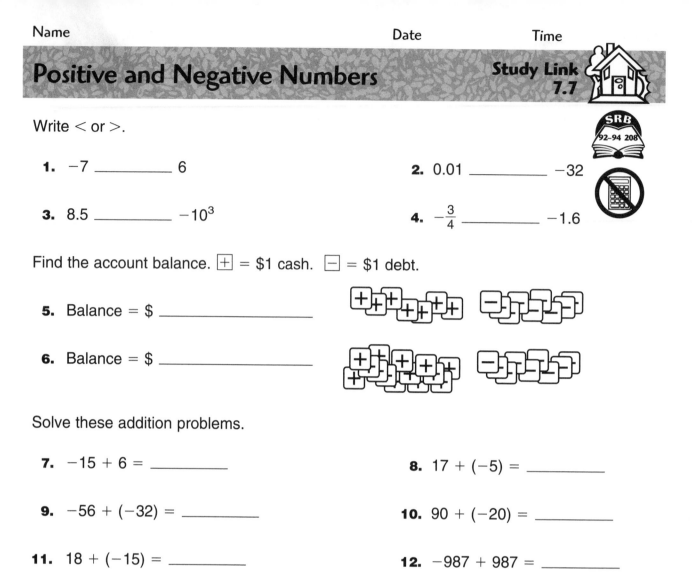

6. Balance = \$ ______________

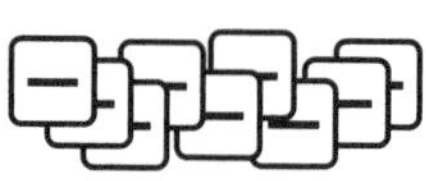

Solve these addition problems.

7. $-15 + 6 =$ ________

8. $17 + (-5) =$ ________

9. $-56 + (-32) =$ ________

10. $90 + (-20) =$ ________

11. $18 + (-15) =$ ________

12. $-987 + 987 =$ ________

13. Use the rule to complete the table.

−200

in

Rule

out = −25 + in

out

−225

in	out
25	
50	
−25	
−100	
100	
0	

Name Date Time

Addition and Subtraction Problems

Study Link 7.8

> *Reminder:*
> To subtract a number, you can add the opposite of that number.

Solve each problem. Be careful. Some problems are additions and some are subtractions.

1. $-25 + (-16) =$ ________

2. $0 - (-43) =$ ________

3. $-4 - (-4) =$ ________

4. $-4 - 4 =$ ________

5. $29 - (-11) =$ ________

6. $9 - (-11) =$ ________

7. $-100 + 15 =$ ________

8. $10 - 10.5 =$ ________

9. $9.7 + (-6.7) =$ ________

10. $4\frac{1}{2} + (-2\frac{1}{2}) =$ ________

11. $10 +$ ________ $= -5$

12. $10 -$ ________ $= 20$

13. For each temperature change in the table, two number models are shown in the "Temperature after Change" column. Only one of the number models is correct. Cross out the incorrect number model. Then complete the correct number model.

Temperature before Change	Temperature Change	Temperature after Change	
40°	up 7°	$40 + 7 =$ ______	$40 + (-7) =$ ______
10°	down 8°	$10 - (-8) =$ ______	$10 - 8 =$ ______
−15° (15° below zero)	up 10°	$-15 + 10 =$ ______	$15 + 10 =$ ______
−20° (20° below zero)	down 10°	$-20 - 10 =$ ______	$20 - (-10) =$ ______

Name　　　　　　　　　　　　　　　　　　　　　　Date　　　　　　Time

Positive and Negative Number Review

Study Link 7.9

Write >, < or =.

1. -8 ________ 5　　2. -3 ________ -10　　3. 10 ________ -20

4. 12 ________ -15　　5. $-\frac{3}{4}$ ________ -1　　6. 3^2 ________ 6

Add or subtract.

7. $-20 + 15 =$ ________　　8. $-14 + (-7) =$ ________

9. $-8 + 12 =$ ________　　10. $3 + (-9) =$ ________

11. $-4 - 7 =$ ________　　12. $-10 - 16 =$ ________

13. $5 - (-11) =$ ________　　14. $8 - 12 =$ ________

Some of the following number sentences are true because they follow the rules for the order of operations. Some of the sentences are false. Make a check mark next to the true number sentences. Insert parentheses in the false number sentences to make them true.

15. $3 + 7 * 5 = 38$　　16. $-5 + 20 \div 5 = -1$

17. $-2 + 3 * 4 = 4$　　18. $-2 + 3 * 4 = 10$

19. $-3 + 5 * 2 - (-6) = 37$　　20. $4^2 + (-3) - (-5) * 2 = 20$

21. a. Julie arrived 20 minutes before the race began. She started right on time. It took her 24 minutes to finish the 6-kilometer race. She stayed 10 minutes after the race to cool off; then she left. If she arrived at the race at 9:10 A.M., what time was it when she left?

____

b. Explain how you found your answer.

____

____

____

Name Date Time

Unit 7 Review

1. Circle the number sentences that are true.

SRB 4-6 8 69 208

$25 + (-6) < -32$ $4^2 < 2^4$ $15 * 15 * 15 < 15^3$

$21 * 21 = 21^3$ $-5 - (-58) = 53$ $25 > 5^2 - (-2)$

Write each number as a power of 10.

2. 1,000,000 ________

3. 10,000 ________

4. 1 hundred-thousand ________

5. 1 billion ________

Match the number written in number-and-word notation with its standard notation. Fill in the oval next to the correct answer.

6. 3 million

O 300,000

O 30,000,000

O 3,000,000

O 30,000

7. 20 thousand

O 200,000

O 20,000

O 2,000,000

O 20,000,000

8. 640 thousand

O 6,400,000

O 64,000,000

O 640,000,000

O 640,000

9. 2.6 million

O 26,000,000

O 2,060,000

O 20,600,000

O 2,600,000

Name Date Time

Unit 7 Review (cont.)

Study Link 7.10

Write each number in scientific notation.

10. 8 million ______________ **11.** 7 billion ______________

12. 3 thousand ______________ **13.** 17 billion ______________

14. Louise bought three 6-pack containers of yogurt. She ate 5 individual containers of yogurt in one week. How many containers did she have left?

Number model: ______________ Answer: ______________

15. The water in Leroy's and Jerod's fish tank had evaporated so that it was about $\frac{5}{8}$ inch below the level it should be. They added water and the water level went up about $\frac{3}{4}$ inch. Did the water level end up above or below where it should be? __________

How much above or below?

Number model: ______________ Answer: ______________

Name Date Time

Family Letter

Study Link 7.11

Unit 8: Fractions and Ratios

In Unit 4, your child reviewed equivalent fractions and developed multiplication and division rules for finding equivalent fractions.

In this unit, your child will apply this knowledge to operations with fractions and mixed numbers. Students will learn that the key to adding, subtracting, and dividing fractions with unlike denominators is to convert them into fractions with the same denominator.

Students will be introduced to fraction multiplication, using folded paper to represent fractions of a whole. Then the class will study fraction multiplication using "area models," which are diagrams that help students visualize dividing a "whole" into parts. This concept building will lead to an algorithm for multiplying fractions:

$$\frac{a}{b} * \frac{c}{d} = \frac{a * c}{b * d}$$

Example: $\frac{2}{5} * \frac{3}{4} = \frac{2 * 3}{5 * 4} = \frac{6}{20}$, or $\frac{3}{10}$

For mixed-number multiplication, students will first rename the mixed numbers as fractions, then use the multiplication of fractions algorithm to find their product, and finally rename the product as a mixed number.

Example: $2\frac{1}{2} * 1\frac{2}{3} = \frac{5}{2} * \frac{5}{3}$

$$= \frac{5 * 5}{2 * 3} = \frac{25}{6} = 4\frac{1}{6}$$

You might want to show your child another way to solve this problem, using partial products:

$2\frac{1}{2} * 1\frac{2}{3}$ can be thought of as $(2 + \frac{1}{2}) * (1 + \frac{2}{3})$. There are 4 partial products, indicated by arrows:

$$(2 + \frac{1}{2}) * (1 + \frac{2}{3})$$

$2 * 1 = 2$

$2 * \frac{2}{3} = \frac{4}{3}$

$\frac{1}{2} * 1 = \frac{1}{2}$

$\frac{1}{2} * \frac{2}{3} = \frac{2}{6}$

Add the partial products: $2 + \frac{4}{3} + \frac{1}{2} + \frac{2}{6} = 2 + \frac{8}{6} + \frac{3}{6} + \frac{2}{6} = 2 + \frac{13}{6} = 4\frac{1}{6}$

Your child will play several games, such as *Build-It* and *Fraction Action, Fraction Friction,* to practice sorting fractions and adding fractions with unlike denominators.

Finally, as part of the American Tour, students will participate in data explorations involving population distributions and household sizes.

Please keep this Family Letter for reference as your child works through Unit 8.

Vocabulary

Important terms in Unit 8:

area model A model for multiplication problems, in which the length and width of a rectangle represent the factors and the area represents the product.

discount The amount by which the regular price of an item is reduced. For example, if a $10 item is on sale for $7, the discount is $3. The discount accounts for 3\10, or 30% of the full price. We say that the percent of discount is 30%.

horizontal Positioned in a left-to-right orientation; parallel to the horizon.

majority A number or amount that is more than half of a total number or amount.

unit fraction A fraction whose numerator is 1. For example, $\frac{1}{2}$, $\frac{1}{3}$, $\frac{1}{8}$, and $\frac{1}{20}$ are all unit fractions.

unit percent One percent (1%).

vertical Positioned in an up-down orientation; perpendicular to the horizon.

Building Skills through Games

In Unit 8, your child will practice skills with fractions and other numbers by playing the following games. For detailed instructions for many games, see the *Student Reference Book.*

Build-It See *Student Reference Book,* p. 263
This game for partners requires a deck of 16 Build–It fraction cards. This game provides practice in comparing and ordering fractions.

Fraction Capture See *Math Masters,* p. 87
Partners roll dice to form fractions and then attempt to capture squares on a Fraction Capture Game Board. This game provides practice in finding equivalent fractions and in adding fractions.

Mixed Number Spin (*Math Masters,* p. 105) **and *Fraction Spin*** (*Math Masters,* p. 110)
Partners use a spinner to randomly select fractions and mixed numbers that are used to complete number sentences. This game provides practice in adding and subtracting fractions and mixed numbers.

Fraction Action/Fraction Friction See *Student Reference Book,* p. 277
This game for partners requires a set of 16 Fraction Action, Fraction Friction cards. The game is similar to blackjack, and provides practice in adding fractions with unlike denominators.

Fraction Multiplication Top-It* and *Fraction/Whole-Number Multiplication Top-It
Partners play a card game using fraction cards. This game provides practice in multiplying fractions and multiplying whole numbers and fractions.

Name That Number See *Student Reference Book,* p. 286
Partners play a card game using a deck of number cards. These games provide practice in using order of operations to write number sentences.

Frac-Tac-Toe See *Student Reference Book,* p. 274–276
This game for partners requires a deck of number cards 0–10 and a Game Board that is similar to a bingo card. The game provides practice in converting among fractions, decimals, and percents.

Do-Anytime Activities

To work with your child on the concepts taught in this unit and in previous units, try these interesting and rewarding activities:

1. Ask your child to measure the lengths of two objects using a ruler. Then ask him or her to calculate the sum and difference of their lengths.

2. Ask your child to explain how to use the fraction operation keys on his or her calculator. For example, ask your child to show you how to enter fractions and mixed numbers, simplify fractions, and convert between fractions and decimals.

3. Help your child identify advertisements in signs, newspapers, and magazines that use percents. Help your child find the sale price of an item that is discounted by a certain percent; for example, a $40 shirt reduced by 25% costs $30.

As You Help Your Child with Homework

As your child brings assignments home, you may want to go over the instructions together, clarifying them as necessary. The answers listed below will guide you through this unit's Study Links.

Study Link 8.1

1. $\frac{3}{6}$ **2.** $\frac{2}{3}$ **3.** $\frac{5}{6}$

4. $\frac{19}{20}$ **5.** $\frac{9}{17}$ **6.** $\frac{4}{7}$

7. Sample answer: A common denominator is $21 * 17$, or 357. $\frac{11}{21} = \frac{11 * 17}{21 * 17} = \frac{187}{357}$, and $\frac{9}{17} = \frac{9 * 21}{17 * 21} = \frac{189}{357}$. So $\frac{9}{17}$ is greater.

8. 0.75 **9.** $0.\overline{6}$ **10.** 0.625

11. 0.7 **12.** 0.55 **13.** 0.84

14. Sample answer: $\frac{1}{8}$ is half of $\frac{1}{4}$ $\left(\frac{0.25}{2} = 0.125\right)$. $\frac{5}{8} = \frac{4}{8} + \frac{1}{8} = 0.5 + 0.125$, or 0.625.

15. > **16.** = **17.** >

18. < **19.** > **20.** >

21. Sample answer: $\frac{6}{7} + \frac{1}{7} = 1$. $\frac{1}{8}$ is less than $\frac{1}{7}$, so $\frac{6}{7} + \frac{1}{8}$ is less than 1.

Study Link 8.2

2. 2 **3.** $10\frac{2}{3}$ **5.** $5\frac{1}{2}$

7. 6 **9.** 14 **11.** $5\frac{1}{4}$

13. $9\frac{3}{8}$ **15.** $8\frac{1}{4}$

Study Link 8.3

1. 11 **3.** 10 **6.** $6\frac{5}{3}$

7. $2\frac{1}{2}$ **9.** $2\frac{1}{5}$ **11.** $5\frac{4}{9}$

13. $2\frac{1}{4}$ **15.** $\frac{1}{2}$

Study Link 8.4

1. $\frac{4}{5}$; $\frac{155}{200}$ **2.** $< \frac{1}{2}$ **3.** $> \frac{1}{2}$

4. $= \frac{1}{2}$ **5.** $< \frac{1}{2}$

6. $\frac{\boxed{6}}{①} + \frac{⟨5⟩}{\boxed{6}} = \frac{41}{6} = 6\frac{5}{6}$

Study Link 8.5

1. $\frac{6}{15}$, or $\frac{2}{5}$ **3.** $\frac{12}{20}$, or $\frac{3}{5}$

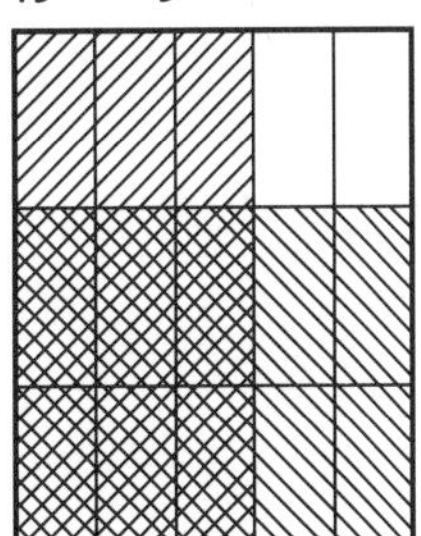

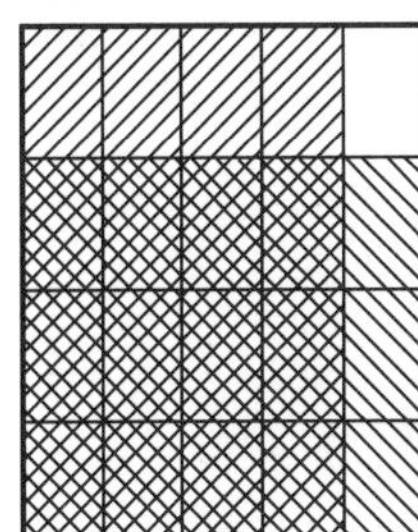

5. Nina: $\frac{1}{2}$; Phillip: $\frac{1}{6}$; Ezra: $\frac{1}{6}$; Benjamin: $\frac{1}{6}$

Study Link 8.6

1. $\frac{1}{3} * \frac{2}{5} = \frac{2}{15}$
3. $\frac{7}{8} * \frac{1}{3} = \frac{7}{24}$
5. $\frac{10}{18}$, or $\frac{5}{9}$
7. $\frac{12}{25}$
9. $\frac{5}{63}$
11. 9; 3

Study Link 8.7

1.

Rule

$\triangle = \square * \frac{3}{5}$

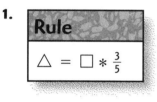

in $\square$	out $\triangle$
$\frac{1}{2}$	$\frac{3}{10}$
2	$\frac{6}{5}$, or $1\frac{1}{5}$
$\frac{4}{5}$	$\frac{12}{25}$
$\frac{3}{4}$	$\frac{9}{20}$
3	$\frac{9}{5}$, or $1\frac{4}{5}$

3.

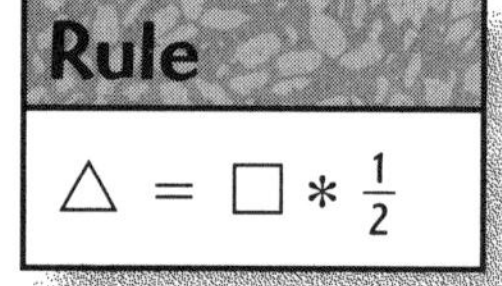

in $\square$	out $\triangle$
$\frac{2}{3}$	$\frac{2}{6}$
$\frac{3}{4}$	$\frac{3}{8}$
$\frac{7}{8}$	$\frac{7}{16}$
3	$1\frac{1}{2}$

5. Rules and tables vary.

Study Link 8.8

1. **a.** $\frac{46}{24}$, or $1\frac{11}{12}$ **b.** $\frac{10}{40}$, or $\frac{1}{4}$
   c. $\frac{85}{24}$, or $3\frac{13}{24}$ **d.** $\frac{175}{24}$, or $7\frac{7}{24}$
   e. $\frac{296}{60}$, or $4\frac{14}{15}$ **f.** $\frac{364}{40}$, or $9\frac{1}{10}$
2. **a.** $8\frac{5}{9}$ **b.** $5\frac{1}{2}$ **c.** $2\frac{1}{12}$
3. **a.** 5 **b.** $5\frac{5}{8}$

Study Link 8.9

1. $\frac{45}{100}$; 0.45; 45%
   $\frac{3}{10}$; 0.3; 30%
   $\frac{2}{10}$; 0.2; 20%
   $\frac{15}{100}$; 0.15; 15%
2. Calculated discounts: \$100.00; \$1,600.00; \$7.84; \$0.75; \$8.70; \$5.28; \$810.00; \$385.00

Study Link 8.10

1. 4;20
3. 1,200 miles
5. 32 cookies
7. yes
9. \$350; \$70

Study Link 8.11

Sample answers for Problems 1–4:

1. $\frac{14}{16}, \frac{28}{32}, \frac{35}{40}$
2. $\frac{6}{8}, \frac{9}{12}, \frac{12}{16}$
3. $\frac{1}{2}, \frac{2}{4}, \frac{3}{6}$
4. $\frac{4}{6}, \frac{6}{9}, \frac{8}{12}$
5. $\frac{3}{8}$
6. $\frac{5}{9}$
7. $\frac{7}{9}$
8. $\frac{7}{12}$
9. Sample answer: I changed $\frac{4}{10}$ and $\frac{7}{12}$ to fractions with a common denominator. $\frac{4}{10} = \frac{24}{60}$ and $\frac{7}{12} = \frac{35}{60}$. Since $\frac{1}{2} = \frac{30}{60}$, $\frac{7}{12}$ is $\frac{5}{60}$ away from $\frac{1}{2}$ and $\frac{4}{10}$ is $\frac{6}{60}$ away from $\frac{1}{2}$. So, $\frac{7}{12}$ is closer to $\frac{1}{2}$.
11. $\frac{13}{20}$
13. $\frac{11}{18}$
15. $\frac{17}{24}$
17. $\frac{3}{10}$
19. $3\frac{1}{3}$

Study Link 8.12

1. 27
3. 5
5. $3\frac{4}{5}$
7. $1\frac{5}{9}$
9. $8\frac{5}{12}$
11. 6
13. $11\frac{1}{4}$
15. $4\frac{1}{2}$

Use with Lesson 7.11.

Name Date Time

Comparing Fractions

Study Link 8.1

SRB 66–68 83–88

Circle the greater fraction for each pair.

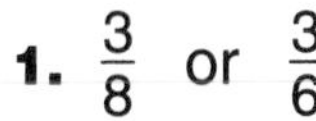

1. $\frac{3}{8}$ or $\frac{3}{6}$ **2.** $\frac{2}{3}$ or $\frac{2}{9}$ **3.** $\frac{4}{7}$ or $\frac{5}{6}$

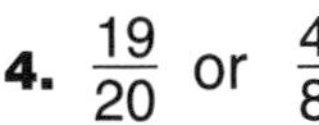

4. $\frac{19}{20}$ or $\frac{4}{8}$ **5.** $\frac{11}{21}$ or $\frac{9}{17}$ **6.** $\frac{4}{7}$ or $\frac{6}{11}$

7. Explain how you got your answer for Problem 5.

____

____

____

Write the decimal equivalent for each fraction.

8. $\frac{3}{4}$ = ________ **9.** $\frac{2}{3}$ = ________ **10.** $\frac{5}{8}$ = ________

11. $\frac{7}{10}$ = ________ **12.** $\frac{11}{20}$ = ________ **13.** $\frac{21}{25}$ = ________

14. Explain how you can do Problem 10 without using a calculator.

____

____

Use $>$, $<$, or $=$ to make each number sentence true.

15. $\frac{1}{2} + \frac{5}{8}$ ______ 1 **16.** $\frac{2}{3} + \frac{2}{6}$ ______ 1

17. $\frac{7}{9} + \frac{3}{5}$ ______ 1 **18.** 1 ______ $\frac{6}{10} + \frac{5}{20}$

19. 1 ______ $\frac{3}{8} + \frac{4}{9}$ **20.** 1 ______ $\frac{6}{7} + \frac{1}{8}$

21. Explain how you found the answer to Problem 20.

____

____

____

Name Date Time

Addition of Mixed Numbers

Study Link 8.2

Rename each mixed number in simplest form.

1. $3\frac{6}{5} = $ $4\frac{1}{5}$

2. $\frac{16}{8} = $ ______

3. $9\frac{5}{3} = $ ______

4. $1\frac{7}{5} = $ ______

5. $4\frac{6}{4} = $ ______

6. $5\frac{10}{6} = $ ______

Add. Write each sum as a whole number or mixed number in simplest form.

7. $3\frac{1}{4} + 2\frac{3}{4} = $ ______

8. $4\frac{1}{5} + 3\frac{4}{5} = $ ______

9. $9\frac{1}{3} + 4\frac{2}{3} = $ ______

10. $3\frac{5}{7} + 8\frac{6}{7} = $ ______

11. $\frac{15}{8} + 3\frac{3}{8} = $ ______

12. $4\frac{2}{9} + 5\frac{5}{9} = $ ______

Add. Rename the sum in simplest form and circle your final answer.

13. $2\frac{5}{8} + 6\frac{3}{4}$

14. $7\frac{1}{2} + 3\frac{2}{3}$

15. $4\frac{6}{9} + 3\frac{7}{12}$

16. $5\frac{3}{4} + 2\frac{4}{5}$

Name Date Time

Subtraction of Mixed Numbers

Study Link 8.3

Fill in the missing numbers.

1. $3\frac{3}{8} = 2\frac{\square}{8}$

2. $4\frac{5}{6} = \square\frac{11}{6}$

3. $2\frac{1}{9} = 1\frac{\square}{9}$

4. $6\frac{3}{7} = \square\frac{10}{7}$

5. $4\frac{3}{5} = 3\frac{\square}{5}$

6. $7\frac{2}{3} = \square\frac{\square}{3}$

Subtract. Write your answers in simplest form.

7. $5\frac{3}{4} - 3\frac{1}{4}$

8. $6\frac{2}{3} - 4\frac{1}{3}$

9. $5\frac{4}{5} - 3\frac{3}{5}$

10. $4 - \frac{3}{8} =$ ______

11. $6 - \frac{5}{9} =$ ______

12. $5 - 2\frac{3}{10} =$ ______

13. $7 - 4\frac{3}{4} =$ ______

14. $3\frac{2}{5} - 1\frac{3}{5} =$ ______

15. $4\frac{3}{8} - 3\frac{7}{8} =$ ______

Name Date Time

More Fraction Problems

Study Link 8.4

1. Circle all the fractions below that are greater than $\frac{3}{4}$.

$\frac{4}{5}$ $\frac{13}{20}$ $\frac{1}{2}$ $\frac{18}{25}$ $\frac{9}{12}$ $\frac{155}{200}$ $\frac{7}{11}$

Decide whether the sum or difference is greater than $\frac{1}{2}$, less than $\frac{1}{2}$, or equal to $\frac{1}{2}$. Circle your answer. (*Hint:* Find a common denominator for each problem.)

2. $\frac{1}{10} + \frac{2}{7}$ $> \frac{1}{2}$ $< \frac{1}{2}$ $= \frac{1}{2}$

3. $\frac{5}{6} - \frac{1}{4}$ $> \frac{1}{2}$ $< \frac{1}{2}$ $= \frac{1}{2}$

4. $\frac{18}{20} - \frac{2}{5}$ $> \frac{1}{2}$ $< \frac{1}{2}$ $= \frac{1}{2}$

5. $\frac{3}{4} - \frac{1}{3}$ $> \frac{1}{2}$ $< \frac{1}{2}$ $= \frac{1}{2}$

Fraction Puzzle

Goal To select and place three different numbers so that the sum is as large as possible.

Procedure Select three different numbers from this list: 1, 2, 3, 4, 5, 6.

- Write the same number in each square.
- Write a different number in the circle.
- Write a third number in the hexagon.
- Add the two fractions.

$\frac{\square}{\bigcirc} + \frac{\hexagon}{\square} =$ ____________

Example If $\square$ = 2, ⬡ = 3, and $\bigcirc$ = 4, then the sum is 2.

$\frac{2}{4} + \frac{3}{2} = \frac{8}{4} = 2$

Name Date Time

Fractions of Fractions

Study Link 8.5

Example

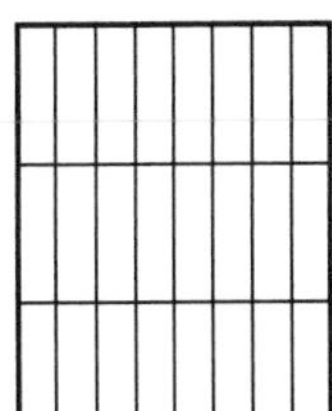

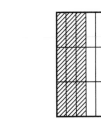

The whole rectangle represents ONE.

Shade $\frac{3}{8}$ of the interior.

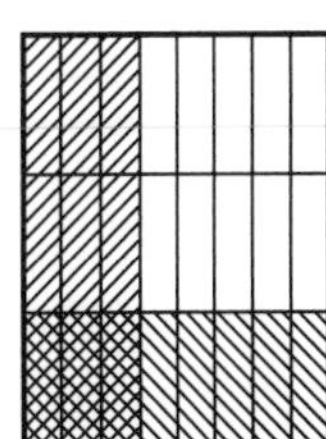

Shade $\frac{1}{3}$ of the interior in a different way.

The double shading shows that $\frac{1}{3}$ of $\frac{3}{8}$ is $\frac{3}{24}$, or $\frac{1}{8}$.

In each of the following problems, the whole rectangle represents ONE.

1. Shade $\frac{3}{5}$ of the interior.

Shade $\frac{2}{3}$ of the interior in a different way.

The double shading shows that

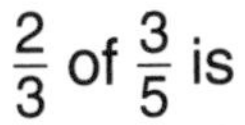

$\frac{2}{3}$ of $\frac{3}{5}$ is ____________________.

2. Shade $\frac{3}{4}$ of the interior.

Shade $\frac{1}{3}$ of the interior in a different way.

The double shading shows that

$\frac{1}{3}$ of $\frac{3}{4}$ is ____________________.

3. Shade $\frac{4}{5}$.

Shade $\frac{3}{4}$ of the interior in a different way.

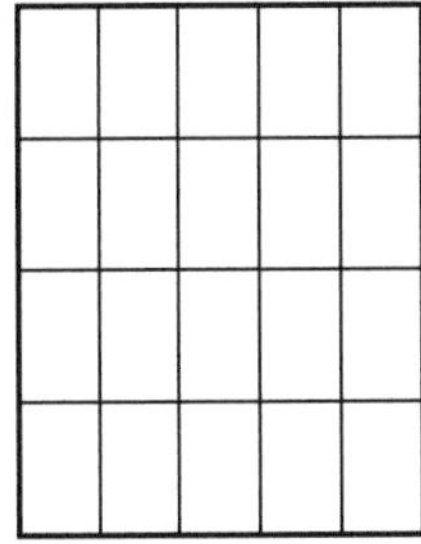

The double shading shows that

$\frac{3}{4}$ of $\frac{4}{5}$ is ____________________.

4. Shade $\frac{5}{8}$.

Shade $\frac{3}{5}$ of the interior in a different way.

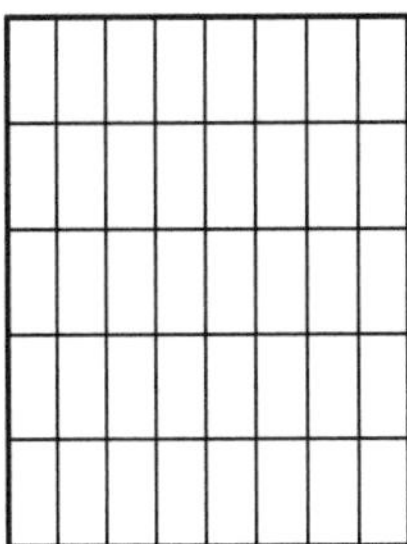

The double shading shows that

$\frac{3}{5}$ of $\frac{5}{8}$ is ____________________.

5. Nina and Phillip cut Mr. Ferguson's lawn. Nina worked alone on her half, but Phillip shared his half equally with his friends, Ezra and Benjamin. What fraction of the earnings should each person get?

____

Name Date Time

Multiplying Fractions

Study Link 8.6

Write a number model for each area model.

Example

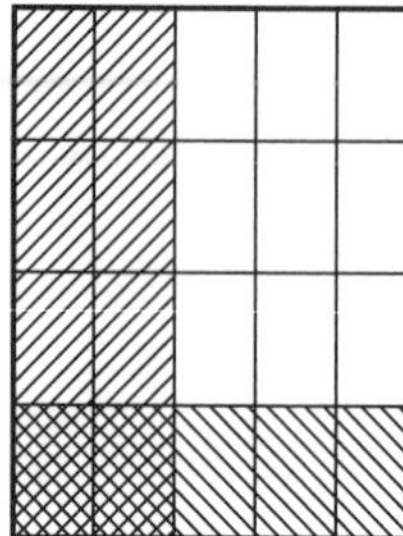

$\frac{1}{4} * \frac{2}{5} = \frac{2}{20}$, or $\frac{1}{10}$

1.

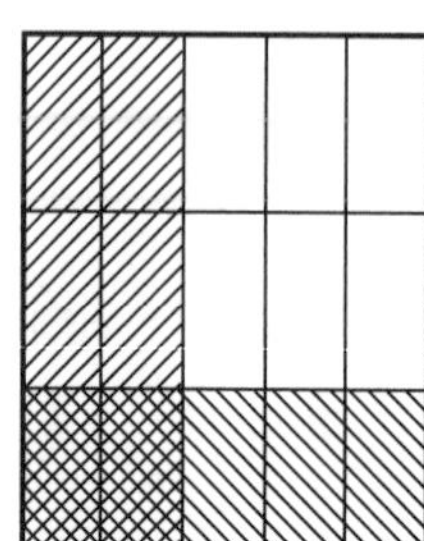

____

2.

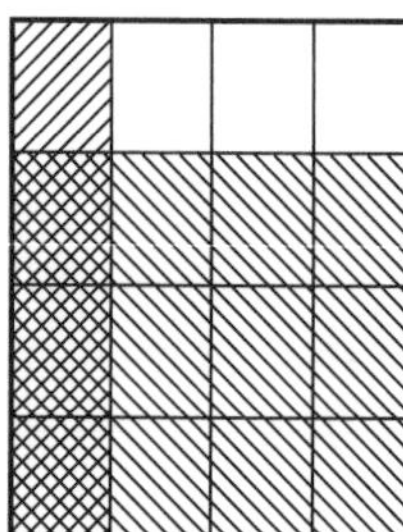

____

3.

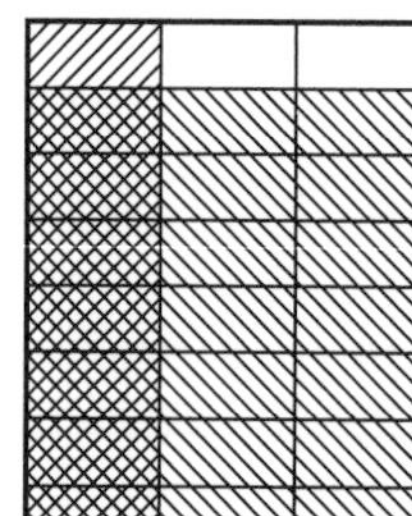

____

Multiply.

4. $\frac{3}{7} * \frac{2}{10} =$ ______________

5. $\frac{5}{6} * \frac{2}{3} =$ ______________

6. $\frac{1}{2} * \frac{1}{4} =$ ______________

7. $\frac{4}{5} * \frac{3}{5} =$ ______________

8. $\frac{2}{3} * \frac{3}{8} =$ ______________

9. $\frac{1}{7} * \frac{5}{9} =$ ______________

10. Matt is making cookies for the school fund-raiser. The recipe calls for $\frac{2}{3}$ cup of chocolate chips. He decides to triple the recipe. How many cups of chocolate chips does he need? ________ cups

11. The total number of goals scored by both teams in the field-hockey game was 15. Julie's team scored $\frac{3}{5}$ of the goals. Julie scored $\frac{1}{3}$ of her team's goals. How many goals did Julie's team score? ________ goals

How many goals did Julie score? ________ goals

12. Girls are one-half of the fifth grade class. Two-tenths of these girls have red hair. Red-haired girls are what fraction of the fifth grade class? ______________

Name Date Time

"What's My Rule?"

Study Link 8.7

Use the given rule to complete each table.

1. Rule

$\triangle = \square * \frac{3}{5}$

in ($\square$)	out ($\triangle$)
$\frac{1}{2}$	
2	
$\frac{4}{5}$	
$\frac{3}{4}$	
3	

2. Rule

$\triangle = \square * 4$

in ($\square$)	out ($\triangle$)
$\frac{2}{3}$	
$\frac{4}{5}$	
$\frac{8}{9}$	
$\frac{5}{4}$	
$\frac{7}{3}$	

What is the rule for each table?

3. Rule

in ($\square$)	out ($\triangle$)
$\frac{2}{3}$	$\frac{2}{6}$
$\frac{3}{4}$	$\frac{3}{8}$
$\frac{7}{8}$	$\frac{7}{16}$
3	$1\frac{1}{2}$

4. Rule

in ($\square$)	out ($\triangle$)
2	$\frac{1}{2}$
3	$\frac{3}{4}$
$\frac{5}{6}$	$\frac{5}{24}$
$\frac{2}{3}$	$\frac{1}{6}$

5. Make and complete your own "What's My Rule?" table on the back of this page.

Name Date Time

Multiplying Fractions and Mixed Numbers

Study Link 8.8

1. Multiply.

a. $5\frac{3}{4} * \frac{2}{6} =$ ________ **b.** $\frac{5}{8} * \frac{2}{5} =$ ________ **c.** $4\frac{1}{4} * \frac{5}{6} =$ ________

d. $2\frac{1}{3} * 3\frac{1}{8} =$ ________ **e.** $3\frac{1}{12} * 1\frac{3}{5} =$ ________ **f.** $2\frac{4}{5} * 3\frac{2}{8} =$ ________

2. Find the area of each figure below.

Area of a Rectangle	Area of a Triangle	Area of a Parallelogram
$A = b * h$	$A = \frac{1}{2} * b * h$	$A = b * h$

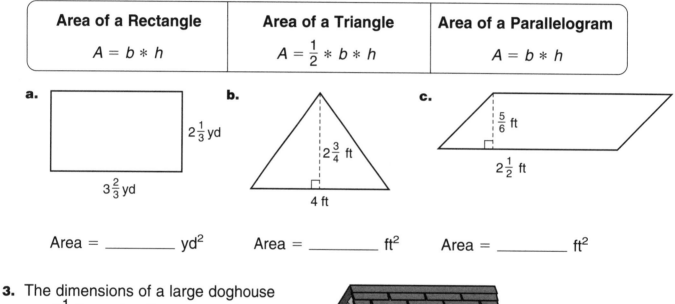

a.

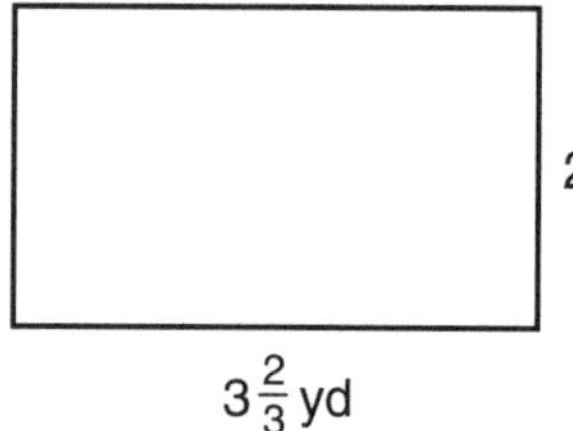

Area = ________ yd^2

b.

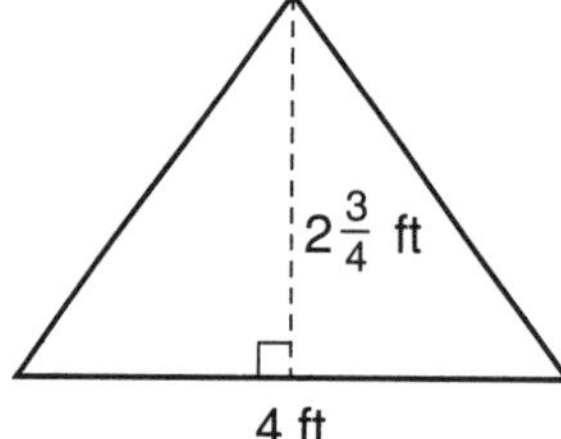

Area = ________ ft^2

c.

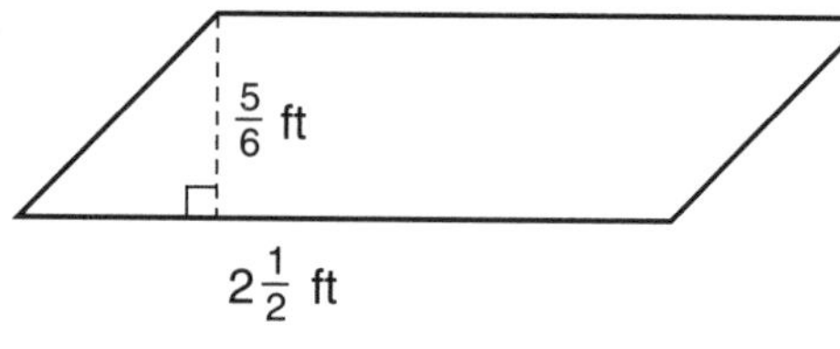

Area = ________ ft^2

3. The dimensions of a large doghouse are $2\frac{1}{2}$ times the dimensions of a small doghouse.

a. If the width of the small doghouse is 2 feet, what is the width of the large doghouse?

 feet

b. If the length of the small doghouse is $2\frac{1}{4}$ feet, what is the length of the large doghouse?

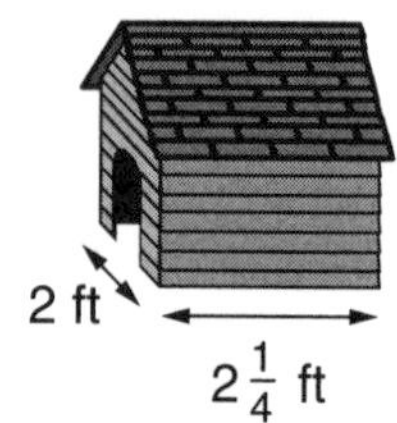

 feet

Name Date Time

Fractions, Decimals, and Percents

Study Link 8.9

SRB 26 48 51 83 89

1. Complete the table so that each number is shown as a fraction, decimal, and percent.

Fraction	Decimal	Percent
		45%
	0.3	
$\frac{2}{10}$		
	0.15	

2. Use your percent sense to estimate the discount for each item. Then calculate the discount for each item. (If necessary, round to the nearest cent.)

Item	List Price	Percent of Discount	Estimated Discount	Calculated Discount
Saguaro cactus with arms	$400.00	25%		
Life-sized wax figure of yourself	$10,000.00	16%		
Manhole cover	$78.35	10%		
Live scorpion	$14.98	5%		
10,000 honeybees	$29.00	30%		
Dinner for one on the Eiffel Tower	$88.00	6%		
Magician's box for sawing a person in half	$4,500.00	18%		
Fire hydrant	$1,100.00	35%		

Source: Everything Has Its Price

Name Date Time

Unit Fractions

Study Link 8.10

Finding the worth of the unit fraction will help you to solve each problem below.

SRB 52 53 74 75

1. If $\frac{4}{5}$ of a number is 16, what is $\frac{1}{5}$ of the number? ______

What is the number? ______

2. Our football team won $\frac{3}{4}$ of the games that it played.

It won 12 games. How many games did it play? ______ (unit)

3. When a balloon had traveled 800 miles it had completed $\frac{2}{3}$ of its journey. What was the total length of its trip? ______ (unit)

4. Neil's box of mixed fruit contains 15 oranges. These oranges are worth $\frac{3}{5}$ of the total number of pieces of fruit in the box. How many pieces of fruit does Neil have? ______ pieces

5. Grandma baked cookies. Twenty cookies were oatmeal raisin. The oatmeal raisin cookies represent $\frac{5}{8}$ of all the cookies. How many cookies did Grandma bake? ______ cookies

6. Tiana jogged $\frac{6}{8}$ of the way to school in 12 minutes. If she continues at the same speed, how long will her entire jog to school take? ______ minutes

7. After 35 minutes, Hayden had completed $\frac{7}{10}$ of his math test. If he has a total of 55 minutes to complete the test, do you think he will finish on time? ______

8. Ian bought a video game that was on sale for \$45. He paid 75% of the original price. How much would the game have cost if it had not been on sale? \$ ______

9. An ad for a computer printer stated that you could buy the printer for only \$280, or 80% of the original price. What was the original price of the printer? \$ ______

How much would you save? \$ ______

Name Date Time

Fraction Review

Study Link 8.11

Write three equivalent fractions for each fraction.

1. $\frac{7}{8}$ ______________________

2. $\frac{3}{4}$ ______________________

3. $\frac{6}{12}$ ______________________

4. $\frac{2}{3}$ ______________________

Circle the fraction that is closer to $\frac{1}{2}$.

5. $\frac{3}{8}$ or $\frac{4}{5}$

6. $\frac{4}{7}$ or $\frac{5}{9}$

7. $\frac{7}{8}$ or $\frac{7}{9}$

8. $\frac{4}{10}$ or $\frac{7}{12}$

9. Explain how you found your answer for Problem 8.

____

____

____

____

____

Solve. Write your answers in simplest form.

10. $\frac{3}{5} + \frac{9}{10} =$ __________

11. $\frac{2}{5} + \frac{1}{4} =$ __________

12. __________ $= \frac{5}{6} + \frac{3}{4}$

13. $\frac{7}{9} - \frac{1}{6} =$ __________

14. $8 - \frac{2}{3} =$ __________

15. $\frac{7}{8} - \frac{1}{6} =$ __________

16. $\frac{2}{3}$ of $\frac{1}{2}$ is __________.

17. $\frac{3}{4}$ of $\frac{2}{5}$ is __________.

18. $\frac{2}{7} * \frac{3}{4} =$ __________

19. $4 * \frac{5}{6} =$ __________

Name Date Time

Mixed Number Review

Fill in the missing numbers.

1. $3\frac{3}{8} = \frac{\square}{8}$

2. $6\frac{2}{3} = 5\frac{\square}{3}$

3. $4\frac{1}{4} = 3\frac{\square}{4}$

4. $\frac{\square}{5} = 3\frac{7}{5}$

Solve. Write your answers in simplest form.

5. $1\frac{3}{5} + 2\frac{1}{5} =$ ________

6. $3\frac{3}{8} - 1\frac{5}{8} =$ ________

7. $7\frac{4}{9} - 5\frac{8}{9} =$ ________

8. $3\frac{2}{7} + 1\frac{4}{5} =$ ________

9. $5\frac{2}{3} + 2\frac{3}{4} =$ ________

10. $4 - 1\frac{3}{4} =$ ________

11. $2\frac{2}{5} + 3\frac{3}{5} =$ ________

12. $4\frac{1}{4} + 5\frac{3}{4} =$ ________

13. $3 * 3\frac{3}{4} =$ ________

14. $4\frac{2}{3} * \frac{6}{7} =$ ________

15. ________ $= 2\frac{1}{2} * 1\frac{4}{5}$

16. $\frac{3}{10} * 8\frac{1}{3} =$ ________

Name Date Time

Family Letter

Study Link 8.13

Unit 9: Coordinates, Area, Volume, and Capacity

The beginning of this unit will provide your child with practice in naming and locating ordered number pairs on a coordinate grid. Whole numbers, fractions, and negative numbers will be used as coordinates. Your child will play the game *Hidden Treasure* (similar to the commercially available *Battleship*™), which provides additional practice with coordinates. You may wish to challenge your child to a round.

In previous grades, your child studied the perimeters (distances around) and the areas (amounts of surface) of geometric figures. *Fourth Grade Everyday Mathematics* developed and applied formulas for the areas of rectangles, parallelograms, and triangles. In this unit, your child will review these formulas and explore new area topics, including the rectangle method for finding areas of regular and irregular shapes.

Students will also examine how area, perimeter, and angle measurements are affected when a figure is changed by mathematical transformations. These transformations resemble changes and motions in the physical world. In some transformations, figures are enlarged in one or two dimensions; in other transformations, figures are translated (slid) or reflected (flipped over).

In the exploration "Earth's Water Surface," students review locating places on Earth with latitude and longitude. Then they use latitude and longitude in a sampling experiment that enables them to estimate, without measuring, the percent of Earth's surface that is covered by water. In a second exploration, "School's Land Area," students use actual measurements and scale drawings to estimate the land area covered by their school.

The unit concludes with a look at volume (the amount of space an object takes up) and capacity (the amount of material a container can hold). Students develop a formula for the volume of a prism (volume = area of the base * the height). They observe the metric equivalents 1 liter = 1,000 milliliters = 1,000 cubic centimeters, and they practice making conversions between U.S. customary measures (1 gallon = 4 quarts, and so on).

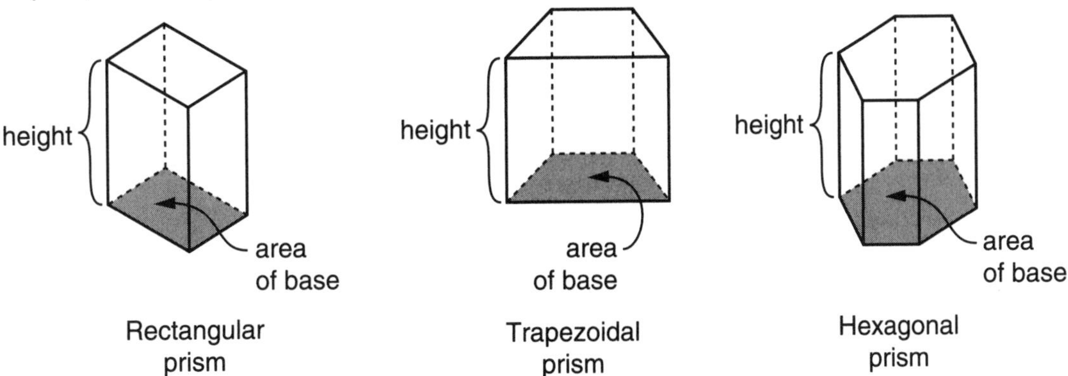

Please keep this Family Letter for reference as your child works through Unit 9.

Vocabulary

Important terms in Unit 9:

area The amount of surface inside a closed boundary. Area is measured in square units, such as square inches and square centimeters.

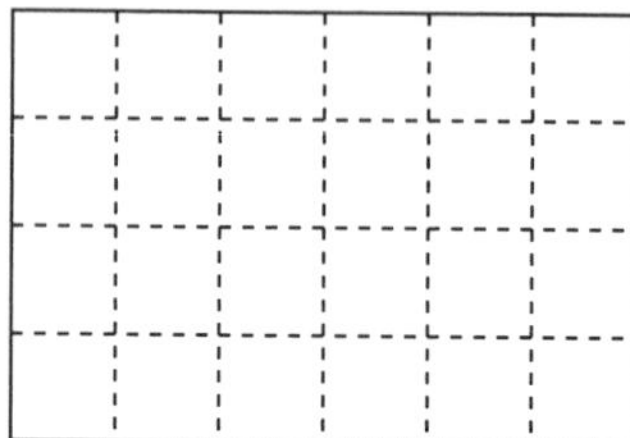

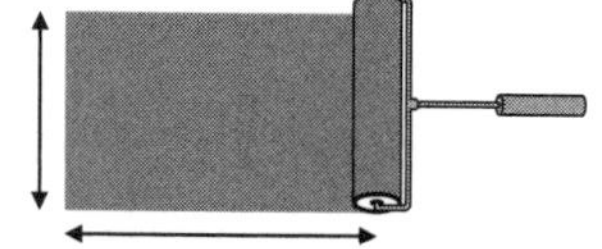

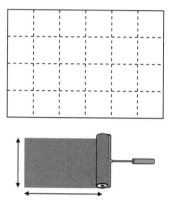

Two ways to model area

axis Either of the two number lines that intersect to form a coordinate grid.

capacity The amount a container can hold, usually in such units as *quart, gallon, cup,* and *liter.*

coordinate A number used to locate a point on a number line, or one of two numbers used to locate a point on a coordinate grid.

coordinate grid A device for locating points in a plane using ordered number pairs, or coordinates.

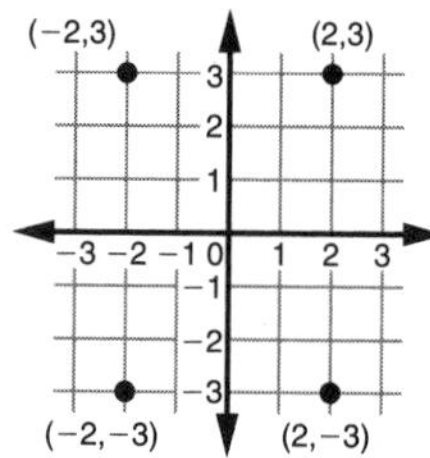

Coordinate grid

formula A general rule for finding the value of something. A formula is often written using letters, called *variables,* that stand for the quantities involved. For example, the formula for the area of a rectangle may be written as $A = l * w$, where A represents the area of the rectangle, l represents the length, and w represents the width.

height A measure of how tall something is. In geometry, height is the same thing as altitude.

latitude A measure, in degrees, of the distance of a place north or south of the Equator.

longitude A measure, in degrees, of how far east or west of the prime meridian a place is.

opposite of a number A number that is the same distance from zero on the number line as a given number, but on the opposite side of zero. For example, the opposite of $+3$ is -3 and the opposite of -5 is $+5$.

ordered number pair Two numbers that are used to locate a point on a *coordinate grid.* The first number gives the position along the horizontal axis; the second number gives the position along the vertical axis. Ordered number pairs are usually written in parentheses: (5,3).

perpendicular Meeting at right angles. Lines, rays, line segments, and planes that meet at right angles are perpendicular. The symbol $\perp$ means "is perpendicular to."

rectangle method A method for finding area in which one or more rectangles are drawn around a figure or parts of a figure.

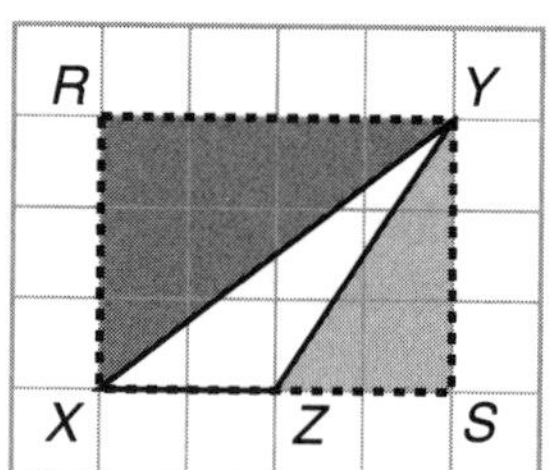

To find the area of triangle *XYZ,* subtract the areas of the two darkly shaded triangles from the area of rectangle *XRYS.*

transformation Something done to a geometric figure that produces a new figure. The most common transformations are translations (slides), reflections (flips), and rotations (turns).

variable A letter or symbol that represents a number. A variable can represent one specific number or it can stand for many different numbers.

volume The amount of space inside a 3-dimensional object. Volume is usually measured in cubic units, such as cubic centimeters, cubic inches, or cubic feet. Sometimes volume is measured in units of capacity, such as gallons or liters.

Do-Anytime Activities

To work with your child on concepts taught in this unit, try these interesting and rewarding activities:

1. Find an atlas or map that uses letter-number pairs to locate places. (For example, an atlas might say that Chattanooga, Tennessee is located at D-9.) Use the letter-number pairs to locate places you have visited or would like to visit.

2. Estimate the area of a room in your home. Use a tape measure or ruler to measure the room's length and width, and multiply to find the area. Make a simple sketch of the room, including the length, the width, and the area. If you can, find the area of other rooms, or even of your entire home.

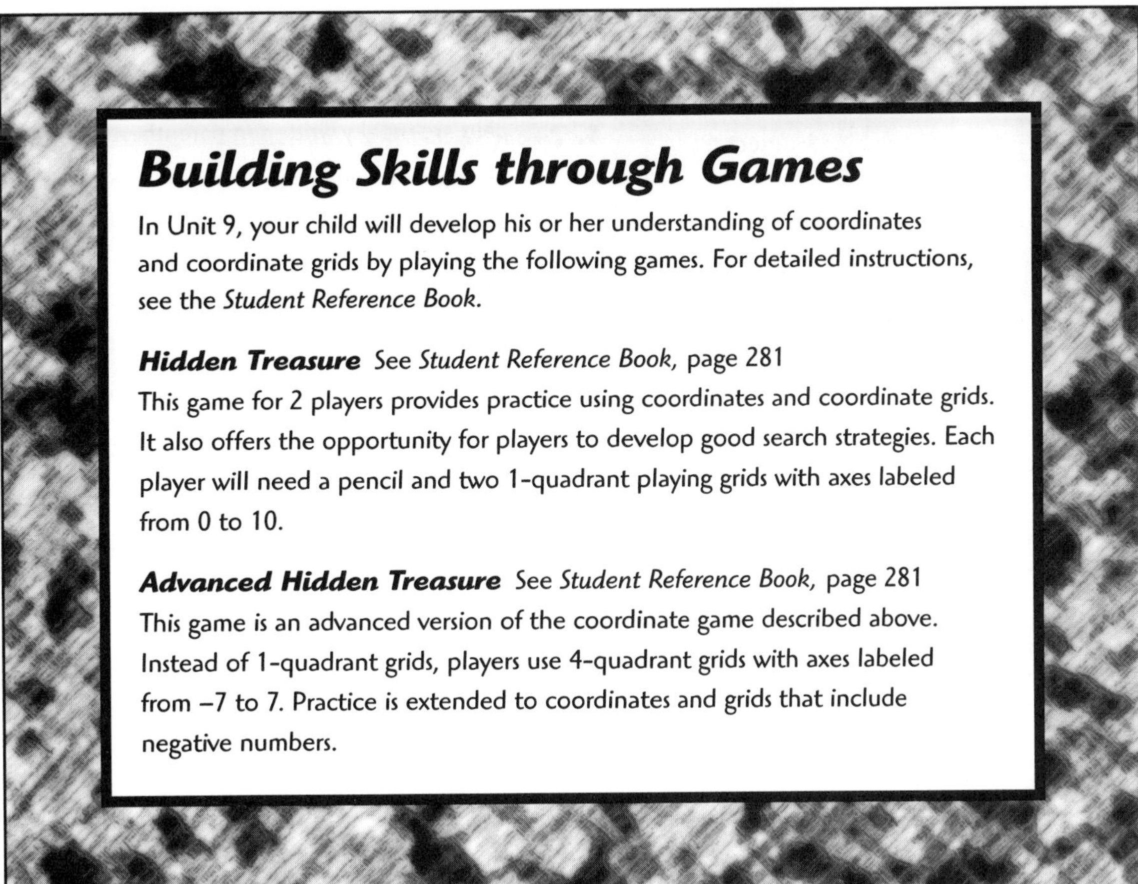

Building Skills through Games

In Unit 9, your child will develop his or her understanding of coordinates and coordinate grids by playing the following games. For detailed instructions, see the *Student Reference Book.*

Hidden Treasure See *Student Reference Book,* page 281
This game for 2 players provides practice using coordinates and coordinate grids. It also offers the opportunity for players to develop good search strategies. Each player will need a pencil and two 1-quadrant playing grids with axes labeled from 0 to 10.

Advanced Hidden Treasure See *Student Reference Book,* page 281
This game is an advanced version of the coordinate game described above. Instead of 1-quadrant grids, players use 4-quadrant grids with axes labeled from −7 to 7. Practice is extended to coordinates and grids that include negative numbers.

As You Help Your Child with Homework

As your child brings assignments home, you may want to go over the instructions together, clarifying them as necessary. The answers listed below will guide you through some of the Study Links in this unit.

Study Link 9.1

2. Rectangular prism

3. a. (11,7)

Study Link 9.3

2. The first number

3.

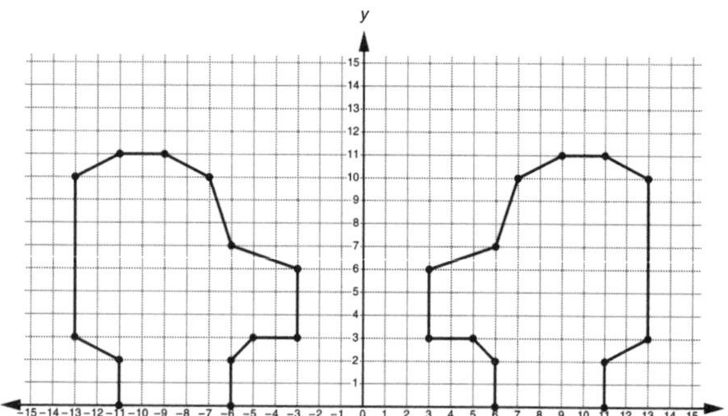

Study Link 9.4

1. $12\frac{1}{2}$ hr

2. 114 square feet

3. 80 yd^2 **4.** 33 ft^2

5.

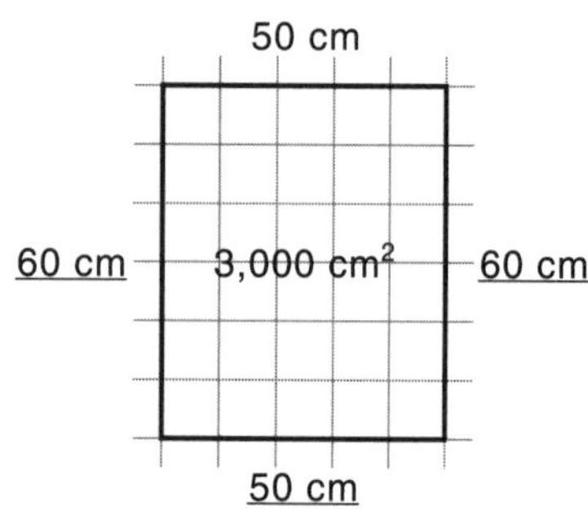

6.

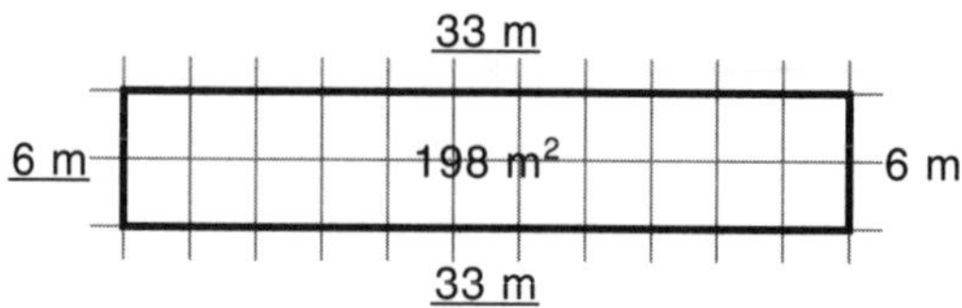

Study Link 9.5

1. 4 cm^2 **2.** 7.5 cm^2 **3.** 6 cm^2

4. 16 cm^2 **5.** 10 cm^2 **6.** 15 cm^2

Study Link 9.6

1. 4.5 cm^2; $\frac{1}{2} * 3 * 3 = 4.5$

2. 7.5 cm^2; $\frac{1}{2} * 5 * 3 = 7.5$

3. 3 cm^2; $\frac{1}{2} * 2 * 3 = 3$

4. 24 cm^2; $6 * 4 = 24$

5. 12 cm^2; $4 * 3 = 12$

6. 8 cm^2; $4 * 2 = 8$

Study Link 9.7

1. ft^2, yd^2 **2.** cm^2, $in.^2$ **3.** cm^2

4. $A = \frac{1}{2} * b * h$; 130 ft^2 **5.** $A = b * h$; 16 cm^2

6. $A = \frac{1}{2} * b * h$; 77 yd^2 **7.** $A = b * h$; 76 m^2

Study Link 9.8

1. 15 cm^2; 15 cm^3; 45 cm^3 **2.** 8 cm^2; 8 cm^3; 16 cm^3

3. 9 cm^2; 9 cm^3; 27 cm^3 **4.** 14 cm^2; 14 cm^3; 56 cm^3

Study Link 9.9

1. 72 cm^3 **2.** 144 cm^3 **3.** 70 $in.^3$

4. 162 cm^3 **5.** 45 $in.^3$ **6.** 140 m^3

Study Link 9.10

2. $A = \frac{1}{2} * 7 * 6$; 21 cm^2

3. $A = 8 * 6$; 48 $in.^2$

Use with Lesson 8.13.

Name Date Time

Plotting Points

Study Link 9.1

1. Plot the following points onto the grid below. After you plot each point, draw a line segment to connect it to the last point you plotted. *Remember to use your straightedge!*

(3,6); (11,11); (15,11); (15,7); (7,2); (3,2); (3,6); (7,6)

Draw a line segment connecting (7,6) and (7,2).
Draw a line segment connecting (7,6) and (15,11).

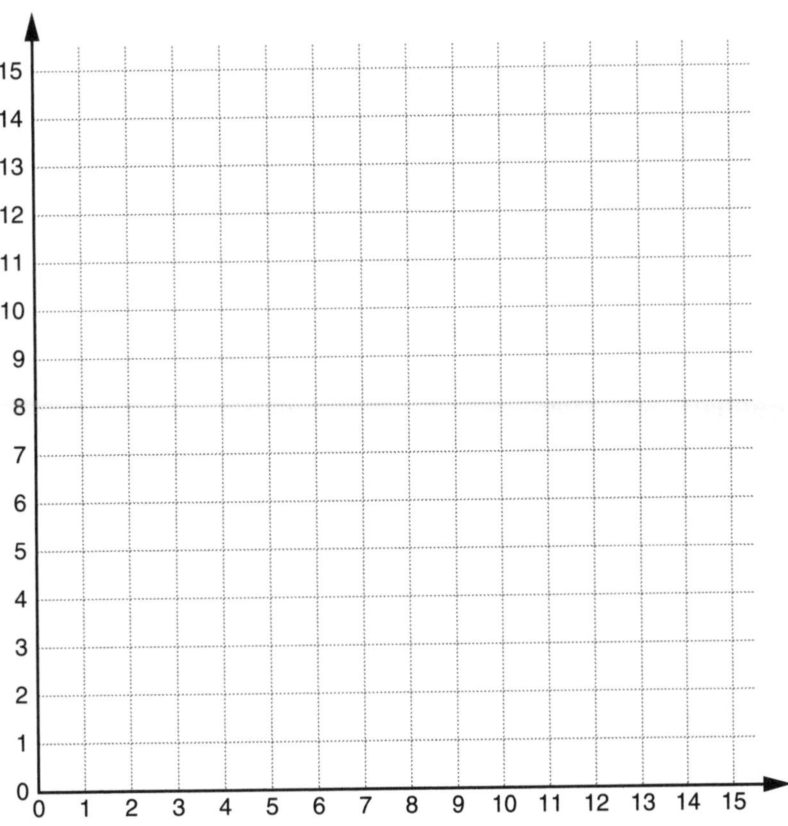

Challenge

2. What 3-dimensional shape could this drawing represent?

____

3. a. If the shape were a prism, what ordered pair would name the missing vertex?

____

b. Draw the missing vertex and then add dashed lines for the missing edges.

Name Date Time

Plotting Figures on a Coordinate Grid

Study Link 9.2

SRB 192 134–136

1. Plot three points and make a triangle on the grid below. Label the points: *A, B,* and *C.* List the coordinates of the points you drew.

   A: (____,____) *B:* (____,____) *C:* (____,____)

2. Circle the name of the kind of triangle you drew.

   scalene equilateral isosceles

3. Plot four points and make a parallelogram on the grid below. Label the points: *M, N, O,* and *P.* List the coordinates of the points you drew.

   M: (____,____) *N:* (____,____) *O:* (____,____) *P:* (____,____)

4. Circle another name for the parallelogram you drew.

   quadrangle rhombus rectangle square

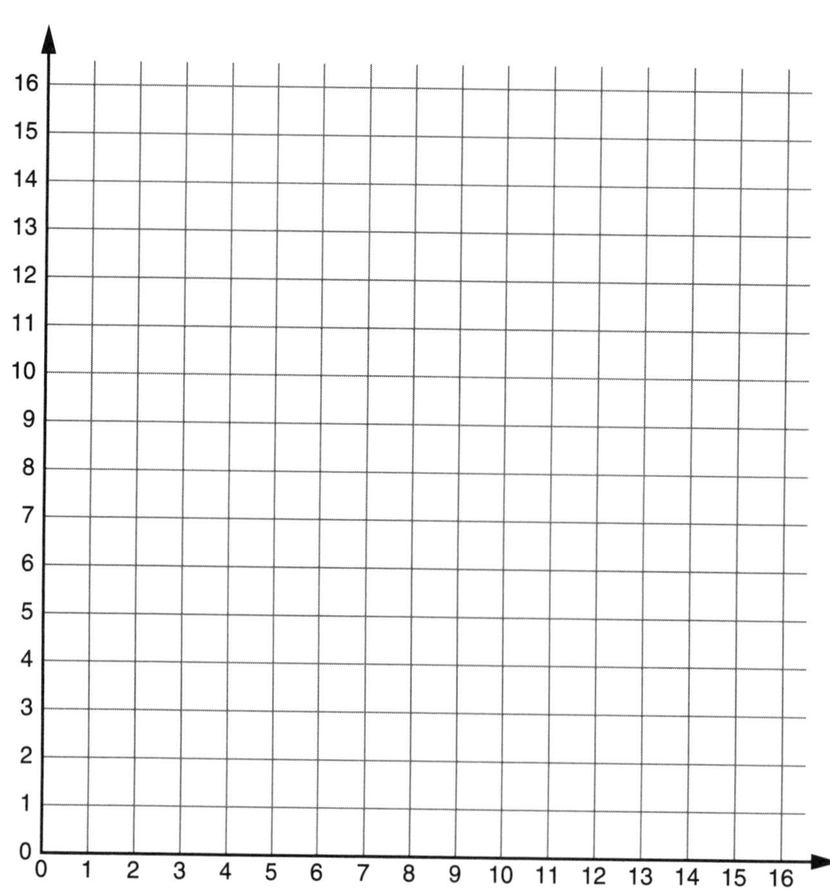

Use with Lesson 9.2.

Name Date Time

Reflections on a Grid

Study Link 9.3

1. Plot the points listed below. Use a straightedge to connect the points in the same order that you plot them.

(6,0); (6,2); (5,3); (3,3); (3,6); (6,7); (7,10); (9,11); (11,11); (13,10); (13,3); (11,2); (11,0)

2. Which number (the first number or the second number) in the pair do you need to change to the opposite in order to draw the reflection of this design on the other side of the *y*-axis?

____

3. Draw the reflection described above. Plot the points and connect them.

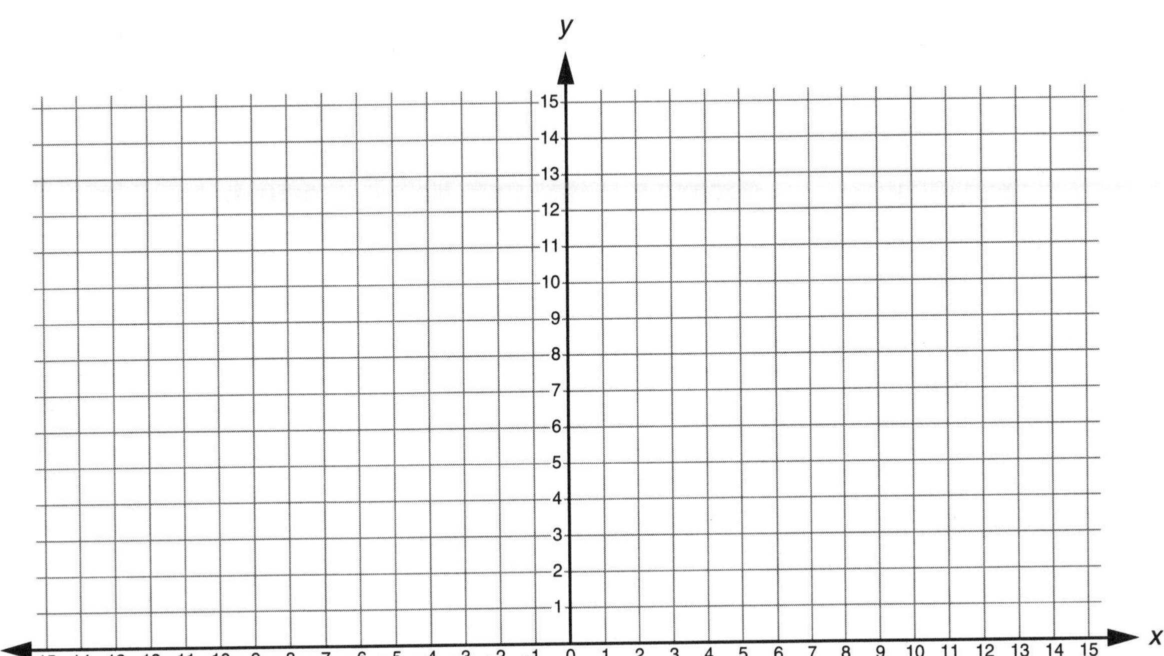

Name Date Time

More Area Problems

Study Link 9.4

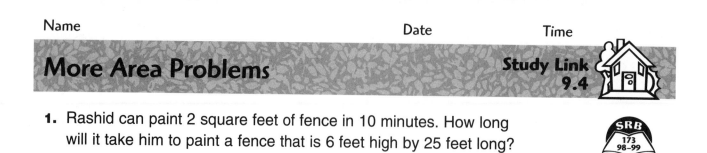

1. Rashid can paint 2 square feet of fence in 10 minutes. How long will it take him to paint a fence that is 6 feet high by 25 feet long?

SRB 173 98–99

______

2. Regina wants to cover one wall of her room with wallpaper. The wall is 9 feet high and 15 feet wide. There is a doorway in the wall that is 3 feet wide and 7 feet tall. How many square feet of wallpaper will she need to buy?

______

Calculate the areas for the figures below.

3.

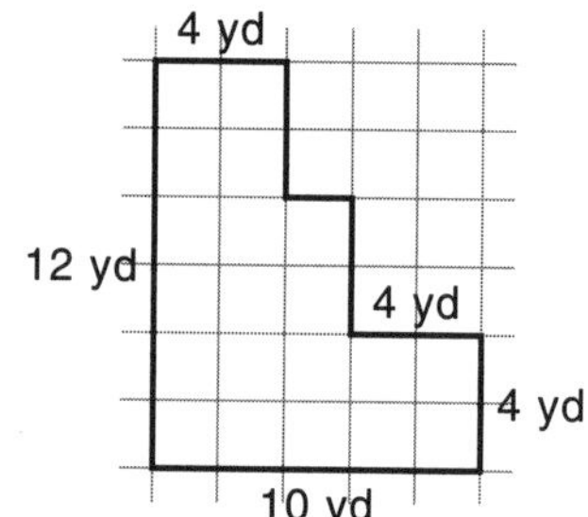

Area = ______ yd^2

4.

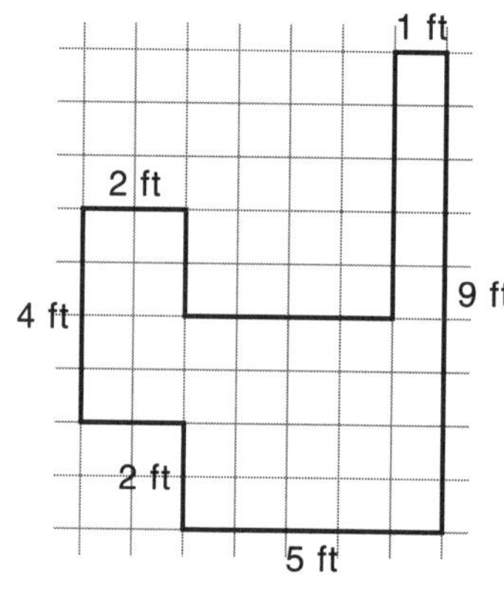

Area = ______ ft^2

Fill in the missing lengths for the figures below.

5.

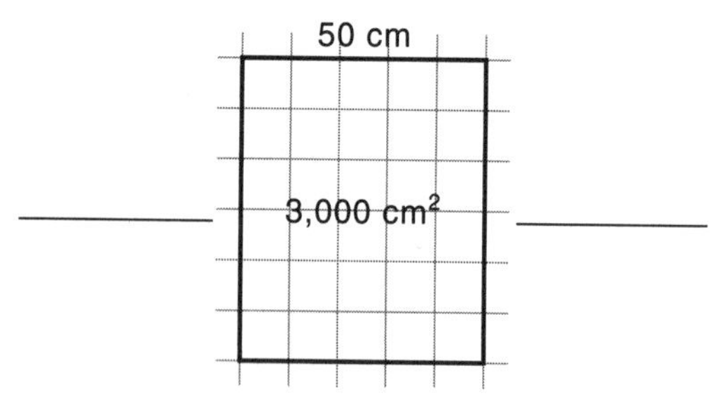

6.

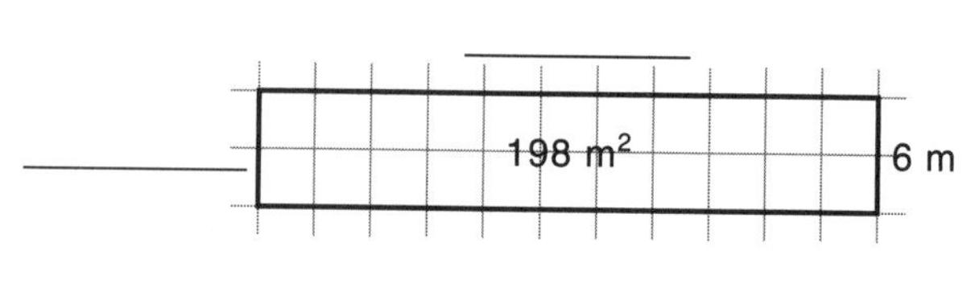

7. On the back of this page, explain how you found the area for Problem 4.

Name Date Time

The Rectangle Method

Study Link 9.5

Use the rectangle method to find the area of each triangle and parallelogram below.

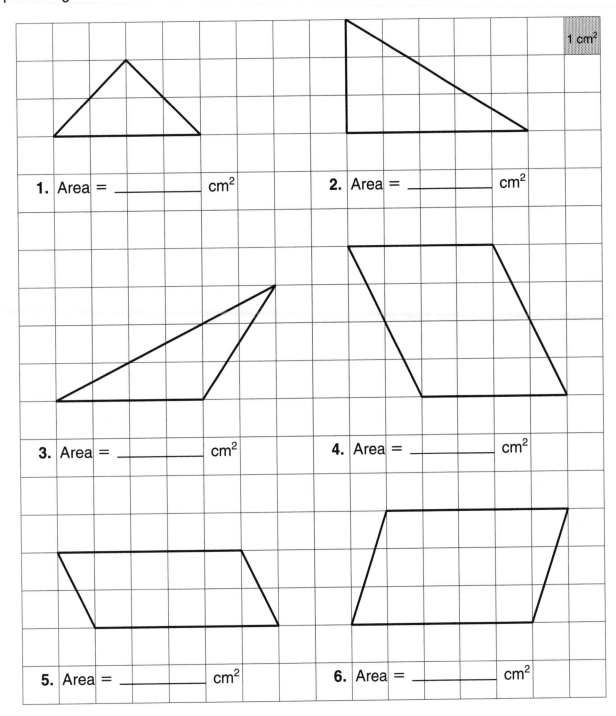

1 cm^2

1. Area = ________ cm^2

2. Area = ________ cm^2

3. Area = ________ cm^2

4. Area = ________ cm^2

5. Area = ________ cm^2

6. Area = ________ cm^2

Name Date Time

Area Formulas

Study Link 9.6

Area of a parallelogram: $A = b * h$

Area of a triangle: $A = \frac{1}{2} * b * h$

For each figure below, label the base and the height; find the area; and record the number model you used to find the area.

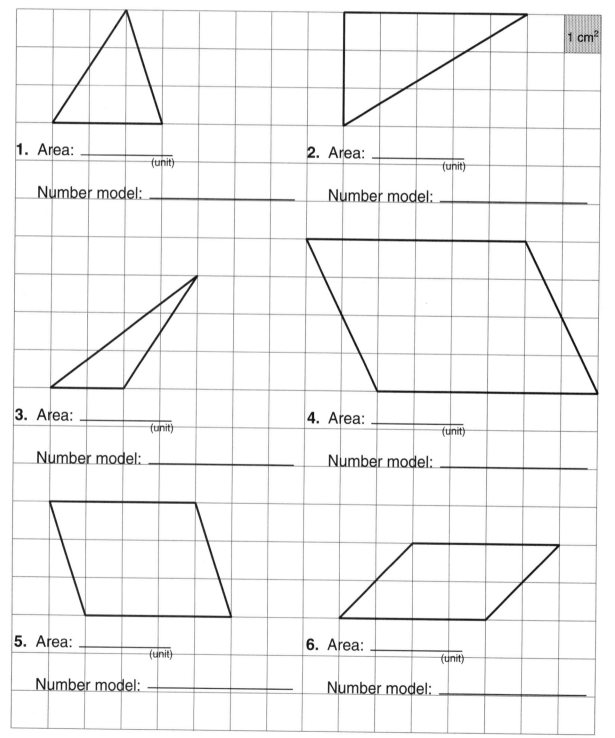

1 cm²

1. Area: ______ (unit)

   Number model: ______

2. Area: ______ (unit)

   Number model: ______

3. Area: ______ (unit)

   Number model: ______

4. Area: ______ (unit)

   Number model: ______

5. Area: ______ (unit)

   Number model: ______

6. Area: ______ (unit)

   Number model: ______

Use with Lesson 9.6.

Name Date Time

An Area Review

Study Link 9.7

Circle the most appropriate unit or units to use for measuring the area of each object.

1. The area of a football field — cm^2 ft^2 yd^2 $in.^2$

2. The area of your hand — cm^2 ft^2 yd^2 $in.^2$

3. The area of a postage stamp — cm^2 ft^2 yd^2 $in.^2$

Find the area of the figures shown below.
Write the formula you used to find the area.

Area of a triangle: $A = \frac{1}{2} * b * h$
Area of a parallelogram: $A = b * h$

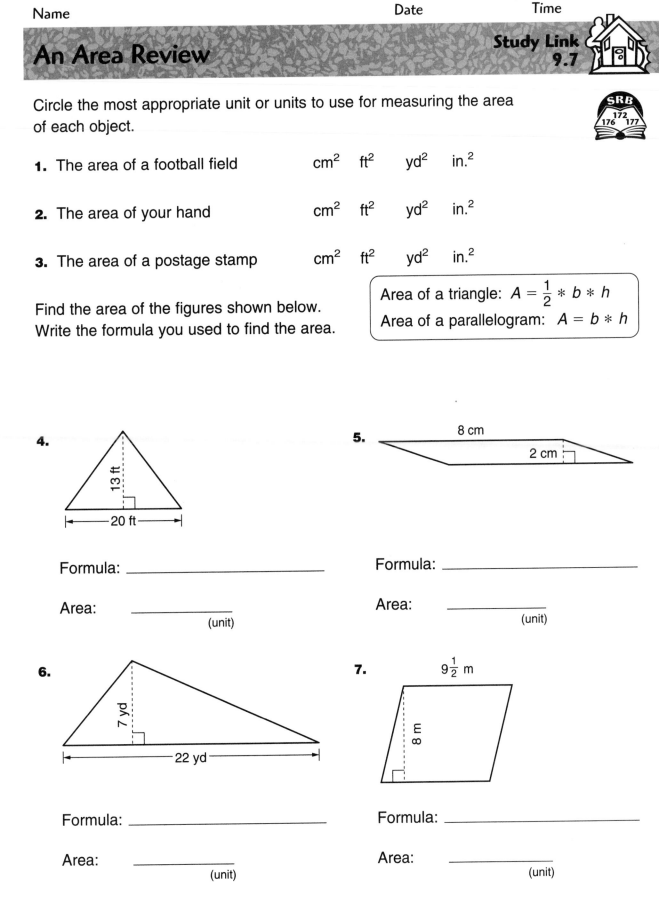

4.

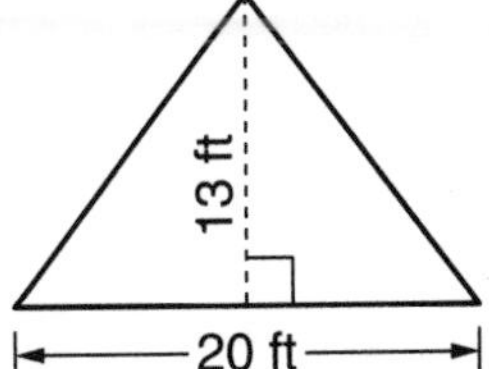

Formula: ______________________

Area: ____________ (unit)

5.

8 cm
2 cm

Formula: ______________________

Area: ____________ (unit)

6.

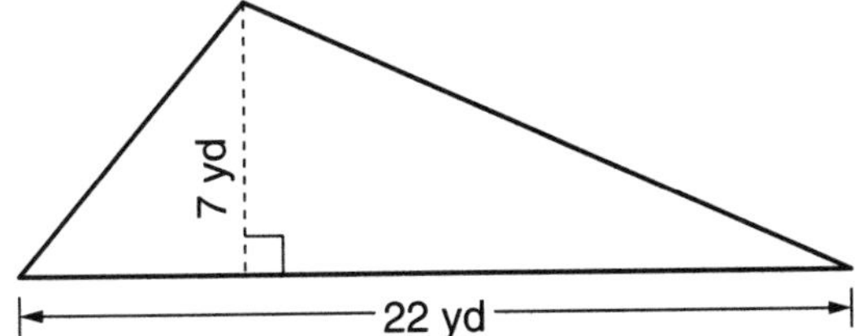

Formula: ______________________

Area: ____________ (unit)

7.

$9\frac{1}{2}$ m

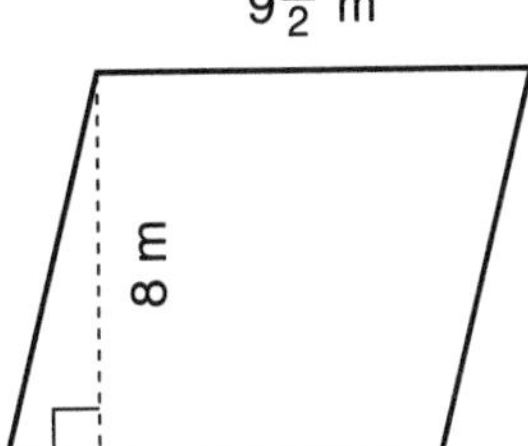

Formula: ______________________

Area: ____________ (unit)

Name Date Time

Volumes of Cube Structures

Study Link 9.8

The structures below are made up of centimeter cubes.

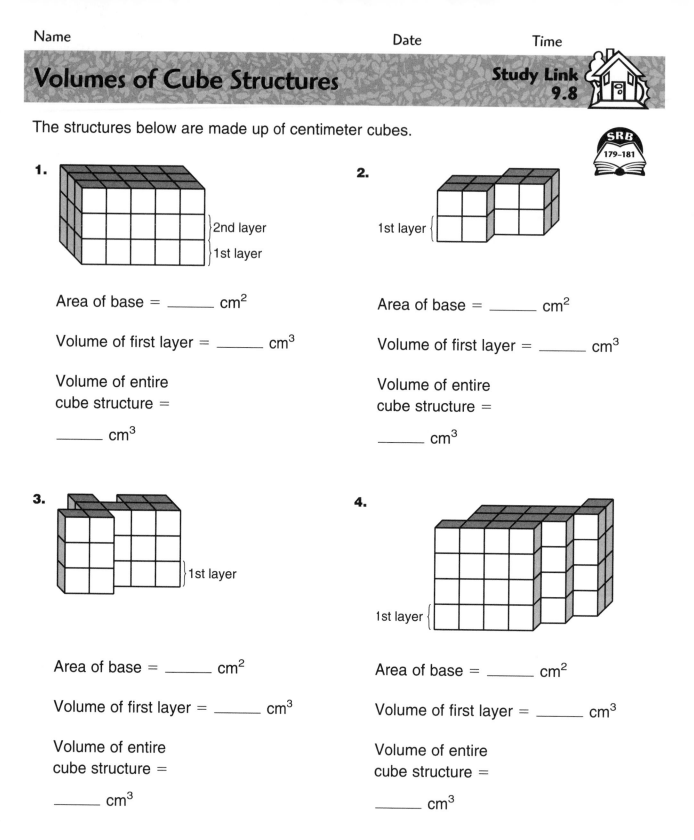

SRB 179–181

1.

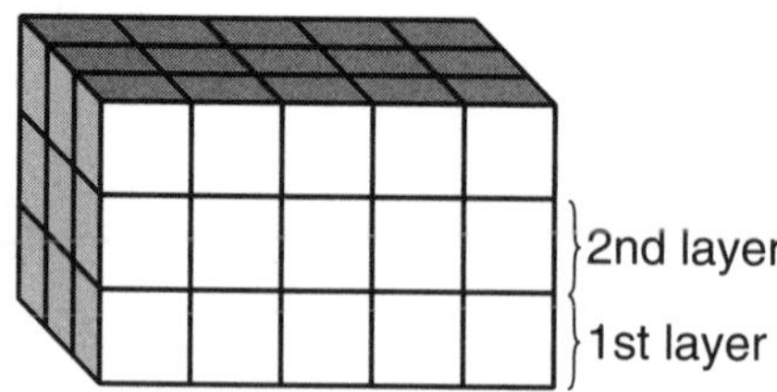

Area of base = ______ cm^2

Volume of first layer = ______ cm^3

Volume of entire cube structure =

______ cm^3

2.

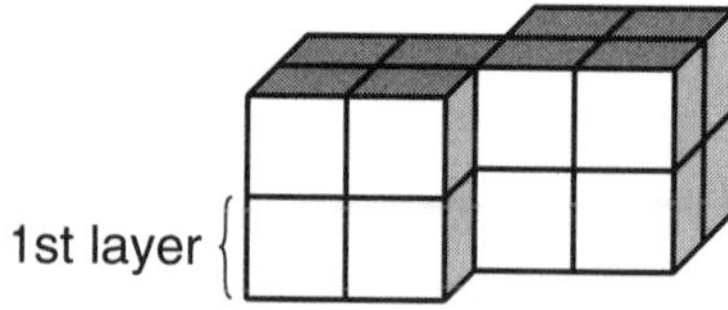

Area of base = ______ cm^2

Volume of first layer = ______ cm^3

Volume of entire cube structure =

______ cm^3

3.

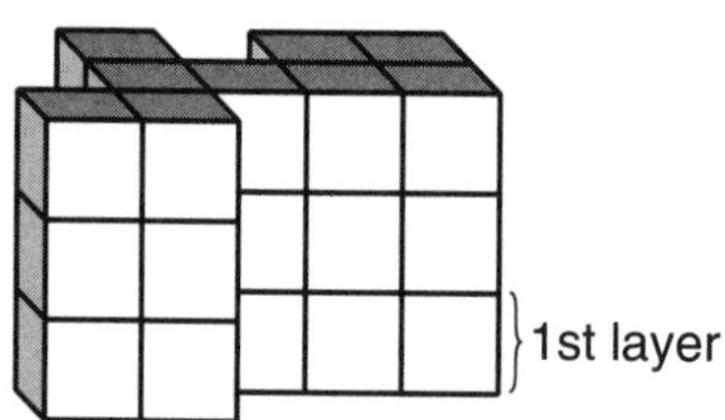

Area of base = ______ cm^2

Volume of first layer = ______ cm^3

Volume of entire cube structure =

______ cm^3

4.

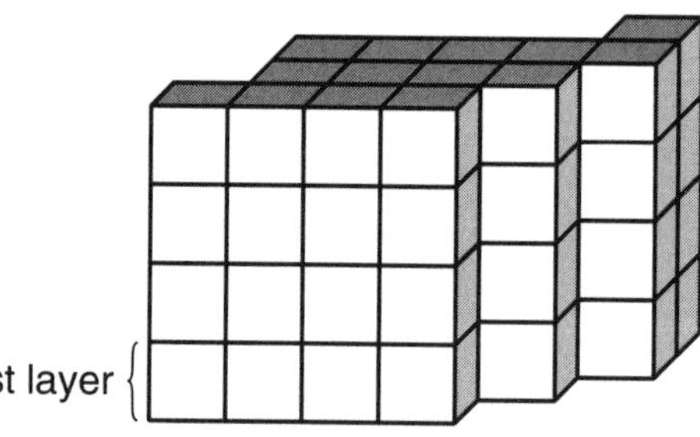

Area of base = ______ cm^2

Volume of first layer = ______ cm^3

Volume of entire cube structure =

______ cm^3

Name Date Time

Volumes of Prisms

The volume V of any prism can be found with the formula $V = B * h$, where B is the area of the base of the prism, and h is the height of the prism for that base.

1.

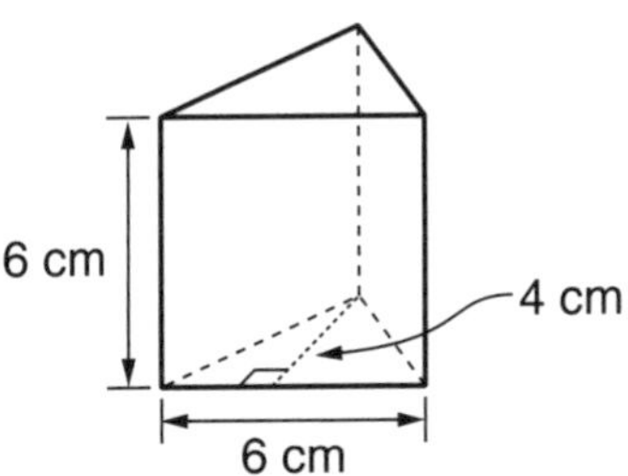

Volume = ________ cm^3

2.

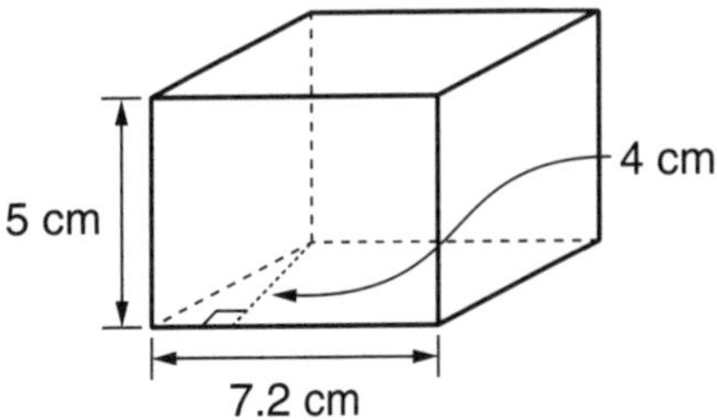

Volume = ________ cm^3

3.

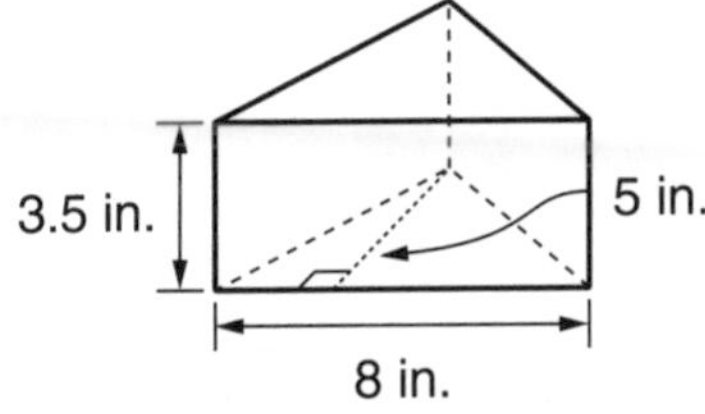

Volume = ________ $in.^3$

4.

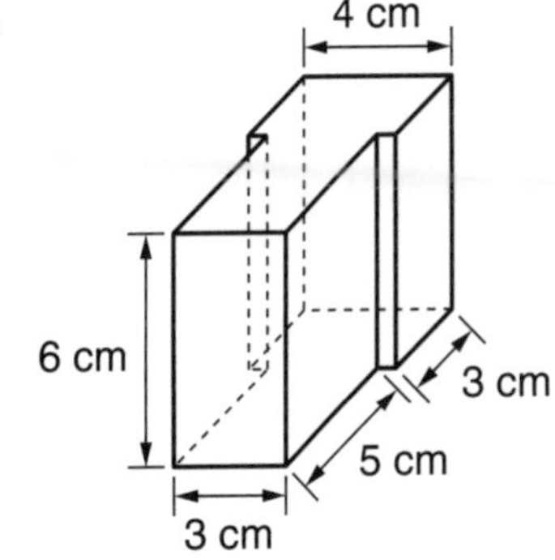

Volume = ________ cm^3

5.

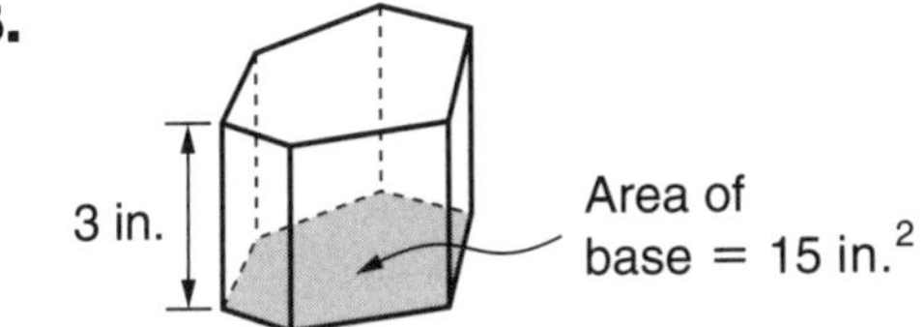

Volume = ________ $in.^3$

6.

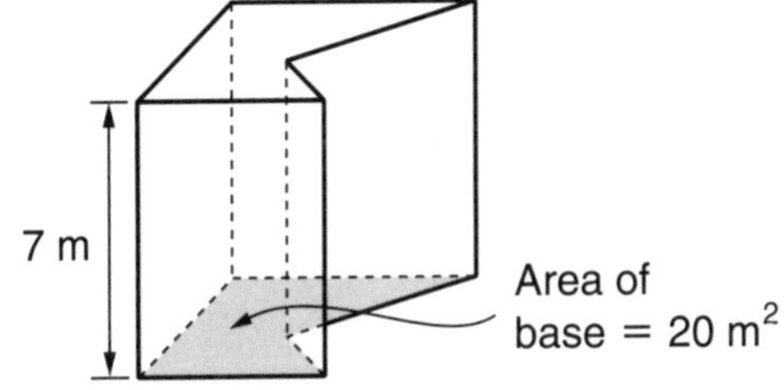

Volume = ________ m^3

Name Date Time

Unit 9 Review

1. Plot 6 points on the grid below and connect them to form a hexagon. List the coordinates of the points you plotted.

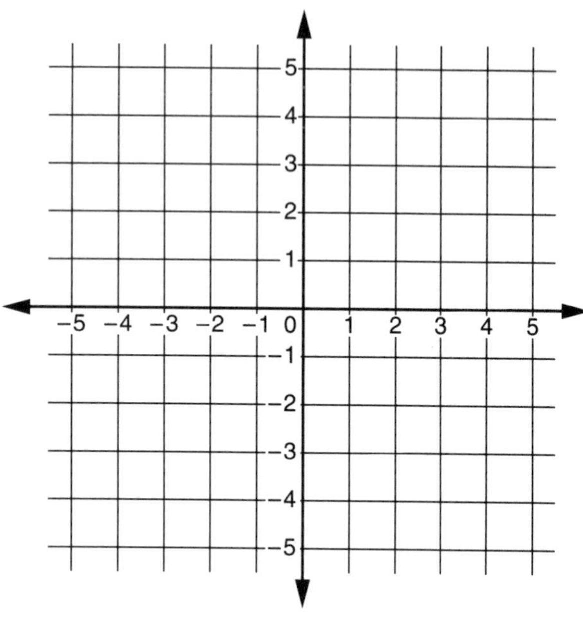

(_____, _____)
(_____, _____)
(_____, _____)
(_____, _____)
(_____, _____)
(_____, _____)

Find the area of the figures shown below. Write the number model you used to find the area.

Area of a rectangle: $A = b * h$
Area of a parallelogram: $A = b * h$
Area of a triangle: $A = \frac{1}{2} * b * h$

2. 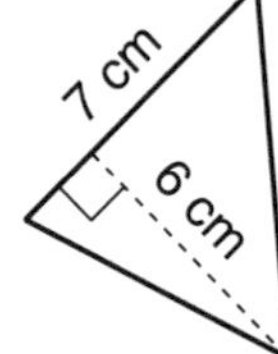

Number model: ____________________

Area: ____________________ (unit)

3. 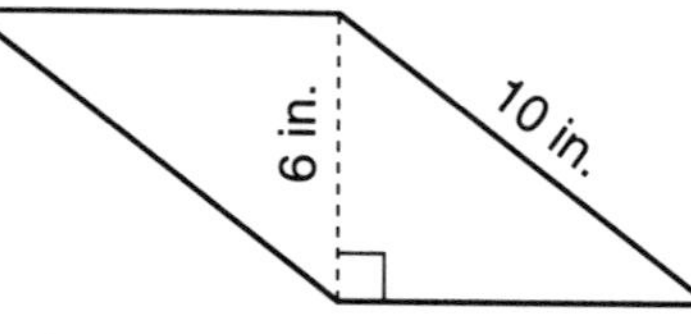

Perimeter = 36 in.

Number model: ____________________

Area: ____________________ (unit)

4. On the back of this page, explain how you solved Problem 3.

Name Date Time

Family Letter

Study Link 9.11

Unit 10: Algebra Concepts and Skills

In this unit, your child will be introduced to solving simple equations with a pan balance, thus developing basic skills of algebra. For example, a problem might be to find how many marbles in the illustration below weigh as much as a cube. You can solve this problem by removing 3 marbles from the left pan and 3 marbles from the right pan. Then the pans will still balance. Therefore, you know that one cube weighs the same as 11 marbles.

You can think of this pan-balance problem as a model for the equation $c + 3 = 14$, in which the value of c is 11.

A "What's My Rule?" table has been a routine since the early grades of *Everyday Mathematics*. In this unit, your child will follow rules to complete tables, such as the one below and will then graph the data. Your child will also determine rules from information provided in tables and graphs. Students will begin to express such rules using algebraic expressions containing variables.

Rule
out = in + 6

in	out
−1	5
2	8
5	
	12
12	
	15

As the American Tour continues, your child will work with variables and formulas to predict eruption times of the famous geyser, Old Faithful, in Yellowstone National Park.

In previous grades, your child studied the perimeter (distance around) and the area (amount of surface) of geometric figures. In Unit 9, students developed and applied formulas for the area of rectangles, parallelograms, and triangles. In this unit, your child will explore and apply formulas for the circumference (distance around) and area of circles.

Please keep this Family Letter for reference as your child works through Unit 10.

Vocabulary

Important terms in Unit 10:

algebraic expression An expression that contains a variable. For example, if Maria is 2 inches taller than Joe, and if the variable M represents Maria's height, then the algebraic expression $M - 2$ represents Joe's height.

coordinate A number used to locate a point on a number line, or one of two numbers used to locate a point on a coordinate grid.

formula A general rule for finding the value of something. A formula is often written using letters, called *variables*, that stand for the quantities involved. For example, the formula for the area of a rectangle may be written as $A = l * w$, where A represents the area of the rectangle, l represents its length, and w represents its width.

line graph A graph in which data points are connected by line segments.

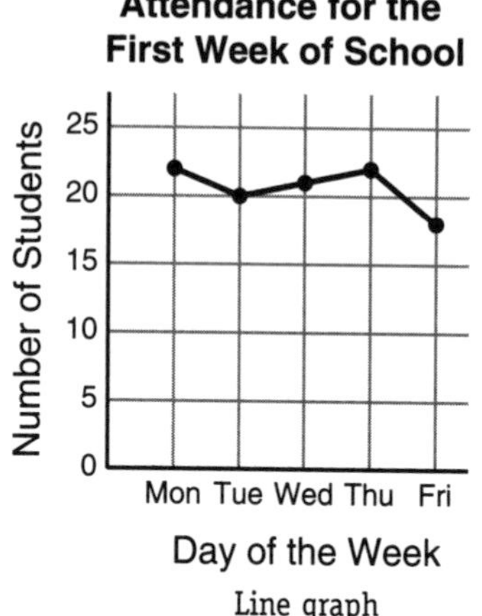

Line graph

ordered number pair Two numbers that are used to locate a point on a *coordinate grid.* The first number gives the position along the horizontal axis, and the second number gives the position along the vertical axis. The numbers in an ordered pair are called *coordinates.* Ordered pairs are usually written inside parentheses: (2,3).

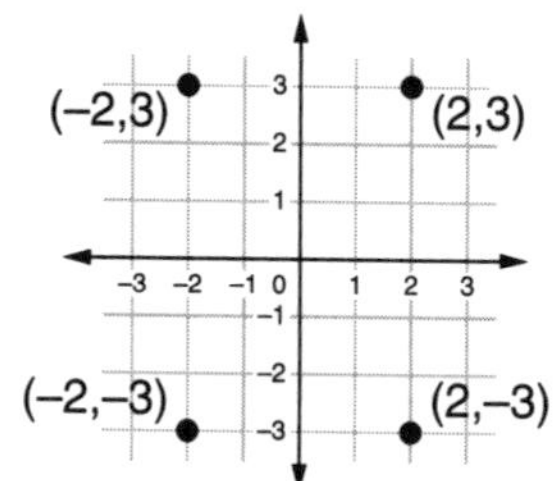

Coordinate grid

pan balance A tool used to weigh objects or compare weights.

Pan balance

predict To tell what will happen ahead of time; to make an educated guess about what might happen.

rate A comparison by division of two quantities with unlike units. For example, a speed such as 55 miles per hour is a rate that compares distance with time.

variable A letter or other symbol that represents a number. A variable can represent one specific number or it can stand for many different numbers.

Do-Anytime Activities

To work with your child on concepts taught in this unit and in previous units, try these interesting and rewarding activities:

1. Have your child list different timed distances for a mile. For example, the fastest mile run by man and by a race car; your child's own fastest mile completed by running, biking, or walking; the fastest mile run for a handicapped athlete; the fastest mile completed by a swimmer, and so on.
2. Have your child keep a running tally of when the school bus arrives. Or have your child time himself or herself to see how long it takes to walk to school in the morning compared to walking home in the afternoon. After a week, have your child describe landmarks for their data, and interpret these landmarks.

Building Skills through Games

In this unit, your child will practice using algebraic expressions containing variables by playing the following game. For more detailed instructions, see the *Student Reference Book.*

First to 100 See *Student Reference Book,* page 273
This is a game for two to four players and requires 32 Problem Cards and a pair of six-sided dice. Players answer questions after substituting numbers for the variable on Problem Cards. The questions offer practice on a variety of mathematical topics.

As You Help Your Child with Homework

As your child brings assignments home, you may want to go over the instructions together, clarifying them as necessary. The answers listed below will guide you through some of the Study Links in this unit.

Study Link 10.1

1. 3 **2.** 3 **3.** 36 **4.** 4 **5.** 3

Study Link 10.2

1. 5, 10 **2.** 2, 2 **3.** 4, 6 **4.** true
5. true **6.** false **7.** false **8.** 26
9. 2 **10.** 50 **11.** 0

Study Link 10.3

1.

in	out
−5	−11
8	2
10	4
2	−4
3	−3

2.

□	△
4	20
7	35
6	30
12	60
1.2, $\frac{6}{5}$, or $1\frac{1}{5}$	6
7.2, $\frac{36}{5}$, or $7\frac{1}{5}$	36

3.

in	out
−15	−7.5
37	44.5
−3.5	4
−20	−12.5

4.

□	△
3	21
2	$\frac{63}{2}$, 31.5, or $31\frac{1}{2}$
10	6.3, $\frac{63}{10}$, or $6\frac{3}{10}$
6	10.5
1	63

Study Link 10.4

1.

in (n)	out ($15 - n$)
1	14
2	13
8	7
10	5
18	−3
15	0

3.

in (x)	out $((2 * x) + 3)$
1	5
2	7
3	9
6	15
8	19
0	3

5. Rule: $(n * 2) - 1$; Multiply "in" by 2 and then subtract 1.

in	out
1	1
2	3
3	5
4	7
5	9
10	19

Study Link 10.5

1. 60°F **2.** 72°F **3. a.** 70°F **b.** 67°F

4. Sample answer: Some types of crickets may chirp more slowly than others. The formulas predict higher temperatures for crickets that chirp at faster rates.

Study Link 10.6

°C	−20	−10	0	10	20	30
°F (formula)	−4	14	32	50	68	86
°F (rule of thumb)	−8	12	32	52	72	92

Study Link 10.7

Answers vary.

Study Link 10.8

1. a. 22.0 **b.** 40.2
2. a. 85 **b.** 85
3. a. 21

Study Link 10.9

1. circumference **2.** area **3.** area
4. circumference **5.** 50 cm^2
6. 6 in. **7.** 5 m

8. Sample answer: The circumference is 31.4 meters, and this equals $\pi * d$, or about $3.14 * d$. Since $3.14 * 10 = 31.4$, the diameter is about 10 meters. The radius is half the diameter, or about 5 meters.

Name Date Time

Pan-Balance Problems

Study Link 10.1

Solve these pan-balance problems. In each figure, the two pans are in perfect balance.

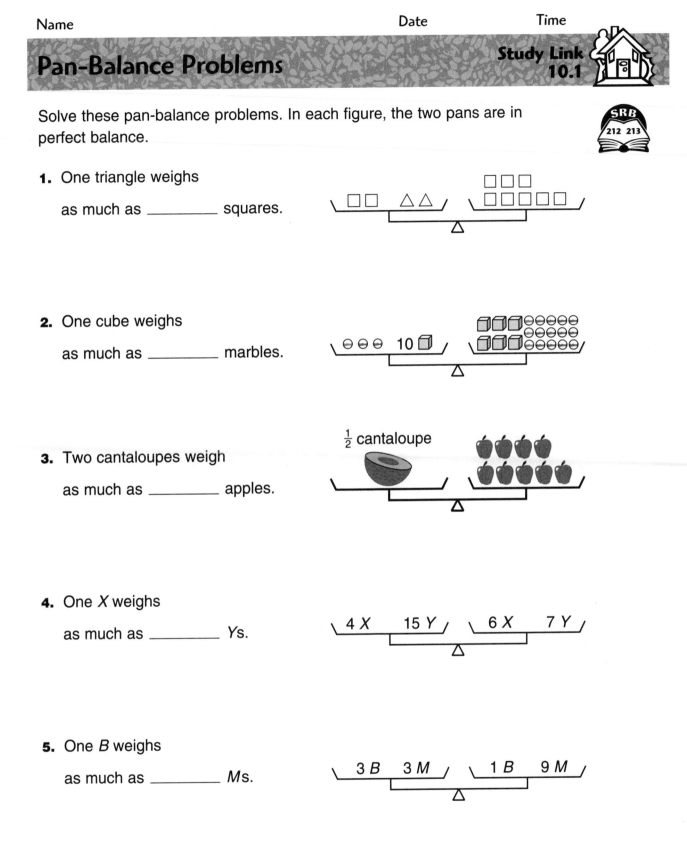

1. One triangle weighs as much as ________ squares.

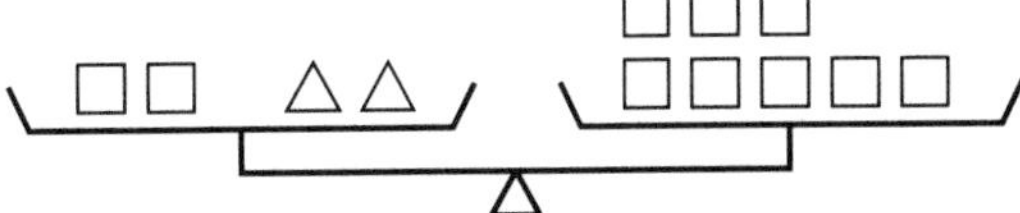

2. One cube weighs as much as ________ marbles.

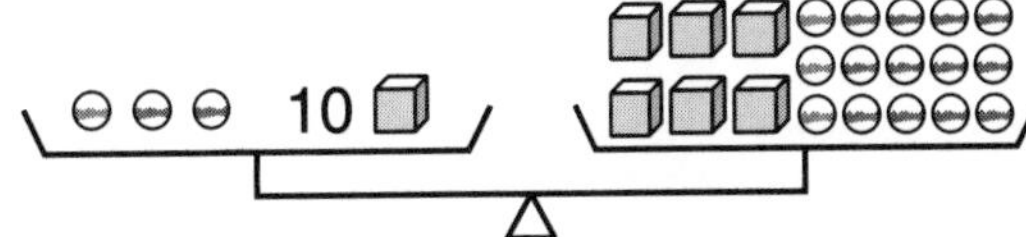

3. Two cantaloupes weigh as much as ________ apples.

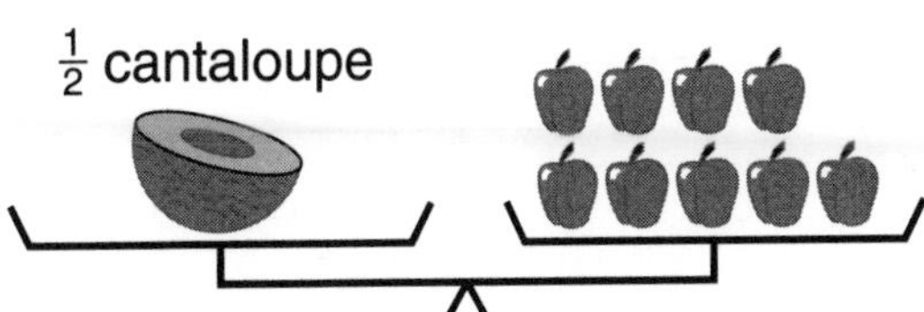

4. One *X* weighs as much as ________ *Y*s.

4 *X* 15 *Y* | 6 *X* 7 *Y*

5. One *B* weighs as much as ________ *M*s.

3 *B* 3 *M* | 1 *B* 9 *M*

Name Date Time

More Pan-Balance Problems

Study Link 10.2

In each figure below, the two pans are in perfect balance. Solve these pan-balance problems.

1.

M weighs

as much as ________ marbles.

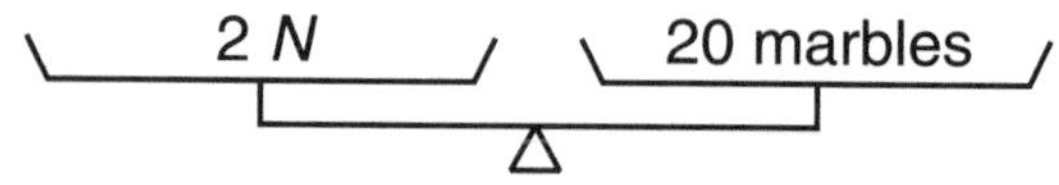

N weighs

as much as ________ marbles.

2.

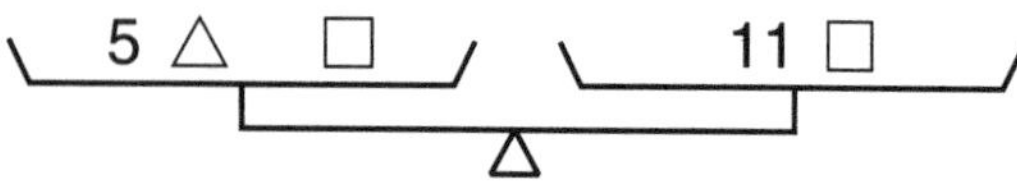

One △ weighs

as much as ________ □s.

One □ weighs

as much as ________ marbles.

3.

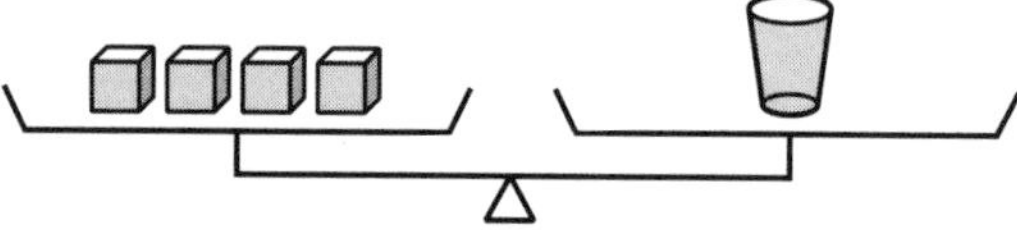

One cup of juice weighs

as much as ________ blocks.

One apple weighs

as much as ________ blocks.

True or false?

4. (5 + 16) ∗ 3 = 63 ________

5. 30 = ((9 + 7) − 1) ∗ 2 ________

6. 38 = 2 + ((8 ∗ 6) − 10) ________

7. 34 ∗ (2 + 26) = 94 ________

Fill in the missing numbers to make true sentences.

8. ________ = (7 + 45) / 2

9. ((28 / 7) + 12) / 8 = ________

10. ((14 ∗ 3) + 14) − 6 = ________

11. ________ = (3 − 3) ∗ ((34 / 2) ∗ 115)

Use with Lesson 10.2.

Name Date Time

"What's My Rule?"

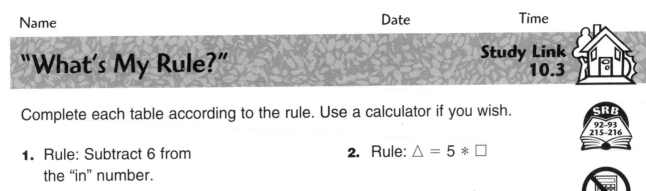

Study Link 10.3

Complete each table according to the rule. Use a calculator if you wish.

1. Rule: Subtract 6 from the "in" number.

in	out
−5	−11
8	
10	
	−4
	−3

2. Rule: △ = 5 ∗ □

□	△
4	
7	
6	
12	60
	6
	36

3. Rule: Add 7.5 to the "in" number.

in	out
−15	
37	
	4
−20	

4. Rule: △ = (9 ∗ 7) / □

□	△
3	
2	
10	
	10.5
	63

Name Date Time

"What's My Rule?"

Study Link 10.4

Complete each table below according to the rule.

1. Rule: Subtract the "in" number from 15.

in (n)	out ($15 - n$)
1	
2	
8	
	5
18	
	0

2. Rule: Triple the "in" number.

in (d)	out ($3 * d$)
7	
12	
	24
0.3	
	1
$\frac{1}{2}$	

3. Rule: Double the "in" number and add 3.

in (x)	out ($((2 * x) + 3)$)
1	
2	
3	
	15
8	
	3

Complete each table below. Write the rule in words or as a formula.

4. Rule: ______________________

____

____

in	out
6	3
9	$4\frac{1}{2}$
1	0.5
12	
	8
440	

5. Rule: ______________________

____

____

in	out
1	1
2	3
3	5
4	
5	
	19

6. Make up your own.

Rule: ______________________

____

in	out

Use with Lesson 10.4.

Name Date Time

Cricket Formulas

Study Link 10.5

SRB 201

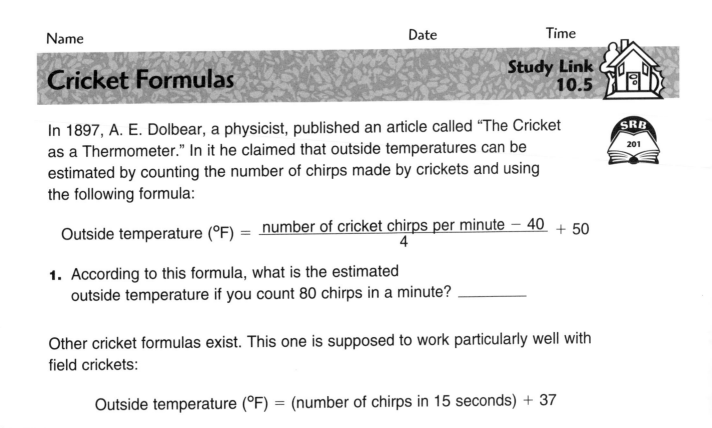

In 1897, A. E. Dolbear, a physicist, published an article called "The Cricket as a Thermometer." In it he claimed that outside temperatures can be estimated by counting the number of chirps made by crickets and using the following formula:

$$\text{Outside temperature } (^\circ\text{F}) = \frac{\text{number of cricket chirps per minute} - 40}{4} + 50$$

1. According to this formula, what is the estimated outside temperature if you count 80 chirps in a minute? ________

Other cricket formulas exist. This one is supposed to work particularly well with field crickets:

$$\text{Outside temperature } (^\circ\text{F}) = (\text{number of chirps in 15 seconds}) + 37$$

2. What outside temperature would be predicted if you counted 35 chirps in 15 seconds? ________

3. Compare the two formulas. If you counted 30 chirps in 15 seconds, what temperature would each formula predict?

   a. First formula: ________

   b. Second formula: ________

4. Why might the type of cricket you are listening to affect the accuracy of the prediction?

____

____

____

____

____

Source: It's Raining Frogs and Fishes: Four Seasons of Natural Phenomena and Oddities of the Sky

Name Date Time

Converting Celsius to Fahrenheit

In the U.S. customary system, temperature is measured in degrees Fahrenheit (°F). In the metric system, temperature is measured in degrees Celsius (°C). The temperature at which water freezes is 0°C, or 32°F.

You can use the following formula to convert temperatures measured in degrees Celsius to degrees Fahrenheit, where F stands for the number of degrees Fahrenheit and C for the number of degrees Celsius:

Formula: $F = (1.8 * C) + 32$

If you want to get a rough estimate of the temperature in degrees Fahrenheit, you can use the following rule of thumb:

Rule of thumb: Double the number of degrees Celsius and add the Fahrenheit freezing temperature.

$F = (2 * C) + 32$

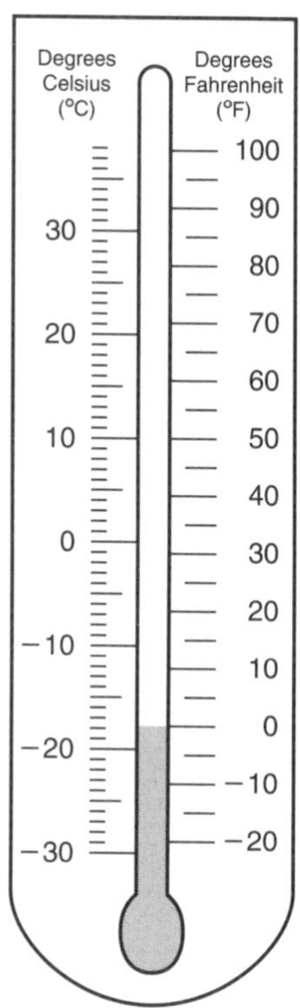

Convert the Celsius temperatures in the table to Fahrenheit temperatures, first using the formula and then the rule of thumb. Compare the results.

°C	−20	−10	0	10	20	30
°F (Use the formula.)						
°F (Use the rule of thumb.)						

Do you think that the results you get using the rule of thumb are close enough in most situations? ________

Explain. ____

____

If you were sick and you took your temperature with a Celsius thermometer, would you use the formula or the rule of thumb to convert your temperature to degrees Fahrenheit? ______________________

Explain. ____

____

Name Date Time

Mystery Graphs

Create a mystery graph on the grid below. Be sure to label the horizontal and vertical axes. Describe the situation that goes with your graph on the lines provided.

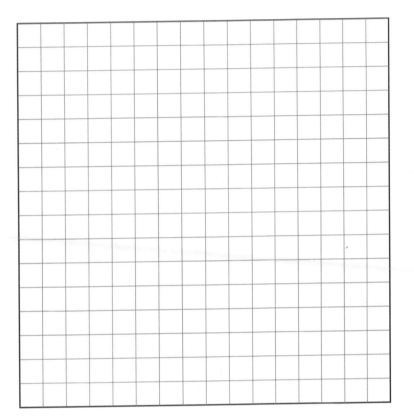

Name Date Time

Finding Circumferences

Study Link 10.8

The formula for the circumference of a circle is:

Circumference = $\pi * $ **diameter** or just $C = \pi * d$

Use the (π) key on your calculator to solve these problems. If your calculator doesn't have a (π) key, enter 3.14 each time you need π.

1. Find the circumference of each circle below. Show answers to the nearest tenth.

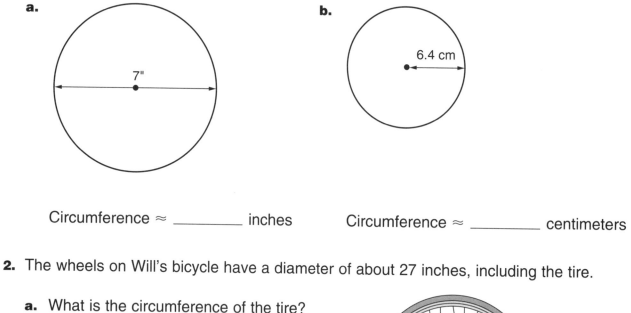

a.

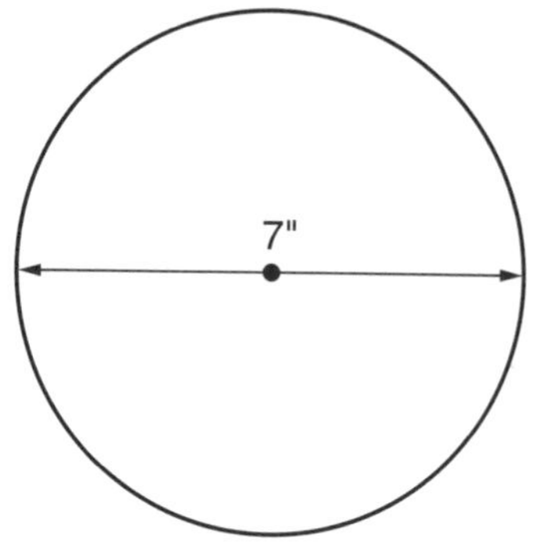

Circumference ≈ ________ inches

b.

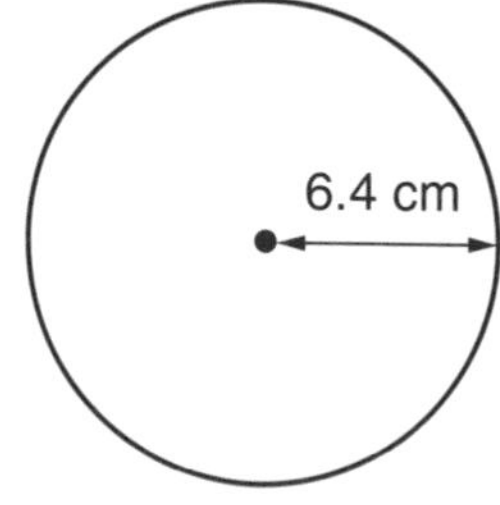

Circumference ≈ ________ centimeters

2. The wheels on Will's bicycle have a diameter of about 27 inches, including the tire.

a. What is the circumference of the tire?

About ________ inches

b. About how far will Will's bicycle travel if the wheels go around exactly once?

About ________ inches

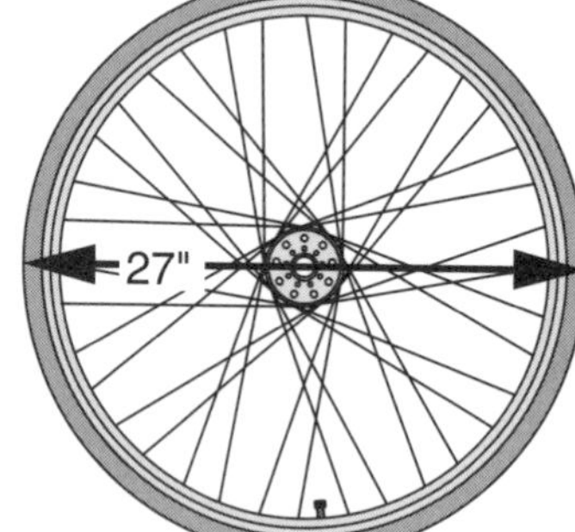

3. Sofia measured the circumference of her bicycle tire. She found it was 66 inches. What is the diameter of the tire?

About ________ inches

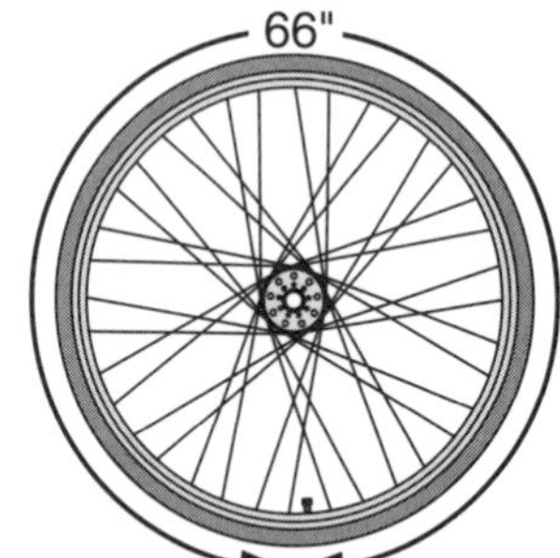

Use with Lesson 10.8.

Name Date Time

Area and Circumference

Study Link 10.9

SRB 171 178

Circle the best measurement for each situation described below.

1. What size hat to buy (*Hint:* The hat has to fit around the head.)

area circumference perimeter

2. How much frosting covers the top of a round birthday cake

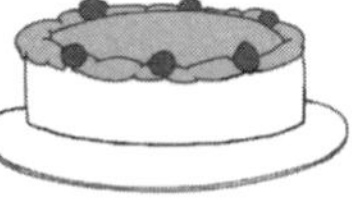

area circumference perimeter

3. The amount of yard that will be covered by a circular inflatable swimming pool

area circumference perimeter

4. The length of the top of a can label when you pull it off of the can

area circumference perimeter

Fill in the oval next to the measurement that best completes each statement.

Area of a circle: $A = \pi * r^2$
Circumference of a circle: $C = \pi * d$

5. The radius of a circle is about 4 cm. The area of the circle is about

○ 12 cm^2 ○ 39 cm^2 ○ 50 cm^2 ○ 25 cm^2

6. The area of a circle is about 28 in.^2. The diameter of the circle is about

○ 3 in. ○ 6 in. ○ 9 in. ○ 18 in.

7. The circumference of a circle is about 31.4 meters. The radius of the circle is about

○ 3 m ○ 5 m ○ 10 m ○ 15 m

8. Explain how you found your answer for Problem 7.

____

____

____

____

____

Family Letter

Study Link 10.10

Unit 11: Volume

Unit 11 focuses on developing your child's ability to think spatially. Many times, students may feel that concepts of area and volume are of little use in their everyday lives compared with their computation skills. Encourage your child to become more aware of the importance and relevance of 2- and 3-dimensional shapes. Point out geometric solids (such as pyramids, cones, and cylinders) as well as 2-dimensional shapes (such as squares, circles, and triangles) in your surroundings.

Volume (or capacity) is the measure of the amount of space inside a 3-dimensional geometric figure. Your child will develop formulas to calculate the volume of rectangular and curved solids in cubic units. The class will also review units of capacity, such as cups, pints, quarts, and gallons. They will use units of capacity to estimate the volume of irregular objects by measuring the amount of water each object displaces when submerged. Your child will also explore the relationship between weight and volume by calculating the weight of rice an "average" Thai family of four consumes in one year and estimating how many cartons of a certain size would be needed to store a year's supply.

Area is defined as the number of units (usually squares) that can fit onto a bounded surface, without gaps or overlaps. Your child will review formulas for finding the area of rectangles, parallelograms, triangles, and circles and use these formulas in calculating the surface area of 3-dimensional shapes.

It is not the goal of this unit to have students memorize formulas, but rather to help them develop an appreciation for their use and application in various settings. By the end of this unit, your child will have had many experiences using 2- and 3-dimensional geometry.

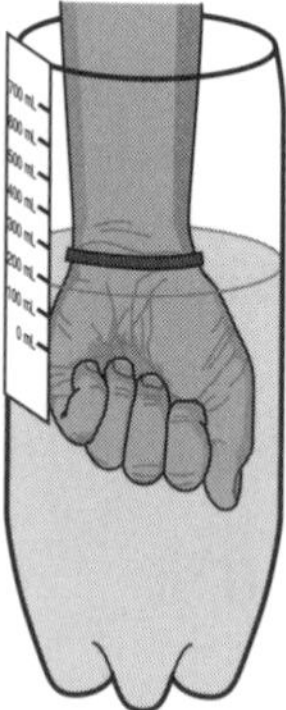

Using a calibrated bottle, your child will find the volume of an irregular object by submerging it in water and measuring the volume of water it displaces.

Please keep this Family Letter for reference as your child works through Unit 11.

Vocabulary

Important terms in Unit 11:

apex In a pyramid or cone, the vertex opposite the base.

base of a polygon A side on which a polygon "sits". The height of a polygon may depend on which side is called the base.

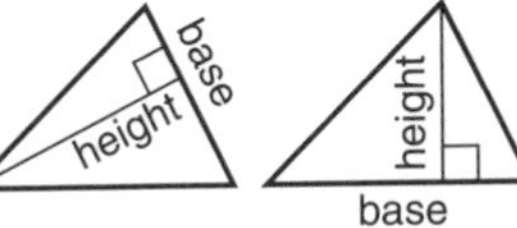

base of a prism or cylinder Either of the two parallel and congruent faces that define the shape of a prism or a cylinder.

base of a pyramid or cone The face of a pyramid or cone that is opposite its apex.

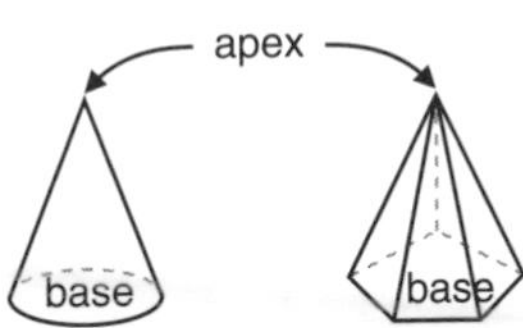

calibrate To divide or mark something, such as a thermometer, with gradations.

cone A 3-dimensional shape that has a circular *base,* a curved surface, and one vertex, which is called the *apex.*

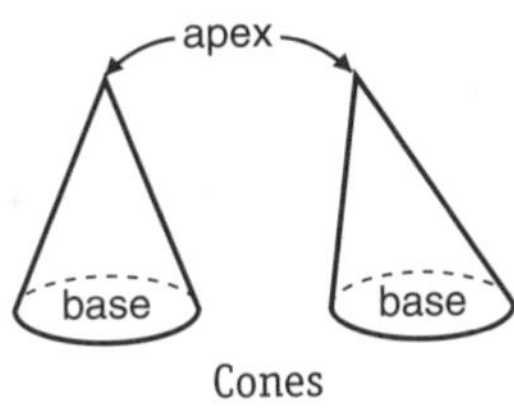

Cones

cube A polyhedron with 6 square faces. A cube has 8 vertices and 12 edges.

cylinder A 3-dimensional shape that has two circular or elliptical bases that are parallel and congruent and are connected by a curved surface. A can is shaped like a cylinder.

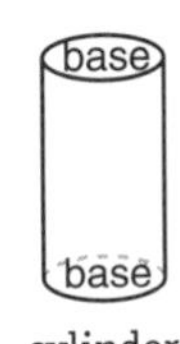

cylinder

edge A line segment where two faces of a polyhedron meet.

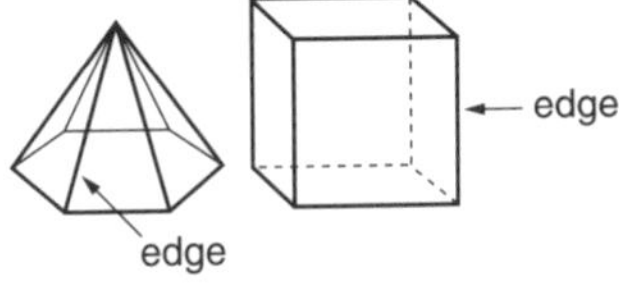

face A flat surface on a 3-dimensional shape.

geometric solid A 3-dimensional shape, such as a prism, pyramid, cylinder, cone, or sphere. Despite its name, a geometric solid is "hollow"; it does not contain the points in its interior.

polyhedron A closed 3-dimensional figure whose surfaces, or faces, are all formed by polygons and their interiors.

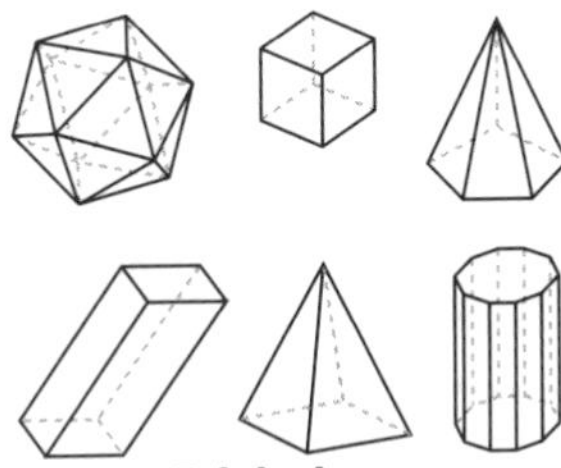
Polyhedrons

prism A solid with two parallel *faces,* called *bases,* that are congruent polygons; all of its other faces all parallelograms. Prisms get their names from the shapes of their bases.

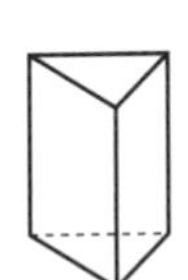

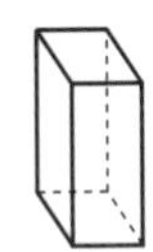

pyramid A solid in which one face, the *base,* is any polygon and all the other faces are triangles that come together at a point called the *vertex* or *apex.* Pyramids get their names from the shapes of their bases.

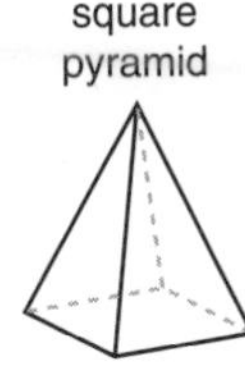

regular polyhedron A polyhedron whose faces are formed by a single kind of congruent regular polygon and in which every vertex looks exactly the same as every other vertex. There are five regular polyhedrons.

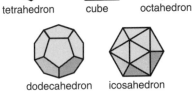

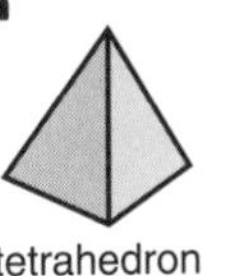

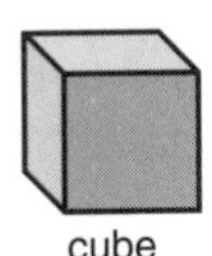

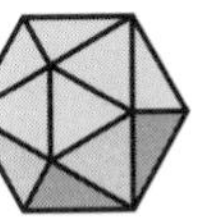

sphere The set of all points in space that are a given distance from a given point. The given point is the center of the sphere and the given distance is the radius.

surface area A measure of the surface of a 3-dimensional figure.

vertex (vertices or vertexes) The point where the rays of an angle, the sides of a polygon, or the edges of a polyhedron meet.

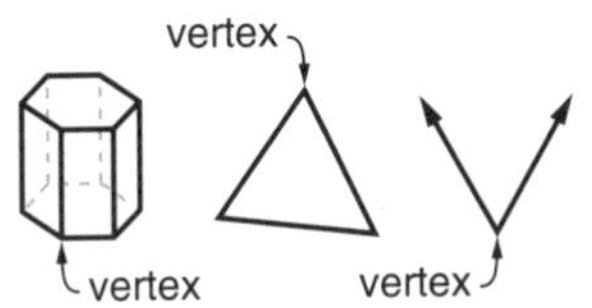

Do-Anytime Activities

To work with your child on the concepts taught in this unit, try these interesting and rewarding activities:

1. Have your child compile a 2- and 3-dimensional shapes portfolio or create a collage of labeled shapes. Images can be taken from newspapers, magazines, photographs, and so on.

2. **Explore Kitchen Measures**
The most common use of measuring volume is cooking. Work with your child to make a favorite recipe. (Doubling the recipe can be good practice in computing with fractions.) Ask your child to use measuring spoons and cups to find the capacity of various containers. The data can be organized in a table:

Container	Capacity
Coffee mug	$1\frac{1}{4}$ cups
Egg cup	3 tablespoons

Building Skills through Games

In Unit 11, your child will practice operations with whole numbers and geometry skills by playing the following games. Detailed instructions for each game are in the *Student Reference Book.*

Name That Number See *Student Reference Book,* page 286
This is a game for two or three players using the Everything Math Deck or a complete deck of number cards. Playing *Name That Number* helps students review operations with whole numbers, including the order of operations.

Polygon Capture See *Student Reference Book,* page 289
This game uses 16 polygons and 16 Property Cards, and is played by partners or 2 teams each with 2 players. *Polygon Capture* gives students practice in identifying properties of polygons that involve sides and angles.

3-D Shape Sort See *Student Reference Book,* page 293
This game is similar to *Polygon Capture.* Partners or 2 teams each with 2 players need 16 Property Cards and 12 Shape Cards to play. *3-D Shape Sort* gives students practice in identifying properties of 3-dimensional shapes.

As You Help Your Child with Homework

As your child brings assignments home, you may want to go over the instructions together, clarifying them as necessary. The answers listed below will guide you through some of this unit's Study Links.

Study Link 11.1

1. Answers vary.
2. D

Study Link 11.2

1. Rectangular prism: 6 faces; 8 vertices; 12 edges
   Tetrahedron: 4 faces; 4 vertices; 6 edges
   Triangular prism: 5 faces; 6 vertices; 9 edges
   Rectangular pyramid: 5 faces; 5 vertices; 8 edges
   Octahedron: 8 faces; 6 vertices; 12 edges
2. **a.** Sample answer: The sum of the numbers of faces and vertices is 2 more than the number of edges.

   b. $e = (f + v) - 2$

Study Link 11.3

Answers vary for Problems 1–4.

Study Link 11.4

1. <
2. <
3. >
4. Sample answer: Since both pyramids have the same height, compare the areas of the bases. The base of the square pyramid has an area of $5 * 5 = 25 \text{ m}^2$. The base area of the triangular pyramid is $\frac{1}{2} * 5 * 5$, or $12\frac{1}{2} \text{ m}^2$.
5. **a.** Sample answer: Displacement means moving something out of its proper place.

   b. Sample answer: To calibrate is to divide or mark to show measurements, as on a thermometer.

Study Link 11.5

Sample answer: Cotton is not very dense, so it did not displace too much water.

Study Link 11.6

1. >	**2.** =	**3.** <
4. <	**5.** <	**6.** =

7. cubic inches
8. gallons
9. gallons
10. milliliters
11. cubic centimeters
12. capacity
13. volume
14. Sample answer: Capacity is a measure of how much of a pourable substance or liquid a container can hold. Volume is a measure of the amount of space occupied by a 3-dimensional shape.

Study Link 11.7

1. 88 in.^2; Sample answers: I found the area of each of the 6 sides and then the total. Or, I found the area of the top, front, and one side; I added these 3 areas and doubled the result.
2. Yes. A 4 in. $\times$ 4 in. $\times$ $3\frac{1}{2}$ in. box has a volume = 56 in.^3 and surface area = 88 in.^2
3. Volume: 502.7 cm^3; Surface area: 351.9 cm^3
4. Volume: 216 in.^3; Surface area: 216 in.^3

Name Date Time

Cube Patterns

Study Link 11.1

There are four patterns below. Three of the patterns can be folded to form a cube.

1. Try to guess which one of the patterns below cannot be folded into a cube.

My guess: Pattern ________ (A, B, C, or D) cannot be folded into a cube.

2. Cut and fold the pattern to check your guess. Did you make the correct guess? If not, try other patterns until you find the one that does not form a cube.

My answer: Pattern ________ (A, B, C, or D) cannot be folded into a cube.

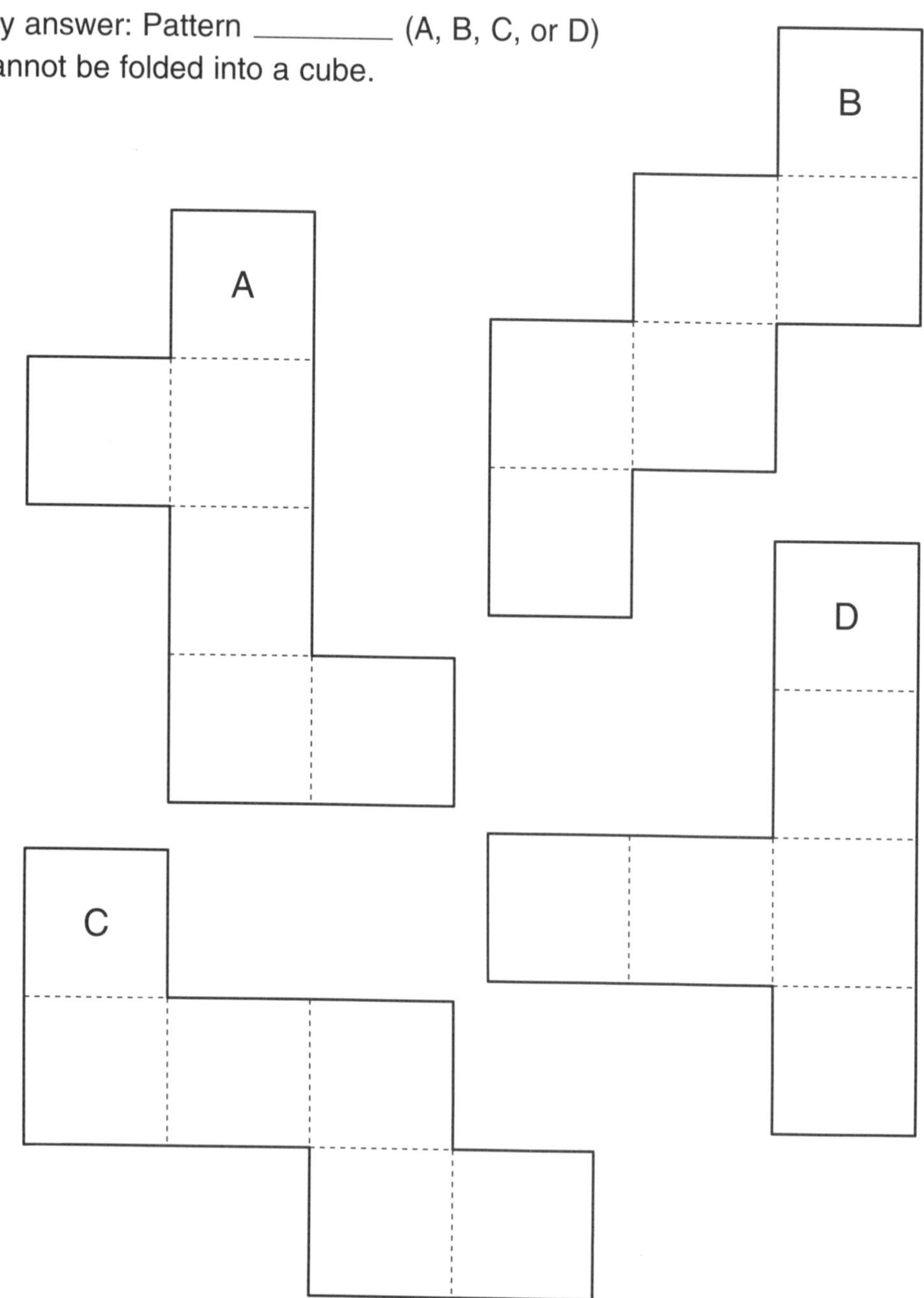

Name Date Time

Faces, Vertices, and Edges

Study Link 11.2

SRB 137–138

1. Refer to the pictures of polyhedrons on the next page to complete the following table:

Polyhedron	Number of Faces (f)	Number of Vertices (v)	Number of Edges (e)
Rectangular prism	6		
Tetrahedron		4	
Triangular prism			9
Rectangular pyramid			
Octahedron			

2. Look for a pattern in the results in your table.

a. If you know the numbers of faces and vertices in a polyhedron, how can you calculate the number of edges, without counting them?

____

____

____

b. Express your calculation as a formula. Let f represent the number of faces, let v represent the number of vertices, and let e represent the number of edges in the polyhedron.

e = ______________________

c. Check that this formula is true for other polyhedrons.

This formula is sometimes called Euler's Formula, named after the 18th-century Swiss mathematician and physicist, Leonhard Euler.

Name Date Time

Faces, Vertices, and Edges (cont.)

Study Link 11.2

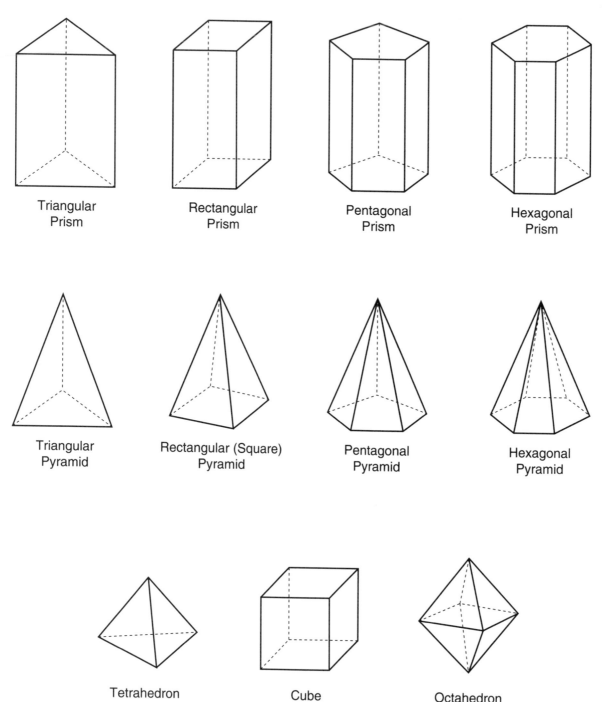

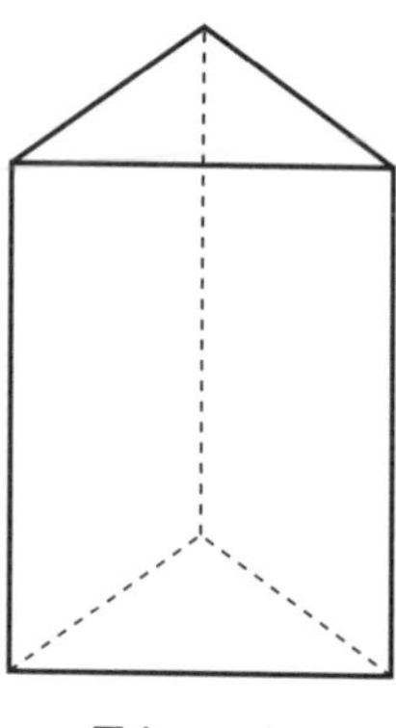
Triangular Prism

Rectangular Prism

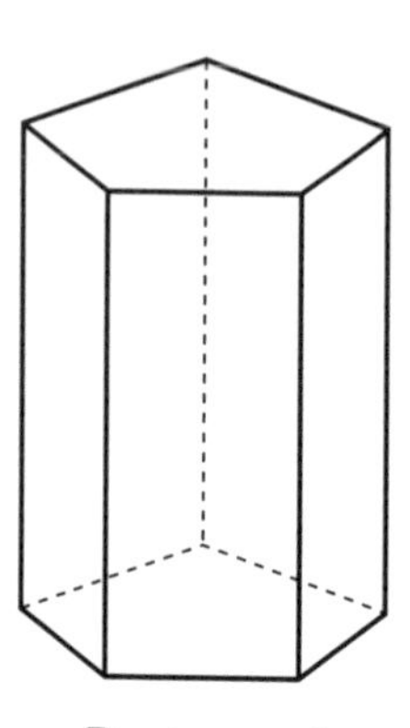
Pentagonal Prism

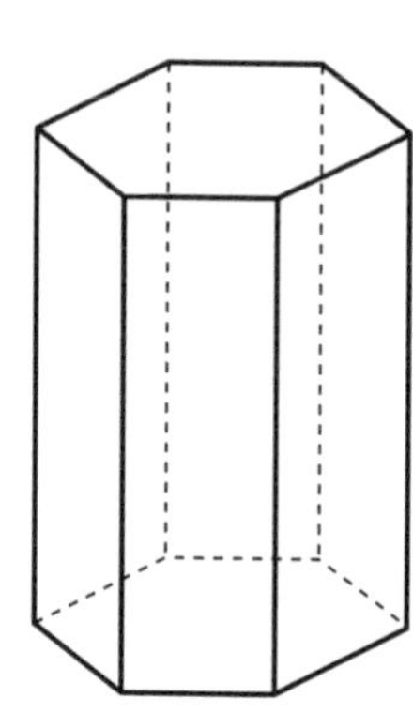
Hexagonal Prism

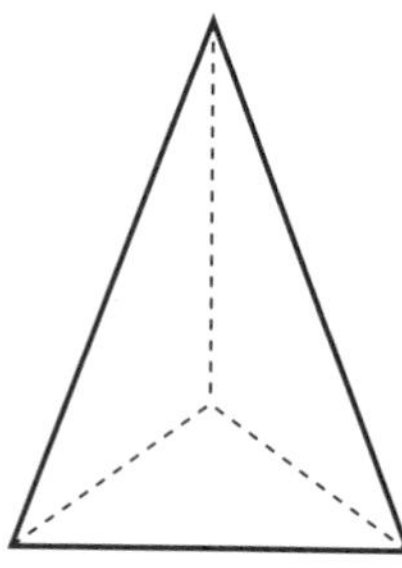
Triangular Pyramid

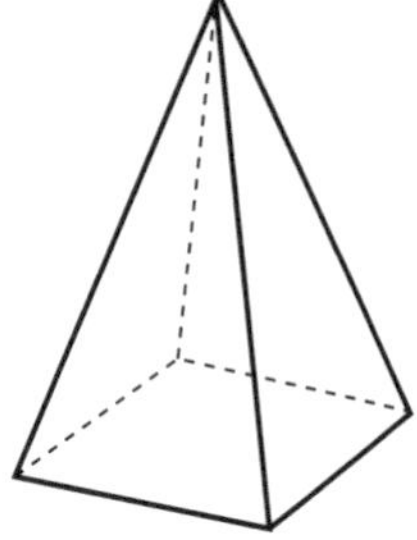
Rectangular (Square) Pyramid

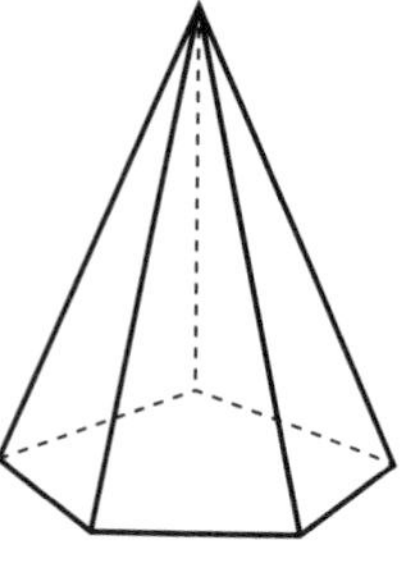
Pentagonal Pyramid

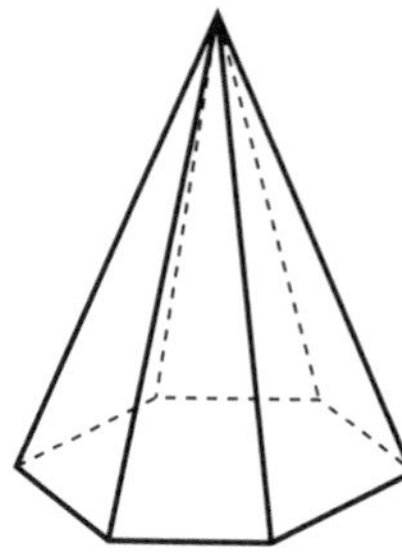
Hexagonal Pyramid

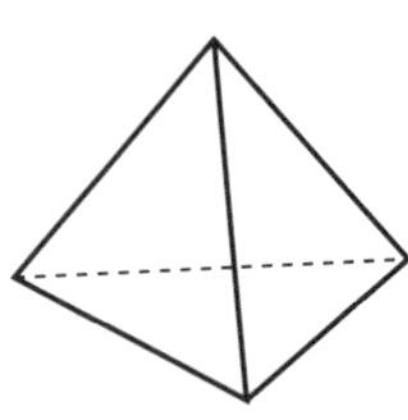
Tetrahedron

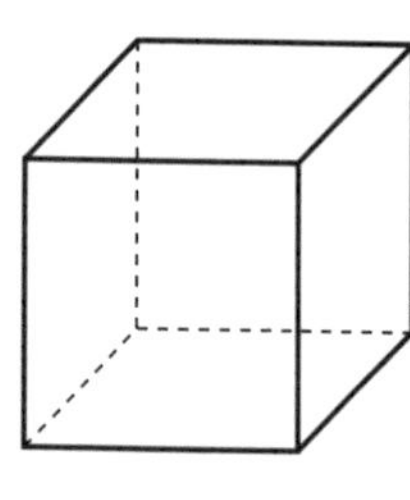
Cube

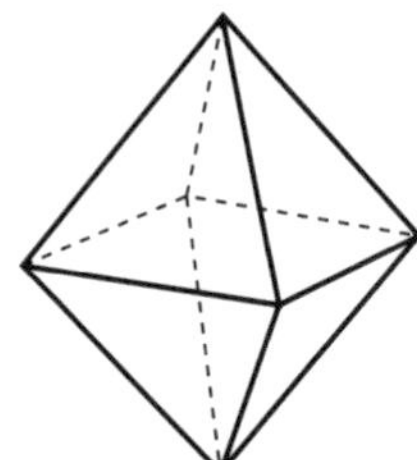
Octahedron

Use with Lesson 11.2.

Name Date Time

Volume of Cylinders

Study Link 11.3

Use these two formulas to solve the problems below.

SRB 178, 181–182

Formula for the Volume of a Cylinder

$$V = B * h$$

where V is the volume of the cylinder, B is the area of the cylinder's base, and h is the height of the cylinder.

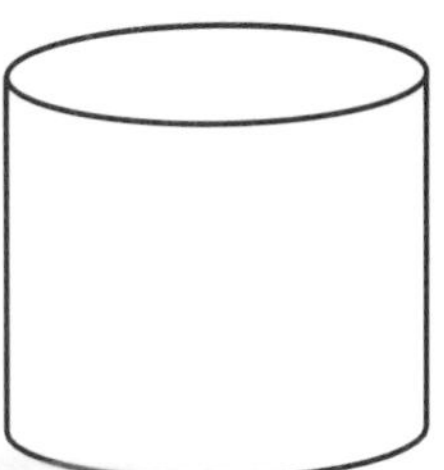

Formula for the Area of a Circle

$$A = \pi * r^2$$

where A is the area of the circle and r is the length of the radius of the circle.

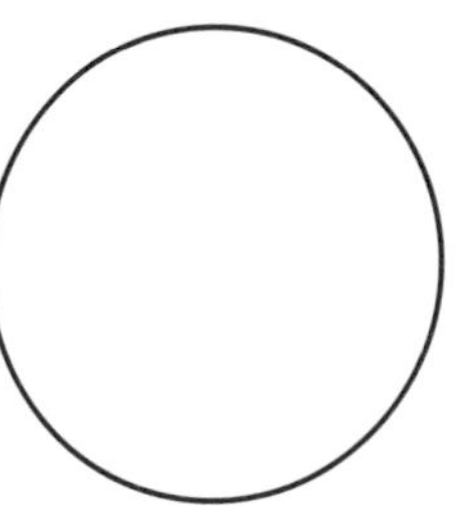

1. Find the smallest cylinder in your home. Record its dimensions and calculate its volume.

   radius = ____________ height = ____________

   Area of base = ____________ Volume = ____________

2. Find the largest cylinder in your home. Record its dimensions and calculate its volume.

   radius = ____________ height = ____________

   Area of base = ____________ Volume = ____________

3. Is the volume of the largest cylinder more or less than the volume of your toaster? ____________

   About how much more or less? ____________

4. Is the volume of the largest cylinder more or less than the volume of your television set? ____________

   About how much more or less? 

Name Date Time

Comparing Volumes

Study Link 11.4

Use $>$, $<$, or $=$ to compare the volumes of the two figures in each problem below.

SRB 180–183

1.

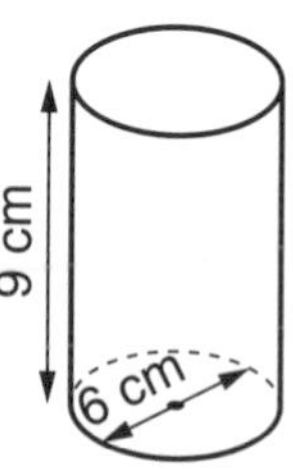

____

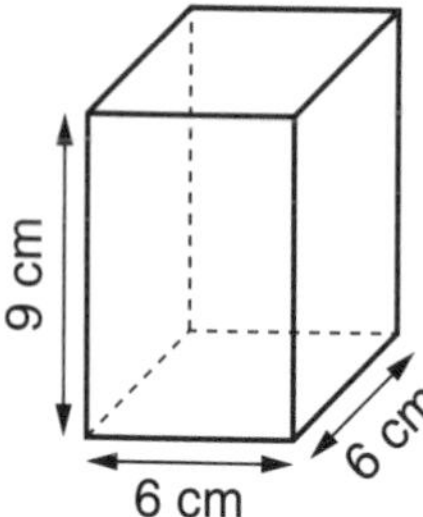

2.

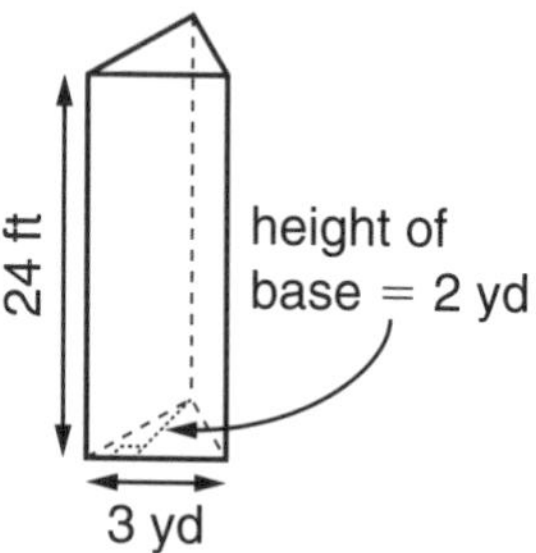

____

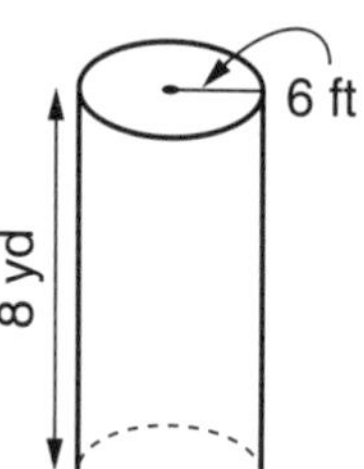

3.

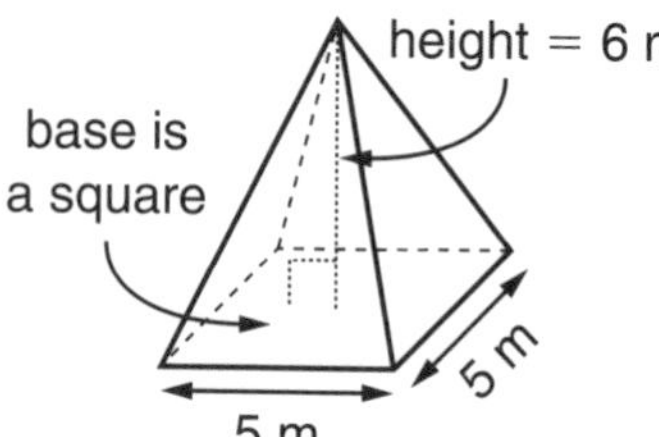

____

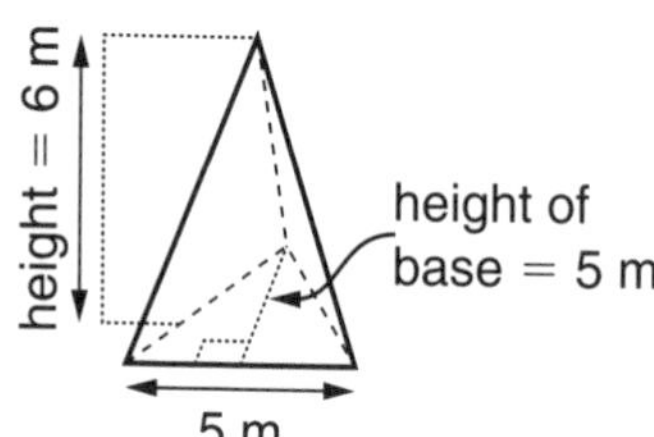

4. Explain how you got your answer for Problem 3.

____

____

____

____

5. Use a dictionary to find the meaning(s) of each of the following words:

a. displacement: _______________

____

b. calibrate: _______________

____

Name Date Time

A Displacement Experiment

Try this experiment at home.

Materials

- ❑ drinking glass
- ❑ water
- ❑ 2 large handfuls of cotton (Be sure to use real cotton. Synthetic materials will not work.)

Directions

- Fill the drinking glass almost to the top with water.
- Put the cotton bit by bit into the glass. Fluff it as you go.

If you are careful, you should be able to fit all of the cotton into the glass without spilling a drop of water.

Think about what you know about displacement and volume. Why do you think you were able to fit the cotton into the glass without the water overflowing?

Name Date Time

Units of Volume and Capacity

Study Link 11.6

SRB 179

Write >, <, or = to compare the measurements below.

1. 5 cups _____ 1 quart
2. 30 mL _____ 30 cm^3
3. 1 quart _____ 1 liter
4. 15 pints _____ 8 quarts
5. 100 cm^3 _____ 1 gallon
6. 10 cups _____ 5 pints

Circle the unit you would use to measure each of the following.

7. The volume of a square pyramid

   gallons   cubic inches   ounces   meters

8. The amount of milk a fifth grader drinks in a week

   gallons   milliliters   ounces   meters

9. The amount of water used to fill a swimming pool

   gallons   milliliters   ounces   meters

10. The amount of penicillin given in a shot

    gallons   milliliters   liters   meters

11. The volume of a rectangular prism

    gallons   cubic centimeters   liters   meters

12. Would you find the **volume** or the **capacity** if you wanted to know how much juice a jug holds? _______________

13. Would you find the **volume** or the **capacity** if you wanted to know how much closet space a stack of boxes would take up? _______________

Challenge

14. Explain the difference between capacity and volume.

____

____

____

____

Name Date Time

Volume and Surface Area

Study Link 11.7

SRB 181–182, 184–185

Area of rectangle:
$A = l * w$

Volume of rectangular prism:
$V = l * w * h$

Circumference of circle:
$C = \pi * d$

Area of circle:
$A = \pi * r^2$

Volume of cylinder:
$V = \pi * r^2 * h$

1. Marge wants to give her best friend a box of chocolates. Figure out the least number of square inches of wrapping paper Marge needs to wrap the box. (To simplify the problem, assume that she will cover the box completely, with no overlaps.)

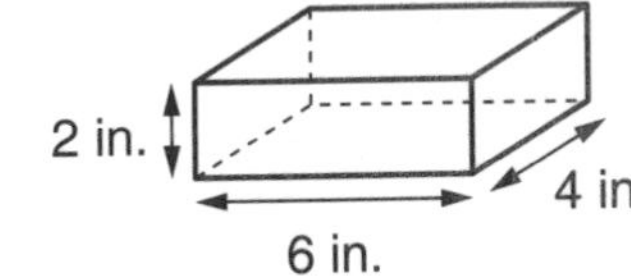

Amount of paper needed: ____________

Explain how you found the answer.

____

____

____

2. Could Marge use the same amount of wrapping paper to cover a box with a larger volume than the box pictured in Problem 1? ________ Explain.

____

____

Find the volume and the surface area of the two figures in Problems 3 and 4.

3. Volume:

____

Surface area:

____

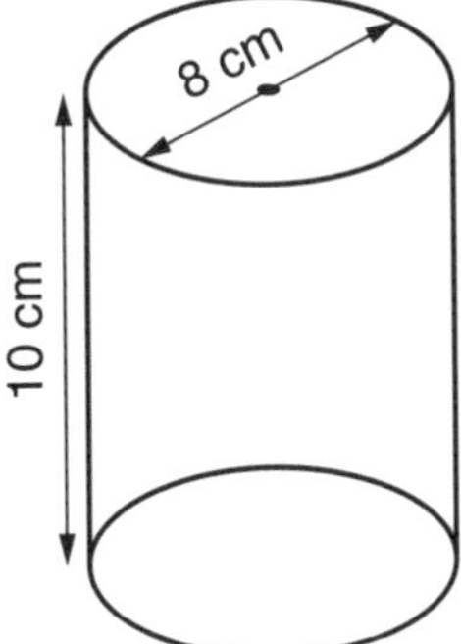

4. Volume:

____

Surface area:

____

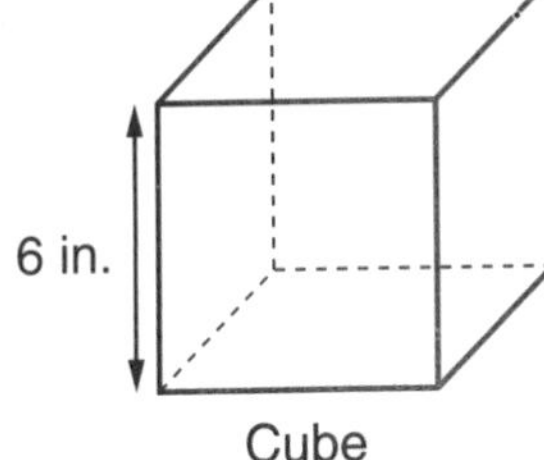

Name Date Time

Family Letter

Study Link 11.8

Unit 12: Probability, Ratios, and Rates

A **ratio** is a comparison of two quantities with the same unit. For example, if one house has a floor area of 2,000 square feet, and a second house has a floor area of 3,000 square feet, the ratio of the areas is 2,000 to 3,000 or (simplified) 2 to 3.

To prepare students for working with ratios in algebra, the class will review the meanings and forms of ratios, and will solve number stories involving ratios of part of a set to the whole set. Your child will find, write, and solve many number models (equations) for ratio problems.

Your child will continue to use the American Tour as part of the discussion of ratios. We will also be doing projects based on information in the American Tour.

A **rate** is a comparison of two quantities with different units. For example, speed is expressed in miles per hour. In our study of rates, students will determine their own heart rates (heartbeats per minute). Then they will observe the effect of exercise on heart rate, and represent the class results graphically.

We will continue our study of probability by looking at situations in which a sequence of choices is made. For example, if a menu offers you 2 choices of appetizer, 4 choices of entrée, and 3 choices of dessert, and you choose one of each kind, there are 2 * 3 * 4 or 24 different possible combinations for your meal. If all the choices were equally appealing (which is unlikely), and you chose at random, the probability of any one combination would be $\frac{1}{24}$.

Your child will play *Frac-Tac-Toe,* which was introduced in Unit 4, as well as a new game, *Spoon Scramble,* to practice operations and equivalencies with fractions, decimals, and percents.

You can help your child by asking questions about homework problems; by pointing out fractions, percents, and ratios that you encounter in everyday life; and by playing *Frac-Tac-Toe* or *Spoon Scramble* to sharpen skills.

Please keep this Family Letter for reference as your child works through Unit 12.

Vocabulary

Important terms in Unit 12:

common factor Any number that is a factor of two or more numbers. The common factors of 18 and 24 are 1, 2, 3, and 6.

equal chance or equally likely When each of the possible outcomes for some situation has the same chance of occurring, the outcomes are said to have an equal chance or to be equally likely. For example, in tossing a coin there is an equal chance of getting heads or tails. Heads and tails are equally likely outcomes.

factor tree A method used to obtain the prime factorization of a number. The original number is written as a product of factors. Then each of these factors is written as a product of factors, and so on, until the factors are all prime numbers. A factor tree looks like an upside down tree with the root (the original number) at the top, and the leaves (the factors) beneath it.

30
6 * 5
2 * 3 * 5

Factor tree for 30

greatest common factor The largest factor that two or more numbers have in common. For example, the common factors of 24 and 36 are 1, 2, 3, 4, 6, and 12. Thus, the greatest common factor of 24 and 36 is 12.

least common multiple The smallest number that is a multiple of two or more numbers. For example, while some common multiples of 6 and 8 are 24, 48, and 72, the least common multiple of 6 and 8 is 24.

multiplication counting principle A way of determining the total number of possible outcomes for two or more separate choices. Suppose, for example, you roll a die and then flip a coin. There are 6 choices for which face of the die shows and 2 choices for which side of the coin shows. Then there are 6 * 2, or 12 possible outcomes all together: (1,H), (1,T), (2,H), (2,T), (3,H), (3,T), (4,H), (4,T), (5,H), (5,T), (6,H), (6,T).

prime factorization A whole number expressed as a product of prime factors. For example, the prime factorization of 24 is 2 * 2 * 2 * 3.

probability A number from 0 to 1 that tells the chance that an event will happen. For example, the probability that a fair coin will show heads is $\frac{1}{2}$. The closer a probability is to 1, the more likely it is that the event will happen. The closer a probability is to 0, the less likely it is that the event will happen.

rate A comparison by division of two quantities with unlike units. For example, traveling 100 miles in 2 hours can be expressed as 100 mi/2 hr, or 50 miles per hour. In this case, the rate compares distance (miles) to time (hours).

ratio A comparison by division of two quantities with the same units. Ratios can be expressed as fractions, decimals, or percents, as well as in words. Ratios can also be written with a colon between the two numbers being compared. For example, if a team wins 3 out of 5 games played, the ratio of wins to total games can be written as $\frac{3}{5}$, 3/5, 0.6, 60%, 3 to 5, or 3:5 (read "three to five").

tree diagram A diagram such as a factor tree or a probability tree. A tree diagram is a network of points connected by line segments. One special point is the root of the tree and closed loops are not allowed. Tree diagrams can be used to factor numbers and to represent probability situations in which there is a series of events.

The first tree diagram below represents flipping one coin two times. The second tree diagram below shows the prime factorization of 30.

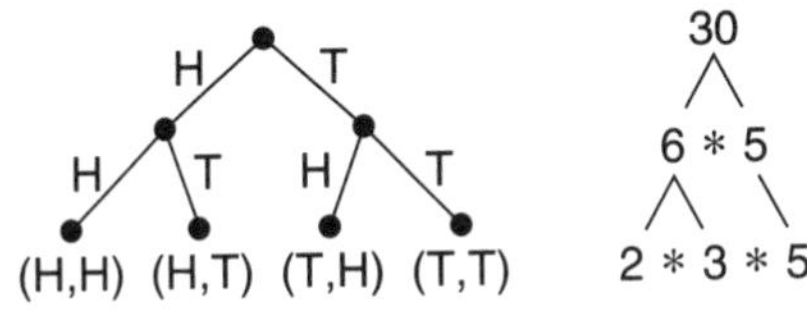

Tree diagrams

Do Anytime Activities

To work with your child on the concepts taught in this unit and in previous units, try these interesting and rewarding activities:

1. Identify different ratios and ask your child to write each ratio using words, a fraction, a decimal, a percent, and a colon. For example, the ratio of 1 adult for every 5 students could be written as 1 to 5, $\frac{1}{5}$, 0.2, 20%, or 1:5.

2. Play one of the games in this unit with your child: *Frac-Tac-Toe, Name That Number,* or *Spoon Scramble.*

3. Read the book *Jumanji* with your child and review the possible outcomes when rolling two dice. Ask your child to verify the probabilities of rolling certain number combinations by recording the outcomes for 100 rolls of a pair of dice.

4. Identify rate situations in everyday life and ask your child to solve problems involving rates. For example, find the number of miles your car travels for each gallon of gas, or find the number of calories that are burned each hour or minute for different types of sports activities.

Building Skills through Games

In Unit 12, your child will practice skills with probability, ratios, and rates by playing the following games. For detailed instructions, see the *Math Masters* and the *Student Reference Book.*

Frac-Tac-Toe See *Student Reference Book,* pp. 274–276
This is a game for two players. Game materials include 4 each of the number cards 0–10, pennies or counters of two colors, a calculator, and a gameboard. The gameboard is a 5-by-5 number grid that resembles a bingo card. Several versions of the gameboard are shown in the *Student Reference Book. Frac-Tac-Toe* provides students with practice in converting fractions to decimals and percents.

Name That Number See *Student Reference Book,* p. 286
This is a game for two or three players. Game materials include the Everything Math Deck or a complete deck of number cards. Playing *Name That Number* provides students with practice in working with operations and in using the order of operations.

Spoon Scramble See *Math Masters,* p. 174
This game provides students with practice identifying equivalent expressions for finding a fraction, decimal, or percent of a number. Four players use 3 spoons and a deck of 16 *Spoon Scramble* Cards to play this game.

As You Help Your Child with Homework

As your child brings assignments home, you may want to go over the instructions together, clarifying them as necessary. The answers listed below will guide you through this unit's Study Links.

Study Link 12.1

Sample answers:

1. a. 30; 3 * 10; 3 * 2 * 5

b.

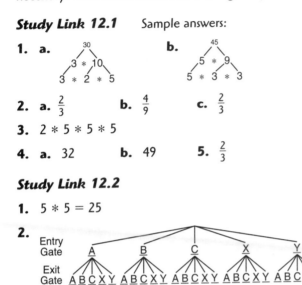

2. a. $\frac{2}{3}$ **b.** $\frac{4}{9}$ **c.** $\frac{2}{3}$

3. 2 * 5 * 5 * 5

4. a. 32 **b.** 49 **5.** $\frac{2}{3}$

Study Link 12.2

1. 5 * 5 = 25

2.

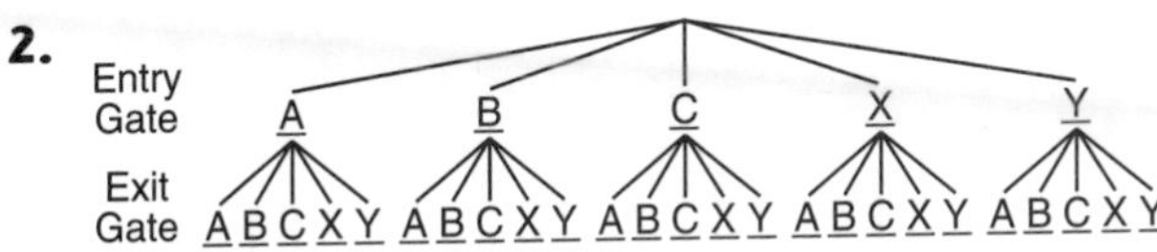

3. no; Sample answer: Some gates will probably be used more than other gates.

4. 20

5. a.

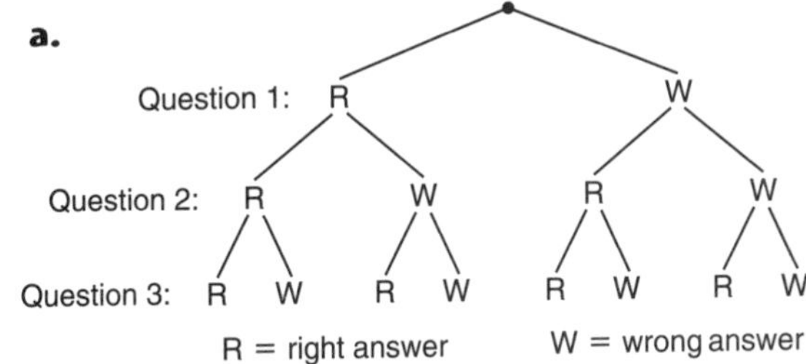

b. $\frac{1}{8}$

Study Link 12.3

1. Sixteen out of twenty-five

2. $\frac{16}{25}$ **3.** 64% **4.** 16:25

5. 23:50; 0.46 of the cars were blue

6. $\frac{2}{3}$; 6:9; $66\frac{2}{3}$% of the people were swimmers

7. 7 out of 8; 35:40 of the caps sold were baseball caps

Study Link 12.4

1. a. 4 **b.** 16

2. 15

3. 16 **4.** 8 **5.** 32

Study Link 12.5

1. 8 **2.** 24 **3.** 45

4. 60 **5.** 20 **6.** 26

7. $\frac{2}{5} = \frac{\square}{115}$; 46 students

8. $\frac{3}{4} = \frac{\square}{156}$; 117 students

9. $\frac{1.50}{3} = \frac{\square}{90}$; \$45

10. 210 tickets

Study Link 12.6

1. a.

Number of spiders	27,000	54,000	81,000	108,000	135,000
Pounds of spider web	1	2	3	4	5

b. 270,000

2. a.

Miles	13	26	39	52	65
Minutes	1	2	3	4	5

b. 780

3. 1,000 **4.** 930 **5.** $7\frac{1}{2}$, or 7.5

Study Link 12.8

3. 15 clarinetists

4. a. 12 **b.** 6 **c.** 4 **d.** 2

Name Date Time

Factor Trees

Study Link 12.1

1. Make factor trees for the following numbers. An example has been done for you.

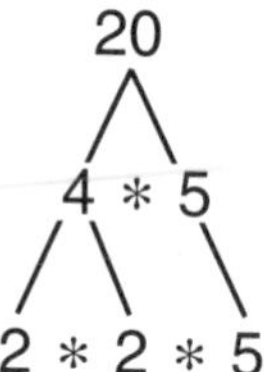

a. 30

b. 45

2. Write each fraction in simplest form. Use factor trees to help you.

a. $\frac{20}{30}$ = ______ **b.** $\frac{20}{45}$ = ______ **c.** $\frac{30}{45}$ = ______

3. Find the prime factorization for 250. ______________________________

4. **a.** Circle the number below that has the most prime factors. (You can use factor trees to help you.)

   63 32 49 100

   b. Which has the fewest prime factors? ________

Challenge

5. Simplify the fraction below. Use factor trees or some other method.

$\frac{150}{225}$ = ______

Name Date Time

Probability Investigations

Study Link 12.2

Multiplication Counting Principle

Suppose you can make a first choice in *m* ways and a second choice in *n* ways. Then there are $m * n$ ways to make the first choice followed by the second choice. Three or more choices can be counted in the same way, by multiplying.

SRB 124

1. A person can enter the stadium shown at the right through any gate, and can exit through any gate. In how many different ways can a person enter and exit the stadium?

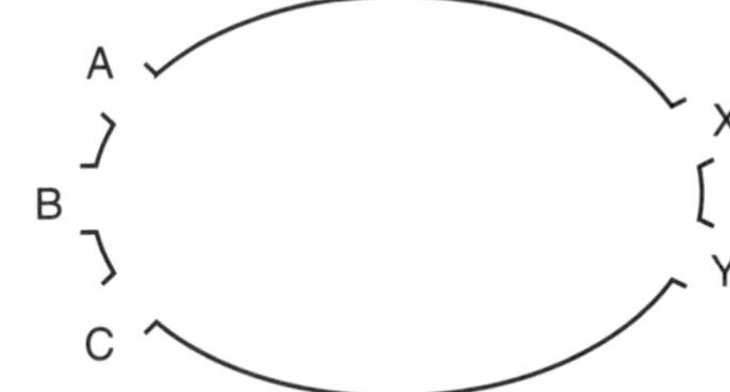

________ * ________ = ________

(ways to enter) (ways to exit) (total ways to enter and exit)

2. Draw a **tree diagram** to show all possible ways to enter and exit the stadium.

Entry gate: ___ ___ ___ ___ ___

Exit gate: __

3. Do you think that all of the ways to enter and exit are equally likely? ________

Explain your answer. ______________________________

____

4. How many ways are there to enter and exit the same stadium if a person may not leave by the same gate through which he or she entered? ________

5. Sally takes a quiz with three true-false questions. She does not know the answer to any of the questions, so she guesses on all three.

a. On the back of this page, draw a tree diagram to show Sally's possible results.

b. What is the probability that she will get all three questions correct? ________

Name Date Time

Ratios

Study Link 12.3

Ratios can be stated or written in a variety of ways. Sometimes a ratio is easier to understand or will make more sense if it is rewritten in another form.

Example In a group of 25 students, 16 students walk to school and 9 take a bus. The ratio of students who take a bus, to all students in the group, can be expressed in the following ways:

- With words: Nine out of twenty-five students take a bus.
- With a fraction: $\frac{9}{25}$ of the students take a bus.
- With a percent: 36% of the students take a bus.
- With a colon between the two numbers being compared: The ratio of students who take a bus, to all students in the group, is 9:25 ("nine out of twenty-five").

Revise the above statements to express the ratio of students who walk to school, to all students.

1. With words: ______________________ students walk to school.

2. With a fraction: ______________ of the students walk to school.

3. With a percent: ______________ of the students walk to school.

4. With a colon: The ratio of students who walk to school to all students is ______________.

In each problem, fill in the ovals next to all of the correct ratios.

5. Fifty cars drove past in 10 minutes. Twenty-three cars were blue.

O 23:50 of the cars were blue. O 23% of the cars were blue. O 0.46 of the cars were blue.

6. In a group of 9 people, 6 were swimmers.

O $\frac{2}{3}$ of the people were swimmers. O 6:9 of the people were swimmers. O $66\frac{2}{3}$% of the people were swimmers.

7. In a sports shop, 35 of the 40 caps sold the day before the World Series were baseball caps.

O 7 out of 8 caps sold were baseball caps. O 35% of the caps sold were baseball caps. O 35:40 of the caps sold were baseball caps.

Use with Lesson 12.3.

Name Date Time

Ratio Problems

SRB 100–102

1. Draw 20 tiles so that 2 out of 10 tiles are white and the rest are shaded.

   a. How many tiles are white? ________ tiles

   b. How many tiles are shaded? ________ tiles

2. Draw 9 shaded tiles.

   Add white tiles so that 2 out of 5 tiles are white.

   How many tiles are there in all? ________ tiles

3. Imagine 48 tiles. If 4 out of 12 tiles are white, how many tiles are white? ________ tiles

4. There are 24 players on the soccer team. Two out of every 3 players have not scored a goal yet this year.

   How many players have scored goals this year? ________ players

5. For every 8 spelling tests Justine took, she earned 3 perfect scores. If Justine earned 12 perfect scores this year, how many spelling tests did she take? ________ tests

6. Make up and solve your own ratio number story. Be prepared to share it with the class.

   ____

   ____

   ____

   ____

   Answer: ______________________________________

Name Date Time

Ratio Problems

Study Link 12.5

Find the missing number.

1. $\frac{1}{5} = \frac{x}{40}$ $x =$ ______

2. $\frac{2}{3} = \frac{16}{y}$ $y =$ ______

3. $\frac{5}{6} = \frac{m}{54}$ $m =$ ______

4. $\frac{1}{4} = \frac{15}{n}$ $n =$ ______

5. $\frac{5}{8} = \frac{f}{32}$ $f =$ ______

6. $\frac{13}{50} = \frac{g}{100}$ $g =$ ______

Write a number model for each problem. Then solve the problem.

7. Of the 115 students in the sixth grade, 2 out of 5 belong to the Drama Club. How many students are members of the Drama Club?

   Number model: ______ Answer: ______ (unit)

8. Three out of 4 students at Highland School ordered a hot lunch today. There are 156 students at the school. How many students ordered a hot lunch?

   Number model: ______ Answer: ______ (unit)

9. Gina and the other members of her troop sell cookies for $3 a box. For each box they sell, the troop earns $1.50. One week, Gina's troop sold $90 worth of cookies. How much did the troop earn?

   Number model: ______ Answer: $ ______

Challenge

10. 30% of the tickets sold by a movie theater for the Friday night show were children's tickets at $4 each. The rest of the tickets were sold at the full price of $8.50. The movie theater collected $252 for the children's tickets.

    How many tickets did they sell in all? Answer: ______ (unit)

    On the back of this page, explain or show how you got your answer.

Name Date Time

Rates

Study Link 12.6

Complete each table using the given information. Then answer the question below each table.

SRB 97–99

1. a. It would take 27,000 spiders, each spinning a single web, to produce a pound of spider web.

Number of Spiders	27,000	54,000			
Pounds of Spider Web	1	2	3	4	5

b. At this rate, how many spiders, each spinning a single web, would be needed to produce 10 pounds of spider web? __________ spiders

2. a. The deer botfly flies so fast that it is almost invisible to the human eye. In 1 minute it can travel 13 miles.

Miles	13				
Minutes	1	2	3	4	5

b. At this rate, how far could a deer botfly travel in 1 hour? __________ miles

Solve the following rate problems. Make a table if it will help you.

3. About 50 gallons of maple sap are needed to make 1 gallon of maple syrup. How many gallons of maple sap are needed to make 20 gallons of maple syrup?

About __________ gallons

4. For 186 days a year, the sun is not visible at the North Pole. During a 5-year period, for about how many days is the sun not visible?

About __________ days

5. In a beehive, about $1\frac{1}{2}$ ounces of beeswax are used to build a honeycomb that holds 4 pounds of honey. How much beeswax is needed to build a honeycomb that could hold 20 pounds of honey?

About __________ ounces

Source: 2201 Fascinating Facts

Name Date Time

Rate and Pan-Balance Problems

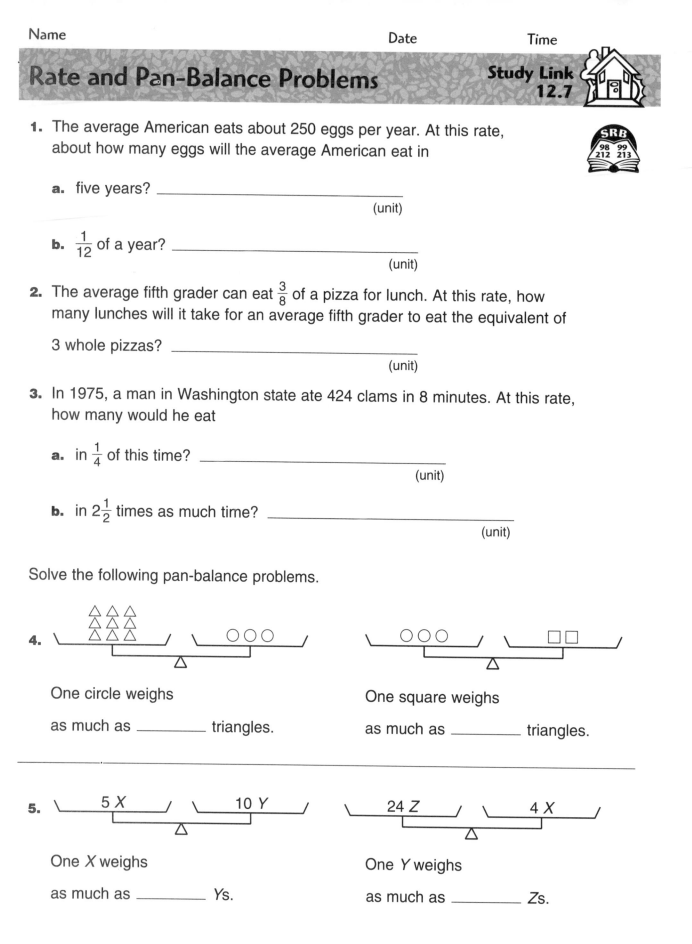

Study Link 12.7

1. The average American eats about 250 eggs per year. At this rate, about how many eggs will the average American eat in

   a. five years? ______________________ (unit)

   b. $\frac{1}{12}$ of a year? ______________________ (unit)

2. The average fifth grader can eat $\frac{3}{8}$ of a pizza for lunch. At this rate, how many lunches will it take for an average fifth grader to eat the equivalent of 3 whole pizzas? ______________________ (unit)

3. In 1975, a man in Washington state ate 424 clams in 8 minutes. At this rate, how many would he eat

   a. in $\frac{1}{4}$ of this time? ______________________ (unit)

   b. in $2\frac{1}{2}$ times as much time? ______________________ (unit)

Solve the following pan-balance problems.

4. △△△ △△△ △△△ | ○○○

One circle weighs as much as ________ triangles.

One square weighs as much as ________ triangles.

5. 5 X | 10 Y

One X weighs as much as ________ Ys.

One Y weighs as much as ________ Zs.

Name Date Time

Musical Ratios

Study Link 12.8

Piano/Keyboard	21 million
Guitar	19 million
Organ	6 million
Flute	4 million
Clarinet	4 million
Drums	3 million
Trumpet	3 million
Violin	2 million
Harmonica	1.7 million
Saxophone	1 million

Source: America by the Numbers

At the left is a list of musical instruments played by people living in the United States and the approximate number of these people who play each instrument.

1. **a.** What is the ratio of flute players to harmonica players? ____________

   b. What is the ratio of drum players to piano players? ____________

   c. Record the ratio of violin and saxophone players to trumpet players. ____________

2. Which two pairs of instrument players have a 1-to-1 ratio? ____________

   ____

3. In a fifth-grade band, the ratio of saxophonists to clarinetists is 2:3. If there are 10 saxophonists, how many clarinetists are there? ____________

Challenge

4. The school orchestra is performing tonight. There are 24 orchestra members. There are 6 violas. The ratio of violins to violas is 2:1. The ratio of cellos to basses is 2:1. There are no other instruments. How many chairs are needed in each section?

   a. Violins ____________ **b.** Violas ____________

   c. Cellos ____________ **d.** Basses ____________

Name Date Time

Operations with Fractions

Study Link 12.9

1. In the Malagasay Indian tribes, it is against the law for a son to be taller than his father. If a son is taller, he must give his father money or an ox. Suppose a father is 5 feet $10\frac{1}{2}$ inches tall and his son is 5 feet $6\frac{3}{4}$ inches tall. How many more inches can the son grow before he is as tall as his father?

   ____________ (unit)

2. In the state of Indiana, it is illegal to travel on a bus within 4 hours of eating garlic. If you lived in Indiana and had eaten a bowl of pasta with garlic bread $2\frac{1}{3}$ hours ago, how many more hours would you need to wait before you could legally travel on a bus?

   ____________ (unit)

3. In Idaho, it is against the law to give a person a box of candy that weighs more than 50 pounds. It is Valentine's Day, and you give your mother a box of candy that weighs $48\frac{1}{4}$ pounds. How much more could the box weigh without breaking the law?

   ____________ (unit)

4. The body of an average jellyfish is about $\frac{9}{10}$ water. What fraction of the jellyfish is not water?

   ____

5. The world record for a jump by a frog is 19 feet $3\frac{1}{8}$ inches. How much farther would a frog need to jump to set a new world record of 7 yards?

   ____________ (unit)

6. The maximum length for a typical king cobra is about $5\frac{4}{5}$ meters. If 6 of these snakes were lined up end to end, how far would they stretch?

   ____________ (unit)

7. An average trumpeter swan weighs about $16\frac{4}{5}$ kilograms. What is the approximate weight of 3 average trumpeter swans?

   ____________ (unit)

Sources: The Top 10 of Everything; Beyond Belief!

Name Date Time

Family Letter

Study Link 12.10

End-of-Year Family Letter

Congratulations!

By completing *Fifth Grade Everyday Mathematics,* your child has accomplished a great deal. Thank you for all of your support!

This Family Letter is here for you to use as a resource throughout your child's vacation. It includes an extended list of Do-Anytime Activities, directions for games that can be played at home, a list of mathematics-related books to check out over vacation, and a sneak preview of what your child will be learning in *Sixth Grade Everyday Mathematics.* Enjoy your vacation!

Do-Anytime Activities

Mathematics means more when it is rooted in real-life situations. To help your child review many of the concepts he or she has learned in fifth grade, we suggest the following activities for you and your child to do together over vacation. These activities will help your child build on the skills he or she has learned this year and help prepare him or her for *Sixth Grade Everyday Mathematics.*

1. Review multiplication facts. Include the basic facts such as 7 * 8 = 56, and "extended facts," such as 70 * 8 = 560 and 70 * 80 = 5,600.
2. Create opportunities to work with rulers, yardsticks, metersticks, tape measures, and scales. Have your child measure using both metric and U.S. customary units.
3. Ask your child to solve multiplication and division problems that are based on real-life situations. Vary the problems so that some are suitable for mental computation, some require paper-and-pencil calculation, and others require the use of a calculator.
4. Practice using percents by asking your child to calculate sales tax, percent discounts, sports statistics, and so on.
5. Continue the American Tour by reading about important people, events, inventions, explorations, and other topics in American history. Focus on data displays such as bar, line, and circle graphs; and on color-coded maps.

Building Skills through Games

The following section lists rules for games that can be played at home. The number cards used in some games can be made from 3" by 5" index cards.

1	2	2	2	2	2
2	3	3	3	3	3
3	4	4	4	4	5
5	5	5	6	6	7
7	8	8	9	9	10
10	11	12	13	14	15
16	18	20	21	22	24
25	26	27	28	30	32

Factor Captor number grid

Factor Captor

1. To start the first round, Player 1 (James) chooses a 2-digit number on the number grid. James covers it with a counter, and records the number on scratch paper. This is James's score for the round.
2. Player 2 (Emma) covers all of the factors of James's number. Emma finds the sum of the factors, and records it on scratch paper. This is Emma's score for the round.

   A factor may only be covered once during a round.
3. If Emma missed any factors, James can cover them with counters and add them to his score.
4. In the next round, players switch roles. Player 2 (Emma) chooses a number that is not covered by a counter. Player 1 (James) covers all factors of that number.
5. Any number that is covered by a counter is no longer available and may not be used again.
6. The first player in a round may not cover a number less than 10, unless no other numbers are available.
7. Play continues with players trading roles in each round, until all numbers on the grid have been covered. Players then use their calculators to find their total scores. The player with the higher total score wins the game.

EXAMPLE

Round 1: James covers 27 and scores 27 points. Emma covers 1, 3, and 9, and scores 1 + 3 + 9 = 13 points.

Round 2: Emma covers 18 and scores 18 points. James covers 2, 3, and 6, and scores 2 + 3 + 6 =11 points. Emma covers 9 with a counter, because 9 is also a factor of 18. Emma adds 9 points to her score.

Frac-Tac-Toe (2-4-5-10 version)

Advance Preparation: Separate the cards into two piles—a numerator pile and a denominator pile. For a 2-4-5-10 game, place two each of the 2, 4, 5, and 10 cards in the denominator pile. All other cards are placed on the numerator pile.

Shuffle the cards in each pile. Place the piles facedown. When the numerator pile is completely used, reshuffle that pile, and place it facedown. When the denominator pile is completely used, turn it over and place it facedown without reshuffling it.

1. Players take turns. When it is your turn:
   - ▷ Turn over the top card from each pile to form a fraction (numerator card over denominator card).
   - ▷ Try to match the fraction shown with one of the grid squares on the Game Board. (Use either of the gameboards shown) If a match is found, cover that grid square with your counter and your turn is over. If no match is found, your turn is over.

Game Boards for the 2-4-5-10 versions of *Frac-Tac-Toe*

>1.0	0 or 1	>2.0	0 or 1	>1.0
0.1	0.2	0.25	0.3	0.4
>1.5	0.5	>1.5	0.5	>1.5
0.6	0.7	0.75	0.8	0.9
>1.0	0 or 1	>2.0	0 or 1	>1.0

>100%	0% or 100%	>200%	0% or 100%	>100%
10%	20%	25%	30%	40%
>100%	50%	>200%	50%	>100%
60%	70%	75%	80%	90%
>100%	0% or 100%	>200%	0% or 100%	>100%

2. To change the fraction shown by the cards to a decimal or percent, players *may* use a calculator.
3. **Scoring** The first player covering three squares in a row in any direction (horizontal, vertical, diagonal) is the winner.

Variations:

▷ For a 2-4-8 game, place two each of the 2, 4, and 8 cards in the denominator pile. Use the game boards shown in the margin.

▷ For a 3-6-9 game, place two each of the 3, 6, and 9 cards in the denominator pile. Use the game boards shown in the margin.

Multiplication Bull's-eye

1. Shuffle a deck of number cards (4 each of the numbers 0–9) and place them facedown on the playing surface.
2. Players take turns. When it is your turn:
   - ▷ Roll a six-sided die. Look up the target range of the product in the table.
   - ▷ Take four cards from the top of the deck.
   - ▷ Use the cards to try to form two numbers whose product falls within the target range. **Do not use a calculator.**
   - ▷ Multiply the two numbers on your calculator to determine whether the product falls within the target range. If it does, you have hit the bull's-eye and score 1 point. If it doesn't, you score 0 points.
   - ▷ Sometimes it is impossible to form two numbers whose product falls within the target range. If this happens, you score 0 points for that turn.
3. The game ends when each player has had five turns.
4. The player scoring more points wins the game.

EXAMPLE

Tom rolls a 3, so the target range of the product is from 1,001 to 3,000.

He turns over a 5, a 7, a 2, and a 9.

Tom uses estimation to try to form two numbers whose product falls within the target range—for example, 97 and 25.

He finds the product on the calculator:
97 * 25 = 2,425.

Since the product is between 1,001 and 3,000, Tom has hit the bull's-eye and scores 1 point.

Some other possible winning products from the 5, 7, 2, and 9 cards are:
25 * 79, 27 * 59, 9 * 257, and 2 * 579.

Number on Die	Target Range of Product
1	500 or less
2	501–1,000
3	1,001–3,000
4	3,001–5,000
5	5,001–7,000
6	more than 7,000

2-4-8 Frac-Tac-Toe Game Boards

>2.0	0 or 1	>1.5	0 or 1	>2.0
1.5	0.125	0.25	0.375	1.5
>1.0	0.5	0.25 or 0.75	0.5	>1.0
2.0	0.625	0.75	0.875	2.0
>2.0	0 or 1	1.125	0 or 1	>2.0

>200%	0% or 100%	>150%	0% or 100%	>200%
150%	$12\frac{1}{2}\%$	25%	$37\frac{1}{2}\%$	150%
>100%	50%	25% or 75%	50%	>100%
200%	$62\frac{1}{2}\%$	75%	$87\frac{1}{2}\%$	200%
>200%	0% or 100%	$112\frac{1}{2}\%$	0% or 100%	>200%

3-6-9 Frac-Tac-Toe Game Boards

>1.0	0 or 1	$0.\overline{1}$	0 or 1	>1.0
$0.1\overline{6}$	$0.\overline{2}$	$0.\overline{3}$	$0.\overline{3}$	$0.\overline{4}$
>2.0	$0.\overline{5}$	>1.0	$0.\overline{6}$	>2.0
$0.\overline{6}$	$0.\overline{7}$	$0.8\overline{3}$	$0.\overline{8}$	$1.\overline{3}$
>1.0	0 or 1	$1.\overline{6}$	0 or 1	>1.0

>100%	0% or 100%	11.1%	0% or 100%	>100%
$16\frac{2}{3}\%$	22.2%	$33\frac{1}{3}\%$	33.3%	44.4%
>200%	55.5%	>100%	66.6%	>200%
$66\frac{2}{3}\%$	77.7%	$83\frac{1}{3}\%$	88.8%	$133\frac{1}{3}\%$
>100%	0% or 100%	$166\frac{2}{3}\%$	0% or 100%	>100%

Vacation Reading with a Mathematical Twist

Books can contribute to children's learning by presenting mathematics in a combination of real-world and imaginary contexts. The titles listed below were recommended by teachers who use *Everyday Mathematics* in their classrooms. They are organized by mathematical topic. Visit your local library and check out these mathematics-related books with your child.

Numeration

The Rajah's Rice: A Mathematical Folktale from India by David Barry

Operations and Computation

Counting on Frank by Rod Clement

Data and Chance

Jumanji by Chris Van Allsburg

Geometry

A Cloak for the Dreamer by Aileen Friedman; *Flatland* by Edwin Abbott; *The Boy Who Reversed Himself* by William Sleator

Measurement and Reference Frames

Spaghetti and Meatballs for All!: A Mathematical Story by Marilyn Burns; *Mr. Archimedes' Bath* by Pamela Allen

Looking Ahead: Sixth Grade Everyday Mathematics

Next year your child will ...

- ▷ continue to collect, display, describe, and interpret data
- ▷ maintain and extend skills for comparing, adding, subtracting, multiplying, and dividing fractions and mixed numbers
- ▷ use scientific notation to write large and small numbers; explore scientific notation on a calculator
- ▷ continue the study of variables, expressions, equations, and other topics in algebra; use variables in spreadsheets; and solve equations and inequalities
- ▷ extend skills in geometry, including constructions, transformations of figures, and volumes of 3-dimensional figures
- ▷ maintain and apply skills for adding, subtracting, multiplying, and dividing whole numbers, decimals, and positive and negative numbers

Name Date Time

Unit 1 Checking Progress

1. Mr. Martin has 24 tulip bulbs. He wants to plant them in a rectangular array consisting of *at least* 2 rows with *at least* 2 tulips in each row. On the grid at the right, draw three possible arrays.

2. Is 24 an even or an odd number?

   ____

3. List all the factors of 24.

   ____

4. Is 24 a prime or a composite number?

   ____

   How can you tell? ______________________________

   ____

   ____

5. Circle the factors in Problem 3 that are prime numbers.

6. Write the prime factorization for 24.

   ____

7. Write the prime factorization of 24 using exponents.

   ____

8. Fill in the missing numbers.

   a. $7^2 =$ ________ **b.** $9^2 =$ ________ **c.** ________ $= 6^2$

   d. $\_\_\_\_^2 = 25$ **e.** $\_\_\_\_^2 = 100$ **f.** $8 * 8 = \_\_\_\_^2$

Name Date Time

Unit 1 Checking Progress (cont.)

9. Pretend that you are playing *Factor Captor* on the number grid at the right. The crossed-out numbers have already been picked. Which number would you choose next?

____

Why? _______________

____

____

~~1~~	2	~~3~~	4	~~5~~
6	~~7~~	8	9	10
11	12	13	14	15
16	17	18	19	20
~~21~~	22	~~23~~	24	~~25~~
26	27	28	~~29~~	30

10. If you chose 28 on the grid in Problem 9, what numbers would your opponent be able to capture? _______________

11. Name a number between 200 and 300 that is divisible by 3 but not by 2.

____

12. Name a number between 200 and 300 that is divisible by 2, 3, and 5.

____

13. At the right is a calendar for a month. Use the following clues to figure out on what date the Bret Harte School won its last basketball game.

- The date is not an even number.
- The date is not a square number.
- The date is not a prime number.
- The date is a multiple of 5.

On what day of the month did the school win its last basketball game? _______________

S	M	T	W	T	F	S
	1	2	3	4	5	6
7	8	9	10	11	12	13
14	15	16	17	18	19	20
21	22	23	24	25	26	27
28	29	30	31			

14. Is 231 a prime or a composite number? _______________

Explain your answer. _______________

____

____

Name Date Time

Unit 2 Checking Progress

Solve at least one problem using the partial-sums addition method and at least one problem using the trade-first subtraction method. Use any method you want to solve the rest of the problems. Show your work.

1. 734 + 893 = ____________

2. 24.7 + 103.9 = ____________

3. ____________ = 58.2 + 76.08

4. 692 − 348 = ____________

5. 150.4 − 63.7 = ____________

6. ____________ = 28.3 − 13.71

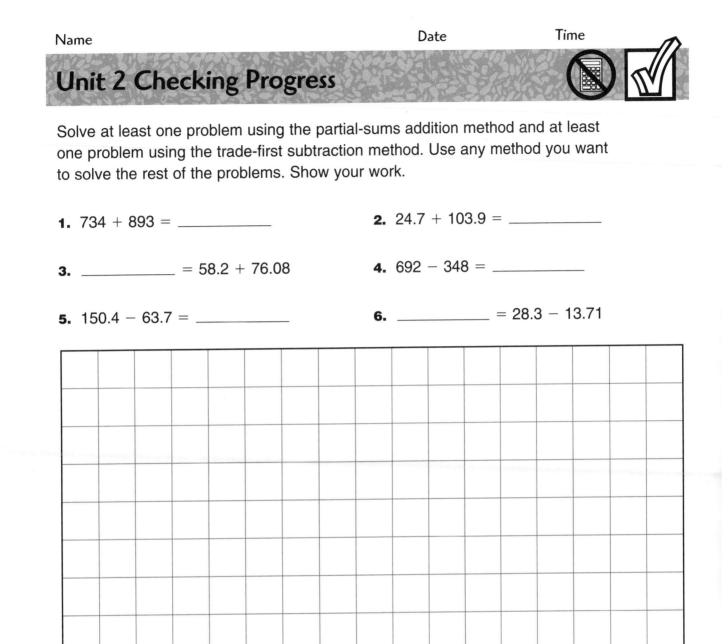

Name Date Time

Unit 2 Checking Progress (cont.)

Round to the nearest ...

7. hundred.

a. 84 ____________

b. 1,659 ____________

c. 46,310 ____________

8. one.

a. 243.6 ____________

b. 170.3 ____________

c. 1,419.78 ____________

9. tenth.

a. 604.37 ____________

b. 291.06 ____________

c. 12.74 ____________

10. ten.

a. 493 ____________

b. 1,508 ____________

c. 124.63 ____________

11. Write the number that has
6 in the ones place,
4 in the thousands place,
7 in the ten-thousands place,
2 in the tenths place,
and 5 in all of the remaining places. ___ ___ , ___ ___ ___ . ___ ___ ___

12. Identify the errors in the following problems and correct them.

a.

```
   28
 × 46
   80
  120
  320
+  48
  488
```

b.

	3	**6**	
0	0 / 6	6 / 2	**2**
4	1 / 5	0 / 3	**5**
	7	3	

13. Choose one of the problems above and explain why making a quick estimate of the answer before solving the problem would be helpful.

____

____

____

Name Date Time

Unit 2 Checking Progress (cont.)

For each problem, make a magnitude estimate. Circle the appropriate box. Then solve the problem. Show your work.

14. 64 * 83 = ____________

10s	100s	1,000s	10,000s

15. 5 * 209 = ____________

10s	100s	1,000s	10,000s

16. 12.2 * 1.56 = ____________

10s	100s	1,000s	10,000s

17. 25 * 15.3 = ____________

10s	100s	1,000s	10,000s

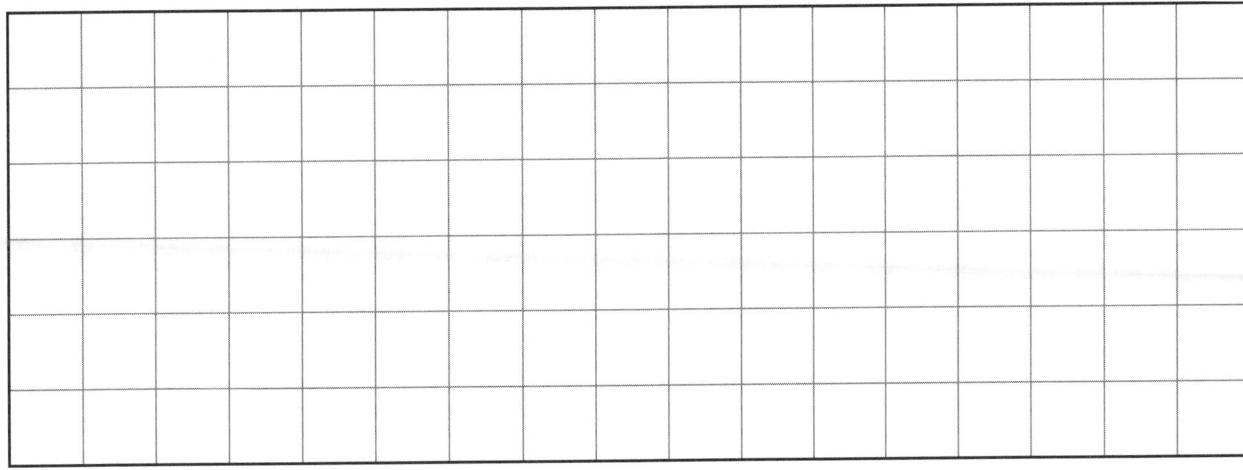

18. Elise had the following scores on her spelling tests: 78, 84, 94, 98, 62, 96, 89, 94, 92. For this set of data, find ...

a. the maximum ________ **b.** the minimum ________

c. the range ________ **d.** the mode ________ **e.** the median ________

19. Caitlin's great-grandmother was born in 1919. Her family had a big party for her on her 75th birthday. There were 52 family members at the party. In what year did they have the party?

a. List the numbers needed to solve the problem. ____________________

b. Describe what you want to find. ____________________

c. Open sentence: ____________________

d. Solution: ____________ **e.** Answer: ____________________

Name Date Time

Unit 3 Checking Progress

Find the missing angle measures without measuring.

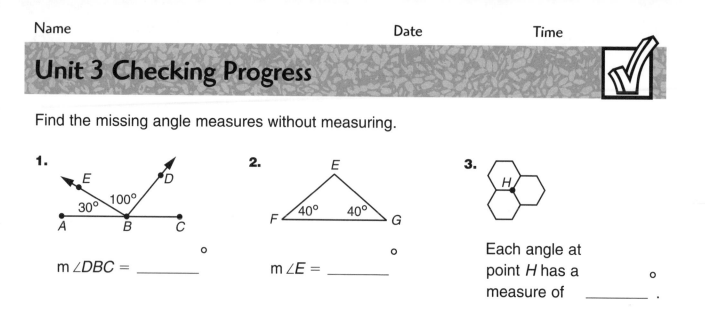

1.

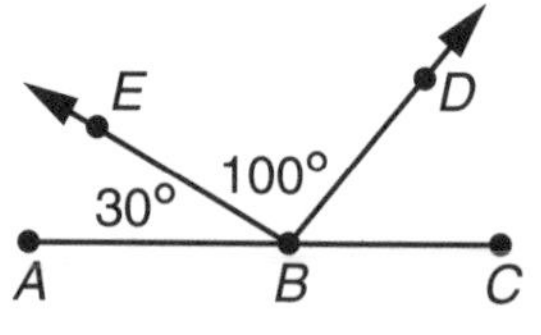

m ∠DBC = ________ °

2.

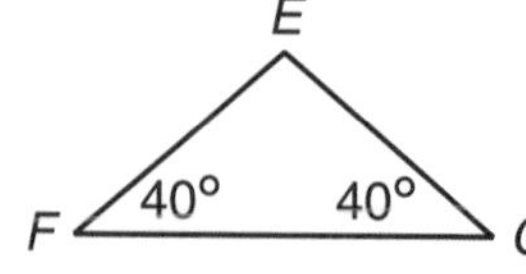

m ∠E = ________ °

3.

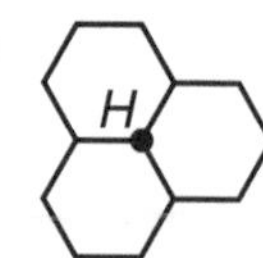

Each angle at point *H* has a measure of ________ °.

Measure each angle below with a protractor. Then fill in an oval to tell what kind of angle it is.

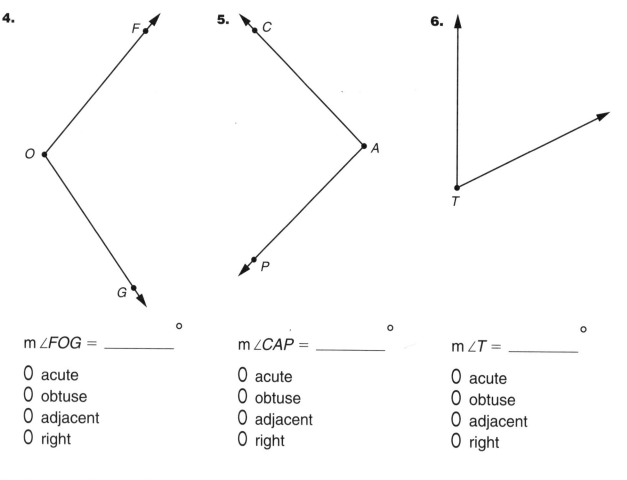

4.

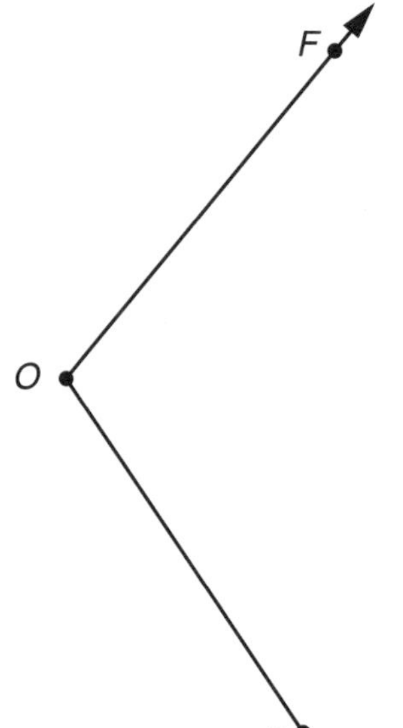

m ∠FOG = ________ °

0 acute
0 obtuse
0 adjacent
0 right

5.

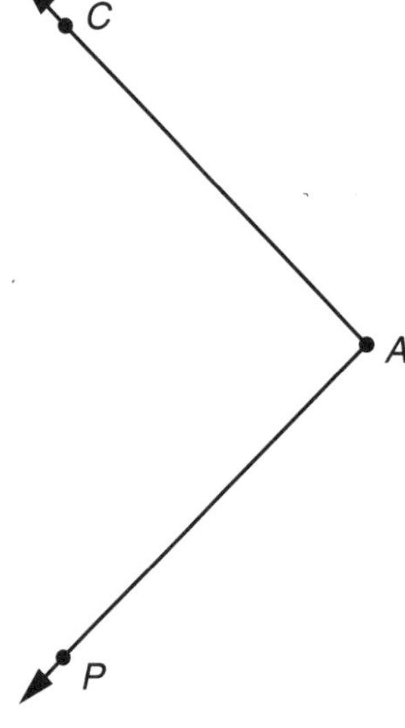

m ∠CAP = ________ °

0 acute
0 obtuse
0 adjacent
0 right

6.

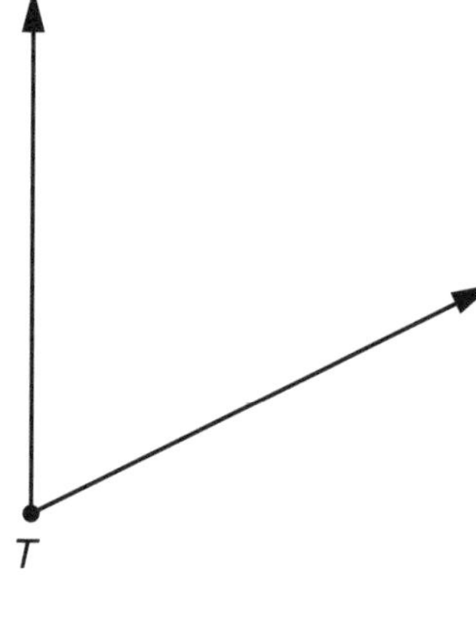

m ∠T = ________ °

0 acute
0 obtuse
0 adjacent
0 right

7. Explain what a reflex angle is.

____

____

Name Date Time

Unit 3 Checking Progress (cont.)

8. **a.** At the right, use a straightedge to draw a pair of adjacent angles. Make one of the angles obtuse. Use letters to name the angles.

b. Tell which angle is obtuse. ∠ ____________

c. Without using your protractor, estimate the measure of each angle to the nearest 10°.

m ∠ ________ is about ________°. m ∠ ________ is about ________°.

9. Write the number that has
4 in the ones place,
a digit in the hundred-thousands place that is twice the digit in the ones place,
the smallest odd digit in the millions place,
7 in the tenths place, and
0 in all other places.

_____ , _____ _____ _____ , _____ _____ _____ . _____

Use your Geometry Template to do the following:

10. Draw an equilateral triangle.

11. Draw an isosceles triangle that is not equilateral.

12. Draw a scalene triangle.

13. List at least one way in which an equilateral triangle and a scalene triangle are the same. ____

____

14. List at least one way in which an equilateral triangle and a scalene triangle are different. ____

____

____

Name Date Time

Unit 3 Checking Progress (cont.)

15. In the space below, use the pattern-block shapes on your Geometry Template to make a pattern that tessellates. (The pattern-block shapes are marked PB.)

16. Explain why your pattern above is a tessellation.

____

____

For each polygon below, fill in the ovals next to the true statements.

17.

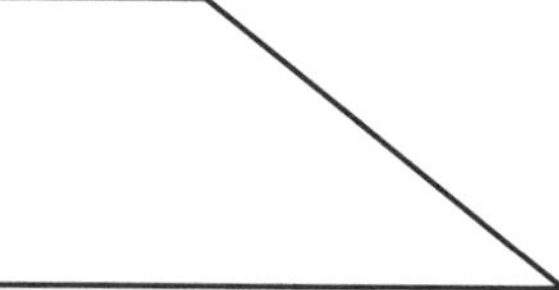

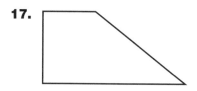

O This polygon is a quadrangle.
O At least two sides are parallel.
O At least two angles are congruent.
O This is a regular polygon.

18.

O This polygon is a quadrangle.
O At least two sides are parallel.
O At least one angle is acute.
O At least two angles are congruent.
O This is a regular polygon.

Name Date Time

Unit 4 Checking Progress

Use a "friendly number" strategy to solve these problems mentally.

1. 84 divided by 6 equals ________.

____
(friendly parts for 84)

2. 104 divided by 8 equals ________.

____
(friendly parts for 104)

Solve. Show your work.

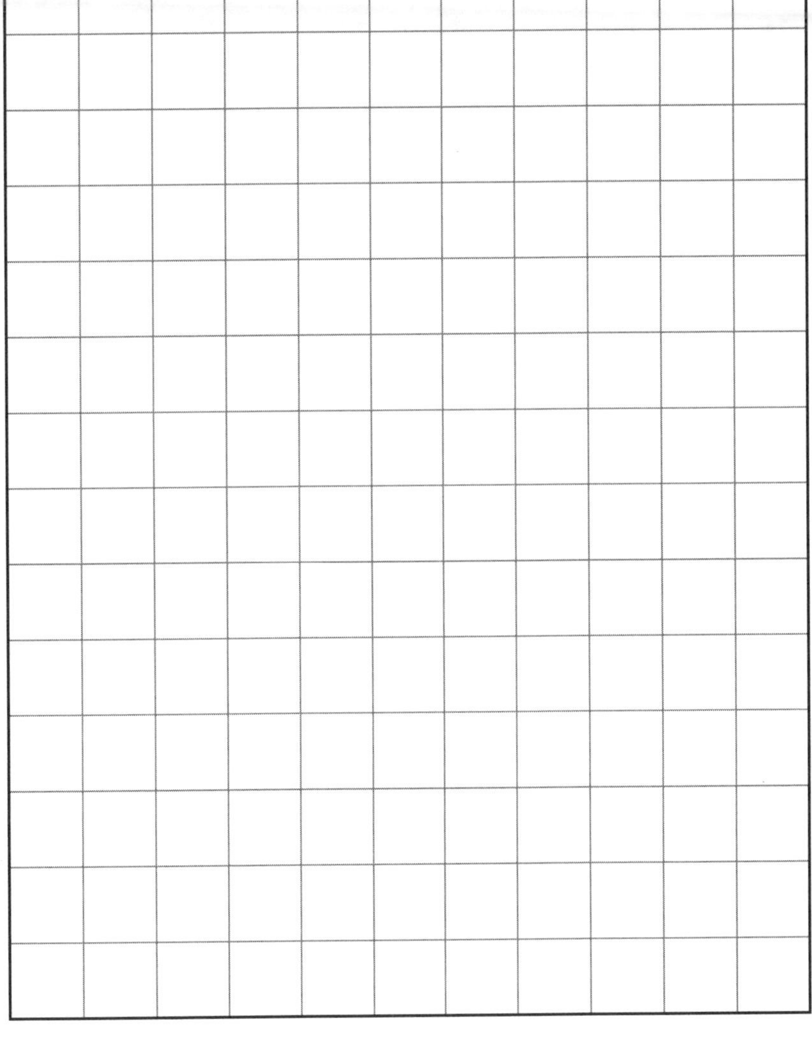

3. 126 / 6 = ________

4. 9 * ________ = 243

5. 703 ÷ 14 → ________

6. 482 ÷ 34 → ________

Circle your magnitude estimate.
Then solve.

7. $5\overline{)88.5}$

0.1s	1s	10s	100s

8. $14\overline{)2.94}$

0.1s	1s	10s	100s

Name Date Time

Unit 4 Checking Progress (cont.)

In Problems 9 and 10:

- Write a number sentence to represent the number story.
- Use a division algorithm to solve the problem.
- Decide what to do about the remainder.
- Tell why you did what you did about the remainder.

9. Tammy has 130 photographs. She can tape 8 photos onto each page of her photo album. How many pages will she need to tape all of her photos in the album?

Number sentence: ______________________ Solution: ______ pages

What does the remainder represent? ______________________

____

What did you do about the remainder? Circle the answer.

Ignored it. Reported it as a fraction or decimal. Rounded the answer up.

10. For a relay race, the gym teacher divided the class into 4 teams with an equal number of students on each team. There were 30 students in the class. Extra students didn't race. How many members were on each team?

Number sentence: ______________________ Solution: ______ members

What does the remainder represent? ______________________

____

What did you do about the remainder? Circle the answer.

Ignored it. Reported it as a fraction or decimal. Rounded the answer up.

In Problems 11 and 12:

- Find the value of x in the first number sentence.
- Use this value to complete the second number sentence.

11. $x = 100 - 95$; $x^2 =$ ______ **12.** $x = \frac{1}{2}$ of a dozen; $30 * x =$ ______

13. Write an open sentence you can use to solve the number story below. Then solve the number story.

Four friends rented a car. The total rental cost was $150, including tax. The friends split the cost evenly. How much did each friend contribute?

Number sentence: ______________________ Solution: $______

Name Date Time

Unit 5 Checking Progress

Write three equivalent fractions for each fraction below.

1. $\frac{3}{7}$ ______________

2. $\frac{6}{9}$ ______________

3. $\frac{9}{10}$ ______________

Fill in the oval next to each equivalent fraction or mixed number. (*Hint:* There may be more than one correct answer.)

4. $\frac{12}{5}$

- O 3
- O $2\frac{4}{5}$
- O $1\frac{7}{5}$
- O $2\frac{2}{5}$

5. $\frac{18}{8}$

- O 2
- O $2\frac{1}{4}$
- O $3\frac{1}{8}$
- O $2\frac{2}{8}$

6. $3\frac{4}{9}$

- O $\frac{7}{9}$
- O $\frac{31}{9}$
- O $\frac{15}{9}$
- O $\frac{34}{9}$

7. $5\frac{7}{3}$

- O $\frac{35}{3}$
- O $\frac{12}{3}$
- O $\frac{15}{3}$
- O $\frac{22}{3}$

8. Explain one way to find the equivalent percent for $\frac{3}{5}$ without using a calculator.

____

____

Write the mixed number and fraction for each diagram below. In each diagram, the square is worth 1.

Whole
square

9. 

Mixed number ______________ Fraction ______________

10. 

Mixed number ______________ Fraction ______________

11. 

Mixed number ______________ Fraction ______________

Name Date Time

Unit 5 Checking Progress (cont.)

Use fraction sticks to add the fractions.

12.

$\frac{1}{8} + \frac{3}{8} =$ ______________

13.

$\frac{1}{2} + \frac{1}{4} =$ ______________

14.

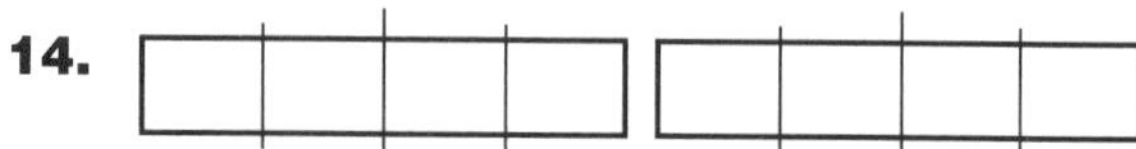

$\frac{3}{4} + \frac{1}{2} =$ ______________

Write <, =, or > to make the sentence true.

15. $\frac{3}{8}$ ______ $\frac{3}{5}$

16. $\frac{9}{10}$ ______ $\frac{1}{2}$

17. $\frac{6}{8}$ ______ $\frac{9}{12}$

18. $\frac{7}{20}$ ______ $\frac{17}{20}$

19. $\frac{6}{7}$ ______ $\frac{5}{6}$

20. $3\frac{2}{3}$ ______ $\frac{10}{3}$

21. First, estimate the size of each piece of the circle graph at the right. Then use your Percent Circle to find the actual percent.

Flavor	Estimate	Percent
Chocolate	______	______
Strawberry	______	______
Vanilla	______	______
Cookie Dough	______	______
Other	______	______

Favorite Ice Cream Flavors

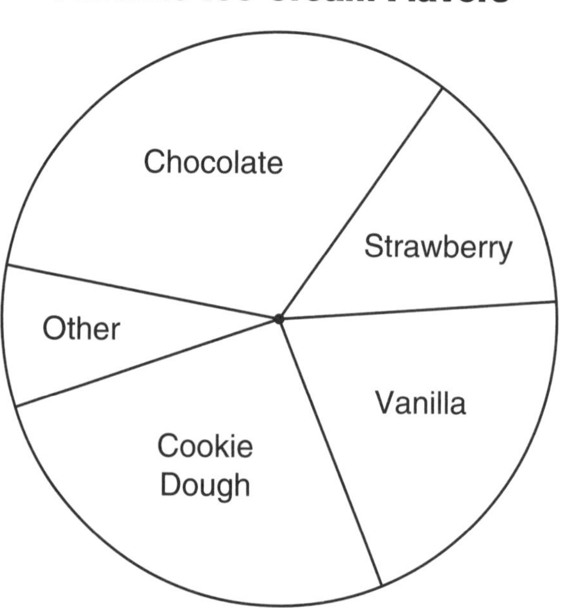

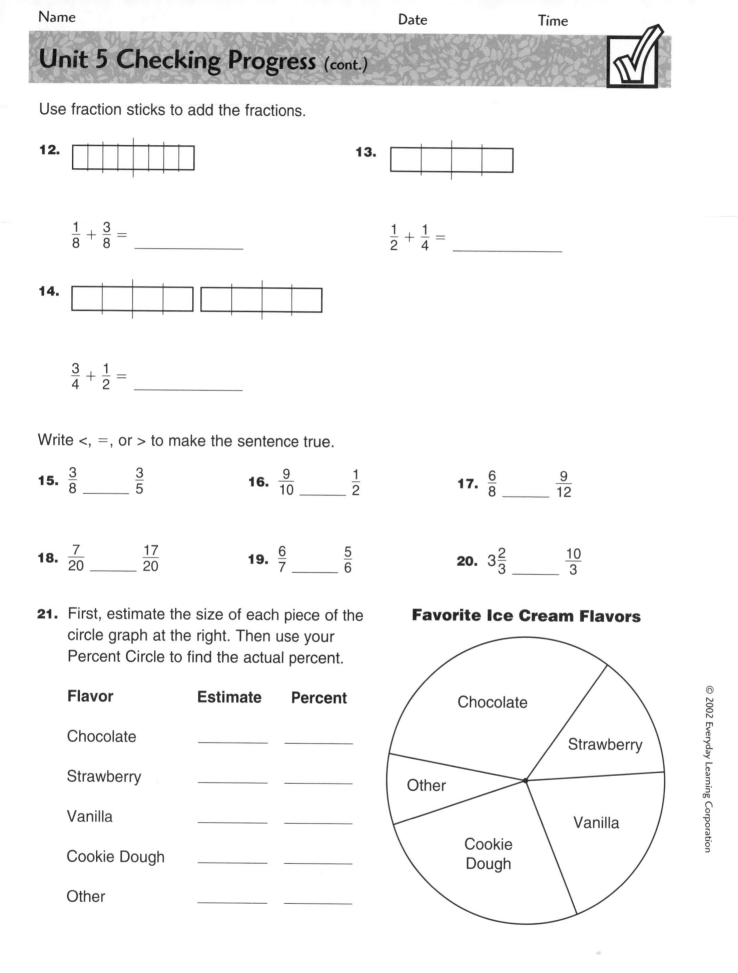

Name Date Time

Unit 5 Checking Progress (cont.)

22. Why is it helpful to make an estimate before finding the size of a piece of a circle graph?

____

____

A survey reported favorite types of books for fifth graders. The results of the survey were as follows:

38% Adventure books 30% Mystery books 22% Humor books 10% Other

23. Make a circle graph for this data on the circle below. Use your Percent Circle.

Favorite Books

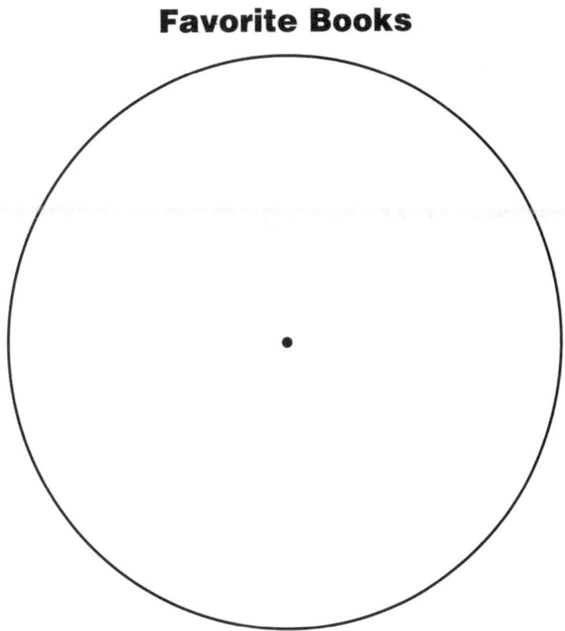

24. If 100 students answered the survey, how many of them chose "adventures"? ________

25. If 10 students answered the survey, how many of them chose "other"?

____

26. If 50 students answered the survey, how many of them chose "mysteries"?

____

Name Date Time

Unit 6 Checking Progress

Fill in the ovals to match the words with their definitions.

1. Median

- O smallest value
- O largest value
- O most frequent value
- O middle value

2. Maximum

- O smallest value
- O largest value
- O most frequent value
- O middle value

3. Mode

- O smallest value
- O largest value
- O most frequent value
- O middle value

4. Minimum

- O smallest value
- O largest value
- O most frequent value
- O middle value

5. Sonia asked seven girls in her fifth grade class how many CDs they own. Here are the results of her survey:

2 0 6 5 7 5 1

a. What was the median number of CDs owned? ______________

b. Sonia concluded: *The typical fifth grader owns about 5 CDs.*

Do you agree with her conclusion? ________

Explain. ______________________________

c. Describe two ways Sonia could improve her survey. ______________________________

____

6. Explain one way to rename $\frac{3}{5}$ as a percent without using a calculator.

____

____

7. Circle each stem-and-leaf plot with a median of 24. Put an X through each stem-and-leaf plot with a mode of 28. (There may be more than one.)

Stems (10s)	Leaves (1s)
1	3 4 7
2	0 2 4 4 4 4 8
3	0

Stems (10s)	Leaves (1s)
1	5 6 7
2	3 3 4 8 8 8 9
3	0

Stems (10s)	Leaves (1s)
1	8 9
2	3 4 8 8 8 9 9
3	0 1

Name Date Time

Unit 6 Checking Progress *(cont.)*

8. One survey reported favorite types of books for fifth graders. The results of the survey were as follows:

adventure books: 38%
mystery books: 30%
comedies: 22%
other: 10%

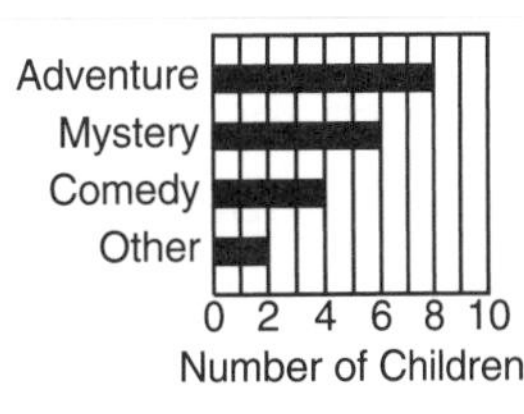

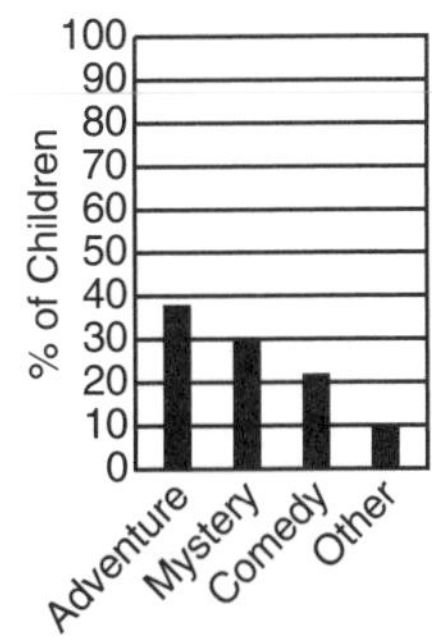

a. Circle the bar graph that best represents the survey results.

b. If 100 students answered the survey, how many of them chose "adventures"? ______

c. If 10 students answered the survey, how many of them chose "other"? ______

d. If 50 students answered the survey, how many of them chose "mysteries"? ______

e. If you were trying to decide what kinds of books to buy for the library in your town, how many fifth graders would you interview? ______

Explain why you chose that number. ______

Solve.

9. $\frac{4}{5} + \frac{2}{5} =$ ______

10. $1 - \frac{3}{4} =$ ______

11. $\frac{5}{8} - \frac{3}{8} =$ ______

12. $\frac{9}{16} + \frac{2}{8} =$ ______

13. $\frac{7}{8} - \frac{1}{2}$

14. $\frac{2}{3} + \frac{2}{5}$

15. $\frac{5}{6} - \frac{3}{8}$

16. $\frac{2}{3} + \frac{3}{4}$

17. a. Use your ruler to draw a line segment that is $2\frac{3}{8}$ inches long.

b. If you erased $\frac{3}{4}$ inch from this line segment, how long would it be? ______

c. If you drew a line segment twice as long as the original line segment, how long would it be? ______

18. Circle the fraction pair that is represented in the drawing below.

$\frac{2}{15}$ and $\frac{3}{5}$ $\frac{5}{3}$ and $\frac{9}{5}$

$\frac{2}{3}$ and $\frac{3}{4}$ $\frac{4}{15}$ and $\frac{2}{15}$

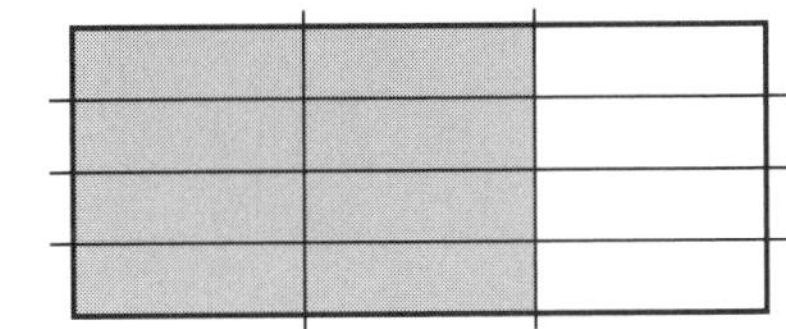
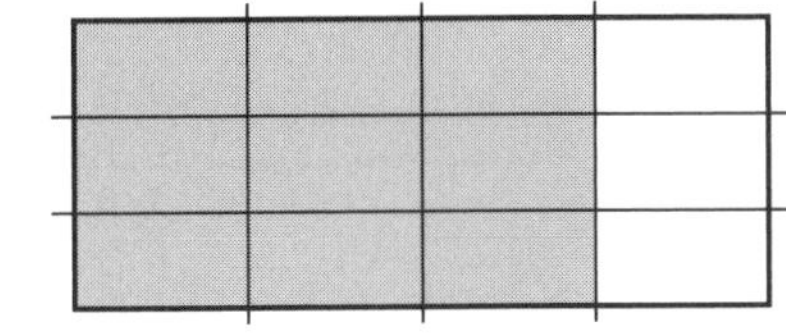

Name Date Time

Unit 6 Checking Progress (cont.)

19. Write a pair of fractions with common denominators for the pictures in Problem 18. _______ _______

20. Explain how you would use the multiplication rule to find common denominators for the fraction pair you circled in Problem 18.

____

____

21. David was writing a report on sleep and dreams. He gave a survey to the 21 students in his class. The following were three of the questions:

A. About how many hours do you sleep each night?

B. About how many dreams do you remember having in an average week?

C. What time do you usually get up on a school day?

The graphs below show the answers to two of these questions. Match the questions with their graphs. (Write A, B, or C under each graph.)

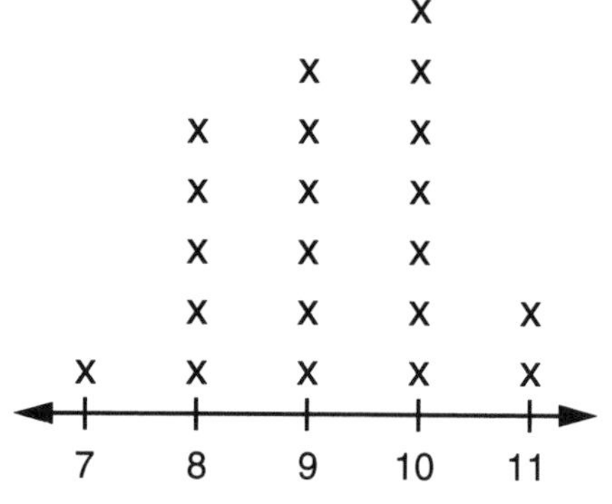

____

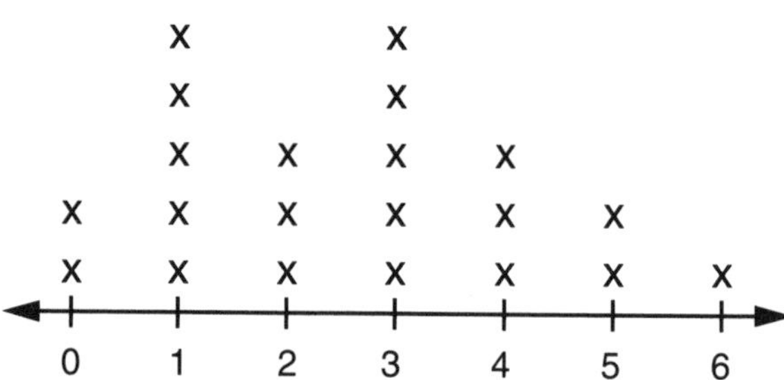

____

22. Martha's class was estimating the number of jellybeans in a jar. They made the following estimates:

128, 126, 135, 139, 132, 130, 145, 147, 155, 120, 191, 135, 145, 135, 137, 158

a. Explain the mistake in the stem-and leaf plot for the jellybean estimates.

____

____

____

____

Stems (10s)	Leaves (1s)
12	8 6 0
13	5 9 2 0 7
14	5 7
15	5 8
19	1

b. Correct the stem-and-leaf plot at the right.

Name Date Time

Unit 7 Checking Progress

Write each number in standard notation and in number-and-word notation.

	Number	Standard Notation	Number-and-Word Notation
1.	10^5		
2.	10^9		
3.	$6 * 10^7$		
4.	$3.2 * 10^6$		

Write >, <, or =.

5. -4 ______ 3

6. -12 ______ -10

7. 37 ______ -42

8. 10^2 ______ -200

9. $-\frac{3}{8}$ ______ -1

10. 9^2 ______ 6^3

11. -8 ______ $5 + (-13)$

12. $-4 + (-4)$ ______ -11

13. $12 + (-6)$ ______ -15

14. $-3 + (-3)$ ______ -6

15. 7 ______ $-1 - (-10)$

16. $24 / 3$ ______ $6 - (-7)$

17. Some of the expressions below are not number sentences. Cross them out. Then circle the number sentences that are true.

$14 + (-25) > -50$ $\quad$ $6^2 = 2^6$ $\quad$ $11 * 11 * 11 = 33^3$

$2 * 10^3$ $\quad$ $-21 - (-39) = 60$ $\quad$ $38 < 7^2 - (-20)$

$\frac{3}{4} + \frac{3}{4} > 1$ $\quad$ 19 $\quad$ $-5 = 20 + (-25)$

18. Explain why the expressions you crossed out in Problem 17 are not number sentences.

____

____

____

Name Date Time

Unit 7 Checking Progress (cont.)

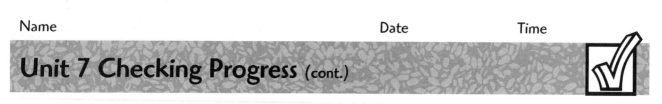

19. Draw a line from each story to the number model that matches.

a. Sandy baked 4 trays of chocolate-chip cookies with one dozen on each tray. She and her brother ate 6 of the cookies while they were still warm.

$4 * 12 - 6$

$6 * 12 - 4$

b. Charlie baked 4 trays of chocolate-chip cookies. He started with one dozen on each tray, but then his mom came and removed 6 cookies from each tray to send to Charlie's grandmother.

$6 * (12 - 4)$

$4 * (12 - 6)$

20. Explain your answers to Problem 19.

____

____

____

____

____

____

____

____

____

Insert parentheses when necessary to make the number sentences true. (Because of the rules of order of operations, some of the problems do not need parentheses.)

21. $9 + 2 * 5 = 19$

22. $9 + 2 * 5 = 55$

23. $12 + 8 \div 2 = 16$

24. $12 + 8 \div 2 = 10$

25. $-8 + 43 \div 5 = 7$

26. $12 + 4 \div 8 = 12\frac{1}{2}$

27. $-3 + 5 * 2 - (-6) = 16$

28. $4^2 + (-3) - (-5) * 2 = 20$

Use with Lesson 7.11.

Name Date Time

Unit 7 Checking Progress (cont.)

Use your ⊞ and ⊟ counters.

29. Draw a picture that shows an account with a balance of −$6.

30. Draw a picture that shows a balance of $8, using exactly 10 counters.

31. What is your balance if you have the same number of ⊞ and ⊟ counters? ________

There are 15 ⊞ and 10 ⊟ counters in a container.

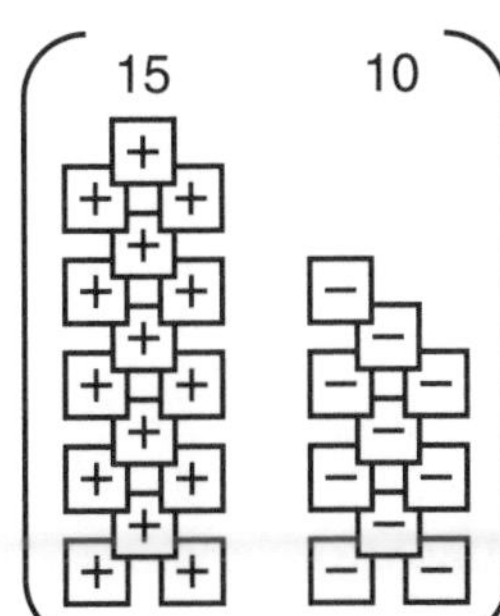

32. What is the balance in the container? ________

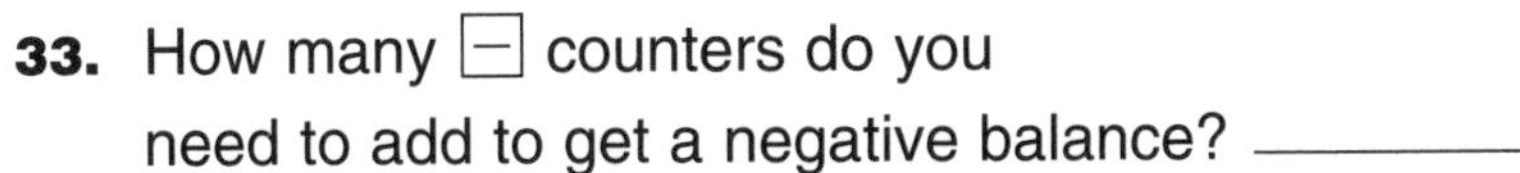

33. How many ⊟ counters do you need to add to get a negative balance? ________

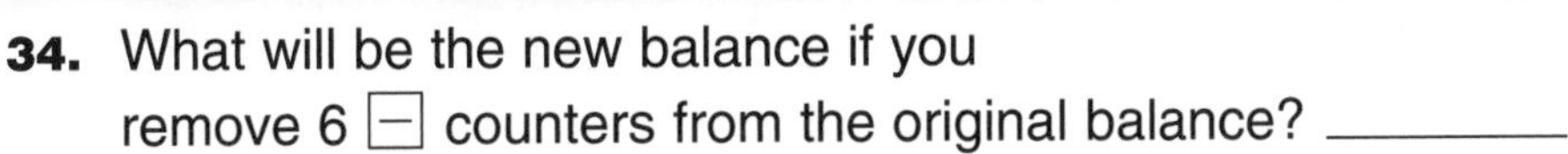

34. What will be the new balance if you remove 6 ⊟ counters from the original balance? ________

35. What will be the new balance if you ...

a. remove 7 ⊟ counters from the original balance? ________

b. add 3 ⊟ counters to the original balance? ________

Solve. You may use your ⊞ and ⊟ counters or your slide rule to help you.

36. $6 + (-8) =$ ________

37. $(-9) + (-6) =$ ________

38. $16 + (-5) =$ ________

39. $(-7) + 13 =$ ________

40. $(-14) - 3 =$ ________

41. $(-8) - (-5) =$ ________

42. $6 -$ ________ $= 17$

43. $17 - 20 =$ ________

44. Kerri is playing a game. She is 8 points "in the hole." (She has −8 points.)

a. She gets 12 points on her next turn. What is her score now? ________

b. If she loses 12 points instead, what will her score be? ________

Name Date Time

Unit 8 Checking Progress

Write each fraction as a decimal and a percent.

1. $\frac{7}{10}$ ____________

2. $\frac{8}{25}$ ____________

3. What is a common denominator for $\frac{1}{4}$ and $\frac{4}{7}$? ________

4. Explain how you found the common denominator in Problem 3.

____

____

5. Is $\frac{13}{25}$ greater than or less than $\frac{1}{2}$? ____________

6. Explain how you decided on your answer for Problem 5.

____

____

7. a. Use your ruler to draw a line segment $2\frac{1}{4}$ inches long.

   b. If you erased $\frac{3}{4}$ inch from this line segment, how long would the new line segment be? ________ in.

8. If you drew a line segment twice as long as the original $2\frac{1}{4}$-inch line segment, how long would the new line segment be? (Circle one.)

$4\frac{6}{16}$ in. $4\frac{2}{4}$ in. $4\frac{3}{8}$ in. $4\frac{3}{16}$ in.

Add or subtract. Write your answer in simplest form.

9. $\frac{5}{8} + \frac{3}{4} =$ ______

10. $1 - \frac{2}{3}$

11. $\frac{5}{8} - \frac{1}{2}$

12. $\frac{3}{4} + 1\frac{1}{2}$

13. $3\frac{3}{7} - 1\frac{6}{7} =$ ______

14. $3\frac{1}{3} + 1\frac{7}{8} =$ ______

15. $2\frac{1}{5} - 1\frac{4}{5} =$ ______

Name Date Time

Unit 8 Checking Progress (cont.)

Solve each problem.

16. Bobbie measured the growth of her corn plant every week. One Friday, it was $3\frac{7}{8}$ inches tall. The following Friday, it was $6\frac{3}{8}$ inches tall. How much had it grown in one week? ________ in.

17. Explain how you found your answer for Problem 16.

____

____

18. How many minutes are there in $\frac{1}{3}$ of an hour? ______ min

19. Mary Lou baked 36 cupcakes for the bake sale. If 75% of them had chocolate frosting, how many cupcakes had chocolate frosting? ______ cupcakes

Fill in the missing number.

20. $3\frac{5}{8} = 2\frac{\square}{8}$ **21.** $5\frac{2}{6} = \square\frac{8}{6}$ **22.** $3\frac{1}{7} = 2\frac{\square}{7}$ **23.** $6\frac{5}{9} = \square\frac{14}{9}$

24. Fill in the oval next to possible common denominators for each fraction pair. (There may be more than one correct answer.)

a. $\frac{1}{3}$ and $\frac{4}{9}$	**b.** $\frac{3}{4}$ and $\frac{5}{6}$	**c.** $\frac{5}{8}$ and $\frac{2}{3}$	**d.** $\frac{3}{12}$ and $\frac{2}{5}$
O 3	O 4	O 3	O 5
O 6	O 6	O 8	O 7
O 9	O 12	O 12	O 30
O 12	O 24	O 24	O 60

25. List the eight fractions from Problem 24 in order from smallest to largest.

____ ____ ____ ____ ____ ____ ____ ____
smallest largest

Multiply. Write your answer in simplest form.

26. $\frac{3}{8} * \frac{4}{5} =$ ______ **27.** $\frac{2}{3} * \frac{3}{4} =$ ______ **28.** $1\frac{1}{2} * 2\frac{3}{5} =$ ______ **29.** $3\frac{1}{5} * 4\frac{5}{8} =$ ______

Name Date Time

Unit 9 Checking Progress

Use the grid at the right for Problems 1–4.

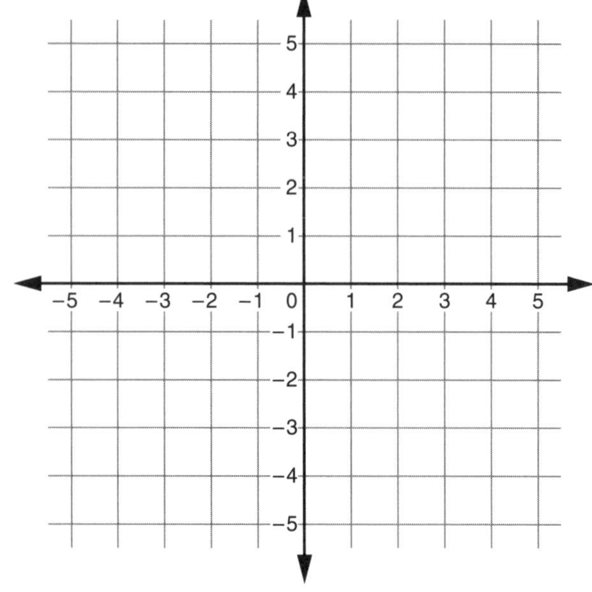

1. a. Plot and label the following points:
A: (1,1) *B:* (2,3) *C:* (5,3) *D:* (4,1)

b. Draw line segments to connect the points as follows:
A to *B*, *B* to *C*, *C* to *D*, and *D* to *A*.

c. Describe the figure you have drawn.

____

____

____

____

2. Plot points on the grid to make a reflection of the figure. Begin with the reflection of point *A* at (1,−1).

3. Record the points you used below.

Point	Original Figure	Reflected Figure
A	(1,1)	(_____ , _____)
B	(2,3)	(_____ , _____)
C	(5,3)	(_____ , _____)
D	(4,1)	(_____ , _____)

4. Describe a rule for changing the points from the original figure to get the reflected figure.

____

____

____

____

Use with Lesson 9.11.

Name Date Time

Unit 9 Checking Progress (cont.)

5. Jim wants to build a fence around his rectangular garden. The garden is 15 feet by 5 feet.

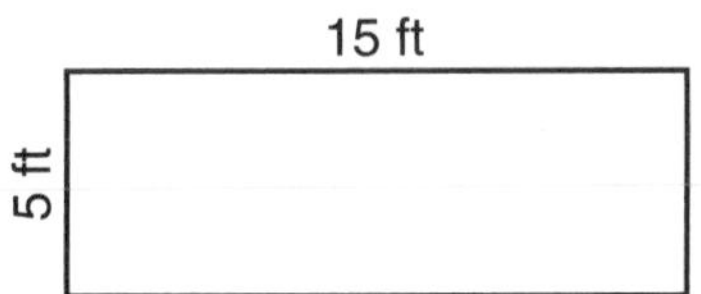

a. In order to build a fence, does Jim need to find the area or the perimeter of the garden? ________________

b. What amount of fence does he need? ________________ (unit)

Find the area of the figures below. Use the formulas to help you.

Area of rectangle = length of base * height: $A = b * h$
Area of parallelogram = length of base * height: $A = b * h$
Area of triangle = $\frac{1}{2}$ * length of base * height: $A = \frac{1}{2} * b * h$

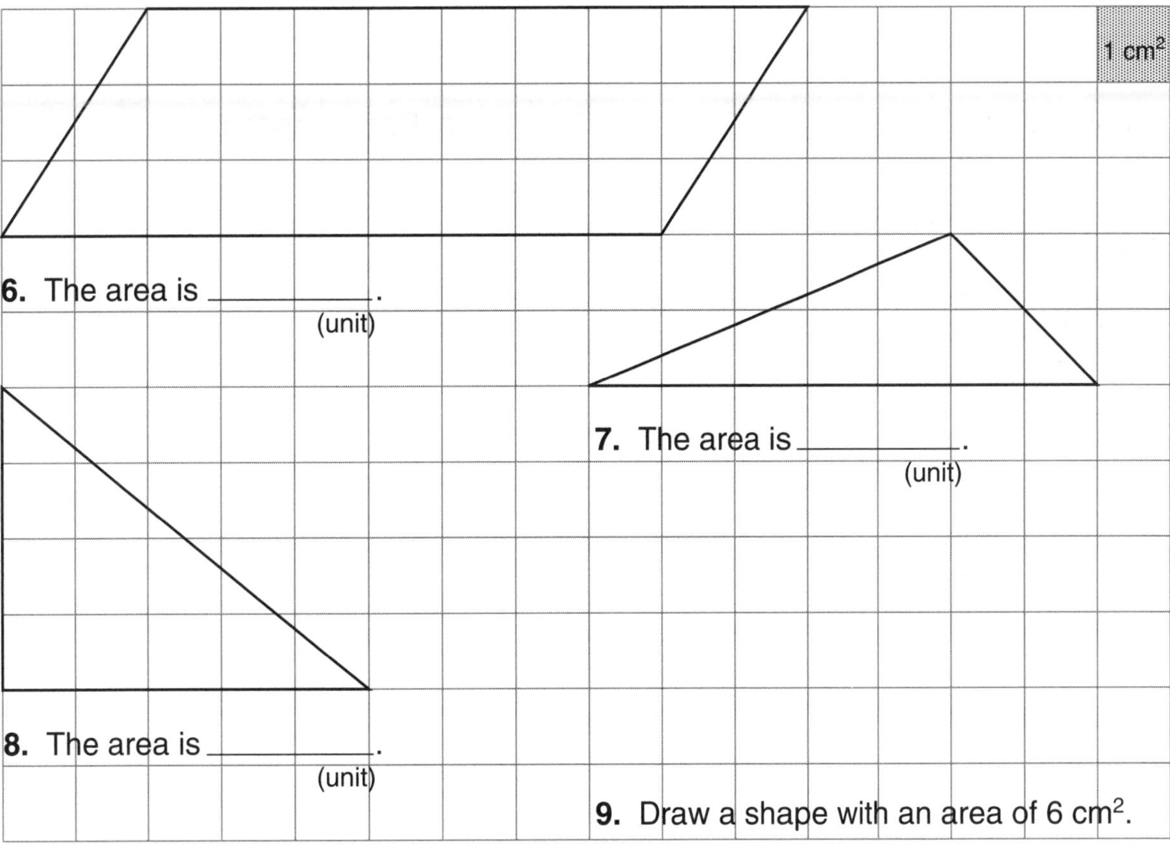

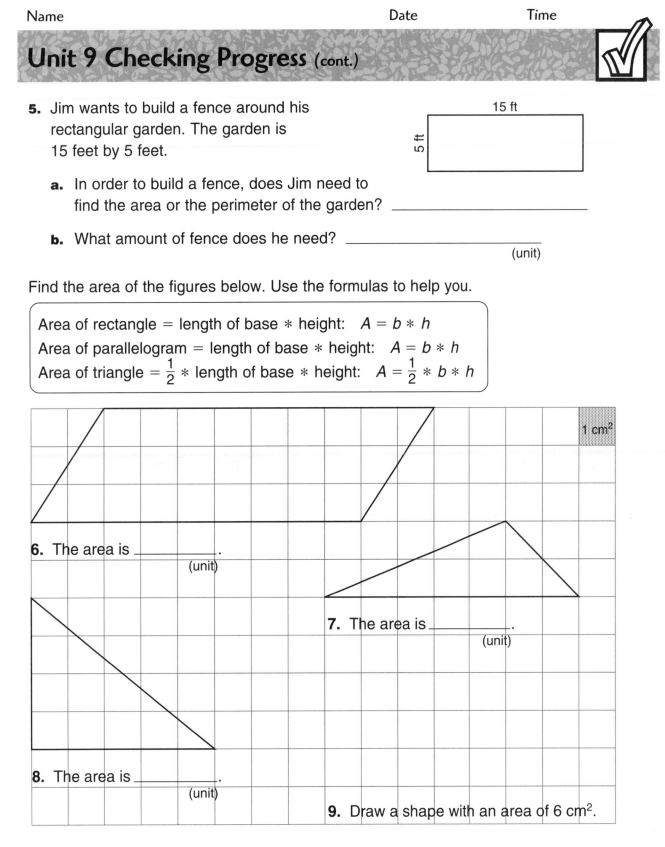

6. The area is ____________. (unit)

7. The area is ____________. (unit)

8. The area is ____________. (unit)

9. Draw a shape with an area of 6 cm^2.

10. Label the base and height on the figures in Problems 6–9.

11. Explain what the area of a figure is. ____

____

____

Name Date Time

Unit 9 Checking Progress (cont.)

12. What ordered number pair names Point *A* in the coordinate grid at the right?

____

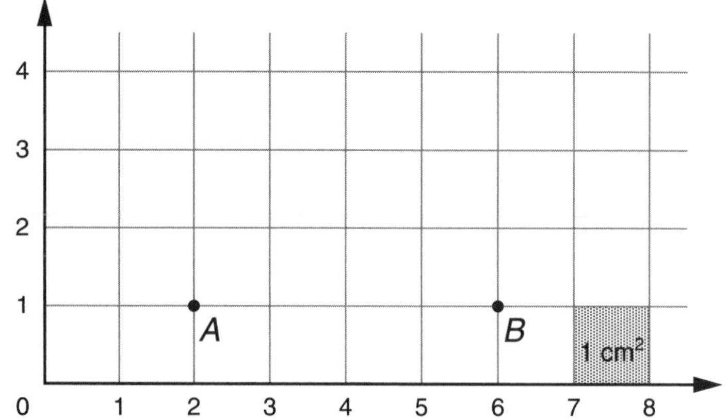

13. Plot and label a Point *C* in the grid so that triangle *ABC* has an area of 4 cm^2. What ordered number pair names Point *C*?

____

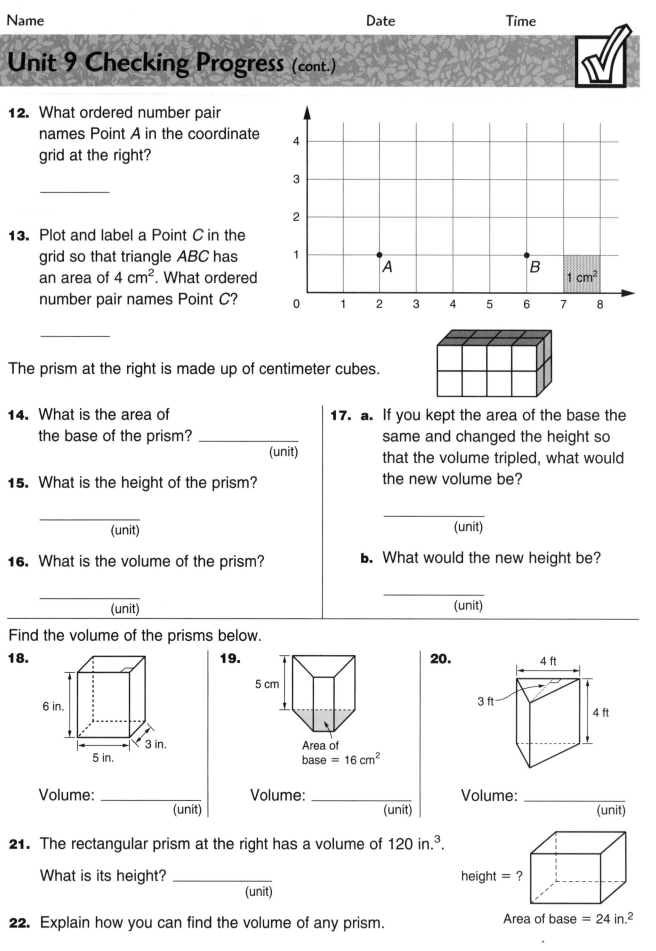

The prism at the right is made up of centimeter cubes.

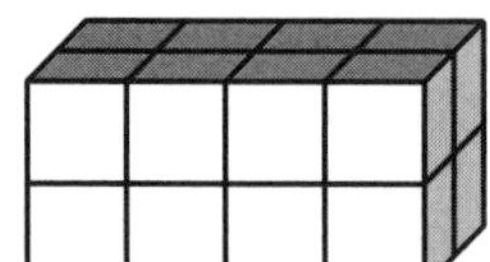

14. What is the area of the base of the prism? _______ (unit)

15. What is the height of the prism?

_______ (unit)

16. What is the volume of the prism?

_______ (unit)

17. a. If you kept the area of the base the same and changed the height so that the volume tripled, what would the new volume be?

_______ (unit)

b. What would the new height be?

_______ (unit)

Find the volume of the prisms below.

18.

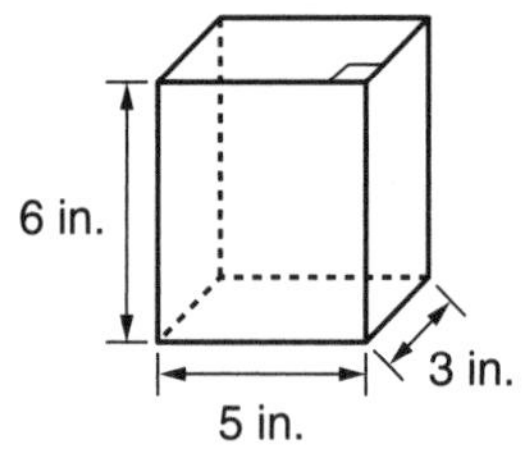

Volume: _______ (unit)

19.

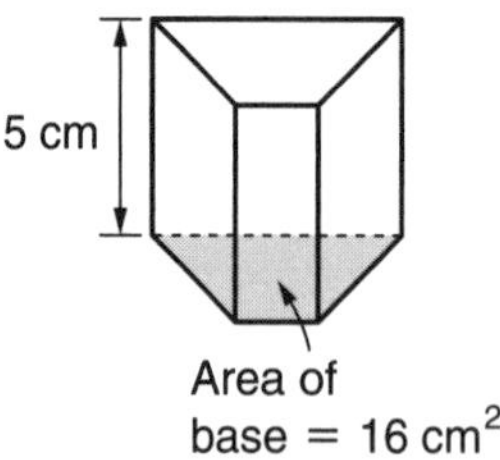

Volume: _______ (unit)

20.

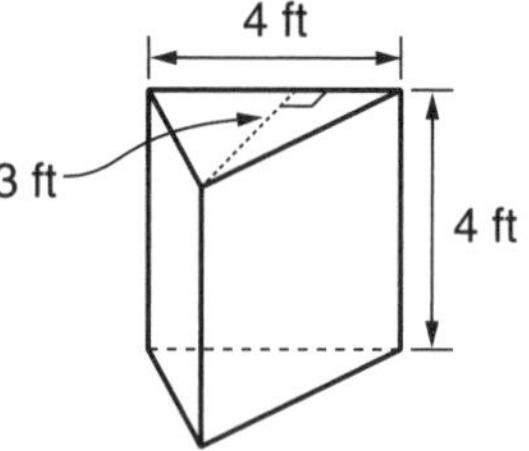

Volume: _______ (unit)

21. The rectangular prism at the right has a volume of 120 $in.^3$.

What is its height? _______ (unit)

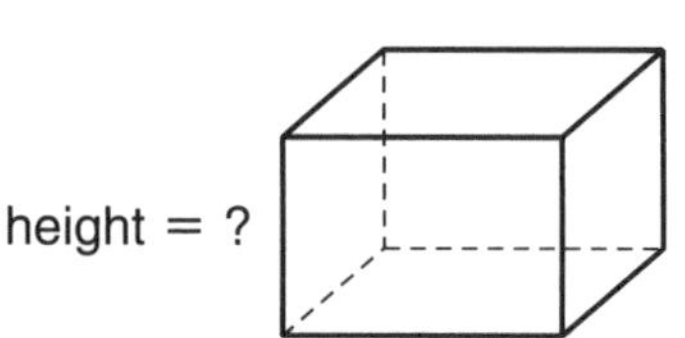

22. Explain how you can find the volume of any prism.

____

Name Date Time

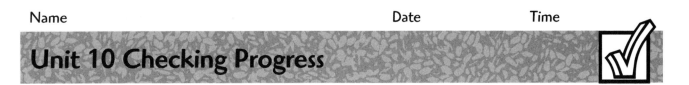

Unit 10 Checking Progress

Marge earns D dollars an hour.

1. Tom earns $5 an hour more than Marge. How much does he earn per hour? (Circle the answer.)

$5 * D$ $D - 5$ $D + 5$ $D + D$

2. Marge's aunt earns twice as much as Marge. How much does she earn per hour? (Circle the answer.)

$2 * D$ $2 + D$ $D - 2$ $\frac{1}{2} * D$

3. Write an expression that shows how much Marge earns in 40 hours.

____

4. The copy machine in the school office can make 40 copies per minute.
This is given below as a rule.
Complete the table. Then graph the data in the table.
Rule: Number of copies = 40 $*$ number of minutes

Time (min)	Number of Copies
1	
	80
3	
	100
$4\frac{1}{2}$	
	220

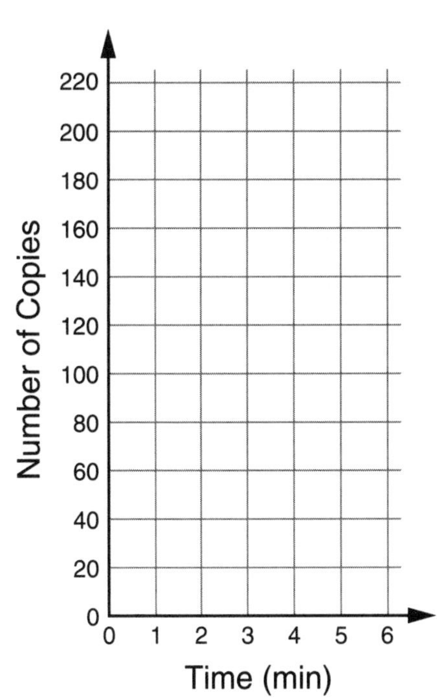

5. Ms. Southern needs to make 150 copies.

About how long will this take? _______________________________

Name Date Time

Unit 10 Checking Progress (cont.)

Solve the pan-balance problems below.

6. One apple weighs

as much as ________ marbles.

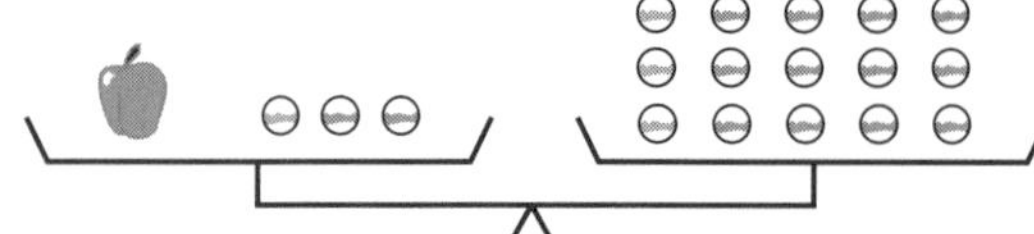

7. One block weighs

as much as ________ marbles.

8. One ball weighs

as much as ________ blocks.

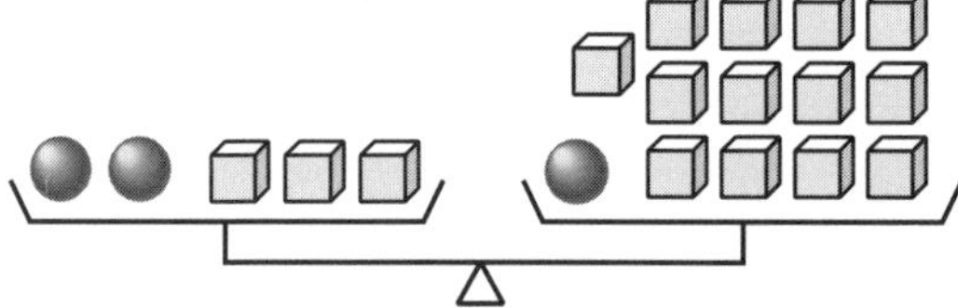

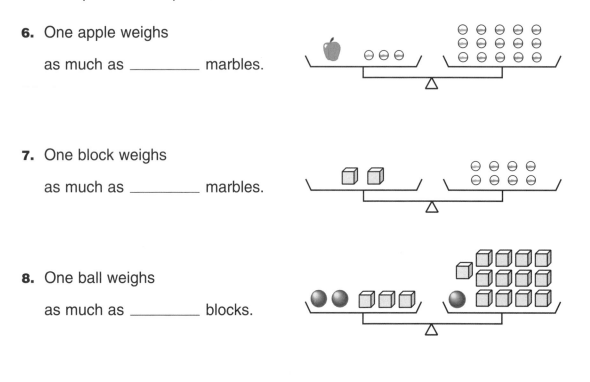

9. Shawna wrote an equation but covered one number.

$15 + 7 = \square + 12$. What is the covered number? ________

10. Pete set up a pan balance. He found that 2 calculators balance 16 marbles. He then used the pan balance and found that 5 marbles balance 3 marbles and 10 paper clips. Fill in the blanks below.

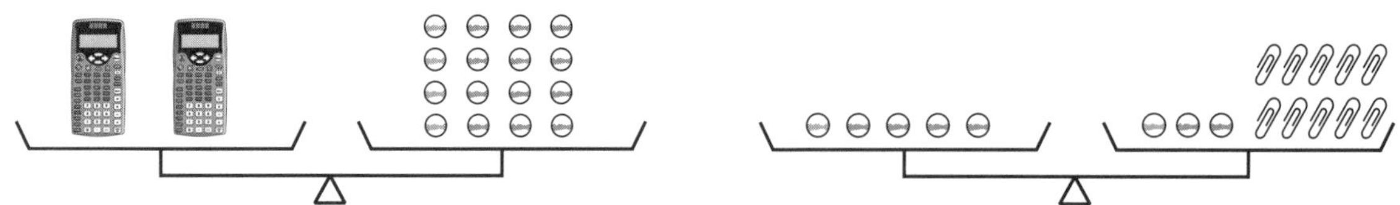

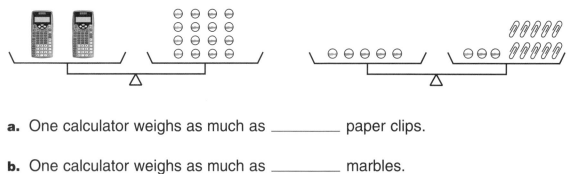

a. One calculator weighs as much as ________ paper clips.

b. One calculator weighs as much as ________ marbles.

Use with Lesson 10.10.

Name Date Time

Unit 10 Checking Progress (cont.)

Circumference of a circle = $\pi * \text{diameter}$

Area of a circle = $\pi * \text{radius}^2$

Complete each of the following sentences, rounding each answer to the nearest centimeter. Use the π key on your calculator or use 3.14 as an approximation for π.

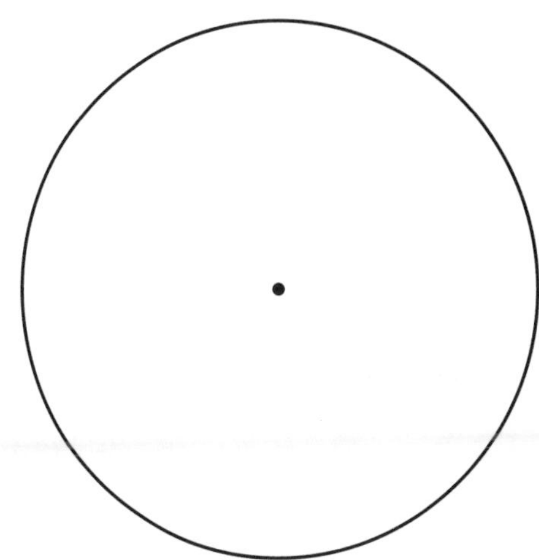

11. The diameter is about ________ cm.

12. The radius is about ________ cm.

13. The circumference is about ________ cm.

14. The area is about ________ cm^2.

To solve each of the following problems, would you need to find the circumference, perimeter, or area? Circle the answer.

15. Mario ran around a circular track 20 times.
How far did he run? circumference area

16. Mr. Li is planting tomatoes in his garden.
He wants one plant for every 2 square feet.
How many plants should he buy? perimeter area

17. Jill is building a fence around her swimming pool.
How many feet of fencing should she buy? perimeter area

Name Date Time

Unit 10 Checking Progress (cont.)

18. Mrs. Griffin surveyed her class. She asked three questions. The class made the line plots below to show the results for each question.

Write the number of the line plot next to the question it represents.

- How many complete months are there until your next birthday? Plot ______
- How many years old is the oldest child living at your house? Plot ______
- How many books did you read last summer? Plot ______

Plot #1

0	1	2	3	4	5	6	7	8	9	10	11
		X	X				X	X	X		
	X	X	X		X		X	X	X	X	X
X	X	X	X		X		X	X	X	X	X

Plot #2

0	1	2	3	4	5	6	7	8	9	10	11	12	13	14	15	16	17	18	19	20
	X		X																	
	X	X	X																	
	X	X	X					X												
	X	X	X		X		X	X												
X	X	X	X		X		X	X				X								X

Plot #3

10	11	12	13	14	15	16	17	18	19	20
	X									
	X									
	X									
	X									
	X	X		X						
	X	X	X	X						
	X	X	X	X	X	X				
	X	X	X	X	X	X		X		

Name Date Time

Unit 11 Checking Progress

Complete each sentence with one of the following names of geometric solids:

pyramid cone rectangular prism cylinder

1. I have exactly two bases and no vertices. I am a ______________________.

2. All of my faces are triangular. I am a ______________________.

3. I have one base and one curved surface. I am a ______________________.

4. I have a pair of bases and exactly eight vertices. I am a ______________________.

The prism at the right is made of centimeter cubes.

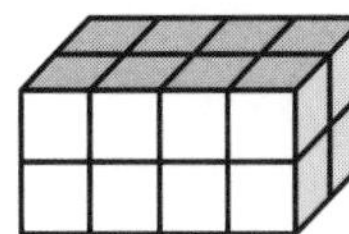

5. What is the area of the base of the prism? _________________

6. What is the height of the prism? _________________

7. What is the volume of the prism? _________________

8. What is the surface area of the prism? _________________

9. Explain how you found your answer for Problem 8.

____

____

____

____

10. If you kept the base the same, but tripled the volume of this prism, what would be the height? _________________

11. Write a number sentence to show how you solved Problem 10. _________________

Name Date Time

Unit 11 Checking Progress (cont.)

Area of rectangle: $A = l * w$	**Circumference of circle:** $C = \pi * d$
Volume of rectangular prism: $V = l * w * h$	**Area of circle:** $A = \pi * r^2$
	Volume of cylinder: $V = \pi * r^2 * h$

12. What is the area of the base of the cylinder at the right?

____

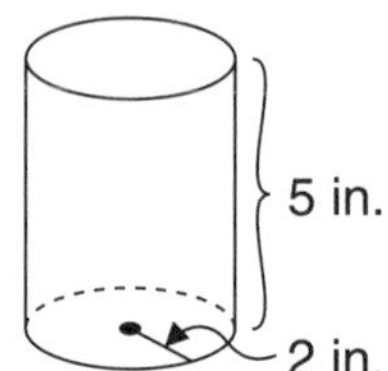

13. What is the volume of the cylinder?

____

14. What information do you need to know to figure out how many square inches of paint you would use if you painted the entire cylinder (top, bottom, and sides)?

____

15. If you place a cone inside of the cylinder in Problem 13 and the cone is an exact "fit" (that is, the apex of the cone touches the bottom of the cylinder, and the base of the cone fits exactly at the top of the cylinder), what would the volume of the cone be? _______________

Write a number sentence to show how you found your answer. _______________

16. Which of the boxes below has the greatest volume? _______________

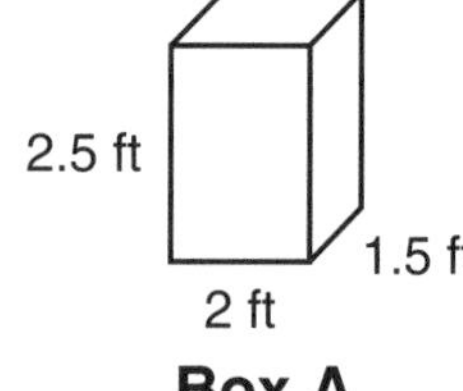

Box A

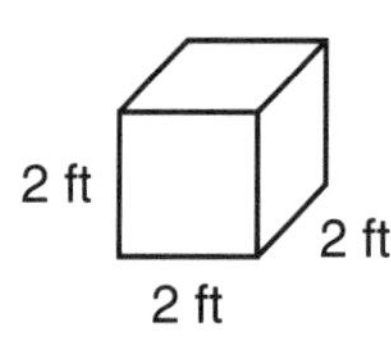

Box B

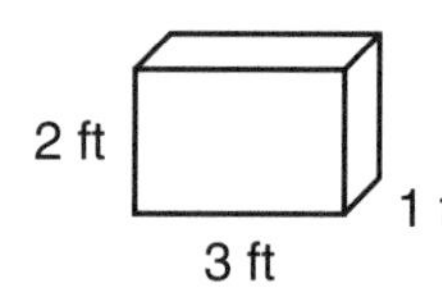

Box C

Explain how you know. _______________

____

____

____

____

____

Name Date Time

Unit 11 Checking Progress (cont.)

17. The rectangular prism at the right has a volume of 120 cubic inches.

What is its height? ________

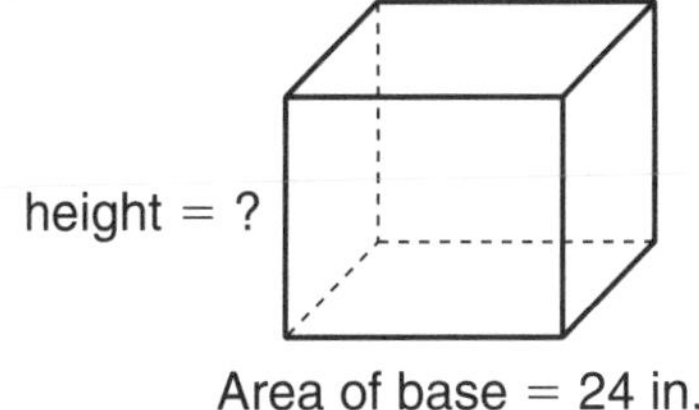

18. The pyramid at the right has the same height as the prism in Problem 17.

What is the volume of the pyramid? ________

Write a number sentence to show how you found your answer. ________________________

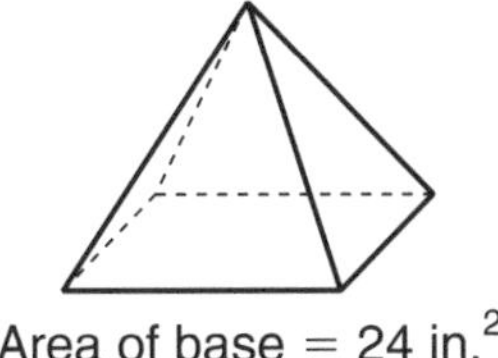

Joan wants to add medicine to her fish tank. The instructions suggest adding one drop of medicine for every 4 liters of water. The base of Joan's fish tank measures 40 cm by 25 cm. The tank is filled with water to a height of about 20 centimeters.

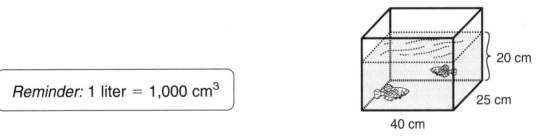

Reminder: 1 liter = 1,000 cm^3

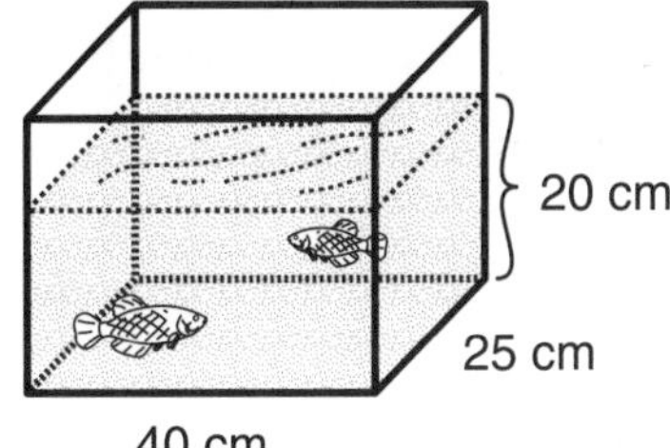

19. How many drops of medicine should Joan add to her tank? ________

20. Explain what you did to find the answer.

____

____

____

____

Name Date Time

Unit 12 Checking Progress

For each number below, draw a factor tree and write the prime factorization.

1. 60 **2.** 84

60 = ____________________ 84 = ____________________

3. What prime factors do 60 and 84 have in common? ____________________

4. What is the greatest common factor of 60 and 84? ____________________

Explain how you found it. ____________________

____

____

5. What is the least common multiple of 60 and 84? ____________________

Explain how you found it. ____________________

____

____

____

____

Rewrite each fraction pair with a common denominator.

6. $\frac{3}{8}$ and $\frac{5}{12}$ ________ and ________ **7.** $\frac{6}{7}$ and $\frac{5}{10}$ ________ and ________

8. Explain how you found the answer to Problem 6.

____

____

____

____

Name Date Time

Unit 12 Checking Progress (cont.)

9. Darin rolls a 6-sided die and then flips a coin.

How many different ways can the die roll and coin toss turn out?

a. Use the Multiplication Counting Principle to answer. ________ different ways

b. Draw a tree diagram to show all the possible ways.
Suggestion: Use the letters H and T to represent HEADS and TAILS.

c. Which method do you think is easier for finding the number of possible results? ________________

d. Explain your answer to Part c. ________________

____

____

10. In Problem 9, what is the probability that Darin

a. rolls a 5 and the coin lands on HEADS? ________

b. rolls an even number and the coin lands on TAILS? ________

c. rolls a prime number? ________

d. tosses the coin so that it lands on HEADS? ________

Name Date Time

Unit 12 Checking Progress (cont.)

11. Sven bought a large pizza. He wants to cut the pizza so that it can be shared equally by 2 people, 3 people, 4 people, 6 people, or 8 people. Into how many slices should Sven cut the pizza? ____________ (unit)

12. There are 30 students in Linda's class. Two-thirds of her class rides to school on the school bus. The other students walk to school. How many students walk to school? ____________ (unit)

13. Matt was playing *Name That Number*. Of the 5 cards he turned over, 60% were black. How many black cards were there? ____________ (unit)

14. Three out of 7 cars parked on one street were red. If there were 28 cars, how many cars were red? ____________ (unit)

15. What is the ratio of cars that were not red to total cars in Problem 14? ____________

Explain how you found your answer. ____________________________

____

____

Name Date Time

Unit 12 Checking Progress (cont.)

Write a number model for each problem. Then solve the problem.

16. Rosalyn's family was driving from home to their aunt's house. After going 48 miles, they were $\frac{3}{4}$ of the way there. How far from home was their aunt's house?

Number model: ________________ Answer: ________ miles

17. In Doreen's first basketball game, she made a basket 9 times out of 15 attempts. She made the same ratio of baskets out of 25 attempts in the second game. How many baskets did she make in her 25 attempts?

Number model: ________________ Answer: ________ baskets

18. Explain how you found your answer to Problem 17.

____

____

____

____

____

19. Marcus's heart beats 11 times in 10 seconds. At this rate, about how many times would it beat in 1 minute? ________ times

20. Carlo exchanged U.S. dollars for French francs. He got 7 francs for each dollar. He received a total of 224 francs. How many U.S. dollars did he exchange? ________ dollars

Name Date Time

Mid-Year Assessment

Solve the problems below.

1. 28 * 9 = ____________ 2. 47 * 68 = ____________ 3. 235 * 56 = ____________

4. 715 + 308 = __________ 5. 9.43 + 7.6 = __________ 6. 51.2 + 17.6 = __________

7. 247 − 196 = __________ 8. 50.3 − 27.6 = __________ 9. 80.3 − 5.17 = __________

Solve for *y*.

10. $15 - y = 9$ __________ 11. $8 * y = 72$ __________ 12. $150 / y = 30$ __________

13. Circle all the numbers below that are factors of 48.

    2 4 5 6 12 14 20 24

Evelyn timed how long it took her to travel to work on nine different days. Following are the times in minutes:

45 42 45 55 48 50 35 58 44

14. What was the median time? ________ minutes

15. What was the maximum time? ________ minutes

16. What was the minimum time? ________ minutes

17. What was the range of times? ________ minutes

18. If you were Evelyn, how much time would you allow to travel to work based on these data? ____________________

19. Explain your answer to Problem 18.

____

____

____

Name Date Time

Mid-Year Assessment (cont.)

20. Circle all of the numbers below that are greater than $\frac{1}{2}$.

$\frac{1}{4}$ $\frac{9}{10}$ 0.66 $\frac{5}{20}$ $\frac{4}{8}$ 0.09

21. On the back of this page, draw a rectangle that has a base 4 cm long and a height of 6.5 cm. Use your ruler or any other tool that you wish.

22. Find the perimeter of the rectangle you drew on the back of this page.

Perimeter: ________________
(unit)

23. Circle all of the expressions below that are equivalent to $\frac{3}{4}$.

0.75 $\frac{8}{6}$ $\frac{6}{12}$ $\frac{9}{16}$ $\frac{15}{20}$ 34%

24. Measure each angle below. Record your answer to the nearest degree.

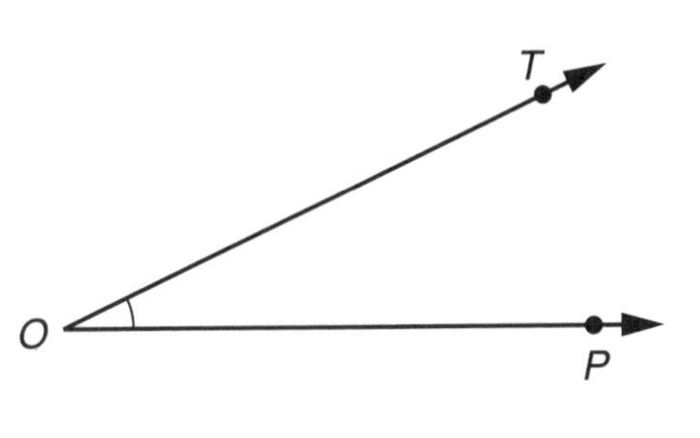

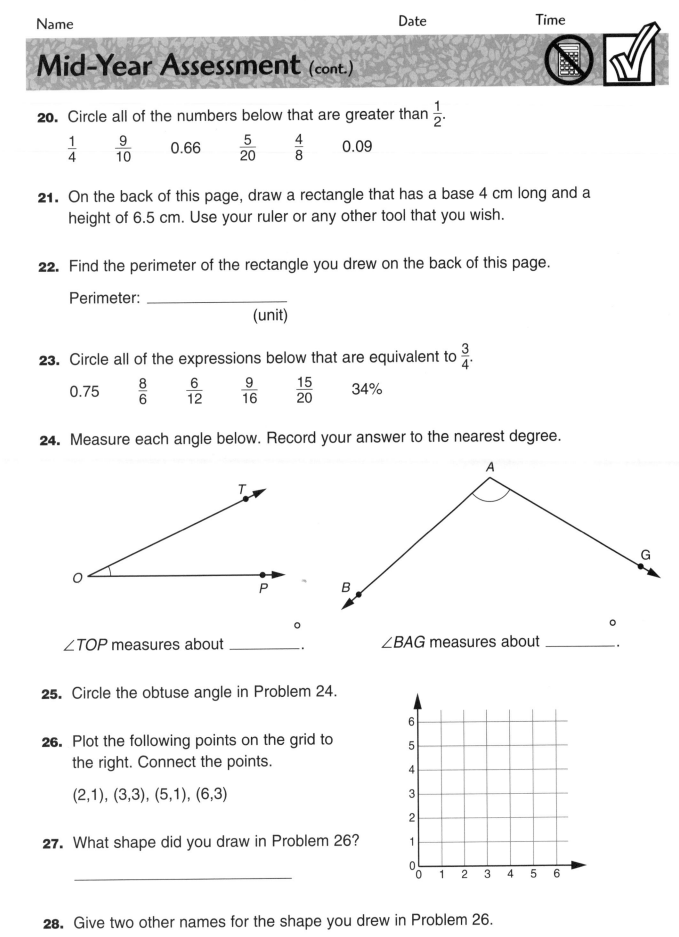

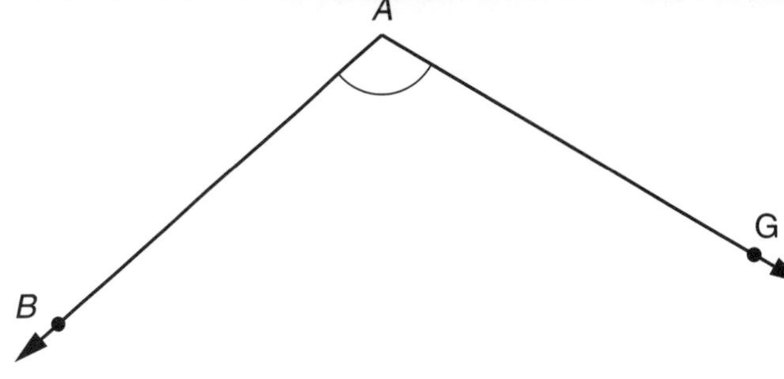

$\angle TOP$ measures about ________°.

$\angle BAG$ measures about ________°.

25. Circle the obtuse angle in Problem 24.

26. Plot the following points on the grid to the right. Connect the points.

(2,1), (3,3), (5,1), (6,3)

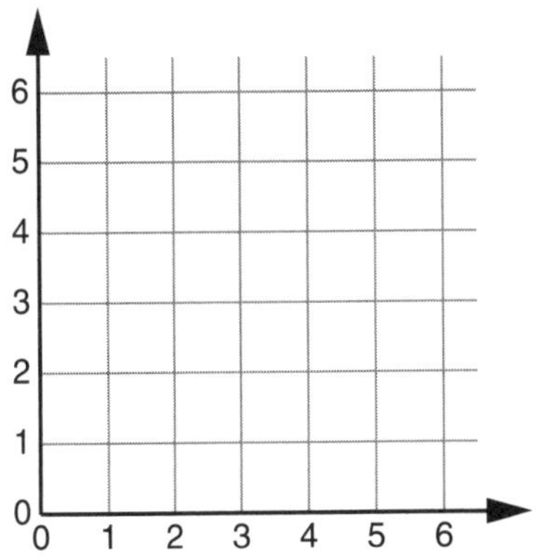

27. What shape did you draw in Problem 26?

____

28. Give two other names for the shape you drew in Problem 26.

________________________________ ________________________________

Name Date Time

Mid-Year Assessment (cont.)

29. Jianhua buys a carton of milk for 59 cents, a hamburger for $1.25, and a salad for $1.50. He pays with a five-dollar bill.

How much did he spend? ____________

How much change should he get? ____________

30. Name a number between 400 and 500 that is divisible by 3 but not by 2. ____________

Explain how you found your number.

____

____

____

____

31. Is 71 prime or composite? ____________

Explain how you know.

____

____

____

____

Round to the nearest...

32. thousand.

65,389 ____________

104,032 ____________

1,029,754 ____________

33. tenth.

0.784 ____________

17.493 ____________

25.815 ____________

Name Date Time

Mid-Year Assessment (cont.)

34. Explain the errors in the following problem.

```
  24
* 96
----
  18
 360
  12
 240
----
 630
```

____

____

____

____

____

35. Make a magnitude estimate for the product in Problem 34. Circle the appropriate box.

10s 100s 1000s 10,000s

36. Write the 8-digit number that has a 4 in the hundreds place, a 5 in the thousandths place, a 9 in the ten-thousands place and 1s in all other places.

___ ___, ___ ___ ___. ___ ___ ___

Write this number in words:

____

____

Add. Use the fraction sticks to help.

37. $\frac{1}{2} + \frac{1}{4} =$ ______

38. $\frac{3}{8} + \frac{1}{4} =$ ______

39. $\frac{3}{4} + \frac{3}{4} =$ ______

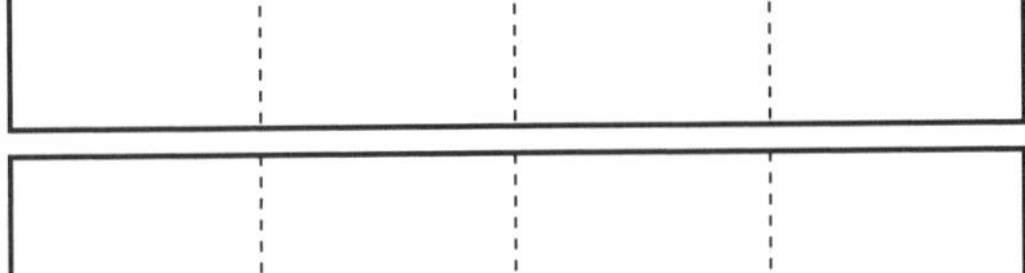

40. $\frac{1}{8} + \frac{1}{2} =$ ______

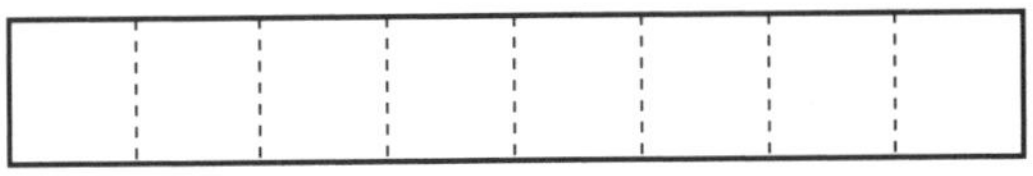

Name Date Time

Mid-Year Assessment (cont.)

Simeon was writing a report on trees in his town. He counted the different types of trees in his neighborhood and made a circle graph. Use his circle graph to answer these questions:

41. What was the most common type of tree? ____________

42. Which types of trees made up one-fourth or more of the sample?

____

43. If there were a total of 200 trees in his sample, how many would be oaks? ____________

Explain how you got your answer.

____

____

____

____

____

____

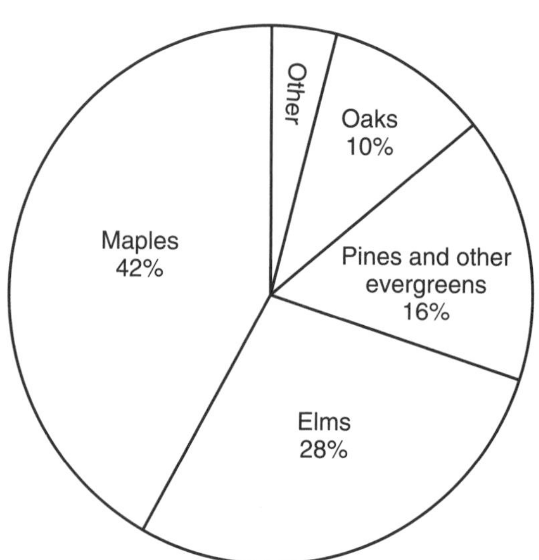

44. Simeon concluded that maples are the most common type of tree in the U.S. Do you agree? ________

Explain. ____________

____

Use with Lesson 6.11.

Name Date Time

End-of-Year Assessment

1. A figure is partly hidden. Which of the following might it be? (Circle all possible answers.)

rectangle triangle trapezoid square

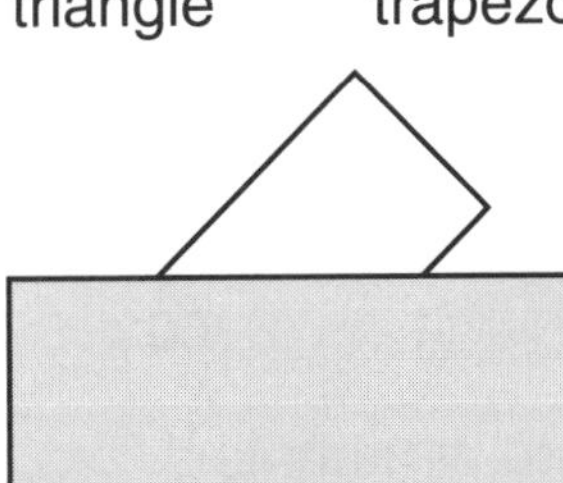

2. A package of hot-dog buns contains 12 buns. Mrs. Hudson is expecting 35 people at her picnic. She wants to have enough hot dog buns for each person to have 2. How many packages of buns should she buy? ____________________

3. Below is a data set. Put two more numbers in it so that

- the median of the new data set is 5,
- the maximum is 15, and
- the range is 13.

4 5 4 11 8 ______ ______

4. A board is $6\frac{1}{8}$ inches long. If you cut off $\frac{3}{4}$ of an inch, how much is left? ____________________ inches

5. Jean combined $\frac{1}{3}$ cup of corn flour with $\frac{3}{4}$ cup of white flour. Is the total flour more or less than 1 cup? ____________________

Explain. ____

____

____

Name Date Time

End-of-Year Assessment (cont.)

For each fraction below, circle all the numbers to the right of the fraction that are equivalent to it.

6.	$\frac{3}{8}$	$\frac{6}{16}$	1.25	38%	$\frac{24}{64}$	0.375
7.	$\frac{6}{10}$	0.600	$\frac{3}{5}$	$\frac{2}{3}$	60%	0.6
8.	$\frac{19}{20}$	0.95	19%	$\frac{38}{40}$	$\frac{48}{50}$	95%

Each square in the grid below has an area of 1 square centimeter.

9. What is the area of triangle *END?* ________ cm^2

10. Draw a rectangle that has an area of 12 cm^2.

11. What is the perimeter of this rectangle? ________ cm

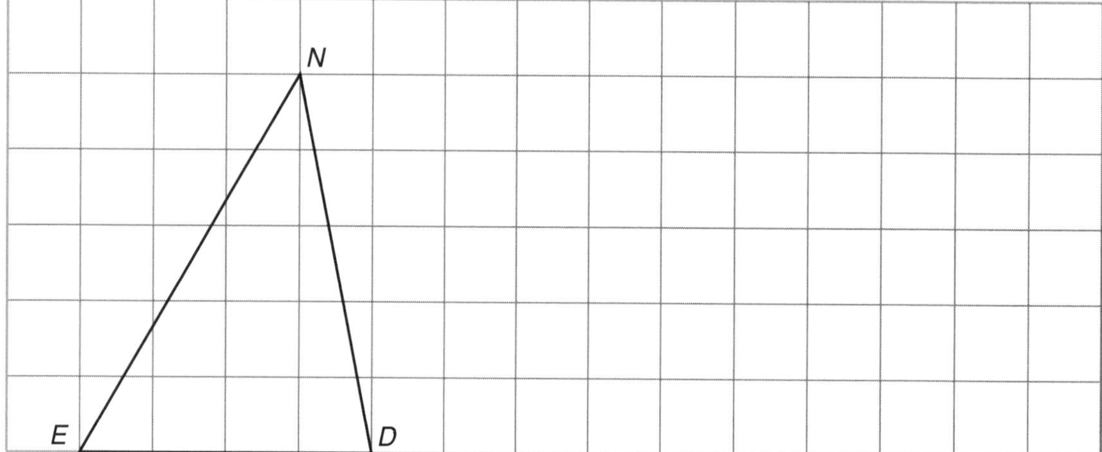

12. What is the volume of the prism to the right?

____
(unit)

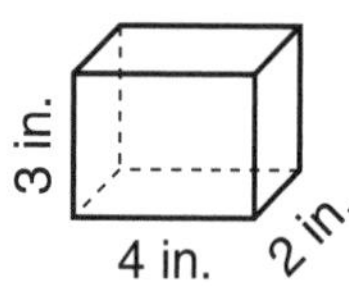

Volume of a prism: $V = B * h$

13. A cylindrical can has a base with an area of 21.5 square centimeters. It has a height of 10 centimeters.

What is its volume? ____________
(unit)

Volume of a cylinder: $V = B * h$

14. Write the 8-digit number that has a 5 in the tens place, a 3 in the hundredths place, a 4 in the hundred-thousands place, and 8 in all the other places. ___ ___ ___, ___ ___ ___. ___ ___

15. Write the number that is 4,000 less than the number you wrote in Problem 14. ________________

Name Date Time

End-of-Year Assessment (cont.)

16. Round the number your wrote in Problem 15 to the nearest

tenth. ________________ thousand. ________________

17. Mark the following points on the ruler.

A: $\frac{7}{8}$ B: $\frac{3}{4}$ C: $1\frac{5}{16}$ D: $2\frac{11}{16}$ E: $\frac{5}{10}$

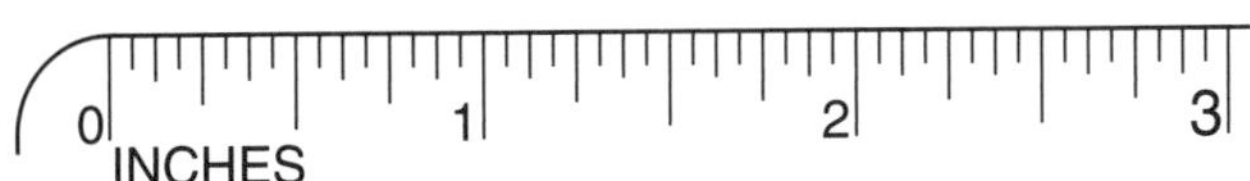

Use >, <, or =.

18. $\frac{3}{8}$ ______ $\frac{3}{7}$

19. 0.38 ______ $\frac{3}{10}$

20. $3\frac{2}{3}$ ______ $\frac{24}{10}$

21. 0.05 ______ $\frac{5}{10}$

22. $\frac{18}{25}$ ______ 72%

23. $\frac{5}{15}$ ______ 0.66

24. What is the probability of drawing a king of hearts from a regular deck of 52 cards? ________________

25. What is the probability of drawing a 5 from a regular deck of 52 cards? ________________

26. Measure the angles below.

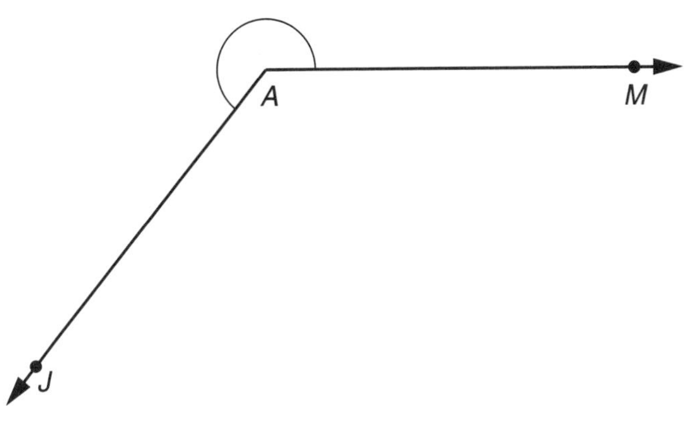

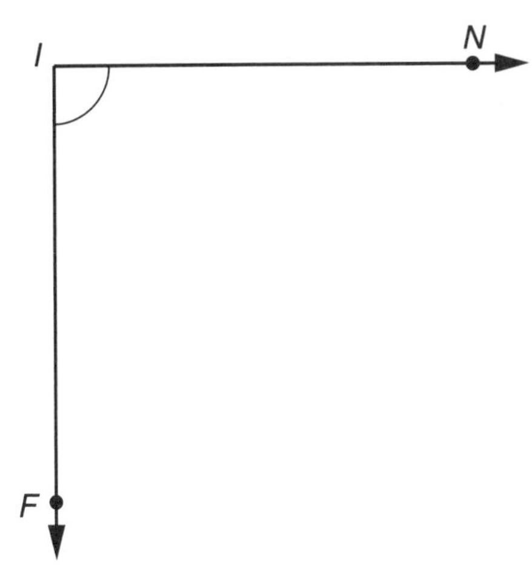

$\angle JAM$ measures about ________.

$\angle FIN$ measures about ________.

27. Circle the reflex angle in Problem 26.

What is the name of the other angle? ________________

End-of-Year Assessment (cont.)

28. In the space below, draw a circle that has a radius of 3 cm.

29. Calculate the circumference and area of the circle you drew in Problem 28.

Circumference of a circle: $C = \pi * d$
Area of a circle: $A = \pi * r^2$

Circumference = ______________ (unit)   Area = ______________ (unit)

30. Describe a situation for which you would calculate circumference.

____

____

____

____

Solve. Do not use a calculator.

31. $756 \div 9 =$ __________   **32.** $308 * 42 =$ __________   **33.** $312 \div 12 =$ __________

34. $5.63 * 28 =$ __________   **35.** $92.4 / 6 =$ __________   **36.** $4.6 * 24.8 =$ __________

37. $3\frac{1}{2} + 2\frac{1}{8} =$ __________   **38.** $2\frac{1}{8} - \frac{5}{3} =$ __________   **39.** $3\frac{5}{10} + \frac{3}{4} =$ __________

Name Date Time

End-of-Year Assessment (cont.)

40. Write the prime factorization for 186. ____________________

41. Mr. Taylor's science class asked 50 students each to name their favorite pet. The results are shown in the table. Complete the percent column of the table.

Animal	Number	Percent
Cat	21	
Dog	13	
Hamster or Gerbil	4	
Bird	8	
Other	4	
Total	50	

42. Did more than $\frac{1}{2}$ or less than $\frac{1}{2}$ of the students name cat or dog as their favorite? ____________________

43. What pet was named by about $\frac{1}{4}$ of the students? ____________________

44. What percent do you think named snake as their favorite pet? (Circle the best answer.)

4% not more than 8% at least 4 of the students

Explain. ____

____

____

____

Name Date Time

End-of-Year Assessment (cont.)

45. Draw a circle graph for the information in Problem 41. Label each section. Use your percent circle on your Geometry Template.

Favorite Pets

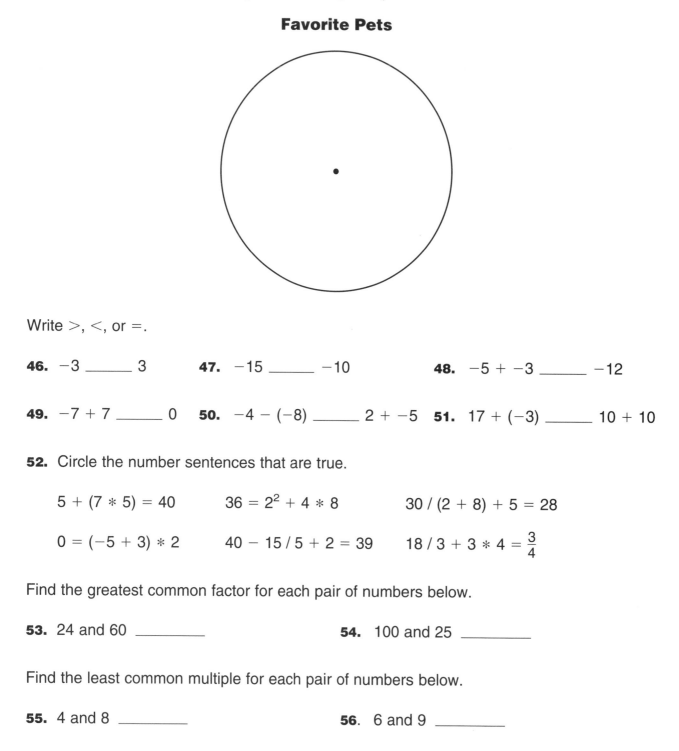

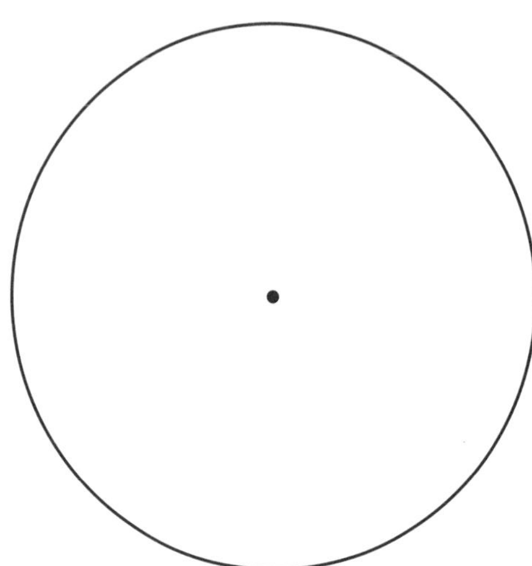

Write $>$, $<$, or $=$.

46. -3 ______ 3 **47.** -15 ______ -10 **48.** $-5 + -3$ ______ -12

49. $-7 + 7$ ______ 0 **50.** $-4 - (-8)$ ______ $2 + -5$ **51.** $17 + (-3)$ ______ $10 + 10$

52. Circle the number sentences that are true.

$5 + (7 * 5) = 40$ $36 = 2^2 + 4 * 8$ $30 / (2 + 8) + 5 = 28$

$0 = (-5 + 3) * 2$ $40 - 15 / 5 + 2 = 39$ $18 / 3 + 3 * 4 = \frac{3}{4}$

Find the greatest common factor for each pair of numbers below.

53. 24 and 60 ________ **54.** 100 and 25 ________

Find the least common multiple for each pair of numbers below.

55. 4 and 8 ________ **56.** 6 and 9 ________

Name Date Time

End-of-Year Assessment (cont.)

57. Complete the table. Then graph the data in the table.

Rule: Number of words = minutes * 46 words

Time (min)	Number of words
1	
4	184
3	
	92
	115

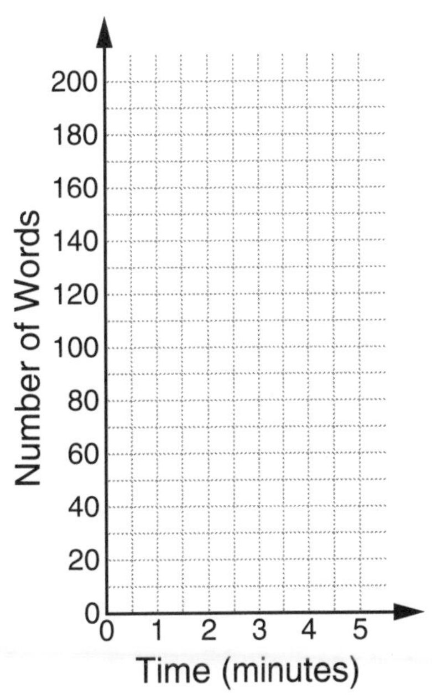

Write a number model for the problem. Then solve the problem.

58. Maureen was cleaning her collection of elephant toys. She had already cleaned 24 of them. If she had cleaned $\frac{6}{7}$ of them, how many did she have left to clean?

Number model: ____________________

Answer: ____________________ (unit)

Explain. ____________________

____

____

____

59. Name at least two characteristics that a cone and a cylinder share.

Explain. ____________________

____

____

Name Date Time

End-of-Year Assessment (cont.)

60. Circle the figure below that has the greatest volume.

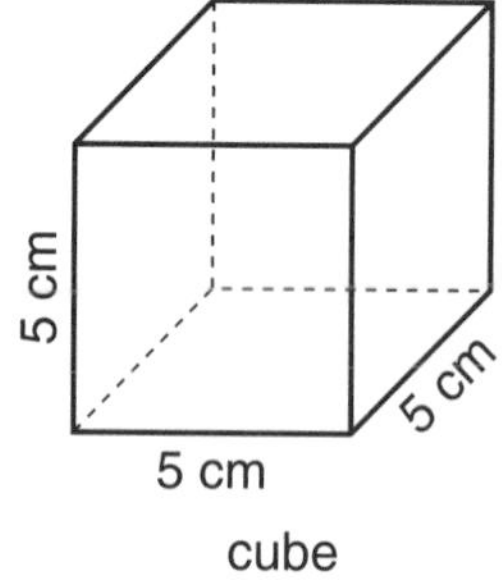

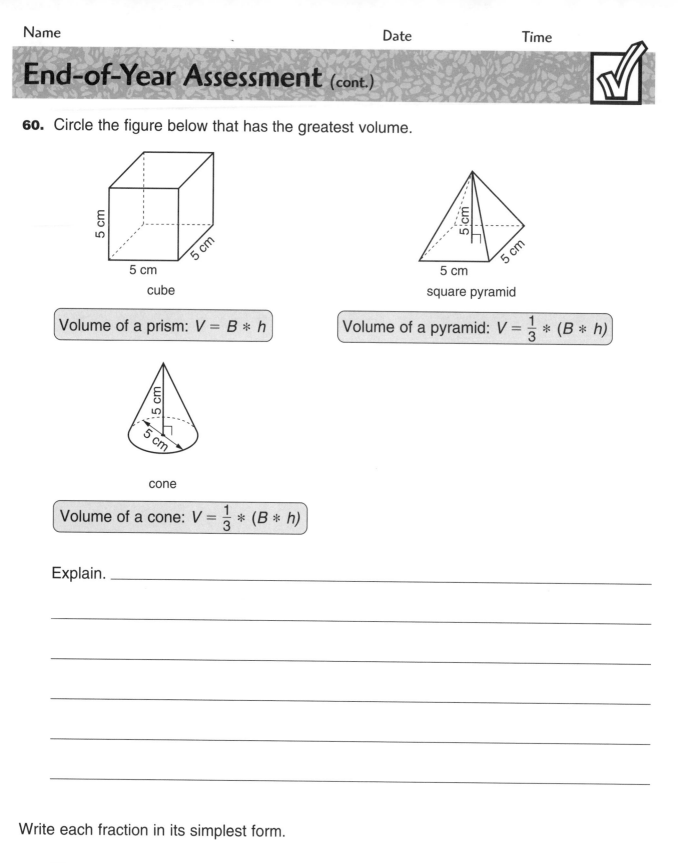

cube

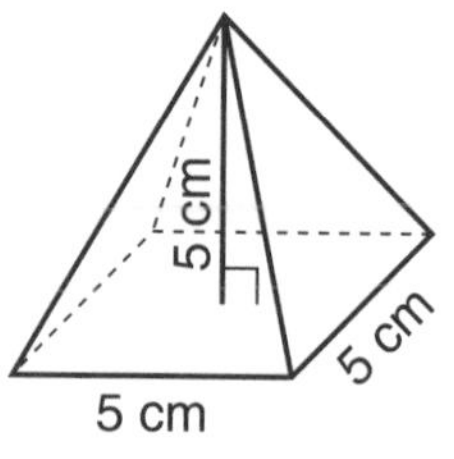

square pyramid

Volume of a prism: $V = B * h$

Volume of a pyramid: $V = \frac{1}{3} * (B * h)$

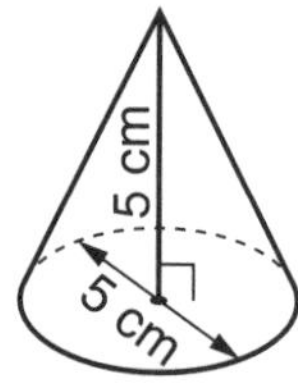

cone

Volume of a cone: $V = \frac{1}{3} * (B * h)$

Explain. ______________________________

____

____

____

____

____

Write each fraction in its simplest form.

61. $\frac{28}{3} =$ ________

62. $4\frac{18}{24} =$ ________

63. $\frac{43}{6} =$ ________

64. $\frac{70}{5} =$ ________

65. $9\frac{36}{60} =$ ________

66. $11\frac{54}{72} =$ ________

Class Checklist: Unit 1

Class ______________________

Dates ______________________

Students' Names	Learning Goals	1a Find the prime factorization of numbers.	1b Rename numbers written in exponential notation.	1c Use a divisibility test to determine if a number is divisible by another number.	1d Identify prime and composite numbers.	1e Understand how square numbers and their square roots are related.	1f Draw arrays to model multiplication.	1g Know basic multiplication facts.	1h Identify even and odd numbers.	1i List the factors of a number.				
1.														
2.														
3.														
4.														
5.														
6.														
7.														
8.														
9.														
10.														
11.														
12.														
13.														
14.														
15.														
16.														
17.														
18.														
19.														
20.														
21.														
22.														
23.														
24.														
25.														
26.														
27.														
28.														
29.														
30.														

Student's Name Date

Individual Profile of Progress: Unit 1

Check ✓				
B	**D**	**S**	**Learning Goals**	**Comments**
			1a Find the prime factorization of numbers.	
			1b Rename numbers written in exponential notation.	
			1c Use a divisibility test to determine if a number is divisible by another number.	
			1d Identify prime and composite numbers.	
			1e Understand how square numbers and their square roots are related.	
			1f Draw arrays to model multiplication.	
			1g Know basic multiplication facts.	
			1h Identify even and odd numbers.	
			1i List the factors of a number.	

Notes to Parents

B = **B**eginning; **D** = **D**eveloping; **S** = **S**ecure

Class Checklist: Unit 2

Class ______________

Dates ______________

Students' Names	Learning Goals	2a Write and solve open sentences for number stories.	2b Round numbers to designated places.	2c Make magnitude estimates.	2d Find the product of multidigit whole numbers and decimals.	2e Know place value to billions.	2f Find the sum and difference of multidigit whole numbers and decimals.	2g Identify the maximum, minimum, median, mode, and mean for a data set.					
1.													
2.													
3.													
4.													
5.													
6.													
7.													
8.													
9.													
10.													
11.													
12.													
13.													
14.													
15.													
16.													
17.													
18.													
19.													
20.													
21.													
22.													
23.													
24.													
25.													
26.													
27.													
28.													
29.													
30.													

Student's Name Date

Individual Profile of Progress: Unit 2

Check ✓				
B	**D**	**S**	**Learning Goals**	**Comments**
			2a Write and solve open sentences for number stories.	
			2b Round numbers to designated places.	
			2c Make magnitude estimates.	
			2d Find the product of multidigit whole numbers and decimals.	
			2e Know place value to billions.	
			2f Find the sum and difference of multidigit whole numbers and decimals.	
			2g Identify the maximum, minimum, median, mode, and mean for a data set.	

Notes to Parents

___

___

___

___

B = **B**eginning; **D** = **D**eveloping; **S** = **S**ecure

Class Checklist: Unit 3

Class ____________________

Dates ____________________

Students' Names	Learning Goals	3a Determine angle measures based on relationships between angles.	3b Estimate the measure of an angle.	3c Measure an angle to within 2°.	3d Identify types of angles.	3e Identify types of triangles.	3f Identify place value in numbers to billions.	3g Know properties of polygons.	3h Define and create tessellations.					
1.														
2.														
3.														
4.														
5.														
6.														
7.														
8.														
9.														
10.														
11.														
12.														
13.														
14.														
15.														
16.														
17.														
18.														
19.														
20.														
21.														
22.														
23.														
24.														
25.														
26.														
27.														
28.														
29.														
30.														

Use with Lesson 3.11.

Student's Name Date

Individual Profile of Progress: Unit 3

Check ✓				
B	**D**	**S**	**Learning Goals**	**Comments**
			3a Determine angle measures based on relationships between angles.	
			3b Estimate the measure of an angle.	
			3c Measure an angle to within 2°.	
			3d Identify types of angles.	
			3e Identify types of triangles.	
			3f Identify place value in numbers to billions.	
			3g Know properties of polygons.	
			3h Define and create tessellations.	

Notes to Parents

B = **B**eginning; **D** = **D**eveloping; **S** = **S**ecure

Class Checklist: Unit 4

Class ______________________

Dates ______________________

Students' Names	Learning Goals	4a Divide decimal numbers by whole numbers with no remainders.	4b Write and solve number sentences with variables for division number stories.	4c Find the quotient and remainder of a whole number divided by a 1-digit whole number.	4d Find the quotient and remainder of a whole number divided by a 2-digit whole number.	4e Make magnitude estimates for quotients of whole and decimal numbers divided by whole numbers.	4f Interpret the remainder in division number stories.	4g Determine the value of a variable; use this value to complete a number sentence.	4h Know place value to hundredths.					
1.														
2.														
3.														
4.														
5.														
6.														
7.														
8.														
9.														
10.														
11.														
12.														
13.														
14.														
15.														
16.														
17.														
18.														
19.														
20.														
21.														
22.														
23.														
24.														
25.														
26.														
27.														
28.														
29.														
30.														

Student's Name Date

Individual Profile of Progress: Unit 4

Check ✓ B	D	S	Learning Goals		Comments
			4a	Divide decimal numbers by whole numbers with no remainders.	
			4b	Write and solve number sentences with variables for division number stories.	
			4c	Find the quotient and remainder of a whole number divided by a 1-digit whole number.	
			4d	Find the quotient and remainder of a whole number divided by a 2-digit whole number.	
			4e	Make magnitude estimates for quotients of whole and decimal numbers divided by whole numbers.	
			4f	Interpret the remainder in division number stories.	
			4g	Determine the value of a variable; use this value to complete a number sentence.	
			4h	Know place value to hundredths.	

Notes to Parents

B = **B**eginning; **D** = **D**eveloping; **S** = **S**ecure

Class Checklist: Unit 5

Class ______________________

Dates ______________________

Students' Names	Learning Goals	5a Add fractions with like denominators.	5b Order and compare fractions.	5c Convert between fractions and percents.	5d Draw a circle graph for a set of data.	5e Measure pieces of a circle graph; interpret a circle graph.	5f Convert between fractions and mixed numbers.	5g Find equivalent fractions.						
1.														
2.														
3.														
4.														
5.														
6.														
7.														
8.														
9.														
10.														
11.														
12.														
13.														
14.														
15.														
16.														
17.														
18.														
19.														
20.														
21.														
22.														
23.														
24.														
25.														
26.														
27.														
28.														
29.														
30.														

Use with Lesson 5.13.

Student's Name Date

Individual Profile of Progress: Unit 5

Check ✓				
B	**D**	**S**	**Learning Goals**	**Comments**
			5a Add fractions with like denominators.	
			5b Order and compare fractions.	
			5c Convert between fractions and percents.	
			5d Draw a circle graph for a set of data.	
			5e Measure pieces of a circle graph; interpret a circle graph.	
			5f Convert between fractions and mixed numbers.	
			5g Find equivalent fractions.	

Notes to Parents

____

____

____

____

B = **B**eginning; **D** = **D**eveloping; **S** = **S**ecure

Class Checklist: Unit 6

Class ______________________

Dates ______________________

Students' Names	Learning Goals	6a Construct stem-and-leaf plots.	6b Read and interpret stem-and-leaf plots.	6c Add and subtract fractions with common denominators.	6d Add and subtract fractions with unlike denominators.	6e Understand how sample size affects results.	6f Find a common denominator.	6g Convert among fractions, decimals, and percents.	6h Find and use data landmarks.					
1.														
2.														
3.														
4.														
5.														
6.														
7.														
8.														
9.														
10.														
11.														
12.														
13.														
14.														
15.														
16.														
17.														
18.														
19.														
20.														
21.														
22.														
23.														
24.														
25.														
26.														
27.														
28.														
29.														
30.														

Use with Lesson 6.11.

Student's Name Date

Individual Profile of Progress: Unit 6

Check ✔ B	D	S	Learning Goals	Comments
			6a Construct stem-and-leaf plots.	
			6b Read and interpret stem-and-leaf plots.	
			6c Add and subtract fractions with common denominators.	
			6d Add and subtract fractions with unlike denominators.	
			6e Understand how sample size affects results.	
			6f Find a common denominator.	
			6g Convert among fractions, decimals, and percents.	
			6h Find and use data landmarks.	

Notes to Parents

B = **B**eginning; **D** = **D**eveloping; **S** = **S**ecure

Class Checklist: Unit 7

Class ______________________

Dates ______________________

Students' Names	Learning Goals	7a Understand and apply scientific notation.	7b Understand and apply powers of 10.	7c Understand and apply order of operations to evaluate expressions and solve number sentences.	7d Add and subtract positive and negative numbers.	7e Understand and apply exponential notation.	7f Identify number sentences. Tell whether a number sentence is true or false.	7g Understand and apply the use of parentheses in number sentences.	7h Order and compare positive and negative numbers.					
1.														
2.														
3.														
4.														
5.														
6.														
7.														
8.														
9.														
10.														
11.														
12.														
13.														
14.														
15.														
16.														
17.														
18.														
19.														
20.														
21.														
22.														
23.														
24.														
25.														
26.														
27.														
28.														
29.														
30.														

Student's Name Date

Individual Profile of Progress: Unit 7

Check ✓ B	D	S	Learning Goals	Comments
			7a Understand and apply scientific notation.	
			7b Understand and apply powers of 10.	
			7c Understand and apply order of operations to evaluate expressions and solve number sentences.	
			7d Add and subtract positive and negative numbers.	
			7e Understand and apply exponential notation.	
			7f Identify number sentences. Tell whether a number sentence is true or false.	
			7g Understand and apply the use of parentheses in number sentences.	
			7h Order and compare positive and negative numbers.	

Notes to Parents

B = **B**eginning; **D** = **D**eveloping; **S** = **S**ecure

Class Checklist: Unit 8

Class ____________________

Dates ____________________

Students' Names	Learning Goals	8a Use an algorithm to multiply mixed numbers.	8b Use an algorithm to multiply fractions.	8c Use an algorithm to subtract mixed numbers with like denominators.	8d Find a percent of a number.	8e Use an algorithm to add mixed numbers.	8f Order and compare fractions.	8g Convert among fractions, decimals, and percents.	8h Convert between fractions and mixed or whole numbers.	8i Find common denominators.				
1.														
2.														
3.														
4.														
5.														
6.														
7.														
8.														
9.														
10.														
11.														
12.														
13.														
14.														
15.														
16.														
17.														
18.														
19.														
20.														
21.														
22.														
23.														
24.														
25.														
26.														
27.														
28.														
29.														
30.														

Student's Name Date

Individual Profile of Progress: Unit 8

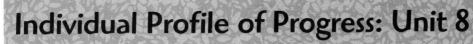

Check ✓ B	D	S	Learning Goals	Comments
			8a Use an algorithm to multiply mixed numbers.	
			8b Use an algorithm to multiply fractions.	
			8c Use an algorithm to subtract mixed numbers with like denominators.	
			8d Find a percent of a number.	
			8e Use an algorithm to add mixed numbers.	
			8f Order and compare fractions.	
			8g Convert among fractions, decimals, and percents.	
			8h Convert between fractions and mixed or whole numbers.	
			8i Find common denominators.	

Notes to Parents

B = **B**eginning; **D** = **D**eveloping; **S** = **S**ecure

Class Checklist: Unit 9

Class ______________________

Dates ______________________

Learning Goals

- **9a** Plot ordered pairs on a four-quadrant coordinate grid.
- **9b** Understand the concept of volume of a figure.
- **9c** Use a formula to find the volume of prisms.
- **9d** Plot ordered pairs on a one-quadrant coordinate grid.
- **9e** Identify the base and height of triangles and parallelograms.
- **9f** Use a formula to find the area of triangles and parallelograms.
- **9g** Understand the concept of area of a figure.
- **9h** Use a formula to find the area of rectangles.

Students' Names	Learning Goals	9a	9b	9c	9d	9e	9f	9g	9h					
1.														
2.														
3.														
4.														
5.														
6.														
7.														
8.														
9.														
10.														
11.														
12.														
13.														
14.														
15.														
16.														
17.														
18.														
19.														
20.														
21.														
22.														
23.														
24.														
25.														
26.														
27.														
28.														
29.														
30.														

Use with Lesson 9.11.

Student's Name Date

Individual Profile of Progress: Unit 9

Check ✓ B	D	S	Learning Goals	Comments
			9a Plot ordered pairs on a four-quadrant coordinate grid.	
			9b Understand the concept of volume of a figure.	
			9c Use a formula to find the volume of prisms.	
			9d Plot ordered pairs on a one-quadrant coordinate grid.	
			9e Identify the base and height of triangles and parallelograms.	
			9f Use a formula to find the area of triangles and parallelograms.	
			9g Understand the concept of area of a figure.	
			9h Use a formula to find the area of rectangles.	

Notes to Parents

____

____

____

____

B = **B**eginning; **D** = **D**eveloping; **S** = **S**ecure

Class Checklist: Unit 10

Class ______________________

Dates ______________________

Students' Names	Learning Goals	10a Solve two-step pan-balance problems.	10b Write algebraic expressions to describe situations.	10c Represent rate problems as formulas, graphs, and tables.	10d Use formulas to find circumference and area of a circle.	10e Distinguish between circumference and area of a circle problems.	10f Solve one-step pan-balance problems.	10g Interpret mystery line plots and graphs.						
1.														
2.														
3.														
4.														
5.														
6.														
7.														
8.														
9.														
10.														
11.														
12.														
13.														
14.														
15.														
16.														
17.														
18.														
19.														
20.														
21.														
22.														
23.														
24.														
25.														
26.														
27.														
28.														
29.														
30.														

Use with Lesson 10.10.

Student's Name Date

Individual Profile of Progress: Unit 10

Check ✓				
B	**D**	**S**	**Learning Goals**	**Comments**
			10a Solve two-step pan-balance problems.	
			10b Write algebraic expressions to describe situations.	
			10c Represent rate problems as formulas, graphs, and tables.	
			10d Use formulas to find circumference and area of a circle.	
			10e Distinguish between circumference and area of a circle problems.	
			10f Solve one-step pan-balance problems.	
			10g Interpret mystery line plots and graphs.	

Notes to Parents

B = **B**eginning; **D** = **D**eveloping; **S** = **S**ecure

Class Checklist: Unit 11

Class ______________________

Dates ______________________

Students' Names	Learning Goals	11a Understand the relationship between the volume of pyramids and prisms, and the volume of cones and cylinders.	11b Find the surface area of prisms.	11c Understand how to find the surface area of cylinders.	11d Understand the concept of and calculate capacity.	11e Use formulas to find the volume of prisms and cylinders.	11f Use formulas to find the area of polygons and circles.	11g Know the properties of geometric solids.						
1.														
2.														
3.														
4.														
5.														
6.														
7.														
8.														
9.														
10.														
11.														
12.														
13.														
14.														
15.														
16.														
17.														
18.														
19.														
20.														
21.														
22.														
23.														
24.														
25.														
26.														
27.														
28.														
29.														
30.														

Use with Lesson 11.8.

Student's Name Date

Individual Profile of Progress: Unit 11

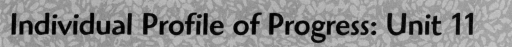

Check ✓				
B	**D**	**S**	**Learning Goals**	**Comments**
			11a Understand the relationship between the volume of pyramids and prisms, and the volume of cones and cylinders.	
			11b Find the surface area of prisms.	
			11c Understand how to find the surface area of cylinders.	
			11d Understand the concept of and calculate capacity.	
			11e Use formulas to find the volume of prisms and cylinders.	
			11f Use formulas to find the area of polygons and circles.	
			11g Know the properties of geometric solids.	

Notes to Parents

B = **B**eginning; **D** = **D**eveloping; **S** = **S**ecure

Class Checklist: Unit 12

Class ____________________

Dates ____________________

Learning Goals

- 12a Use tree diagrams to find all possible ways a sequence of choices can be made.
- 12b Compute the probability of outcomes when choices are equally likely.
- 12c Use the Multiplication Counting Principle to find the total number of possible outcomes of a sequence of choices.
- 12d Find the greatest common factor of two numbers.
- 12e Find the least common multiple of two numbers.
- 12f Solve ratio and rate number stories.
- 12g Find and identify factors of numbers.
- 12h Find the prime factorizations of numbers.

Students' Names		12a	12b	12c	12d	12e	12f	12g	12h				
1.													
2.													
3.													
4.													
5.													
6.													
7.													
8.													
9.													
10.													
11.													
12.													
13.													
14.													
15.													
16.													
17.													
18.													
19.													
20.													
21.													
22.													
23.													
24.													
25.													
26.													
27.													
28.													
29.													
30.													

Use with Lesson 12.10.

Student's Name Date

Individual Profile of Progress: Unit 12

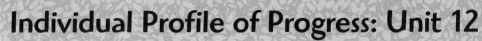

Check ✓				
B	**D**	**S**	**Learning Goals**	**Comments**
			12a Use tree diagrams to find all possible ways a sequence of choices can be made.	
			12b Compute the probability of outcomes when choices are equally likely.	
			12c Use the Multiplication Counting Principle to find the total number of possible outcomes of a sequence of choices.	
			12d Find the greatest common factor of two numbers.	
			12e Find the least common multiple of two numbers.	
			12f Solve ratio and rate number stories.	
			12g Find and identify factors of numbers.	
			12h Find the prime factorizations of numbers.	

Notes to Parents

____

____

____

____

B = **B**eginning; **D** = **D**eveloping; **S** = **S**ecure

Class Checklist: 1st Quarter

Class ______________________

Dates ______________________

Students' Names	Learning Goals	1. Draw arrays to model multiplication. **(1f)**	2. Know basic multiplication facts. **(1g)**	3. Identify even and odd numbers. **(1h)**	4. List the factors of a number. **(1i)**	5. Find the sum and difference of multidigit whole numbers and decimals. **(2f)**	6. Identify place value in numbers to billions. **(3f)**	7. Use a divisibility test to determine if a number is divisible by another number. **(1c)**	8. Identify prime and composite numbers. **(1d)**	9. Understand how square numbers and their square roots are related. **(1e)**	10. Make magnitude estimates. **(2c)**	11. Find the product of multidigit whole numbers and decimals. **(2d)**	12. Know place value to billions. **(2e)**	
1.														
2.														
3.														
4.														
5.														
6.														
7.														
8.														
9.														
10.														
11.														
12.														
13.														
14.														
15.														
16.														
17.														
18.														
19.														
20.														
21.														
22.														
23.														
24.														
25.														
26.														
27.														
28.														
29.														
30.														

Use with Lesson 3.11.

Class Checklist: 1st Quarter (cont.)

Class ____________________

Dates ____________________

Students' Names	Learning Goals	13. Round numbers to designated places. (2b)	14. Rename numbers written in exponential notation. (1b)	15. Find the prime factorization of numbers. (1a)	16. Write and solve open sentences for number stories. (2a)	17. Know properties of polygons. (3g)	18. Define and create tessellations. (3h)	19. Estimate the measure of an angle. (3b)	20. Measure an angle to within 2°. (3c)	21. Identify types of angles. (3d)	22. Identify types of triangles. (3e)	23. Determine angle measures based on relationships between angles. (3a)	24. Identify the maximum, minimum, median, mode, and mean for a data set. (2g)	
1.														
2.														
3.														
4.														
5.														
6.														
7.														
8.														
9.														
10.														
11.														
12.														
13.														
14.														
15.														
16.														
17.														
18.														
19.														
20.														
21.														
22.														
23.														
24.														
25.														
26.														
27.														
28.														
29.														
30.														

Student's Name Date

Individual Profile of Progress: 1st Quarter

B	D	S	Learning Goals	Comments
			1. Draw arrays to model multiplication. **(1f)**	
			2. Know basic multiplication facts. **(1g)**	
			3. Identify even and odd numbers. **(1h)**	
			4. List the factors of a number. **(1i)**	
			5. Find the sum and difference of multidigit whole numbers and decimals. **(2f)**	
			6. Identify place value in numbers to billions. **(3f)**	
			7. Use a divisibility test to determine if a number is divisible by another number. **(1c)**	
			8. Identify prime and composite numbers. **(1d)**	
			9. Understand how square numbers and their square roots are related. **(1e)**	
			10. Make magnitude estimates. **(2c)**	
			11. Find the product of multidigit whole numbers and decimals. **(2d)**	
			12. Know place value to billions. **(2e)**	
			13. Round numbers to designated places. **(2b)**	
			14. Rename numbers written in exponential notation. **(1b)**	
			15. Find the prime factorization of numbers. **(1a)**	
			16. Write and solve open sentences for number stories. **(2a)**	
			17. Know properties of polygons. **(3g)**	
			18. Define and create tessellations. **(3h)**	
			19. Estimate the measure of an angle. **(3b)**	
			20. Measure an angle to within 2°. **(3c)**	

B = **B**eginning; **D** = **D**eveloping; **S** = **S**ecure

Use with Lesson 3.11.

Student's Name Date

Individual Profile of Progress: 1st Quarter

Check ✔ B	D	S	Learning Goals	Comments
			21. Identify types of angles. **(3d)**	
			22. Identify types of triangles. **(3e)**	
			23. Determine angle measures based on relationships between angles. **(3a)**	
			24. Identify the maximum, minimum, median, mode, and mean for a data set. **(2g)**	

Notes to Parents

B = **B**eginning; **D** = **D**eveloping; **S** = **S**ecure

Class Checklist: 2nd Quarter

Class ______________________

Dates ______________________

Students' Names	Learning Goals	1. Know place value to hundredths. (4h)	2. Convert between fractions and mixed numbers. (5f)	3. Find equivalent fractions. (5g)	4. Convert among fractions, decimals, and percents. (6g)	5. Find the quotient and remainder of a whole number divided by a 1-digit whole number. (4c)	6. Find the quotient and remainder of a whole number divided by a 2-digit whole number. (4d)	7. Make magnitude estimates for quotients of whole and decimal numbers divided by whole numbers. (4e)	8. Interpret the remainder in division number stories. (4f)	9. Determine the value of a variable; use this value to complete a number sentence. (4g)	10. Order and compare fractions. (5b)	11. Convert between fractions and percents. (5c)	12. Add and subtract fractions with common denominators. (5a, 6c)	
1.														
2.														
3.														
4.														
5.														
6.														
7.														
8.														
9.														
10.														
11.														
12.														
13.														
14.														
15.														
16.														
17.														
18.														
19.														
20.														
21.														
22.														
23.														
24.														
25.														
26.														
27.														
28.														
29.														
30.														

Class Checklist: 2nd Quarter (cont.)

Class ______________________

Dates ______________________

Students' Names	Learning Goals	13. Add and subtract fractions with unlike denominators. **(6d)**	14. Find a common denominator. **(6f)**	15. Divide decimal numbers by whole numbers with no remainders. **(4a)**	16. Write and solve number sentences with variables for division number stories. **(4b)**	17. Find and use data landmarks. **(6h)**	18. Draw a circle graph for a set of data. **(5d)**	19. Measure pieces of a circle graph; interpret a circle graph. **(5e)**	20. Understand how sample size affects results. **(6e)**	21. Construct stem-and-leaf plots. **(6a)**	22. Read and interpret stem-and-leaf plots. **(6b)**			
1.														
2.														
3.														
4.														
5.														
6.														
7.														
8.														
9.														
10.														
11.														
12.														
13.														
14.														
15.														
16.														
17.														
18.														
19.														
20.														
21.														
22.														
23.														
24.														
25.														
26.														
27.														
28.														
29.														
30.														

Student's Name Date

Individual Profile of Progress: 2nd Quarter

B	D	S	Learning Goals	Comments
			1. Know place value to hundredths. **(4h)**	
			2. Convert between fractions and mixed numbers. **(5f)**	
			3. Find equivalent fractions. **(5g)**	
			4. Convert between fractions, decimals, and percents. **(6g)**	
			5. Find the quotient and remainder of a whole number divided by a 1-digit whole number. **(4c)**	
			6. Find the quotient and remainder of a whole number divided by a 2-digit whole number. **(4d)**	
			7. Make magnitude estimates for quotients of whole and decimal numbers divided by whole numbers. **(4e)**	
			8. Interpret the remainder in division number stories. **(4f)**	
			9. Determine the value of a variable; use this value to complete a number sentence. **(4g)**	
			10. Order and compare fractions. **(5b)**	
			11. Convert between fractions and percents. **(5c)**	
			12. Add and subtract fractions with common denominators. **(5a, 6c)**	
			13. Add and subtract fractions with unlike denominators. **(6d)**	
			14. Find a common denominator. **(6f)**	
			15. Divide decimal numbers by whole numbers with no remainders. **(4a)**	
			16. Write and solve number sentences with variables for division number stories. **(4b)**	
			17. Find and use data landmarks. **(6h)**	
			18. Draw a circle graph for a set of data. **(5d)**	

B = **B**eginning; **D** = **D**eveloping; **S** = **S**ecure

Student's Name Date

Individual Profile of Progress: 2nd Quarter

Check ✓ B	D	S	Learning Goals	Comments
			19. Measure pieces of a circle graph; interpret a circle graph. **(5e)**	
			20. Understand how sample size affects results. **(6e)**	
			21. Construct stem-and-leaf plots. **(6a)**	
			22. Read and interpret stem-and-leaf plots. **(6b)**	

Notes to Parents

B = **B**eginning; **D** = **D**eveloping; **S** = **S**ecure

Class Checklist: 3rd Quarter

Class ______________________

Dates ______________________

Students' Names	Learning Goals	1. Convert among fractions, decimals, and percents. **(8g)**	2. Convert between fractions and mixed or whole numbers. **(8h)**	3. Find common denominators. **(8i)**	4. Understand and apply exponential notation. **(7e)**	5. Identify number sentences. Tell whether a number sentence is true or false. **(7f)**	6. Understand and apply the use of parentheses in number sentences. **(7g)**	7. Order and compare positive and negative numbers. **(7h)**	8. Use an algorithm to add mixed numbers. **(8e)**	9. Order and compare fractions. **(8f)**	10. Understand and apply powers of 10. **(7b)**	11. Understand and apply order of operations to evaluate expressions and solve number sentences. **(7c)**	12. Add and subtract positive and negative numbers. **(7d)**	13. Use an algorithm to multiply fractions. **(8b)**
1.														
2.														
3.														
4.														
5.														
6.														
7.														
8.														
9.														
10.														
11.														
12.														
13.														
14.														
15.														
16.														
17.														
18.														
19.														
20.														
21.														
22.														
23.														
24.														
25.														
26.														
27.														
28.														
29.														
30.														

Use with Lesson 9.11.

Class Checklist: 3rd Quarter (cont.)

Class ______________________

Dates ______________________

Learning Goals

Students' Names	14. Use an algorithm to subtract mixed numbers with like denominators. **(8c)**	15. Find a percent of a number. **(8d)**	16. Understand and apply scientific notation. **(7a)**	17. Use an algorithm to multiply mixed numbers. **(8a)**	18. Identify the base and height of triangles and parallelograms. **(9e)**	19. Understand the concept of area of a figure. **(9g)**	20. Use a formula to find the area of rectangles. **(9h)**	21. Use a formula to find the area of triangles and parallelograms. **(9f)**	22. Understand the concept of volume of a figure. **(9b)**	23. Use a formula to find the volume of prisms. **(9c)**	24. Plot ordered pairs on a one-quadrant coordinate grid. **(9d)**	25. Plot ordered pairs on a four-quadrant coordinate grid. **(9a)**
1.												
2.												
3.												
4.												
5.												
6.												
7.												
8.												
9.												
10.												
11.												
12.												
13.												
14.												
15.												
16.												
17.												
18.												
19.												
20.												
21.												
22.												
23.												
24.												
25.												
26.												
27.												
28.												
29.												
30.												

Student's Name Date

Individual Profile of Progress: 3rd Quarter

Check ✓				
B	**D**	**S**	**Learning Goals**	**Comments**
			1. Convert among fractions, decimals, and percents. **(8g)**	
			2. Convert between fractions and mixed or whole numbers. **(8h)**	
			3. Find common denominators. **(8i)**	
			4. Understand and apply exponential notation. **(7e)**	
			5. Identify number sentences. Tell whether a number sentence is true or false. **(7f)**	
			6. Understand and apply the use of parentheses in number sentences. **(7g)**	
			7. Order and compare negative numbers. **(7h)**	
			8. Use an algorithm to add mixed numbers. **(8e)**	
			9. Order and compare fractions. **(8f)**	
			10. Understand and apply powers of 10. **(7b)**	
			11. Understand and apply order of operations to evaluate expressions and solve number sentences. **(7c)**	
			12. Add and subtract positive and negative numbers. **(7d)**	
			13. Use an algorithm to multiply fractions. **(8b)**	
			14. Use an algorithm to subtract mixed numbers with like denominators. **(8c)**	
			15. Find a percent of a number. **(8d)**	
			16. Understand and apply scientific notation. **(7a)**	
			17. Use an algorithm to multiply mixed numbers. **(8a)**	
			18. Identify the base and height of triangles and parallelograms. **(9e)**	
			19. Understand the concept of area of a figure. **(9g)**	

B = **B**eginning; **D** = **D**eveloping; **S** = **S**ecure

Student's Name Date

Individual Profile of Progress: 3rd Quarter

Check ✓				
B	**D**	**S**	**Learning Goals**	**Comments**
			20. Use a formula to find the area of rectangles. **(9h)**	
			21. Use a formula to find the area of triangles and parallelograms. **(9f)**	
			22. Understand the concept of volume of a figure. **(9b)**	
			23. Use a formula to find the volume of prisms. **(9c)**	
			24. Plot ordered pairs on a one-quadrant coordinate grid. **(9d)**	
			25. Plot ordered pairs on a four-quadrant coordinate grid. **(9a)**	

Notes to Parents

B = **B**eginning; **D** = **D**eveloping; **S** = **S**ecure

Class Checklist: 4th Quarter

Class ______________________

Dates ______________________

Learning Goals

1. Find and identify factors of numbers. **(12g)**
2. Find the prime factorizations of numbers. **(12h)**
3. Solve one-step pan-balance problems. **(10f)**
4. Solve ratio and rate number stories. **(12f)**
5. Write algebraic expressions to describe situations. **(10b)**
6. Represent rate problems as formulas, graphs, and tables. **(10c)**
7. Find the greatest common factor of two numbers. **(12d)**
8. Find the least common multiple of two numbers. **(12e)**
9. Solve two-step pan-balance problems. **(10a)**
10. Know the properties of geometric solids. **(11g)**
11. Use formulas to find the area of polygons and circles. **(11f)**
12. Use formulas to find the volume of prisms and cylinders. **(11e)**

Students' Names	Learning Goals	1.	2.	3.	4.	5.	6.	7.	8.	9.	10.	11.	12.	
1.														
2.														
3.														
4.														
5.														
6.														
7.														
8.														
9.														
10.														
11.														
12.														
13.														
14.														
15.														
16.														
17.														
18.														
19.														
20.														
21.														
22.														
23.														
24.														
25.														
26.														
27.														
28.														
29.														
30.														

Use with Lesson 12.10.

Class Checklist: 4th Quarter (cont.)

Class ______________________

Dates ______________________

Learning Goals

13. Use formulas to find circumference and area of a circle. **(10d)**
14. Distinguish between circumference and area of a circle problems. **(10e)**
15. Understand the relationship between the volume of pyramids and prisms, and the volume of cones and cylinders. **(11a)**
16. Find the surface area of prisms. **(11b)**
17. Understand how to find the surface area of cylinders. **(11c)**
18. Understand the concept of and calculate capacity. **(11d)**
19. Use the Multiplication Counting Principle to find the total number of possible outcomes of a sequence of choices. **(12c)**
20. Use tree diagrams to find all possible ways a sequence of choices can be made. **(12a)**
21. Compute the probability of outcomes when choices are equally likely. **(12b)**
22. Interpret mystery line plots and graphs. **(10g)**

Students' Names	Learning Goals	13.	14.	15.	16.	17.	18.	19.	20.	21.	22.			
1.														
2.														
3.														
4.														
5.														
6.														
7.														
8.														
9.														
10.														
11.														
12.														
13.														
14.														
15.														
16.														
17.														
18.														
19.														
20.														
21.														
22.														
23.														
24.														
25.														
26.														
27.														
28.														
29.														
30.														

Student's Name Date

Individual Profile of Progress: 4th Quarter

Check ✔				
B	**D**	**S**	**Learning Goals**	**Comments**
			1. Find and identify factors of numbers. **(12g)**	
			2. Find the prime factorizations of numbers. **(12h)**	
			3. Solve one-step pan-balance problems. **(10f)**	
			4. Solve ratio and rate number stories. **(12f)**	
			5. Write algebraic expressions to describe situations. **(10b)**	
			6. Represent rate problems as formulas, graphs, and tables. **(10c)**	
			7. Find the greatest common factor of two numbers. **(12d)**	
			8. Find the least common multiple of two numbers. **(12e)**	
			9. Solve two-step pan-balance problems. **(10a)**	
			10. Know the properties of geometric solids. **(11g)**	
			11. Use formulas to find the area of polygons and circles. **(11f)**	
			12. Use formulas to find the volume of prisms and cylinders. **(11e)**	
			13. Use formulas to find circumference and area of a circle. **(10d)**	
			14. Distinguish between circumference and area of a circle problems. **(10e)**	
			15. Understand the relationship between the volume of pyramids and prisms, and the volume of cones and cylinders. **(11a)**	
			16. Find the surface area of prisms. **(11b)**	
			17. Understand how to find the surface area of cylinders. **(11c)**	
			18. Understand the concept of and calculate capacity. **(11d)**	

B = **B**eginning; **D** = **D**eveloping; **S** = **S**ecure

Student's Name Date

Individual Profile of Progress: 4th Quarter

Check ✓				
B	D	S	Learning Goals	Comments
			19. Use the Multiplication Counting Principle to find the total number of possible outcomes of a sequence of choices. **(12c)**	
			20. Use tree diagrams to find all possible ways a sequence of choices can be made. **(12a)**	
			21. Compute the probability of outcomes when choices are equally likely. **(12b)**	
			22. Interpret mystery line plots and graphs. **(10g)**	

Notes to Parents

B = **B**eginning; **D** = **D**eveloping; **S** = **S**ecure

List of Assessment Sources

Ongoing Assessment

Product Assessment

Periodic Assessment

Outside Tests

Other

Use as needed.

Student's Name Date

Individual Profile of Progress

Check ✓				
B	**D**	**S**	**Learning Goals**	**Comments**
			1.	
			2.	
			3.	
			4.	
			5.	
			6.	
			7.	
			8.	
			9.	
			10.	

Notes to Parents

B = **B**eginning; **D** = **D**eveloping; **S** = **S**ecure

Use as needed.

Class Checklist

____
Class

____
Dates

Students' Names	**Learning Goals**													
1.														
2.														
3.														
4.														
5.														
6.														
7.														
8.														
9.														
10.														
11.														
12.														
13.														
14.														
15.														
16.														
17.														
18.														
19.														
20.														
21.														
22.														
23.														
24.														
25.														
26.														
27.														
28.														
29.														
30.														

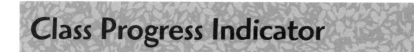

Class Progress Indicator

Mathematical Topic Being Assessed: ______________________________

	BEGINNING	DEVELOPING OR DEVELOPING+	SECURE OR SECURE+
First Assessment After Lesson: ______ Dates included: ______ to ______			
Second Assessment After Lesson: ______ Dates included: ______ to ______			
Third Assessment After Lesson: ______ Dates included: ______ to ______			

Notes

____

____

____

____

Use as needed.

Name Date

Evaluating My Math Class

Interest Inventory

Dislike a Lot 1	Dislike 2	Neither Like nor Dislike 3	Like 4	Like a Lot 5

Use the scale above to describe how you feel about:

1. your math class. ____________
2. working with a partner or in a group. ____________
3. working by yourself. ____________
4. solving problems. ____________
5. making up problems for others to solve. ____________
6. finding new ways to solve problems. ____________
7. challenges in math class. ____________
8. playing mathematical games. ____________
9. working on Study Links. ____________
10. working on projects that take more than a day to complete. ____________

11. Which math lesson has been your favorite so far? Why?

____

____

____

____

____

____

____

____

Use as needed.

Name Date

My Math Class

Interest Inventory

1. In math class, I am good at ____
____
____
____.

2. One thing I like about math is ____
____
____
____.

3. One thing I find difficult in mathematics class is ______________________________
____
____
____.

4. The most interesting thing I have learned in math so far this year is __________
____
____
____.

5. Outside school, I used mathematics when I ______________________________
____
____
____.

6. I would like to know more about ______________________________________
____
____
____.

Name Date

Weekly Math Log

1. What did you study in math this week?

2. Many ideas in math are related to other ideas within math. Think about how the topic(s) you studied in class this week relate to other topics you learned before.

   Your reflection can include what you learned in previous years.

Use as needed.

Name Date

Math Log

Use as needed.

Name Date

Number-Story Math Log

1. Write an easy number story that uses mathematical ideas that you have studied recently. Solve the problem.

Number Story ______________________________

____

____

____

____

Solution ______________________________

____

____

____

2. Write a difficult number story that uses mathematical ideas that you have studied recently. If you can, solve the number story. If you are not able to solve it, explain what you need to know to solve it.

Number Story ______________________________

____

____

____

____

Solution ______________________________

____

____

____

Use as needed.

Name Date

Sample Math Work

Self-Assessment

Attach a sample of your work to this form.

1. This work is an example of:

____

____

____

____

____

____

2. This work shows that I can:

____

____

____

____

____

____

OPTIONAL

3. This work shows that I still need to improve:

____

____

____

____

____

____

____

Name Date

Discussion of My Math Work

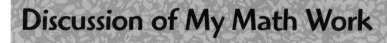

Self-Assessment

Attach a sample of your work to this page. Tell what you think is important about your sample.

Use as needed.

Name Date Time

Exit Slip

Name Date Time

Exit Slip

Use as needed.

Name Date Time

Arithmetic Training: Auto Mode

Solving Problems that the Calculator Gives You

Pressing (◈) puts your calculator into Arithmetic Training: Auto Mode. In Auto mode, the calculator displays a problem for you to solve. The calculator tells you if you are correct and gives hints (> or <) if you are wrong. You have up to three tries for each problem.

After every five problems, the calculator shows a scoreboard with the number of problems you have solved correctly and incorrectly. You can see your scoreboard at any time by pressing (Mode) once. Press (Mode) again to return to the problems. To exit from arithmetic-training mode, press (◈).

1. Press (◈) to enter arithmetic-training mode. Practice 10 basic addition facts. Press (◈) to leave arithmetic-training mode.

2. Complete the following scoreboard for the for the 10 basic addition facts you solved:

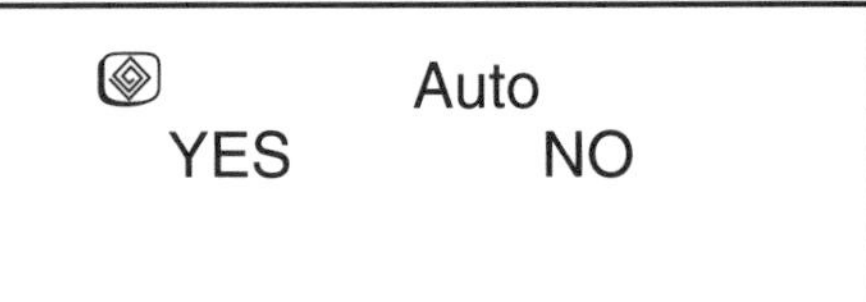

Changing the Kind of Problem that the Calculator Gives You

The calculator has menus for changing the kind of problems it gives you. In each menu, the current choice is underlined. Use (⇦) and (⇨) to go to a different choice. Then press (Enter) to make your new choice active. (If you don't press (Enter), then the old menu choice will still be active.) Press (Mode) to go back to the problems.

The following table shows how to control the kind of problems the calculator gives you:

Key Sequence	Menu	Function
(◈) (Mode) (pause)	◈ Auto AUTO MAN	**Choose the mode.** In AUTO mode, the calculator makes up the problems. In MAN mode, you make up the problems. Press (⇨) (Enter) to change from AUTO to MAN. Press (⇦) (Enter) to change from MAN to AUTO.
(⇩)	◈ Auto 1 2 3	**Choose the level of difficulty.** Level 1 problems are the easiest; level 3 the hardest. Press (⇨), (⇦), and (Enter) to change levels.
(⇩)	◈ Auto + − × ÷ ?	**Choose the operation.** Press (⇨), (⇦), and (Enter) to change operations. If you choose ?, the calculator will give you problems with missing operations.

Name Date Time

Arithmetic Training: Auto Mode (cont.)

The following example shows you how to set the calculator for multiplication problems at the medium level of difficulty:

Example

Key Sequence	Display
◈ Mode (pause) ⇩ ⇨ Enter	◆ Auto 1 2 3 ... ııı ıııı
⇩ ⇨ ⇨ Enter	◆ Auto + − × ÷ ?
Mode	◆ Auto 9 X ? = 720

3. Solve 10 subtraction problems at the medium level of difficulty. Use only the AUTO mode. (You will learn how to use the MAN mode on *Math Masters,* page 482.)

a. Press ◈ Mode to be sure the calculator is in AUTO mode.

b. Press ⇩ ⇨ Enter to select 2, the medium level of difficulty.

c. Press ⇩ ⇨ Enter to select −, subtraction.

d. Press Mode. Solve 10 extended subtraction fact problems.

e. Press ◈ to leave arithmetic-training mode.

4. Complete the following scoreboard for the 10 subtraction problems you solved:

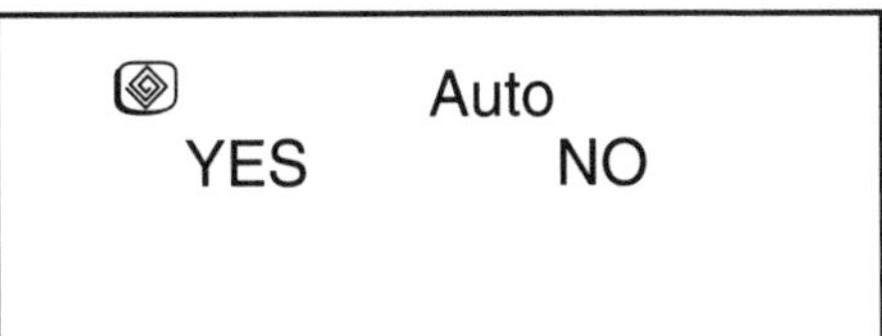

5. Set the calculator for problems that would be good practice for you. Refer to the table on *Math Masters,* page 480 to remind you which keys to press.

a. Be sure the calculator is in AUTO mode.

b. Choose the problem difficulty.

c. Choose the operation.

Name Date Time

Arithmetic Training: Manual Mode

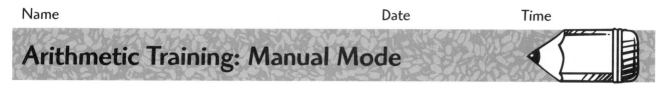

Making Up Your Own Problems to Solve

In Arithmetic Training: Manual Mode, you make up your own problems to solve. Use [?] for a missing number or operation. The calculator tells you how many solutions your problem has. (Only whole numbers are allowed.) To exit from arithmetic-training mode, press [◈].

Example

Key Sequence	Display
[◈] [Mode] (pause) [⇨] [Enter]	AUTO MAN
[Mode] 53 + [?] [Enter] 61 [Enter]	53 + ? = 61 1 SOL
	53 + ? = 61
8 [Enter]	53 + 8 = 61 YES

Set your calculator for MAN-mode arithmetic training.

1. Enter the following problems and then solve them:

a. 75 x 3 = ?　　**b.** 9 x ? = 81　　**c.** 416 ? 8 = 52

Testing whether Inequalities Are True or False

In Manual mode, you can use [<>] to test whether an inequality is true or not. You can use decimals in inequalities in Manual mode. Press [<>] to get <. Press [<>] [<>] to get >.

Example

Key Sequence	Display
[◈] [Mode] (pause) [⇨] [Enter]	AUTO MAN
[Mode] 2 [.] 15 [<>] 2 [Enter]	2.15 < 2 NO

2. Use the calculator to test the following inequalities:

a. 20 < 20.00　　**b.** 1.5 < 1.0500　　**c.** 3.004 > 30.4

Name Date Time

Place Value

Using the Manual Mode to Practice Place Value

When the calculator is in MAN-mode of arithmetic training, you can use [II.] to practice place value. You enter a number, press [II.], and then press one of the red place-value keys ([1000.], [100.], and so on). The calculator will tell how many units of that value are in the number. Press [Clear] to enter another number. To exit from place-value mode, press [Clear]. To exit from arithmetic-training mode, press [◈].

Example

Key Sequence	Display	Explanation
[◈] [Mode] (pause) [⇨] [Enter]	◈ AUTO MAN	
[Mode] 123 [.] 456 [II.]	◈ II. 123.456	
[10.]	◈ II. 123.456 12_.___	There are 12 tens in the number 123.456.

Using the Manual Mode to Find Place Value

You can set the calculator so that it will tell the place value of a digit in a number and also what digit is in a given place in a number.

Example

Key Sequence	Display	Explanation
[◈] [Mode] (pause) [⇨] [Enter]	◈ AUTO MAN	
[⇩] [⇨] [Enter]	◈ II-. -I-.	
[Mode] 123 [.] 456 [II.]	◈ II. 123.456	
[0.01]	◈ II. 123.456 ___._5_	The digit 5 is in the hundredths place.
4	◈ II. 123.456 ___.4__	The digit 4 is in the tenths place.
	◈ II. 123.456 4→0.1	There are 4 tenths in the number 123.456.

1. Enter 987.654. What digit is in the 100s place? ________

2. In the number 987.654, what is the place value of the digit 6? ____________

Name Date Time

Fraction Cards 1

Name Date Time

Fraction Cards 2

Name Date Time

Number Top-It Mat (2-Place Decimals)

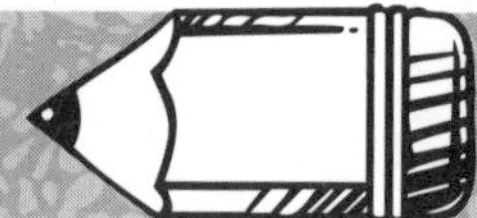

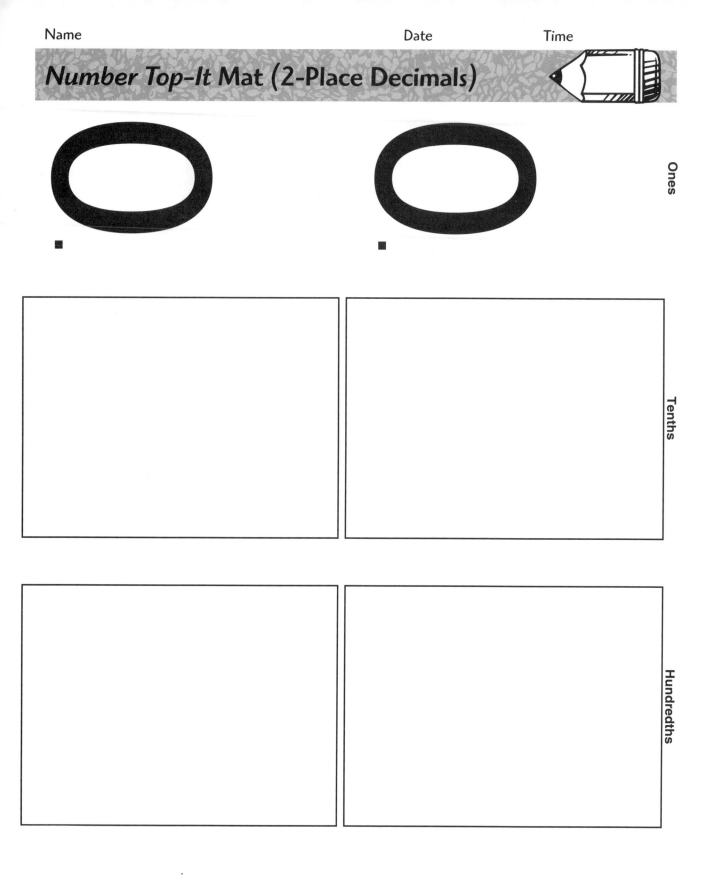

Ones

Tenths

Hundredths

Name Date Time

Number Top-It Mat (3-Place Decimals)

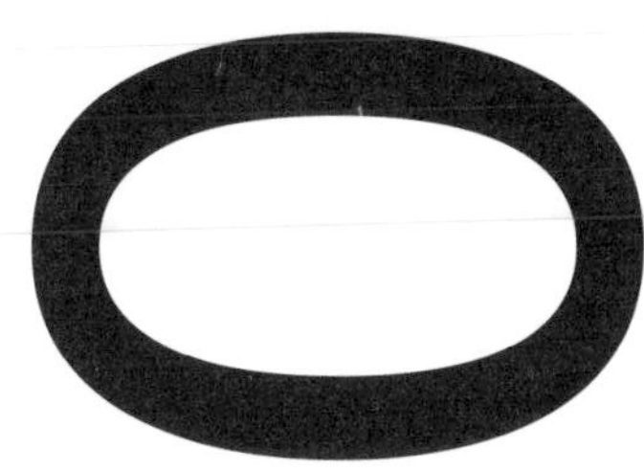

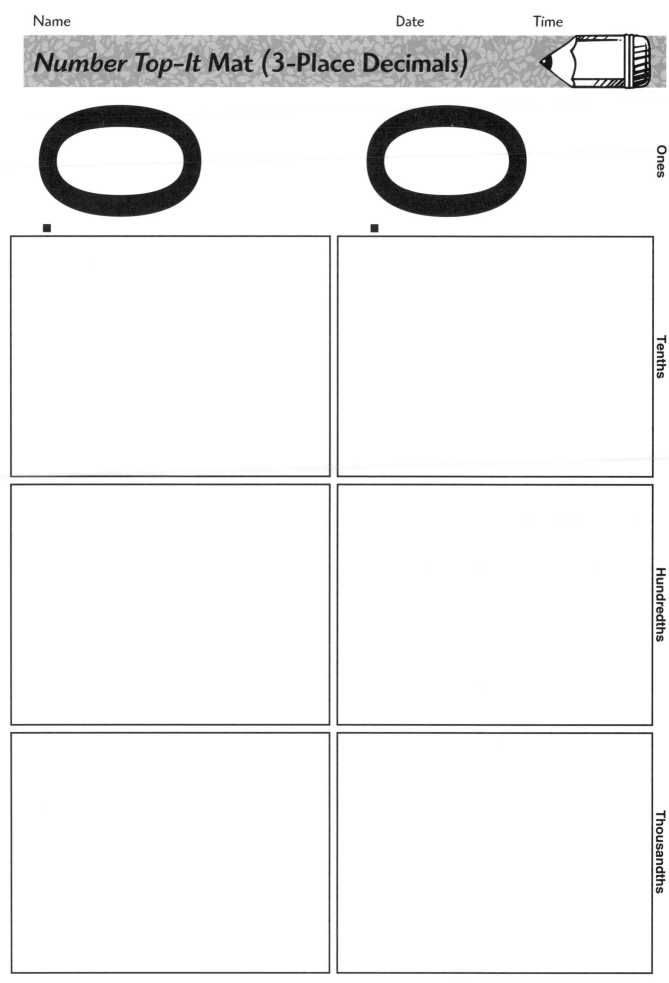

Ones

Tenths

Hundredths

Thousandths